FAST TRACK TO A 5

Preparing for the
AP® Physics 1 and AP® Physics 2 Examinations

To Accompany
College Physics
9th and 10th Editions
by Raymond A. Serway and Chris Vuille

G. Patrick Zober

Patricia Zober

CENGAGE
Learning™

Australia • Brazil • Japan • Korea • Mexico • Singapore • Spain • United Kingdom • United States

AP® and Advanced Placement Program® are trademarks registered and/or owned by the College Board, which was not involved in the production of, and does not endorse, this product.

National Geographic Learning/Cengage Learning is pleased to offer our college-level materials to high schools for Advanced Placement®, honors, and electives courses.
To contact your National Geographic Learning representative, please call us toll-free at **1-888-915-3276** or visit us at **http://ngl.cengage.com**.

For permission to use material from this text or product, submit all requests online at **www.cengage.com/permissions**
Further permissions questions can be emailed to **permissionrequest@cengage.com**.

ISBN: 978-1-285-76264-7

Cengage Learning
20 Channel Center Street
Boston, MA 02210
USA

Cengage Learning is a leading provider of customized learning solutions with office locations around the globe, including Singapore, the United Kingdom, Australia, Mexico, Brazil, and Japan. Locate your local office at: **www.cengage.com/global**.

Cengage Learning products are represented in Canada by Nelson Education, Ltd.

To learn more about Cengage Learning Solutions, visit **www.cengage.com**.

To find online supplements and other instructional support, please visit **www.cengagebrain.com**.

Printed in the United States of America
Print Number: 01   Print Year: 2014

CONTENTS

ABOUT THE AUTHORS

Dr. G. Patrick Zober, PhD Physics, has spent most of his professional career of forty-five years teaching AP B and AP C Physics in western Pennsylvania. He is a former AP Physics Exam grader for the ETS and a current AP Physics Consultant for the College Board. G. Patrick also spends part of his summers conducting AP Physics Workshops for a number of colleges and universities and the State of West Virginia. Besides teaching high school, he has taught Intermediate Mechanics, Engineering Physics, and Modern Physics at several colleges and universities. He has served as a Physics Consultant to the Pennsylvania Department of Education and several higher education publishers. G. Patrick is retired from public education.

Patricia J. Zober, MS Physics, has forty-five years of experience in teaching AP B and AP C Physics at Ringgold High School in western Pennsylvania. An AP Physics Consultant with the College Board and a former AP Physics Exam grader for the College Board, she also presents AP Physics workshops. Before her retirement from public education, Patricia served as science department chairperson and as district-wide science curriculum coordinator. She also has taught Intermediate Mechanics and Engineering Physics at local colleges and universities. Patricia is a member of the Selection Committee for the Pennsylvania Governor's School in Science, and has also served as In-Service Presenter for the Pennsylvania Standards in Science Education.

PREFACE

As a science, physics deals with the *how* of natural phenomena, but being a science of Physics, it is necessarily concerned also with *how much*. This means that you will encounter numerical problems consistently throughout the first course in Physics. Too often, students are intimidated by such problems; many people believe that solving these kinds of problems requires some special intuition that they lack. Our aim is to help you realize that you can solve such problems using strictly logical methods that require no extraordinary gifts. To accomplish this goal, this guide presents a brief summary of the topics covered in the AP Physics 1 and the AP Physics 2 courses, paying special attention to the meanings of the equations of and concepts of physics. These equations are simply shorthand expressions for relationships between physical concepts. Sample problems, worked out in detail, illustrate these equations using a procedure based upon logical approach and careful analysis. In this manner, we hope to help you learn how to set up and tackle the problems and questions of AP Physics 1 and 2.

To solve a problem involving any concept, you must first have a clear understanding of the meaning of that concept. Thus, the topic summaries, definitions, and defining equations that you will find in this guide play particularly important roles. We have focused the presentation of concepts on problem solving, testing your mastery of the concepts with both multiple-choice questions and free-response problems. We hope that this guide will help you view the numerical problems you encounter as applications to the Laws and Principles of Physics, and that you will find it a helpful aid in problem-solving.

G. Patrick Zober
Patricia J. Zober

ACKNOWLEDGMENTS

We are deeply indebted to Karen Ettinger of O'Donnell Learn for all her guidance, input, patience, organizational skills, and the occasional nudges. A special thanks goes to Alison Zetterquist of Cengage Learning for her advice and assistance. The authors wish to thank Paul Pomeroy and Matthew Sckalor for their timely reviews of the many chapters of the manuscript. We extend a special acknowledgment to Joseph A. Sholtis, Jr. and John R. Bell for their invaluable and extensive input and assistance. We express special gratitude to Theo, Vincenzo, and Leonardo for all the timely reminders about mealtime and when it was time to turn off the computers for the night. Finally, we thank Strong Vincent for all of the flawless demonstrations of the physics of projectile motion and flight.

G. Patrick and Patricia Zober

Part I

Strategies for the AP® Test

PREPARING FOR THE AP® PHYSICS 1 AND AP® PHYSICS 2 EXAMINATIONS

Advanced Placement can be exhilarating. Whether you are taking an AP course at your school or you are working on AP independently, the stage is set for a great intellectual experience.

But sometime after New Year's Day, when the examination begins to loom on a very real horizon, Advanced Placement can seem downright intimidating. In fact, offered the opportunity to take the examination for a lark, even adults long out of high school refuse. If you dread taking the test, you are in good company.

The best way to deal with an AP examination is to master it, not let it master you. If you can think of these examinations as a way to show off how much physics you know, you have a leg up. Attitude *does* help. If you are not one of those students, there is still a lot you can do to sideline your anxiety. This book is designed to put you on a fast track. Focused review and practice time will help you master the examination so that you can walk in with confidence and score a 5.

WHAT ARE THE AP PHYSICS 1 AND AP PHYSICS 2 COURSES?

AP Physics 1: Algebra-based and AP Physics 2: Algebra-based is a two-year sequence equivalent to the first and second semesters of a typical introductory, algebra-based college physics course. This two-year sequence gives students the time needed to develop greater depth of conceptual understanding through the use of student-centered, inquiry-based instructional practices. This sequence also gives teachers time to cover the concepts and skills that students will need to demonstrate in order to earn credit for the introductory algebra-based college physics course.

WHAT'S IN THIS BOOK

This book is keyed to *College Physics* by Serway and Vuille, 9th and 10th editions, but because it follows the College Board Concept Outline, it is compatible with all AP Physics textbooks. It is divided into

---

AP® and Advanced Placement Program® are trademarks registered and/or owned by the College Board, which was not involved in the production of, and does not endorse, this product.

three sections. Part I offers suggestions for getting yourself ready, from signing up to take the test and sharpening your pencils to organizing a free-response essay. This is followed by the list of AP Physics learning objectives from the College Board curriculum.

Part II is made up of 19 chapters, again following the College Board Concept Outline. These chapters are not a substitute for your textbook and class work; they simply review the AP Physics 1 course and the AP Physics 2 course. At the end of each chapter, you will find 15 multiple-choice questions and 4 free-response problems based on the material of that chapter. Again, you will find page references at the end of each answer directing you to the discussion on that particular point in *College Physics* and the AP Physics learning objective number covering that point.

Part III has two complete AP Physics 1 and AP Physics 2 level examinations. At the end of each test, you will find the answers, explanations, and references to *College Physics* and the AP Physics learning objective for the multiple-choice questions and the free-response problems.

SETTING UP A REVIEW SCHEDULE

If you have been doing your homework steadily and keeping up with the course work, you are in good shape. Organize your notes, homework, and handouts from class by topic. Reference these materials as well as your textbook and this study guide when you have difficulty in a specific section. Even if you've done all that—or if it's too late to do all that—there are still some more ways to get it all together.

To begin, read Part I of this book. You will be much more comfortable going into the test if you understand how the test questions and problems are designed and how best to approach them.

Take out a calendar and set up a schedule for yourself. If you begin studying early, you can chip away at the review chapters in Part II. You'll be surprised—and pleased—by how much material you can cover in a half an hour a day of study for a month or so before the test. The practice tests in Part III will give you more experience with different kinds of multiple-choice questions and the wide range of free-response problems. Look carefully at the sections of the practice tests; if you missed a number of questions in one particular area, review the chapters that cover that area of the course again.

If time is short, skip reading the review chapters (although you might read through the chapter subheadings) and work on the multiple-choice questions and free-response problems at the end of each review. This will give you a good idea of your understanding of that particular topic. Then take the practice tests in Part III.

If time is *really* short, go straight from Part I to Part III. Taking practice tests over and over again is the fastest, most practical way to prepare. You cannot study physics by reading it like a novel. You must actively do problems to gain understanding and excel in your performance. Athletes don't perform well just by reading books about their sport or by watching others. They must get up and practice. So, you too, just like athletes, must practice, practice, and practice if you want to do your best!

BEFORE THE EXAMINATION

By February, long before the exam, you need to make sure that you are registered to take the examination. Many schools take care of the paperwork and handle the fees for their AP students, but check with your teacher or the AP coordinator to make sure that you are on the list. This is especially important if you have a documented disability and need test accommodations. If you are studying AP independently, call AP Services at the College Board for the name of the local AP coordinator, who will help you through the registration process.

The evening before the exam is not a great time for partying, nor is it a great time for cramming. If you like, look over class notes or drift through your textbook, concentrating on the broad outlines, not the small details, of the course. You might also want to skim through this book and read the AP tips.

The evening before the exam *is* a great time to get your things together for the next day. Sharpen a fistful of no. 2 pencils with good erasers; bring a scientific calculator with fresh batteries. Certain types of calculators are not allowed, so be sure to verify with your teacher or the College Board that your model is acceptable. For example, you cannot use a calculator with a typewriter-style keyboard or a cell phone. Cell phones are not even allowed in the testing room, so you will need a watch, and be certain to turn off the alarm if it has one. Bring a piece of fruit or an energy bar and a bottle of water for the break. Make sure you have your Social Security number and whatever photo identification and admission ticket are required. Then relax. Get a good night's sleep.

On the day of the examination, plan to arrive early. It is wise not to skip breakfast; studies show that students who eat a hot breakfast before testing get higher grades than students who do not. Be careful not to drink a lot of liquids, necessitating a trip to the bathroom during the test. Breakfast will give you the energy you need to power you through the test, and more. You will spend some time waiting while everyone is seated in the correct room for the correct test, and that's before the test has even begun. With a short break between Section I and Section II, the AP Physics 1 exam lasts for three hours and when you take the AP Physics 2 exam it also lasts for three hours. So be prepared for a long day. You do not want to be distracted by a growling stomach or hunger pangs.

Be sure to wear comfortable clothes, taking along a sweater in case the heating or air conditioning is erratic. Be sure, too, to wear clothes you like—everyone performs better when they think they look better—and by all means wear your lucky socks.

You have been on the fast track. Now go get a 5!

TAKING THE AP® PHYSICS 1 AND AP® PHYSICS 2 EXAMINATIONS

Both the AP Physics 1 and the AP Physics 2 examinations each consists of two sections: Section I has 50 multiple-choice questions; Section II in AP Physics 1 has five free-response problems; Section II in AP Physics 2 has four free-response problems. You will have 90 minutes for the multiple-choice portion and are allowed to use a calculator. The questions are collected, and you will be given a short break. You then have 90 minutes for the free-response problems.

AP Physics 1 and 2 Exams—Distribution of Questions and Problems			
	Weighting	Possible Topics	Time Allowed
AP Physics 1, Section I	50%	50 multiple-choice questions	90 minutes
AP Physics 1, Section II	50%	5 free-response problems	90 minutes
AP Physics 2, Section I	50%	50 multiple-choice questions	90 minutes
AP Physics 2, Section II	50%	4 free-response problems	90 minutes

STRATEGIES FOR THE MULTIPLE-CHOICE QUESTION SECTION

Both Section I and Section II of the AP Physics 1 and AP Physics 2 exams come with a table of equations and constants. Here are some rules of thumb to help you work your way through the multiple-choice questions:

■ **There is no guessing penalty** There are 4 possible answers for each question. Each correct answer is worth 1 point, and there is no guessing penalty for each incorrect answer. If you can narrow down the answers even by eliminating one response, it is advantageous to

---

AP® and Advanced Placement Program® are trademarks registered and/or owned by the College Board, which was not involved in the production of, and does not endorse, this product.

guess. If you skip a question, be very careful to skip down that line on the answer sheet.

- **Read the question carefully** Pressured for time, many students make the mistake of reading the questions too quickly or merely skimming them. By reading a question carefully, you may already have some idea about the correct answer. You can then look for it in the responses.

- **Eliminate answers you know are incorrect** You can write on the multiple-choice questions in the test book. As you read through the responses, draw a line through any answer you know is wrong.

- **Read all of the possible answers, then choose the one you feel is correct** AP examinations are written to test your precise knowledge of a subject. Be careful, some of the questions have multiple correct responses. Each correct response is to be recorded to receive credit for the question.

- **Mark and skip tough questions** If you are hung up on a question, mark it in the margin of the question book. You can come back to it later if you have time. Be certain you skip that question on your answer sheet too.

- **Calculational questions** In calculational multiple-choice questions, you may be asked find the solution to a problem that requires mathematics and your calculator.

- **The acceleration due to gravity** In the multiple-choice part of the test it is advisable to use 9.8 m/s² as the acceleration due to gravity unless directed otherwise.

TYPES OF MULTIPLE-CHOICE QUESTIONS

In both the AP Physics 1 and the AP Physics 2 exams, you will encounter a variety of types of multiple-choice questions. Here are some suggestions for approaching each question type.

CLASSIC/BEST RESPONSE TYPE QUESTIONS

As shown below, a body is projected upward with some initial velocity. The altitude of the projectile is shown as a function of time.

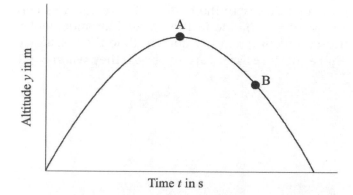

In the absence of air resistance
(A) at point A both the velocity and the acceleration of the projectile are zero
(B) at point A the projectile has a smaller velocity than at point B. The accelerations at Points A and B are the same
(C) the acceleration at point A is zero, but it has a negative value at point B since the projectile is moving downward
(D) the acceleration is the same at points A and B. The velocity at point A is zero and the velocity at point B has some negative value

Answer: D In the absence of air resistance, the acceleration of the projectile is the acceleration due to the gravitational field strength. This is 9.80 $\frac{m}{s^2}$ downward. This eliminates choices (A) and (C). At the apex of the flight, the projectile has no upward velocity. For a fraction of a second, the velocity of the projectile is zero as it stops and changes its direction, increasing its velocity in a downward direction.

RANKING

A series/parallel electrical circuit is shown below.

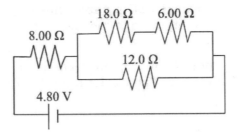

Rank the resistors from the one conducting the highest current to the one conducting the least current.

(A) $I_{18.0\,\Omega} > I_{12.0\,\Omega} > I_{8.00\,\Omega} > I_{6.00\,\Omega}$

(B) $I_{6.00\,\Omega} > I_{8.00\,\Omega} > I_{12.0\,\Omega} > I_{18.0\,\Omega}$

(C) $I_{8.00\,\Omega} > I_{12.0\,\Omega} > \left(I_{18.0\,\Omega} = I_{6.00\,\Omega}\right)$

(D) $I_{8.00\,\Omega} > \left(I_{12.0\,\Omega} = I_{18.0\,\Omega} = I_{6.00\,\Omega}\right)$

Answer: C The entire current in the circuit flows through the 8.00 Ω resistor which is in series with the battery. This eliminates choices (A) and (B). The current will divide in the parallel arrangement with the 12.0 Ω resistor conducting a larger current than the resistances in the top branch. Since these resistors are in series, they will have the same current.

BAR CHARTS

A 50 kg skier approaches a hill with a velocity of 10 $\frac{m}{s}$. The hill has some friction reducing the initial energy of the skier by 50 J. Which of the following bar charts will be the correct choice for the initial and final energy in the system?

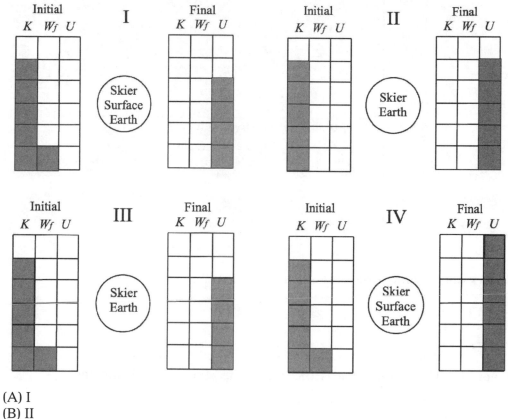

(A) I
(B) II
(C) III
(D) IV

Answer: A The 50 kg skier approaches the hill with a velocity of 10 $\frac{m}{s}$. The initial kinetic energy of the skier is $K = \frac{1}{2}mv^2 = \frac{1}{2}(50 \text{ kg})\left(10 \frac{m}{s}\right)^2 = 250 \text{ J}$. Each block on the bar chart represents 50 J. The hill has some friction that reduces the energy in the system by 50 J. The gravitational potential energy of the skier-Earth system will be 200 J at the top of the hill (4 blocks).

The skier-surface-Earth system links the initial energy before the skier moves up the hill to the final energy at the top of the hill. The system consists of the skier, kinetic energy K, the surface, frictional work W_f, and the Earth-skier U. Any system that does not contain all three is not a correct choice. This eliminates choice II and III. Choice IV does not have the correct bar representing the final gravitational potential energy U. The correct choice is I.

GRAPHING

EXAMPLE 1

A variable force moves a 2.00 kg body through a displacement of 12.0 m.

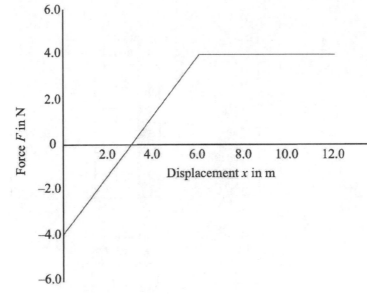

The work done by the force is closest to

(A) 12 J
(B) 18 J
(C) 24 J
(D) 36 J

Answer: C The work done is the area under the curve. From the graph, $A_1 = \frac{1}{2}bh$ is negative and $A_2 = \frac{1}{2}bh$ is positive. The two areas have the same magnitude and give a sum of zero. The work done is therefore the area $A_3 = bh$. This is $(4.0\ \text{N} - 0)(12.0\ \text{m} - 6.0\ \text{m}) = 24.0\ \text{J}$.

EXAMPLE 2

A body undergoes simple harmonic motion with an amplitude of vibration of 0.03 m. The graph of its motion as a function of time is shown below. What is the frequency of oscillation?

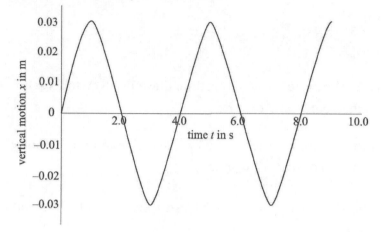

(A) 0.17 Hz
(B) 0.25 Hz
(C) 0.33 Hz
(D) 0.5 Hz

Answer: B   The wave makes one complete cycle of vibration in a period of 4.0 s. Since frequency and period are related by $f = \dfrac{1}{T}$, the frequency is $f = \dfrac{1}{4.0}$ Hz $= 0.25$ Hz.

CALCULATION TYPES

A 2.00 kg body M_1, is pulled to the right across a horizontal table top by a cord that passes over an ideal pulley to a 1.00 kg body, M_2. The coefficient friction of friction μ_k between the 2.00 kg body and the table is 0.10.

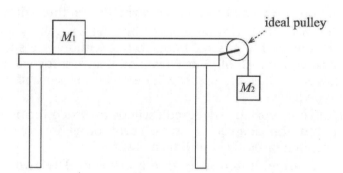

The acceleration of the system is

(A) 2.61 m/s^2

(B) 3.27 m/s^2

(C) 3.92 m/s^2

(D) 4.90 m/s^2

Answer: A The system is accelerating; therefore Newton's second law applies to the problem, $\Sigma|\vec{F}| = m\vec{a}$.

The force of the 1.00 kg hanging body is $\vec{W}_1 = (1.00 \text{ kg})(9.80 \; m/s^2) = 9.80 \text{ N}$.

The friction between the 2.00 kg mass and the table is $|\vec{f}| = \mu_k N = \mu_k M_2 \vec{g}$.

The frictional force is $|\vec{f}| = 0.10(2.00 \text{ kg})(9.80 \; m/s^2) = 1.96 \text{ N}$.

Substitution into $\Sigma|\vec{F}| = m\vec{a}$ is $9.80 \text{ N} - 1.96 \text{ N} = (2.00 \text{ kg} + 1.00 \text{ kg})\vec{a}$.

The acceleration is $7.84 \text{ N} = (3.00 \text{ kg})\vec{a}$. Then $\vec{a} = 2.61 \; m/s^2$.

STRATEGIES FOR THE FREE-RESPONSE PROBLEM SECTION

Both Section I and Section II of the AP Physics 1 and AP Physics 2 exams come with a table of equations and constants. Here are some rules of thumb to help you work your way through the free-response problems:

- Check the radian/degree mode on your calculator. Set it in the degree mode.
- Scan all of the problems and questions in the section you are working in and mark those that you know you can answer correctly. Do these first.
- You will be provided with an answer booklet as well as an insert that contains the same questions as the answer booklet, but without the spaces. You can remove the insert for reference. All of your work and answers for each problem must be shown in the answer booklet. No credit will be given for work shown on the insert, but you may write on it.
- Show all of your work. Partial credit will be awarded for problems if the correct work is shown but the answer is not present or is incorrect. In problems involving calculations, box or circle your final answer.
- Points are awarded in the scoring of a problem. The awarding of the points is done by the problem rubric. Points are never taken away.
- Cross out incorrect answers and work with an "X" rather than spending time erasing.
- Be clear and organized in your work. If a grader cannot clearly understand your work, you may not receive full credit. Neatness goes a long way.

■ Free-response problems will have sets of parts: (a), (b), (c), etc. Attempt to solve each part. Even if your answer to (a) is incorrect, you still may be awarded points for the remaining parts of the question if the work is correct to that point.

■ Some free-response problems may not have numbers associated with them.

■ Questions that ask for an explanation or justification must be technically correct and answered with complete sentences.

■ Laboratory-related questions must be answered with complete sentences.

■ Units are important in your answers. Place units in each and every step and in the final answer.

■ You do not need to work the problems in order.

■ You should be able to recognize that equations of the form $y = mx + b$ are linear with a slope m and a vertical intercept b. An equation of the form $x = at^2 + bt + c$ is parabolic. An equation of the form $PV = k$ is hyperbolic. You should be able to distinguish between these curves.

■ In graphing P vs. V, P is plotted along the vertical axis and V along the horizontal axis. When graphing $s = f(t)$, s is plotted along the vertical axis and t along the horizontal axis.

■ An answer by itself is not enough. The reader (grader) must see how the solution evolves. A good rule of thumb to follow is to write or derive a working equation, substituting using units, and the final answer with correct units. Circle or box the answer.

SAMPLE PROBLEMS AND SCORING

SAMPLE PROBLEM 1

(15 points) A wood block of mass M is held at rest at the top of an inclined plane of length x, height h, and that makes an angle θ with the horizontal. The block is released from rest and undergoes uniform acceleration down the plane. The coefficient of friction between the contact surfaces is μ.

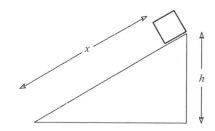

(a) The block slides a short distance down the plane; show and label all of the forces acting on the block.

(b) In terms of the coefficient of friction μ, the mass M of the block, the acceleration due to gravity g, and the angle θ of inclination of the inclined plane, what is the frictional force f acting on the block?

(c) Using energy considerations and in terms of the length of the plane x, μ, g, and θ, what is the velocity of the block at the instant it reaches the bottom of the plane?

(d) In terms of g, μ, and θ, what is the acceleration of the block down the plane?

(e) In terms of M, x, μ, g, and θ, what impulse is generated on the block?

SAMPLE PROBLEM 1 RUBRIC
15 points total

(a) 3 points

1 point is awarded for each correctly drawn and labeled vector.	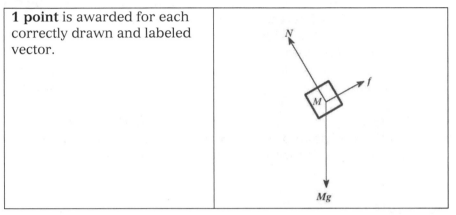

(b) 2 points

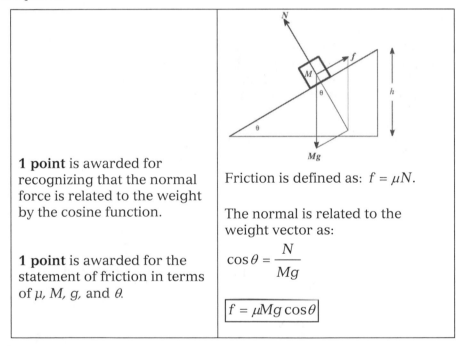

1 point is awarded for recognizing that the normal force is related to the weight by the cosine function.	Friction is defined as: $f = \mu N$. The normal is related to the weight vector as: $\cos\theta = \dfrac{N}{Mg}$
1 point is awarded for the statement of friction in terms of μ, M, g, and θ.	$\boxed{f = \mu Mg \cos\theta}$

(c) 4 points

1 point is awarded for writing an expression of the law of mechanical energy, including work done by a non-conservative force.	$-W_f = \Delta K + \Delta U$ $-fx = K - K_0 + U - U_0$

1 point is awarded for showing that the work done by the non-conservative force is negative (–).	The initial kinetic energy is zero and the final potential energy is zero, giving: $$-fx = K - 0 + 0 - U_0$$ $$K = U_0 - fx$$ Substituting yields: $$\frac{1}{2}Mv^2 = Mgh - (\mu Mg\cos\theta)x$$ h must be eliminated $$h = x\sin\theta$$
1 point is awarded for expressing h in terms of x and θ.	Substituting and dividing out mass M gives: $$\frac{1}{2}v^2 = gx\sin\theta - \mu gx\cos\theta$$ $$v^2 = 2gx(\sin\theta - \mu\cos\theta)$$
1 point is awarded for the expression of v in terms of x, g, μ, and θ.	$$v = \sqrt{2gx(\sin\theta - \mu\cos\theta)}$$

(d) 2 points

1 point is awarded for recognizing the equation to be used.	$$v^2 = v_0^2 + 2ax$$ $$2gx(\sin\theta - \mu\cos\theta) = 0 + 2ax$$
1 point is awarded for the correct expression.	$$a = (\sin\theta - \mu\cos\theta)g$$

(e) 3 points

2 points are awarded for a statement of the impulse-momentum theorem.	$$J = \Delta p$$ $$J = M(v - v_O)$$ $$J = Mv$$
1 point is awarded for the correct expression.	$$J = M\sqrt{2gx(\sin\theta - \mu\cos\theta)}$$

1 additional point is awarded if no extraneous forces are drawn in part (a).

SAMPLE SHORT ANSWER PROBLEM 2

(10 points) A 3.00 g bullet leaves the muzzle of a horizontally mounted rifle with a speed v_0 of 300.0 m/s. The bullet strikes and passes completely through a 0.400 kg wooden block suspended from a long cord. Ignore air resistance.

(a) Explain how you would determine the speed of the bullet as it exits the block. You do not need to do the calculations, but provide complete instructions so that another student could use them to calculate the speed of the bullet as it leaves the block.

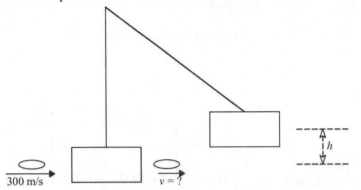

(b) i. How can you determine the work done on the bullet by the block?

ii. How can you find the work done on the block by the bullet?

iii. How can you account for the energy loss in the collision?

(c) What if the bullet, on impact with the block, remains embedded in the block? How high does the block rise compared to the height, h, it reached in part (a)?

_____ greater than h

_____ the same as h

_____ less than h

Justify your answer without making calculations.

SAMPLE SHORT ANSWER PROBLEM RUBRIC

10 points total

(a) 4 points

1 point is awarded for making a statement of the law of conservation of linear momentum.	The total initial momentum of the bullet must equal the total final momentum of the block and the bullet.
1 point is awarded for recognizing that energy is conserved.	The kinetic energy of the block just after the bullet exits will equal the gravitational potential energy the block gains.
1 point is awarded for indicating that the height the block reaches is related to initial speed of the block.	Since the kinetic energy of the block will equal the gain in potential energy, the height the block reaches will give the speed of the block as the bullet exits.
1 point is awarded for the correct statement of substitution of the speed of the block into the initial statement of conservation of momentum.	Substitution of the speed of the block into the initial statement of the conservation of momentum will allow the calculation of the speed of the exiting bullet.

(b) 3 points

1 point is awarded for correct statement.	i. The work done on the bullet by the block is equal to change in the kinetic energy of the bullet.
1 point is awarded for correct statement.	ii. The work done on the block by the bullet equals its change in gravitational potential energy.
1 point is awarded for correct recognition of energy loss.	iii. Possible answers include the thermal energy of the bullet-block system is increased. Energy is transferred into acoustical energy. Work is done by the bullet as it tunnels through the block.

(c) 3 points

1 point is awarded for checking the correct answer.	greater than h
2 points are awarded for the explanation.	The bullet remains embedded in the block and all of the momentum remains within the bullet-block system. The speed of the system as it begins to rise is greater than in part (a). This gives a greater vertical displacement.

AP® PHYSICS
LEARNING OBJECTIVES

The following is the list of learning objectives from the College Board curriculum.

PHYSICS 2	**Learning objective 1.A.2.1** The student is able to construct representations of the differences between a fundamental particle and a system composed of fundamental particles and to relate this to the properties and scales of the systems being investigated.
PHYSICS 2	**Learning objective 1.A.4.1** The student is able to construct representations of the energy level structure of an electron in an atom and to relate this to the properties and scales of the systems being investigated.
PHYSICS 1	**Learning objective 1.A.5.1** The student is able to model verbally or visually the properties of a system based on its substructure and to relate this to changes in the system properties over time as external variables are changed.
PHYSICS 2	**Learning objective 1.A.5.2** The student is able to construct representations of how the properties of a system are determined by the interactions of its constituent substructures.
PHYSICS 1 **PHYSICS 2**	**Learning objective 1.B.1.1** The student is able to make claims about natural phenomena based on conservation of electric charge.
PHYSICS 1 **PHYSICS 2**	**Learning objective 1.B.1.2** The student is able to make predictions, using the conservation of electric charge, about the sign and relative quantity of net charge of objects or systems after various charging processes, including conservation of charge in simple circuits.
PHYSICS 1 **PHYSICS 2**	**Learning objective 1.B.2.1** The student is able to construct an explanation of the two-charge model of electric charge based on evidence produced through scientific practices.

AP® and Advanced Placement Program® are trademarks registered and/or owned by the College Board, which was not involved in the production of, and does not endorse, this product.

PHYSICS 2	**Learning objective 1.B.2.2** The student is able to make a qualitative prediction about the distribution of positive and negative electric charges within neutral systems as they undergo various processes.
PHYSICS 2	**Learning objective 1.B.2.3** The student is able to challenge claims that polarization of electric charge or separation of charge must result in a net charge on the object.
PHYSICS 1 **PHYSICS 2**	**Learning objective 1.B.3.1** The student is able to challenge the claim that an electric charge smaller than the elementary charge has been isolated.
PHYSICS 1	**Learning objective 1.C.1.1** The student is able to design an experiment for collecting data to determine the relationship between the net force exerted on an object, its inertial mass, and its acceleration.
PHYSICS 1	**Learning objective 1.C.3.1** The student is able to design a plan for collecting data to measure gravitational mass and to measure inertial mass, and to distinguish between the two experiments.
PHYSICS 2	**Learning objective 1.C.4.1** The student is able to articulate the reasons that the theory of conservation of mass was replaced by the theory of conservation of mass-energy.
PHYSICS 2	**Learning objective 1.D.1.1** The student is able to explain why classical mechanics cannot describe all properties of objects by articulating the reasons that classical mechanics must be refined and an alternative explanation developed when classical particles display wave properties.
PHYSICS 2	**Learning objective 1.D.3.1** The student is able to articulate the reasons that classical mechanics must be replaced by special relativity to describe the experimental results and theoretical predictions that show that the properties of space and time are not absolute. [Students will be expected to recognize situations in which nonrelativistic classical physics breaks down and to explain how relativity addresses that breakdown, but students will not be expected to know in which of two reference frames a given series of events corresponds to a greater or lesser time interval, or a greater or lesser spatial distance; they will just need to know that observers in the two reference frames can "disagree" about some time and distance intervals.]
PHYSICS 2	**Learning objective 1.E.1.1** The student is able to predict the densities, differences in densities, or changes in densities under different conditions for natural phenomena and design an investigation to verify the prediction.
PHYSICS 2	**Learning objective 1.E.1.2** The student is able to select from experimental data the information necessary to determine the density of an object and/ or compare densities of several objects.

PHYSICS 1 **PHYSICS 2**	**Learning objective 1.E.2.1** The student is able to choose and justify the selection of data needed to determine resistivity for a given material.
PHYSICS 2	**Learning objective 1.E.3.1** The student is able to design an experiment and analyze data from it to examine thermal conductivity.
PHYSICS 1	**Learning objective 2.B.1.1** The student is able to apply $\vec{F} = m\vec{g}$ to calculate the gravitational force on an object with mass m in a gravitational field of strength g in the context of the effects of a net force on objects and systems.
PHYSICS 1	**Learning objective 2.B.2.1** The student is able to apply $g = G\dfrac{M}{r^2}$ to calculate the gravitational field due to an object with mass M, where the field is a vector directed toward the center of the object of mass M.
PHYSICS 1	**Learning objective 2.B.2.2** The student is able to approximate a numerical value of the gravitational field (g) near the surface of an object from its radius and mass relative to those of the Earth or other reference objects.
PHYSICS 2	**Learning objective 2.C.1.1** The student is able to predict the direction and the magnitude of the force exerted on an object with an electric charge q placed in an electric field E using the mathematical model of the relation between an electric force and an electric field: $\vec{F} = q\vec{E}$; a vector relation.
PHYSICS 2	**Learning objective 2.C.1.2** The student is able to calculate any one of the variables — electric force, electric charge, and electric field — at a point given the values and sign or direction of the other two quantities.
PHYSICS 2	**Learning objective 2.C.2.1** The student is able to qualitatively and semi-quantitatively apply the vector relationship between the electric field and the net electric charge creating that field.
PHYSICS 2	**Learning objective 2.C.3.1** The student is able to explain the inverse square dependence of the electric field surrounding a spherically symmetric electrically charged object.
PHYSICS 2	**Learning objective 2.C.4.1** The student is able to distinguish the characteristics that differ between monopole fields (gravitational field of spherical mass and electrical field due to single point charge) and dipole fields (electric dipole field and magnetic field) and make claims about the spatial behavior of the fields using qualitative or semiquantitative arguments based on vector addition of fields due to each point source, including identifying the locations and signs of sources from a vector diagram of the field.

PHYSICS 2	**Learning objective 2.C.4.2** The student is able to apply mathematical routines to determine the magnitude and direction of the electric field at specified points in the vicinity of a small set (2–4) of point charges, and express the results in terms of magnitude and direction of the field in a visual representation by drawing field vectors of appropriate length and direction at the specified points.
PHYSICS 2	**Learning objective 2.C.5.1** The student is able to create representations of the magnitude and direction of the electric field at various distances (small compared to plate size) from two electrically charged plates of equal magnitude and opposite signs, and is able to recognize that the assumption of uniform field is not appropriate near edges of plates.
PHYSICS 2	**Learning objective 2.C.5.2** The student is able to calculate the magnitude and determine the direction of the electric field between two electrically charged parallel plates, given the charge of each plate, or the electric potential difference and plate separation.
PHYSICS 2	**Learning objective 2.C.5.3** The student is able to represent the motion of an electrically charged particle in the uniform field between two oppositely charged plates and express the connection of this motion to projectile motion of an object with mass in the Earth's gravitational field.
PHYSICS 2	**Learning objective 2.D.1.1** The student is able to apply mathematical routines to express the force exerted on a moving charged object by a magnetic field.
PHYSICS 2	**Learning objective 2.D.2.1** The student is able to create a verbal or visual representation of a magnetic field around a long straight wire or a pair of parallel wires.
PHYSICS 2	**Learning objective 2.D.3.1** The student is able to describe the orientation of a magnetic dipole placed in a magnetic field in general and the particular cases of a compass in the magnetic field of the Earth and iron filings surrounding a bar magnet.
PHYSICS 2	**Learning objective 2.D.4.1** The student is able to use the representation of magnetic domains to qualitatively analyze the magnetic behavior of a bar magnet composed of ferromagnetic material.
PHYSICS 2	**Learning objective 2.E.1.1** The student is able to construct or interpret visual representations of the isolines of equal gravitational potential energy per unit mass and refer to each line as a gravitational equipotential.
PHYSICS 2	**Learning objective 2.E.2.1** The student is able to determine the structure of isolines of electric potential by constructing them in a given electric field.

PHYSICS 2	**Learning objective 2.E.2.2** The student is able to predict the structure of isolines of electric potential by constructing them in a given electric field and make connections between these isolines and those found in a gravitational field.
PHYSICS 2	**Learning objective 2.E.2.3** The student is able to qualitatively use the concept of isolines to construct isolines of electric potential in an electric field and determine the effect of that field on electrically charged objects.
PHYSICS 2	**Learning objective 2.E.3.1** The student is able to apply mathematical routines to calculate the average value of the magnitude of the electric field in a region from a description of the electric potential in that region using the displacement along the line on which the difference in potential is evaluated.
PHYSICS 2	**Learning objective 2.E.3.2** The student is able to apply the concept of the isoline representation of electric potential for a given electric charge distribution to predict the average value of the electric field in the region.
PHYSICS 1	**Learning objective 3.A.1.1** The student is able to express the motion of an object using narrative, mathematical, and graphical representations.
PHYSICS 1	**Learning objective 3.A.1.2** The student is able to design an experimental investigation of the motion of an object.
PHYSICS 1	**Learning objective 3.A.1.3** The student is able to analyze experimental data describing the motion of an object and is able to express the results of the analysis using narrative, mathematical, and graphical representations.
PHYSICS 1 **PHYSICS 2**	**Learning objective 3.A.2.1** The student is able to represent forces in diagrams or mathematically using appropriately labeled vectors with magnitude, direction, and units during the analysis of a situation.
PHYSICS 1	**Learning objective 3.A.3.1** The student is able to analyze a scenario and make claims (develop arguments, justify assertions) about the forces exerted on an object by other objects for different types of forces or components of forces.
PHYSICS 1 **PHYSICS 2**	**Learning objective 3.A.3.2** The student is able to challenge a claim that an object can exert a force on itself.
PHYSICS 1 **PHYSICS 2**	**Learning objective 3.A.3.3** The student is able to describe a force as an interaction between two objects and identify both objects for any force.
PHYSICS 2	**Learning objective 3.A.3.4** The student is able to make claims about the force on an object due to the presence of other objects with the same property: mass, electric charge.

PHYSICS 1 **PHYSICS 2**	**Learning objective 3.A.4.1** The student is able to construct explanations of physical situations involving the interaction of bodies using Newton's third law and the representation of action-reaction pairs of forces.
PHYSICS 1 **PHYSICS 2**	**Learning objective 3.A.4.2** The student is able to use Newton's third law to make claims and predictions about the action-reaction pairs of forces when two objects interact.
PHYSICS 1 **PHYSICS 2**	**Learning objective 3.A.4.3** The student is able to analyze situations involving interactions among several objects by using free-body diagrams that include the application of Newton's third law to identify forces.
PHYSICS 1	**Learning objective 3.B.1.1** The student is able to predict the motion of an object subject to forces exerted by several objects using an application of Newton's second law in a variety of physical situations with acceleration in one dimension.
PHYSICS 1	**Learning objective 3.B.1.2** The student is able to design a plan to collect and analyze data for motion (static, constant, or accelerating) from force measurements and carry out an analysis to determine the relationship between the net force and the vector sum of the individual forces.
PHYSICS 1 **PHYSICS 2**	**Learning objective 3.B.1.3** The student is able to reexpress a free-body diagram representation into a mathematical representation and solve the mathematical representation for the acceleration of the object.
PHYSICS 2	**Learning objective 3.B.1.4** The student is able to predict the motion of an object subject to forces exerted by several objects using an application of Newton's second law in a variety of physical situations.
PHYSICS 1 **PHYSICS 2**	**Learning objective 3.B.2.1** The student is able to create and use free-body diagrams to analyze physical situations to solve problems with motion qualitatively and quantitatively.
PHYSICS 1	**Learning objective 3.B.3.1** The student is able to predict which properties determine the motion of a simple harmonic oscillator and what the dependence of the motion is on those properties.
PHYSICS 1	**Learning objective 3.B.3.2** The student is able to design a plan and collect data in order to ascertain the characteristics of the motion of a system undergoing oscillatory motion caused by a restoring force.
PHYSICS 1	**Learning objective 3.B.3.3** The student can analyze data to identify qualitative or quantitative relationships between given values and variables (i.e., force, displacement, acceleration, velocity, period of motion, frequency, spring constant, string length, mass) associated with objects in oscillatory motion to use that data to determine the value of an unknown.

PHYSICS 1	**Learning objective 3.B.3.4** The student is able to construct a qualitative and/or a quantitative explanation of oscillatory behavior given evidence of a restoring force.
PHYSICS 1	**Learning objective 3.C.1.1** The student is able to use Newton's law of gravitation to calculate the gravitational force the two objects exert on each other and use that force in contexts other than orbital motion.
PHYSICS 1	**Learning objective 3.C.1.2** The student is able to use Newton's law of gravitation to calculate the gravitational force between two objects and use that force in contexts involving orbital motion (for circular orbital motion only in Physics 1).
PHYSICS 1 **PHYSICS 2**	**Learning objective 3.C.2.1** The student is able to use Coulomb's law qualitatively and quantitatively to make predictions about the interaction between two electric point charges (interactions between collections of electric point charges are not covered in Physics 1 and instead are restricted to Physics 2).
PHYSICS 1 **PHYSICS 2**	**Learning objective 3.C.2.2** The student is able to connect the concepts of gravitational force and electric force to compare similarities and differences between the forces.
PHYSICS 2	**Learning objective 3.C.2.3** The student is able to use mathematics to describe the electric force that results from the interaction of several separated point charges (generally 2 to 4 point charges, though more are permitted in situations of high symmetry).
PHYSICS 2	**Learning objective 3.C.3.1** The student is able to use right-hand rules to analyze a situation involving a current-carrying conductor and a moving electrically charged object to determine the direction of the magnetic force exerted on the charged object due to the magnetic field created by the current-carrying conductor.
PHYSICS 2	**Learning objective 3.C.3.2** The student is able to plan a data collection strategy appropriate to an investigation of the direction of the force on a moving electrically charged object caused by a current in a wire in the context of a specific set of equipment and instruments and analyze the resulting data to arrive at a conclusion.
PHYSICS 1 **PHYSICS 2**	**Learning objective 3.C.4.1** The student is able to make claims about various contact forces between objects based on the microscopic cause of those forces.
PHYSICS 1 **PHYSICS 2**	**Learning objective 3.C.4.2** The student is able to explain contact forces (tension, friction, normal, buoyant, spring) as arising from interatomic electric forces and that they therefore have certain directions.

PHYSICS 1	**Learning objective 3.D.1.1** The student is able to justify the selection of data needed to determine the relationship between the direction of the force acting on an object and the change in momentum caused by that force.
PHYSICS 1	**Learning objective 3.D.2.1** The student is able to justify the selection of routines for the calculation of the relationships between changes in momentum of an object, average force, impulse, and time of interaction.
PHYSICS 1	**Learning objective 3.D.2.2** The student is able to predict the change in momentum of an object from the average force exerted on the object and the interval of time during which the force is exerted.
PHYSICS 1	**Learning objective 3.D.2.3** The student is able to analyze data to characterize the change in momentum of an object from the average force exerted on the object and the interval of time during which the force is exerted.
PHYSICS 1	**Learning objective 3.D.2.4** The student is able to design a plan for collecting data to investigate the relationship between changes in momentum and the average force exerted on an object over time.
PHYSICS 1	**Learning objective 3.E.1.1** The student is able to make predictions about the changes in kinetic energy of an object based on considerations of the direction of the net force on the object as the object moves.
PHYSICS 1	**Learning objective 3.E.1.2** The student is able to use net force and velocity vectors to determine qualitatively whether kinetic energy of an object would increase, decrease, or remain unchanged.
PHYSICS 1	**Learning objective 3.E.1.3** The student is able to use force and velocity vectors to determine qualitatively or quantitatively the net force exerted on an object and qualitatively whether kinetic energy of that object would increase, decrease, or remain unchanged.
PHYSICS 1	**Learning objective 3.E.1.4** The student is able to apply mathematical routines to determine the change in kinetic energy of an object given the forces on the object and the displacement of the object.
PHYSICS 1	**Learning objective 3.F.1.1** The student is able to use representations of the relationship between force and torque.
PHYSICS 1	**Learning objective 3.F.1.2** The student is able to compare the torques on an object caused by various forces.
PHYSICS 1	**Learning objective 3.F.1.3** The student is able to estimate the torque on an object caused by various forces in comparison to other situations.

Physics 1	**Learning objective 3.F.1.4** The student is able to design an experiment and analyze data testing a question about torques in a balanced rigid system.
Physics 1	**Learning objective 3.F.1.5** The student is able to calculate torques on a two-dimensional system in static equilibrium, by examining a representation or model (such as a diagram or physical construction).
Physics 1	**Learning objective 3.F.2.1** The student is able to make predictions about the change in the angular velocity about an axis for an object when forces exerted on the object cause a torque about that axis.
Physics 1	**Learning objective 3.F.2.2** The student is able to plan data collection and analysis strategies designed to test the relationship between a torque exerted on an object and the change in angular velocity of that object about an axis.
Physics 1	**Learning objective 3.F.3.1** The student is able to predict the behavior of rotational collision situations by the same processes that are used to analyze linear collision situations using an analogy between impulse and change of linear momentum and angular impulse and change of angular momentum.
Physics 1	**Learning objective 3.F.3.2** In an unfamiliar context or using representations beyond equations, the student is able to justify the selection of a mathematical routine to solve for the change in angular momentum of an object caused by torques exerted on the object.
Physics 1	**Learning objective 3.F.3.3** The student is able to plan data collection and analysis strategies designed to test the relationship between torques exerted on an object and the change in angular momentum of that object.
Physics 1	**Learning objective 3.G.1.1** The student is able to articulate situations when the gravitational force is the dominant force and when the electromagnetic, weak, and strong forces can be ignored.
Physics 2	**Learning objective 3.G.1.2** The student is able to connect the strength of the gravitational force between two objects to the spatial scale of the situation and the masses of the objects involved and compare that strength to other types of forces.
Physics 2	**Learning objective 3.G.2.1** The student is able to connect the strength of electromagnetic forces with the spatial scale of the situation, the magnitude of the electric charges, and the motion of the electrically charged objects involved.
Physics 2	**Learning objective 3.G.3.1** The student is able to identify the strong force as the force that is responsible for holding the nucleus together.

PHYSICS 1	**Learning objective 4.A.1.1** The student is able to use representations of the center of mass of an isolated two-object system to analyze the motion of the system qualitatively and semiquantitatively.
PHYSICS 1	**Learning objective 4.A.2.1** The student is able to make predictions about the motion of a system based on the fact that acceleration is equal to the change in velocity per unit time, and velocity is equal to the change in position per unit time.
PHYSICS 1	**Learning objective 4.A.2.2** The student is able to evaluate using given data whether all the forces on a system or whether all the parts of a system have been identified.
PHYSICS 1	**Learning objective 4.A.2.3** The student is able to create mathematical models and analyze graphical relationships for acceleration, velocity, and position of the center of mass of a system and use them to calculate properties of the motion of the center of mass of a system.
PHYSICS 1	**Learning objective 4.A.3.1** The student is able to apply Newton's second law to systems to calculate the change in the center-of-mass velocity when an external force is exerted on the system.
PHYSICS 1	**Learning objective 4.A.3.2** The student is able to use visual or mathematical representations of the forces between objects in a system to predict whether or not there will be a change in the center-of-mass velocity of that system.
PHYSICS 1	**Learning objective 4.B.1.1** The student is able to calculate the change in linear momentum of a two-object system with constant mass in linear motion from a representation of the system (data, graphs, etc.).
PHYSICS 1	**Learning objective 4.B.1.2** The student is able to analyze data to find the change in linear momentum for a constant-mass system using the product of the mass and the change in velocity of the center of mass.
PHYSICS 1	**Learning objective 4.B.2.1** The student is able to apply mathematical routines to calculate the change in momentum of a system by analyzing the average force exerted over a certain time on the system.
PHYSICS 1	**Learning objective 4.B.2.2** The student is able to perform analysis on data presented as a force-time graph and predict the change in momentum of a system.
PHYSICS 1	**Learning objective 4.C.1.1** The student is able to calculate the total energy of a system and justify the mathematical routines used in the calculation of component types of energy within the system whose sum is the total energy.

PHYSICS 1 **Learning objective 4.C.1.2** The student is able to predict changes in the total energy of a system due to changes in position and speed of objects or frictional interactions within the system.

PHYSICS 1 **Learning objective 4.C.2.1** The student is able to make predictions about the changes in the mechanical energy of a system when a component of an external force acts parallel or antiparallel to the direction of the displacement of the center of mass.

PHYSICS 1 **Learning objective 4.C.2.2** The student is able to apply the concepts of conservation of energy and the work-energy theorem to determine qualitatively and/or quantitatively that work done on a two-object system in linear motion will change the kinetic energy of the center of mass of the system, the potential energy of the systems, and/or the internal energy of the system.

PHYSICS 2 **Learning objective 4.C.3.1** The student is able to make predictions about the direction of energy transfer due to temperature differences based on interactions at the microscopic level.

PHYSICS 2 **Learning objective 4.C.4.1** The student is able to apply mathematical routines to describe the relationship between mass and energy and apply this concept across domains of scale.

PHYSICS 1 **Learning objective 4.D.1.1** The student is able to describe a representation and use it to analyze a situation in which several forces exerted on a rotating system of rigidly connected objects change the angular velocity and angular momentum of the system.

PHYSICS 1 **Learning objective 4.D.1.2** The student is able to plan data collection strategies designed to establish that torque, angular velocity, angular acceleration, and angular momentum can be predicted accurately when the variables are treated as being clockwise or counterclockwise with respect to a well-defined axis of rotation, and refine the research question based on the examination of data.

PHYSICS 1 **Learning objective 4.D.2.1** The student is able to describe a model of a rotational system and use that model to analyze a situation in which angular momentum changes due to interaction with other objects or systems.

PHYSICS 1 **Learning objective 4.D.2.2** The student is able to plan a data collection and analysis strategy to determine the change in angular momentum of a system and relate it to interactions with other objects and systems.

Physics 1	**Learning objective 4.D.3.1** The student is able to use appropriate mathematical routines to calculate values for initial or final angular momentum, or change in angular momentum of a system, or average torque or time during which the torque is exerted in analyzing a situation involving torque and angular momentum.
Physics 1	**Learning objective 4.D.3.2** The student is able to plan a data collection strategy designed to test the relationship between the change in angular momentum of a system and the product of the average torque applied to the system and the time interval during which the torque is exerted.
Physics 2	**Learning objective 4.E.1.1** The student is able to use representations and models to qualitatively describe the magnetic properties of some materials that can be affected by magnetic properties of other objects in the system.
Physics 2	**Learning objective 4.E.2.1** The student is able to construct an explanation of the function of a simple electromagnetic device in which an induced emf is produced by a changing magnetic flux through an area defined by a current loop (i.e., a simple microphone or generator) or of the effect on behavior of a device in which an induced emf is produced by a constant magnetic field through a changing area.
Physics 2	**Learning objective 4.E.3.1** The student is able to make predictions about the redistribution of charge during charging by friction, conduction, and induction.
Physics 2	**Learning objective 4.E.3.2** The student is able to make predictions about the redistribution of charge caused by the electric field due to other systems, resulting in charged or polarized objects.
Physics 2	**Learning objective 4.E.3.3** The student is able to construct a representation of the distribution of fixed and mobile charge in insulators and conductors.
Physics 2	**Learning objective 4.E.3.4** The student is able to construct a representation of the distribution of fixed and mobile charge in insulators and conductors that predicts charge distribution in processes involving induction or conduction.
Physics 2	**Learning objective 4.E.3.5** The student is able to plan and/or analyze the results of experiments in which electric charge rearrangement occurs by electrostatic induction, or is able to refine a scientific question relating to such an experiment by identifying anomalies in a data set or procedure.
Physics 2	**Learning objective 4.E.4.1** The student is able to make predictions about the properties of resistors and/or capacitors when placed in a simple circuit, based on the geometry of the circuit element and supported by scientific theories and mathematical relationships.

Physics 2	**Learning objective 4.E.4.2** The student is able to design a plan for the collection of data to determine the effect of changing the geometry and/or materials on the resistance or capacitance of a circuit element and relate results to the basic properties of resistors and capacitors.
Physics 2	**Learning objective 4.E.4.3** The student is able to analyze data to determine the effect of changing the geometry and/or materials on the resistance or capacitance of a circuit element and relate results to the basic properties of resistors and capacitors.
Physics 2	**Learning objective 4.E.5.1** The student is able to make and justify a quantitative prediction of the effect of a change in values or arrangements of one or two circuit elements on the currents and potential differences in a circuit containing a small number of sources of emf, resistors, capacitors, and switches in series and/or parallel.
Physics 2	**Learning objective 4.E.5.2** The student is able to make and justify a qualitative prediction of the effect of a change in values or arrangements of one or two circuit elements on currents and potential differences in a circuit containing a small number of sources of emf, resistors, capacitors, and switches in series and/or parallel.
Physics 2	**Learning objective 4.E.5.3** The student is able to plan data collection strategies and perform data analysis to examine the values of currents and potential differences in an electric circuit that is modified by changing or rearranging circuit elements, including sources of emf, resistors, and capacitors.
Physics 1	**Learning objective 5.A.2.1** The student is able to define open and closed systems for everyday situations and apply conservation concepts for energy, charge, and linear momentum to those situations.
Physics 1	**Learning objective 5.B.1.1** The student is able to set up a representation or model showing that a single object can only have kinetic energy and use information about that object to calculate its kinetic energy.
Physics 1	**Learning objective 5.B.1.2** The student is able to translate between a representation of a single object, which can only have kinetic energy, and a system that includes the object, which may have both kinetic and potential energies.
Physics 1 **Physics 2**	**Learning objective 5.B.2.1** The student is able to calculate the expected behavior of a system using the object model (i.e., by ignoring changes in internal structure) to analyze a situation. Then, when the model fails, the student can justify the use of conservation of energy principles to calculate the change in internal energy due to changes in internal structure because the object is actually a system.

PHYSICS 1	**Learning objective 5.B.3.1** The student is able to describe and make qualitative and/or quantitative predictions about everyday examples of systems with internal potential energy.
PHYSICS 1	**Learning objective 5.B.3.2** The student is able to make quantitative calculations of the internal potential energy of a system from a description or diagram of that system.
PHYSICS 1	**Learning objective 5.B.3.3** The student is able to apply mathematical reasoning to create a description of the internal potential energy of a system from a description or diagram of the objects and interactions in that system.
PHYSICS 1 **PHYSICS 2**	**Learning objective 5.B.4.1** The student is able to describe and make predictions about the internal energy of systems.
PHYSICS 1 **PHYSICS 2**	**Learning objective 5.B.4.2** The student is able to calculate changes in kinetic energy and potential energy of a system, using information from representations of that system.
PHYSICS 1	**Learning objective 5.B.5.1** The student is able to design an experiment and analyze data to examine how a force exerted on an object or system does work on the object or system as it moves through a distance.
PHYSICS 1	**Learning objective 5.B.5.2** The student is able to design an experiment and analyze graphical data in which interpretations of the area under a force-distance curve are needed to determine the work done on or by the object or system.
PHYSICS 1	**Learning objective 5.B.5.3** The student is able to predict and calculate from graphical data the energy transfer to or work done on an object or system from information about a force exerted on the object or system through a distance.
PHYSICS 1 **PHYSICS 2**	**Learning objective 5.B.5.4** The student is able to make claims about the interaction between a system and its environment in which the environment exerts a force on the system, thus doing work on the system and changing the energy of the system (kinetic energy plus potential energy).
PHYSICS 1 **PHYSICS 2**	**Learning objective 5.B.5.5** The student is able to predict and calculate the energy transfer to (i.e., the work done on) an object or system from information about a force exerted on the object or system through a distance.
PHYSICS 2	**Learning objective 5.B.5.6** The student is able to design an experiment and analyze graphical data in which interpretations of the area under a pressure-volume curve are needed to determine the work done on or by the object or system.

PHYSICS 2	**Learning objective 5.B.6.1** The student is able to describe the models that represent processes by which energy can be transferred between a system and its environment because of differences in temperature: conduction, convection, and radiation.
PHYSICS 2	**Learning objective 5.B.7.1** The student is able to predict qualitative changes in the internal energy of a thermodynamic system involving transfer of energy due to heat or work done and justify those predictions in terms of conservation of energy principles.
PHYSICS 2	**Learning objective 5.B.7.2** The student is able to create a plot of pressure versus volume for a thermodynamic process from given data.
PHYSICS 2	**Learning objective 5.B.7.3** The student is able to use a plot of pressure versus volume for a thermodynamic process to make calculations of internal energy changes, heat, or work, based upon conservation of energy principles (i.e., the first law of thermodynamics).
PHYSICS 2	**Learning objective 5.B.8.1** The student is able to describe emission or absorption spectra associated with electronic or nuclear transitions as transitions between allowed energy states of the atom in terms of the principle of energy conservation, including characterization of the frequency of radiation emitted or absorbed.
PHYSICS 1	**Learning objective 5.B.9.1** The student is able to construct or interpret a graph of the energy changes within an electrical circuit with only a single battery and resistors in series and/or in, at most, one parallel branch as an application of the conservation of energy (Kirchhoff's loop rule).
PHYSICS 1	**Learning objective 5.B.9.2** The student is able to apply conservation of energy concepts to the design of an experiment that will demonstrate the validity of Kirchhoff's loop rule ($\Sigma \Delta V = 0$) in a circuit with only a battery and resistors either in series or in, at most, one pair of parallel branches.
PHYSICS 1	**Learning objective 5.B.9.3** The student is able to apply conservation of energy (Kirchhoff's loop rule) in calculations involving the total electric potential difference for complete circuit loops with only a single battery and resistors in series and/or in, at most, one parallel branch.
PHYSICS 2	**Learning objective 5.B.9.4** The student is able to analyze experimental data including an analysis of experimental uncertainty that will demonstrate the validity of Kirchhoff's loop rule ($\Sigma \Delta V = 0$).

PHYSICS 2	**Learning objective 5.B.9.5** The student is able to use conservation of energy principles (Kirchhoff's loop rule) to describe and make predictions regarding electrical potential difference, charge, and current in steady-state circuits composed of various combinations of resistors and capacitors.
PHYSICS 2	**Learning objective 5.B.9.6** The student is able to mathematically express the changes in electric potential energy of a loop in a multiloop electrical circuit and justify this expression using the principle of the conservation of energy.
PHYSICS 2	**Learning objective 5.B.9.7** The student is able to refine and analyze a scientific question for an experiment using Kirchhoff's Loop rule for circuits that includes determination of internal resistance of the battery and analysis of a non-ohmic resistor.
PHYSICS 2	**Learning objective 5.B.9.8** The student is able to translate between graphical and symbolic representations of experimental data describing relationships among power, current, and potential difference across a resistor.
PHYSICS 2	**Learning objective 5.B.10.1** The student is able to use Bernoulli's equation to make calculations related to a moving fluid.
PHYSICS 2	**Learning objective 5.B.10.2** The student is able to use Bernoulli's equation and/or the relationship between force and pressure to make calculations related to a moving fluid.
PHYSICS 2	**Learning objective 5.B.10.3** The student is able to use Bernoulli's equation and the continuity equation to make calculations related to a moving fluid.
PHYSICS 2	**Learning objective 5.B.10.4** The student is able to construct an explanation of Bernoulli's equation in terms of the conservation of energy.
PHYSICS 2	**Learning objective 5.B.11.1** The student is able to apply conservation of mass and conservation of energy concepts to a natural phenomenon and use the equation $E = mc^2$ to make a related calculation.
PHYSICS 2	**Learning objective 5.C.1.1** The student is able to analyze electric charge conservation for nuclear and elementary particle reactions and make predictions related to such reactions based upon conservation of charge.
PHYSICS 2	**Learning objective 5.C.2.1** The student is able to predict electric charges on objects within a system by application of the principle of charge conservation within a system.

Physics 2	**Learning objective 5.C.2.2** The student is able to design a plan to collect data on the electrical charging of objects and electric charge induction on neutral objects and qualitatively analyze that data.
Physics 2	**Learning objective 5.C.2.3** The student is able to justify the selection of data relevant to an investigation of the electrical charging of objects and electric charge induction on neutral objects.
Physics 1	**Learning objective 5.C.3.1** The student is able to apply conservation of electric charge (Kirchhoff's junction rule) to the comparison of electric current in various segments of an electrical circuit with a single battery and resistors in series and in, at most, one parallel branch and predict how those values would change if configurations of the circuit are changed.
Physics 1	**Learning objective 5.C.3.2** The student is able to design an investigation of an electrical circuit with one or more resistors in which evidence of conservation of electric charge can be collected and analyzed.
Physics 1	**Learning objective 5.C.3.3** The student is able to use a description or schematic diagram of an electrical circuit to calculate unknown values of current in various segments or branches of the circuit.
Physics 2	**Learning objective 5.C.3.4** The student is able to predict or explain current values in series and parallel arrangements of resistors and other branching circuits using Kirchhoff's junction rule and relate the rule to the law of charge conservation.
Physics 2	**Learning objective 5.C.3.5** The student is able to determine missing values and direction of electric current in branches of a circuit with resistors and NO capacitors from values and directions of current in other branches of the circuit through appropriate selection of nodes and application of the junction rule.
Physics 2	**Learning objective 5.C.3.6** The student is able to determine missing values and direction of electric current in branches of a circuit with both resistors and capacitors from values and directions of current in other branches of the circuit through appropriate selection of nodes and application of the junction rule.
Physics 2	**Learning objective 5.C.3.7** The student is able to determine missing values, direction of electric current, charge of capacitors at steady state, and potential differences within a circuit with resistors and capacitors from values and directions of current in other branches of the circuit.

PHYSICS 1	**Learning objective 5.D.1.1** The student is able to make qualitative predictions about natural phenomena based on conservation of linear momentum and restoration of kinetic energy in elastic collisions.
PHYSICS 1	**Learning objective 5.D.1.2** The student is able to apply the principles of conservation of momentum and restoration of kinetic energy to reconcile a situation that appears to be isolated and elastic, but in which data indicate that linear momentum and kinetic energy are not the same after the interaction, by refining a scientific question to identify interactions that have not been considered. Students will be expected to solve qualitatively and/or quantitatively for one-dimensional situations and only qualitatively in two-dimensional situations.
PHYSICS 1	**Learning objective 5.D.1.3** The student is able to apply mathematical routines appropriately to problems involving elastic collisions in one dimension and justify the selection of those mathematical routines based on conservation of momentum and restoration of kinetic energy.
PHYSICS 1	**Learning objective 5.D.1.4** The student is able to design an experimental test of an application of the principle of the conservation of linear momentum, predict an outcome of the experiment using the principle, analyze data generated by that experiment whose uncertainties are expressed numerically, and evaluate the match between the prediction and the outcome.
PHYSICS 1	**Learning objective 5.D.1.5** The student is able to classify a given collision situation as elastic or inelastic, justify the selection of conservation of linear momentum and restoration of kinetic energy as the appropriate principles for analyzing an elastic collision, solve for missing variables, and calculate their values.
PHYSICS 2	**Learning objective 5.D.1.6** The student is able to make predictions of the dynamical properties of a system undergoing a collision by application of the principle of linear momentum conservation and the principle of the conservation of energy in situations in which an elastic collision may also be assumed.
PHYSICS 2	**Learning objective 5.D.1.7** The student is able to classify a given collision situation as elastic or inelastic, justify the selection of conservation of linear momentum and restoration of kinetic energy as the appropriate principles for analyzing an elastic collision, solve for missing variables, and calculate their values.
PHYSICS 1	**Learning objective 5.D.2.1** The student is able to qualitatively predict, in terms of linear momentum and kinetic energy, how the outcome of a collision between two objects changes depending on whether the collision is elastic or inelastic.

PHYSICS 1	**Learning objective 5.D.2.2** The student is able to plan data collection strategies to test the law of conservation of momentum in a two-object collision that is elastic or inelastic and analyze the resulting data graphically.
PHYSICS 1	**Learning objective 5.D.2.3** The student is able to apply the conservation of linear momentum to a closed system of objects involved in an inelastic collision to predict the change in kinetic energy.
PHYSICS 1	**Learning objective 5.D.2.4** The student is able to analyze data that verify conservation of momentum in collisions with and without an external friction force.
PHYSICS 1 **PHYSICS 2**	**Learning objective 5.D.2.5** The student is able to classify a given collision situation as elastic or inelastic, justify the selection of conservation of linear momentum as the appropriate solution method for an inelastic collision, recognize that there is a common final velocity for the colliding objects in the totally inelastic case, solve for missing variables, and calculate their values.
PHYSICS 2	**Learning objective 5.D.2.6** The student is able to apply the conservation of linear momentum to a closed system of objects involved in an inelastic collision to predict the change in kinetic energy.
PHYSICS 1	**Learning objective 5.D.3.1** The student is able to predict the velocity of the center of mass of a system when there is no interaction outside of the system but there is an interaction within the system (i.e., the student simply recognizes that interactions within a system do not affect the center of mass motion of the system and is able to determine that there is no external force).
PHYSICS 2	**Learning objective 5.D.3.2** The student is able to make predictions about the velocity of the center of mass for interactions within a defined one-dimensional system.
PHYSICS 2	**Learning objective 5.D.3.3** The student is able to make predictions about the velocity of the center of mass for interactions within a defined two-dimensional system.
PHYSICS 1	**Learning objective 5.E.1.1** The student is able to make qualitative predictions about the angular momentum of a system for a situation in which there is no net external torque.
PHYSICS 1	**Learning objective 5.E.1.2** The student is able to make calculations of quantities related to the angular momentum of a system when the net external torque on the system is zero.

PHYSICS 1	**Learning objective 5.E.2.1** The student is able to describe or calculate the angular momentum and rotational inertia of a system in terms of the locations and velocities of objects that make up the system. Students are expected to do qualitative reasoning with compound objects. Students are expected to do calculations with a fixed set of extended objects and point masses.
PHYSICS 2	**Learning objective 5.F.1.1** The student is able to make calculations of quantities related to flow of a fluid, using mass conservation principles (the continuity equation).
PHYSICS 2	**Learning objective 5.G.1.1** The student is able to apply conservation of nucleon number and conservation of electric charge to make predictions about nuclear reactions and decays such as fission, fusion, alpha decay, beta decay, or gamma decay.
PHYSICS 1	**Learning objective 6.A.1.1** The student is able to use a visual representation to construct an explanation of the distinction between transverse and longitudinal waves by focusing on the vibration that generates the wave.
PHYSICS 1 PHYSICS 2	**Learning objective 6.A.1.2** The student is able to describe representations of transverse and longitudinal waves.
PHYSICS 2	**Learning objective 6.A.1.3** The student is able to analyze data (or a visual representation) to identify patterns that indicate that a particular mechanical wave is polarized and construct an explanation of the fact that the wave must have a vibration perpendicular to the direction of energy propagation.
PHYSICS 1	**Learning objective 6.A.2.1** The student is able to describe sound in terms of transfer of energy and momentum in a medium and relate the concepts to everyday examples.
PHYSICS 2	**Learning objective 6.A.2.2** The student is able to contrast mechanical and electromagnetic waves in terms of the need for a medium in wave propagation.
PHYSICS 1	**Learning objective 6.A.3.1** The student is able to use graphical representation of a periodic mechanical wave to determine the amplitude of the wave.
PHYSICS 1	**Learning objective 6.A.4.1** The student is able to explain and/or predict qualitatively how the energy carried by a sound wave relates to the amplitude of the wave, and/or apply this concept to a real-world example.
PHYSICS 1	**Learning objective 6.B.1.1** The student is able to use a graphical representation of a periodic mechanical wave (position versus time) to determine the period and frequency of the wave and describe how a change in the frequency would modify features of the representation.

PHYSICS 1   **Learning objective 6.B.2.1** The student is able to use a visual representation of a periodic mechanical wave to determine wavelength of the wave.

PHYSICS 2   **Learning objective 6.B.3.1** The student is able to construct an equation relating the wavelength and amplitude of a wave from a graphical representation of the electric or magnetic field value as a function of position at a given time instant and vice versa, or construct an equation relating the frequency or period and amplitude of a wave from a graphical representation of the electric or magnetic field value at a given position as a function of time and vice versa.

PHYSICS 1   **Learning objective 6.B.4.1** The student is able to design an experiment to determine the relationship between periodic wave speed, wavelength, and frequency and relate these concepts to everyday examples.

PHYSICS 1
PHYSICS 2   **Learning objective 6.B.5.1** The student is able to create or use a wave front diagram to demonstrate or interpret qualitatively the observed frequency of a wave, dependent upon relative motions of source and observer.

PHYSICS 2   **Learning objective 6.C.1.1** The student is able to make claims and predictions about the net disturbance that occurs when two waves overlap. Examples should include standing waves.

PHYSICS 2   **Learning objective 6.C.1.2** The student is able to construct representations to graphically analyze situations in which two waves overlap over time using the principle of superposition.

PHYSICS 2   **Learning objective 6.C.2.1** The student is able to make claims about the diffraction pattern produced when a wave passes through a small opening, and to qualitatively apply the wave model to quantities that describe the generation of a diffraction pattern when a wave passes through an opening whose dimensions are comparable to the wavelength of the wave.

PHYSICS 2   **Learning objective 6.C.3.1** The student is able to qualitatively apply the wave model to quantities that describe the generation of interference patterns to make predictions about interference patterns that form when waves pass through a set of openings whose spacing and widths are small compared to the wavelength of the waves.

PHYSICS 2   **Learning objective 6.C.4.1** The student is able to predict and explain, using representations and models, the ability or inability of waves to transfer energy around corners and behind obstacles in terms of the diffraction property of waves in situations involving various kinds of wave phenomena, including sound and light.

PHYSICS 1	**Learning objective 6.D.1.1** The student is able to use representations of individual pulses and construct representations to model the interaction of two wave pulses to analyze the superposition of two pulses.
PHYSICS 1	**Learning objective 6.D.1.2** The student is able to design a suitable experiment and analyze data illustrating the superposition of mechanical waves (only for wave pulses or standing waves).
PHYSICS 1	**Learning objective 6.D.1.3** The student is able to design a plan for collecting data to quantify the amplitude variations when two or more traveling waves or wave pulses interact in a given medium.
PHYSICS 1	**Learning objective 6.D.2.1** The student is able to analyze data or observations or evaluate evidence of the interaction of two or more traveling waves in one or two dimensions (i.e., circular wave fronts) to evaluate the variations in resultant amplitudes.
PHYSICS 1	**Learning objective 6.D.3.1** The student is able to refine a scientific question related to standing waves and design a detailed plan for the experiment that can be conducted to examine the phenomenon qualitatively or quantitatively.
PHYSICS 1	**Learning objective 6.D.3.2** The student is able to predict properties of standing waves that result from the addition of incident and reflected waves that are confined to a region and have nodes and antinodes.
PHYSICS 1	**Learning objective 6.D.3.3** The student is able to plan data collection strategies, predict the outcome based on the relationship under test, perform data analysis, evaluate evidence compared to the prediction, explain any discrepancy and, if necessary, revise the relationship among variables responsible for establishing standing waves on a string or in a column of air.
PHYSICS 1	**Learning objective 6.D.3.4** The student is able to describe representations and models of situations in which standing waves result from the addition of incident and reflected waves confined to a region.
PHYSICS 1	**Learning objective 6.D.4.1** The student is able to challenge with evidence the claim that the wavelengths of standing waves are determined by the frequency of the source regardless of the size of the region.
PHYSICS 1	**Learning objective 6.D.4.2** The student is able to calculate wavelengths and frequencies (if given wave speed) of standing waves based on boundary conditions and length of region within which the wave is confined, and calculate numerical values of wavelengths and frequencies. Examples should include musical instruments.

Physics 1	**Learning objective 6.D.5.1** The student is able to use a visual representation to explain how waves of slightly different frequency give rise to the phenomenon of beats.
Physics 2	**Learning objective 6.E.1.1** The student is able to make claims using connections across concepts about the behavior of light as the wave travels from one medium into another, as some is transmitted, some is reflected, and some is absorbed.
Physics 2	**Learning objective 6.E.2.1** The student is able to make predictions about the locations of object and image relative to the location of a reflecting surface. The prediction should be based on the model of specular reflection with all angles measured relative to the normal to the surface.
Physics 2	**Learning objective 6.E.3.1** The student is able to describe models of light traveling across a boundary from one transparent material to another when the speed of propagation changes, causing a change in the path of the light ray at the boundary of the two media.
Physics 2	**Learning objective 6.E.3.2** The student is able to plan data collection strategies as well as perform data analysis and evaluation of the evidence for finding the relationship between the angle of incidence and the angle of refraction for light crossing boundaries from one transparent material to another (Snell's law).
Physics 2	**Learning objective 6.E.3.3** The student is able to make claims and predictions about path changes for light traveling across a boundary from one transparent material to another at non-normal angles resulting from changes in the speed of propagation.
Physics 2	**Learning objective 6.E.4.1** The student is able to plan data collection strategies, and perform data analysis and evaluation of evidence about the formation of images due to reflection of light from curved spherical mirrors.
Physics 2	**Learning objective 6.E.4.2** The student is able to use quantitative and qualitative representations and models to analyze situations and solve problems about image formation occurring due to the reflection of light from surfaces.
Physics 2	**Learning objective 6.E.5.1** The student is able to use quantitative and qualitative representations and models to analyze situations and solve problems about image formation occurring due to the refraction of light through thin lenses.
Physics 2	**Learning objective 6.E.5.2** The student is able to plan data collection strategies, perform data analysis and evaluation of evidence, and refine scientific questions about the formation of images due to refraction for thin lenses.

PHYSICS 2	**Learning objective 6.F.1.1** The student is able to make qualitative comparisons of the wavelengths of types of electromagnetic radiation.
PHYSICS 2	**Learning objective 6.F.2.1** The student is able to describe representations and models of electromagnetic waves that explain the transmission of energy when no medium is present.
PHYSICS 2	**Learning objective 6.F.3.1)** The student is able to support the photon model of radiant energy with evidence provided by the photoelectric effect.
PHYSICS 2	**Learning objective 6.F.4.1)** The student is able to select a model of radiant energy that is appropriate to the spatial or temporal scale of an interaction with matter.
PHYSICS 2	**Learning objective 6.G.1.1)** The student is able to make predictions about using the scale of the problem to determine at what regimes a particle or wave model is more appropriate.
PHYSICS 2	**Learning objective 6.G.2.1)** The student is able to articulate the evidence supporting the claim that a wave model of matter is appropriate to explain the diffraction of matter interacting with a crystal, given conditions where a particle of matter has momentum corresponding to a de Broglie wavelength smaller than the separation between adjacent atoms in the crystal.
PHYSICS 2	**Learning objective 6.G.2.2)** The student is able to predict the dependence of major features of a diffraction pattern (e.g., spacing between interference maxima), based upon the particle speed and de Broglie wavelength of electrons in an electron beam interacting with a crystal. (de Broglie wavelength need not be given, so students may need to obtain it.)
PHYSICS 2	**Learning objective 7.A.1.1** The student is able to make claims about how the pressure of an ideal gas is connected to the force exerted by molecules on the walls of the container, and how changes in pressure affect the thermal equilibrium of the system.
PHYSICS 2	**Learning objective 7.A.1.2** Treating a gas molecule as an object (i.e., ignoring its internal structure), the student is able to analyze qualitatively the collisions with a container wall and determine the cause of pressure, and at thermal equilibrium, to quantitatively calculate the pressure, force, or area for a thermodynamic problem given two of the variables.
PHYSICS 2	**Learning objective 7.A.2.1** The student is able to qualitatively connect the average of all kinetic energies of molecules in a system to the temperature of the system.
PHYSICS 2	**Learning objective 7.A.2.2** The student is able to connect the statistical distribution of microscopic kinetic energies of molecules to the macroscopic temperature of the system and to relate this to thermodynamic processes.

PHYSICS 2	**Learning objective 7.A.3.1** The student is able to extrapolate from pressure and temperature or volume and temperature data to make the prediction that there is a temperature at which the pressure or volume extrapolates to zero.
PHYSICS 2	**Learning objective 7.A.3.2** The student is able to design a plan for collecting data to determine the relationships between pressure, volume, and temperature, and amount of an ideal gas, and to refine a scientific question concerning a proposed incorrect relationship between the variables.
PHYSICS 2	**Learning objective 7.A.3.3** The student is able to analyze graphical representations of macroscopic variables for an ideal gas to determine the relationships between these variables and to ultimately determine the ideal gas law $PV = nRT$.
PHYSICS 2	**Learning objective 7.B.1.1** The student is able to construct an explanation, based on atomicscale interactions and probability, of how a system approaches thermal equilibrium when energy is transferred to it or from it in a thermal process.
PHYSICS 2	**Learning objective 7.B.2.1** The student is able to connect qualitatively the second law of thermodynamics in terms of the state function called entropy and how it (entropy) behaves in reversible and irreversible processes.
PHYSICS 2	**Learning objective 7.C.1.1** The student is able to use a graphical wave function representation of a particle to predict qualitatively the probability of finding a particle in a specific spatial region.
PHYSICS 2	**Learning objective 7.C.2.1** The student is able to use a standing wave model in which an electron orbit circumference is an integer multiple of the de Broglie wavelength to give a qualitative explanation that accounts for the existence of specific allowed energy states of an electron in an atom.
PHYSICS 2	**Learning objective 7.C.3.1** The student is able to predict the number of radioactive nuclei remaining in a sample after a certain period of time, and also predict the missing species (alpha, beta, gamma) in a radioactive decay.
PHYSICS 2	**Learning objective 7.C.4.1** The student is able to construct or interpret representations of transitions between atomic energy states involving the emission and absorption of photons. [For questions addressing stimulated emission, students will not be expected to recall the details of the process, such as the fact that the emitted photons have the same frequency and phase as the incident photon; but given a representation of the process, students are expected to make inferences such as figuring out from energy conservation that since the atom loses energy in the process, the emitted photons taken together must carry more energy than the incident photon.]

Part II

A Review of AP® Physics 1
and AP® Physics 2

1

VECTORS

FRAMES OF REFERENCE

(*College Physics* 9th ed. page 72/10th ed. pages 73–74)

When you walk into a room and see a picture frame hanging on a wall, it does what it is intended to do, capture your attention. Your eyes focus on the picture that it contains. Picture frames not only keep pictures in place on walls or positioned on tabletops but they are also designed to attract and hold your attention. What else do pictures do? It was once said by an ancient philosopher that a picture is worth a thousand words. That is so true.

Much of physics is about motion and in order to describe movement we must be able to specify where an object has been, where it is, and where it is going to be. We need to create pictures, pictures all worth a thousand words. Our pictures will need a frame; a *frame of reference*, a *coordinate system*. In beginning physics our applications, quantities of interest, are confined to the *xy* plane so we will only need a coordinate system to address the *xy* plane. The most familiar and convenient coordinate system is the *Cartesian coordinate system*, which consists of two mutually perpendicular lines called axes. These axes, designated as *x-axis* and *y-axis*, intersect at a point called the origin where the real number line of each axis has its zero. Every point in two-dimensional space has a set of two numbers known as coordinates. These coordinates are distances measured along each of the axes from the origin. These coordinates are usually written as ordered pairs (*x,y*). The *x*-coordinate can be found by dropping a perpendicular to the *x*-axis and the *y*-coordinate is found by running a perpendicular to the *y*-axis. The intersections with the *x*-axis and the *y*-axis are the coordinates of the point.

SCALAR QUANTITIES AND VECTOR QUANTITIES

(*College Physics* 9th ed. pages 56–58/10th ed. pages 57–60)

Any quantity that can be completely specified by a number and a unit is called a *scalar quantity*. Scalars can be added by ordinary arithmetic: 3.2 m + 2.2 m + 0.3 m = 5.7 m. Mass, volume, temperature, energy, undirected distance, and speed are all classified as scalar quantities.

Other quantities such as displacement and velocity require that direction be specified as well as a number and a unit: 30 m/s east, 12 m vertically upward. These quantities that have both magnitude and geometrical direction are called *vector quantities*. Further examples of vector quantities are force, acceleration, momentum, and torque. There are others. Vectors are pictures in need of a frame of reference.

A vector quantity is conveniently represented by a *vector*; this is an arrow-tipped line segment. The length of a vector indicates the *magnitude* of the vector quantity; the direction of the arrow specifies the *direction* of the vector. An arrowhead, called the tip, on the end of the line segment, indicates the sense of the vector. The other end is referred to as the tail, the beginning of the vector.

VECTOR COMPONENTS

(*College Physics* 9th ed. pages 58–62/10th ed. pages 60–63)

Whereas scalars are treated with ordinary arithmetic, vectors are not; they have their own mathematics we will call vector algebra.

As every point in Cartesian or two-dimensional space has a set of two coordinates, every vector in two-dimensional space has a set of two components: a *horizontal* or *x-component* and a *vertical* or *y-component*. It will be to our advantage to refer to the vector components as *x*- and *y*-components.

We will represent a vector as an *italicized* letter with an arrow over it as with vector $\vec{V}$. Velocity is a vector quantity. It tells us how fast something is moving and in what direction. We denote velocity with a $\vec{v}$ and its units are meters per second or m/s. The velocity of a body at some particular moment of time is called its *instantaneous velocity*. We not only know the magnitude and direction of the body, we also know its location in time or its position or both.

The magnitude of a vector is a scalar quantity since it does not specify direction. We can show the magnitude of a vector $\vec{A}$ as A.

We identify a vector $\vec{V}$, and it has both magnitude, V, and direction, θ. Vector $\vec{V}$ has two components in two-dimensional space, V_x and V_y. Note that we wrote the components in scalar form, italicized without the arrow. Components themselves are vectors but we know the directions of the *x*- and *y*-components so we need to deal only with magnitude.

To calculate the *x*-component of a vector $\vec{V}$ we write $V_x = V\cos\theta$. The *x*-component is related to the cosine, cos, function. We multiply the magnitude of the vector by the cosine of the angle the vector makes with respect to the +x-axis. We call this angle relationship *standard position*.

To calculate the y-component of a vector $\vec{V}$ we write $V_y = V \sin \theta$. The y-component is related to the sine, sin, function. In this case we multiply the sine of the angle expressed in standard position.

Notice below that in the first quadrant, both the x- and y-components are positive. In the second quadrant, the x-component is negative and the y-component positive.

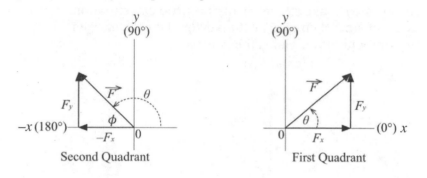

Second Quadrant   First Quadrant

In the third quadrant, both components are negative. In the fourth quadrant, the x-component is positive and the y-component is negative.

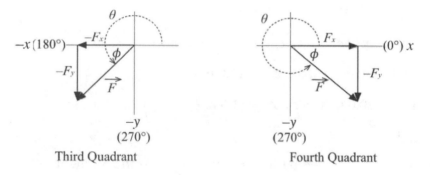

Third Quadrant   Fourth Quadrant

Procedures to calculate the components of a vector:

1. Make a sketch of the situation attaching a frame of reference. Pay attention to the quadrant.

2. Using $V_x = V \cos \theta$ calculate the x-component. Be sure the angle θ is expressed in terms of standard position.

3. Using $V_y = V \sin \theta$ calculate the y-component. Be sure the angle θ is expressed in terms of standard position.

4. Pay attention to the signs of the components. Be sure they reflect the quadrant.

SAMPLE PROBLEM 1

A particle has a velocity of 30.0 m/s at an angle of 50° with respect to the +x-axis. We can use a shorthand way to express this vector: $\vec{v} = 30.0$ m/s @ 50°. Calculate the x- and y-components of this velocity vector.

SOLUTION TO PROBLEM 1

The first thing we do is to make a sketch of the problem situation identifying the quadrant and then put in the vector, label it and its angle. Sketch in the components and label them as well.

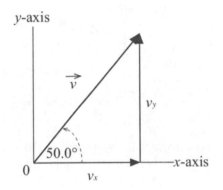

To calculate the x-component of a vector $\vec{V}$: $V_x = V\cos\theta$

To calculate the y-component of a vector $\vec{V}$: $V_y = V\sin\theta$

$$V_x = v\cos\theta = (30.0 \text{ m/s})(\cos 50°) = \textbf{19.3 m / s}$$

$$V_y = v\sin\theta = (30.0 \text{ m/s})(\sin 50°) = \textbf{23.0 m / s}$$

SAMPLE PROBLEM 2

A particle travels along a curved path as shown below. At the moment the particle is at point P, its instantaneous velocity is $\vec{v} = 120.0$ m/s @ 70.0°. Calculate the x- and y-components of $\vec{v}$.

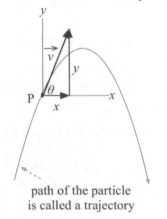

path of the particle
is called a trajectory

SOLUTION TO PROBLEM 2

Attach a frame of reference to the particle, sketch in the components and label everything. To find the components at point P we write the component equations and substitute

$$v_x = v\cos\theta = (120.0 \text{ m/s})(\cos 70.0°) = \textbf{41.0 m/s}$$

$$v_y = v\sin\theta = (120.0 \text{ m/s})(\sin 70.0°) = \textbf{112.8 m/s}$$

In its simplest sense, a *force*, $\vec{F}$, may be defined as a *push* or a *pull* on a body. Forces are vectors. Forces make bodies move or they can cause a body to be at rest. In the SI, the unit of force is the newton (N).

SAMPLE PROBLEM 3

A wooden box is to be pulled across a horizontal floor. A rope is attached to the box as shown below. In physics, we call the forces that exist in ropes by a special name: we call them *tension, $\vec{T}$*. Tension is a vector. If the rope has a tension of 25.0 N and is acting at 135° with respect to the +x-axis, what are the x- and y-components of the tension vector?

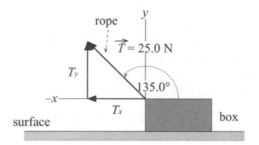

SOLUTION TO PROBLEM 3

The angle is presented in standard position. Write the component equations and substitute in to them

$$T_x = T\cos\theta = (25.0 \text{ N})(\cos 135°) = \textbf{-17.7 N}$$

$$T_y = T\sin\theta = (25.0 \text{ N})(\sin 135°) = \textbf{17.7 N}$$

Notice that in quadrant II the cosine is negative making the x-component negative. The x-component has a magnitude of 17.7 N and points in the negative x direction.

AP Tip

The force in strings, ropes, wires, cables and chains is called tension. Strings, ropes, cables, wires, and chains can only pull. They cannot push.

DETERMINING A VECTOR FROM ITS COMPONENTS

(College Physics 9th ed. pages 59–62/10th ed. pages 60–63)

When a set of vector components are known, they can be resolved into the original vector using the *Pythagorean theorem* and the *inverse tangent function,* $(\tan^{-1})$.

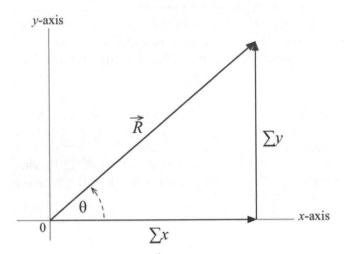

The magnitude of vector $\vec{R}$ is found from its Σx and Σy components by using the Pythagorean theorem:

$$R = |R| = \left|\sqrt{(\Sigma x)^2 + (\Sigma y)^2}\right|$$

The absolute value symbols are a reminder that the magnitude of the resultant is a scalar quantity.

From the inverse tangent function, the angle θ of R is:

$$\theta = \left|\tan^{-1} \frac{\Sigma y}{\Sigma x}\right|$$

SAMPLE PROBLEM 4

A particle following a trajectory is illustrated below. At point Q, the particle has an instantaneous velocity v. The horizontal and vertical components of the velocity vector are $v_x = 12.0$ m/s and $v_y = -7.0$ m/s. Determine the instantaneous velocity of the particle at Q.

SOLUTION TO PROBLEM 4

Notice that the vertical component is negative and the horizontal component is positive. This implies that the instantaneous velocity vector is in quadrant IV.

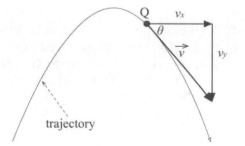

The magnitude of the instantaneous velocity vector is found by the Pythagorean theorem. We write the theorem and make the substitution,

$$v = \left| \sqrt{(v_x)^2 + (v_y)^2} \right| = \left| \sqrt{(12.0 \text{ m/s})^2 + (-7.0 \text{ m/s})^2} \right| = \textbf{13.9 m / s}$$

The direction of v is found using the inverse tangent

$$\theta = \left| \tan^{-1} \frac{v_y}{v_x} \right| = \left| \tan^{-1} \left(\frac{-7 \text{ m/s}}{12.0 \text{ m/s}} \right) \right| = 30.3°.$$

Note that this is an angle in quadrant IV.
To express the angle in standard position we subtract from 360°
$$360° - 30.3° = \textbf{329.7}°$$

At the very moment the particle is at point Q, its instantaneous velocity is **13.9 m / s @ 329.7°**.

RESULTANTS OF TWO OR MORE VECTORS

(*College Physics* 9th ed. pages 59–62/10th ed. pages 60–63)

Vector algebra is loosely based on the arithmetic of parallelograms and as we have seen it involves sine and cosine functions. The resolution of vectors into components is a very powerful tool. The sum of the *x*-components of two or more vectors acting on a body is the *x*-component of the *resultant*. In the same sense, the sum of the *y*-components is the *y*-component of the *resultant*. The resultant is what we call the *result* of adding vectors using vector algebra.

To evaluate and tabulate the components of two forces acting on a body, it is recommended that the beginning physics student construct a table somewhat as follows:

Force	*x*-component	*y*-component
$F_1 @ \theta_1$	$F_1 \cos \theta_1$	$F_1 \sin \theta_1$
$F_2 @ \theta_2$	$F_2 \cos \theta_2$	$F_2 \sin \theta_2$
Sum of the components	$\Sigma x = x_1 + x_2$	$\Sigma y = y_1 + y_2$

The vector problems we will be encountering are ones where the vectors will act at a single point at the same instant. We call these vectors *concurrent* and *simultaneous* vectors.

SAMPLE PROBLEM 5

The *displacement* of a body is the straight-line distance from the starting point to the ending point. Note the "from" and "to" in the previous sentence. Displacement, $\vec{S}$, is a vector since it has both magnitude and direction. An object is moved 24.0 m in a straight line at an angle of 30° with respect to the positive *x*-axis. It is then moved 10.0 m at 60° with respect to the positive *x*-axis. What is the displacement of the object?

SOLUTION TO PROBLEM 5

To find the displacement, we start by making a diagram. First, we attach a frame of reference, a Cartesian coordinate system, to the starting point, the origin. Since both of the object movements are in the first quadrant, our frame of reference is made for the first quadrant only. Note that the diagram is not to scale.

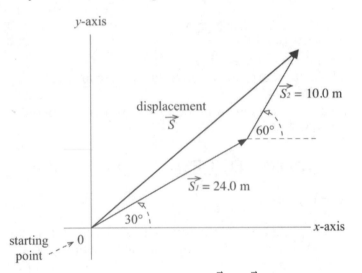

In the diagram, the displacements $\vec{S}_1$, $\vec{S}_2$ and the resultant displacement, $\vec{S}$, are vectors and have both magnitude and direction. To find the displacement, $\vec{S}$, we first calculate the *x*- and *y*-components.

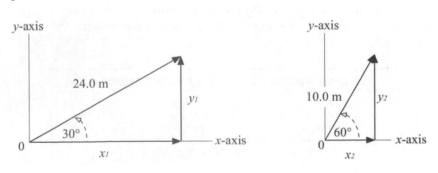

$$x_1 = (24.0 \text{ m})\cos 30° = 20.8 \text{ m} \qquad x_2 = (10.0 \text{ m})\cos 60° = 5.0 \text{ m}$$
$$y_1 = (24.0 \text{ m})\sin 30° = 12.0 \text{ m} \qquad y_2 = (10.0 \text{ m})\sin 60° = 8.7 \text{ m}$$

Compiling the data:

$\vec{S}_1 = 24.0 \text{ m} @ 30°$	S_{1x} $x_1 = S_1 \cos 30°$ $x_1 = 20.8 \text{ m}$	S_{1y} $y_1 = S_1 \sin 30°$ $y_1 = 12.0 \text{ m}$
$\vec{S}_2 = 10.0 \text{ N} @ 60°$	S_{2x} $x_2 = S_2 \cos 60°$ $x_2 = 5.0 \text{ m}$	S_{2Y} $y_2 = S_2 \sin 135°$ $y_2 = 8.7 \text{ m}$
Sum of the components	$\Sigma x = x_1 + x_2$ $\Sigma x = 20.8 \text{ m} + 5.0 \text{ m}$ $\Sigma x = 25.8 \text{ m}$	$\Sigma y = y_1 + y_2$ $\Sigma y = 12.0 \text{ m} + 8.7 \text{ m}$ $\Sigma y = 20.7 \text{ m}$

The sum of all of the x-components is the x-component of the resultant. The same is true of the y-components. Now, we can calculate the resultant displacement, $\vec{R}$.

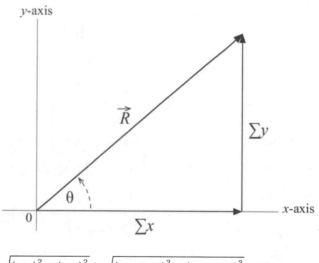

$$R = \sqrt{(\Sigma x)^2 + (\Sigma y)^2} = \sqrt{(25.8 \text{ m})^2 + (20.7 \text{ m})^2} = 33.1 \text{ m}$$

$$\theta = \tan^{-1}\left(\frac{\Sigma y}{\Sigma x}\right) = \tan^{-1}\left(\frac{20.7 \text{ m}}{25.8 \text{ m}}\right) = \tan^{-1}(0.8023) = 38.7°$$

The body is displaced by 33.1 m at an angle of 38.7°. We can write the displacement vector as $\vec{S} = \mathbf{33.1 \text{ m} @ 38.7°}$, which is another picture of the problem.

SAMPLE PROBLEM 6

Two forces, $\vec{A} = 100 \text{ N} @ 30°$ and $\vec{B} = 60 \text{ N} @ 135°$, act concurrently and simultaneously on a body. Use the component method with a table and calculate the

(a) magnitude of the resultant,

(b) angle of the resultant, and

(c) resultant force, R, experienced by the body.

SOLUTION TO PROBLEM 6

First, make a vector diagram sketching in all the forces and their components.

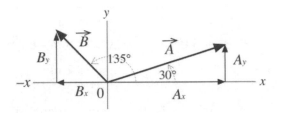

Construct a table. List all of the forces, and calculate the components.

$\vec{A} = 100 \text{ N} @ 30°$	A_x	A_y
	$A_x = A \cos 30°$	$A_y = A \sin 30°$
	$A_x = (100 \text{ N}) \cos 30°$	$A_y = (100 \text{ N}) \sin 30°$
	$A_x = 86.6 \text{ N}$	$A_y = 50.0 \text{ N}$
$\vec{B} = 60.0 \text{ N} @ 135°$	B_x	B_y
	$B_x = B \cos 135°$	$B_y = B \sin 135°$
	$B_x = (60.0 \text{ N}) \cos 135°$	$B_y = (60.0 \text{ N}) \sin 135°$
	$B_x = -42.4 \text{ N}$	$B_y = 42.4 \text{ N}$
Sum of the components	$\Sigma x = A_x + B_x$	$\Sigma y = A_y + B_y$
	$\Sigma x = 86.6 \text{ N} + (-42.4 \text{ N})$	$\Sigma y = 50.0 \text{ N} + 42.4 \text{ N}$
	$\Sigma x = 44.2 \text{ N}$	$\Sigma y = 92.4 \text{ N}$

Observe that both Σx and Σy are positive. This implies that the resultant force, R, is located in the first quadrant. In quadrant I, $90° > \theta > 0°$.

The magnitude of the resultant, $|R|$, is

(a) $|R| = \sqrt{(\Sigma x)^2 + (\Sigma y)^2} = \sqrt{(44.2 \text{ N})^2 + (92.4 \text{ N})^2} = \mathbf{102.4 \text{ N}}$

The angle of the resultant is in quadrant I and is found by

(b) $\theta = \tan^{-1}\left|\dfrac{\Sigma y}{\Sigma x}\right| = \tan^{-1}\left|\dfrac{92.4\text{ N}}{44.2\text{ N}}\right| = \textbf{64.4°}$

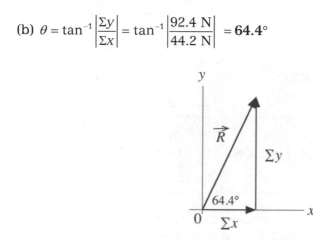

(c) $\vec{R} = \textbf{102.4 N @ 64.4°}$. The body behaves as if a single force of 102.4 N at 64.4° is acting on it.

SAMPLE PROBLEM 7

A set of three concurrent and simultaneous forces are exerted on a particle. If $\vec{F_1} = 200\text{ N}@0°$, $\vec{F_2} = 120\text{ N}@210°$, and $\vec{F_3} = 80.0\text{ N}@340°$, what resultant force will the particle experience?

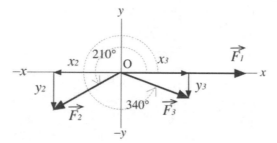

SOLUTION TO PROBLEM 7

$\vec{F_1} = 200\text{ N}@0°$	x_1 $x_1 = F_1\cos 0°$ $x_1 = (200\text{ N})\cos 0°$ $x_1 = 200\text{ N}$	y_1 $y_1 = F_2\sin 0°$ $y_1 = (200\text{ N})\sin 0°$ $y_1 = 0$
$\vec{F_2} = 120\text{ N}@210°$	x_2 $x_2 = F_2\cos 210°$ $x_2 = (120\text{ N})\cos 210°$ $x_2 = -104\text{ N}$	y_2 $y_2 = F_2\sin 210°$ $y_2 = (120\text{ N})\sin 210°$ $y_2 = -60.0\text{ N}$

$\vec{F}_3 = 80.0 \text{ N} @ 340°$	x_3	y_3
	$x_3 = F_3 \cos 340°$	$y_3 = F_3 \sin 340°$
	$x_3 = (80.0 \text{ N})\cos 340°$	$y_3 = (80.0 \text{ N})\sin 340°$
	$x_3 = 75.2 \text{ N}$	$y_3 = -27.4 \text{ N}$
Sum of the components	$\Sigma x = x_1 + x_2 + x_3$	$\Sigma y = y_1 + y_2 + y_3$
	$\Sigma x = 200 \text{ N} - 104 \text{ N} + 75.2 \text{ N}$	$\Sigma y = 0 - 60.0 \text{ N} - 27.4 \text{ N}$
	$\Sigma x = 171 \text{ N}$	$\Sigma y = -87.4 \text{ N}$

Notice that Σx is positive and Σy is negative. This implies that the resultant force, $\vec{R}$, is located in quadrant four and in quadrant four, $360° > \phi > 270°$. The magnitude of the resultant, $|R|$ is

$$|R| = \sqrt{(\Sigma x)^2 + (\Sigma y)^2} = \sqrt{(171 \text{ N})^2 + (-87.4 \text{ N})^2} = 192 \text{ N}$$

The resultant angle is in quadrant four. Since it is an angle in a triangle, the resultant angle must be expressed in standard position and $\theta = 360° - \phi$. First find ϕ:

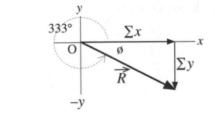

$$\phi = \tan^{-1}\left|\frac{\Sigma y}{\Sigma x}\right| = \tan^{-1}\left|\frac{87.4 \text{ N}}{171 \text{ N}}\right| = 27.1°$$

$$\theta = 360° - \phi = 360° - 27.1° = 333°$$

$\vec{R} = $ **192 N @ 333°**. If the particle in the problem were free to move, it would behave as if a single force of 193 N is moving it at an angle of 333°.

AP Tip

Always remember that a vector has both magnitude and direction. Always solve for both.

A quicker way of determining the resultant of two or more vectors acting on a body is by *inspection*. This method eliminates the force and component table and directly adds the components.

1. Make a sketch showing the concurrent vectors and their components. Be sure all are labeled.

2. Use the following two equations and substitute in the forces and their angles.

3. Solve for Σx and Σy.

$$\Sigma x = F_1 \cos\theta_1 + F_2 \cos\theta_2 + F_3 \cos\theta_3 + \ldots$$

$$\Sigma y = F_1 \sin\theta_1 + F_2 \sin\theta_2 + F_3 \sin\theta_3 + \ldots$$

4. Use the Pythagorean theorem and the inverse tangent and determine the vector or resultant in question.

SAMPLE PROBLEM 8

An object has a set of simultaneous and concurrent forces acting on it. By inspection, calculate the resultant force experienced by the object if: $\vec{A} = 160$ N @ 50°, $\vec{B} = 200$ N @ 100°, and $\vec{C} = 40.0$ N @ 300°.

SOLUTION TO PROBLEM 8

By inspection, first make a vector diagram.

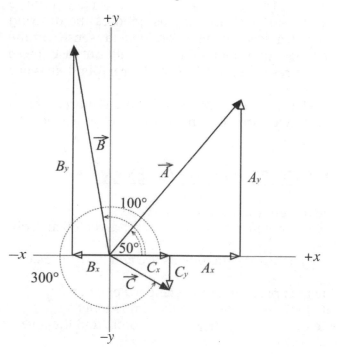

Next, sum the x- and the y-components.

$$\Sigma x = A\cos\theta_A + B\cos\theta_B + C\cos\theta_C$$

$$\Sigma x = A\cos 50° + B\cos 100° + C\cos 300°$$

$$\Sigma x = (160 \text{ N})\cos 50° + (200 \text{ N})\cos 100° + (40.0 \text{ N})\cos 300°$$
$$= 88.1 \text{ N}$$

$$\Sigma y = A\sin\theta_A + B\sin\theta_B + C\sin\theta_C$$

$$\Sigma y = A\sin 50° + B\sin 100° + C\sin 300°$$

$$\Sigma y = (160 \text{ N})\sin 50° + (200 \text{ N})\sin 100° + (40.0 \text{ N})\sin 300° = 285 \text{ N}$$

Solve for the resultant $\vec{R}$.

Both Σx and Σy are positive. This implies that the resultant force, $\vec{R}$, is located in the first quadrant. In quadrant I, $90° > \theta > 0°$.

$$|R| = \sqrt{(\Sigma x)^2 + (\Sigma y)^2} = \sqrt{(88.1 \text{ N})^2 + (285 \text{ N})^2} = 298 \text{ N}$$

$$\theta = \tan^{-1}\left|\frac{\Sigma y}{\Sigma x}\right| = \tan^{-1}\left|\frac{285 \text{ N}}{88.1 \text{ N}}\right| = 72.8°$$

$$\vec{R} = \textbf{298 N @ 72.8°}$$

A NOTE TO THE STUDENT

Several ways exist in which vector situations can be represented and solved. There are graphical methods requiring a pencil, centimeter ruler, a protractor and graph paper, where vector situations are carefully drawn to scale. The graphical methods usually require considerable time and the answers are only as good as the drawing skills of the student. Graphical methods do give a sense of the magnitudes and directions of vectors, but we will not use these methods. They will be presented in class and are found in your textbook.

The analytical method is a calculational method and requires a hand calculator. The method we present and use here is called the *component method*.

VECTORS: STUDENT OBJECTIVES FOR THE AP EXAM

- You should be able to define a frame of reference.
- You should be able to define both a scalar and a vector and give examples of both.
- You should know what vector components are and how to calculate them.
- You should be able to express angles in standard position.
- You should be able to find a vector from its components.
- You should be able to use the Pythagorean theorem and the inverse tangent in problem solving.
- You should be able to define resultant.
- You should be able to define velocity and instantaneous velocity.
- You should be able to define displacement.
- You should be able to add two or more vectors using the component method.

FREE-RESPONSE PROBLEMS

1. Using a table of vectors, calculate the resultant force acting on the body shown below. Vectors $\vec{A}$ and $\vec{B}$ are simultaneous and concurrent.

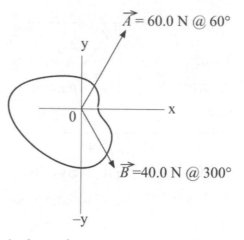

$$\vec{A} = 60.0 \text{ N } @ \ 60°$$

$$\vec{B} = 40.0 \text{ N } @ \ 300°$$

2. A proton travels through space along its trajectory, its path, and at a point Q has an instantaneous velocity $\vec{v}$ with components $v_x = -500.0 \text{ m}/_\text{s}$ and $v_y = -275.0 \text{ m}/_\text{s}$. Calculate the instantaneous velocity of the proton at point Q.

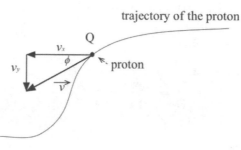

trajectory of the proton

3. Three concurrent and simultaneous force vectors, $\vec{A}$, $\vec{B}$ and $\vec{C}$ are specified by their components as $A_x = 3.0 \text{ N}$, $A_y = 2.0 \text{ N}$; $B_x = -5.0 \text{ N}$, $B_y = -4.0 \text{ N}$; and $C_x = -2.0 \text{ N}$, $C_y = 5.0 \text{ N}$. Determine the resultant of these forces.

4. Vectors $\vec{A} = 120 \text{ N } @ \ 45°$, $\vec{B} = 120 \text{ N } @ \ 135°$, $\vec{C} = 120 \text{ N } @ \ 225°$ and $\vec{D} = 120 \text{ N } @ \ 315°$ all act simultaneously at the center of mass of a body. (a) Are these vectors concurrent? (b) What kind of vectors are these? (c) What resultant do these vectors have?

(*College Physics* 9th ed. pages 61–62/10th ed. pages 57–60)

There are no specific learning objectives for Vectors but their use is required in other Learning Objectives in both AP Physics 1 and AP Physics 2.

Answers

FREE-RESPONSE PROBLEMS

1. Construct a table: list all of the components and calculate their components.

$\vec{A} = 60.0 \text{ N} @ 60°$	A_x $A_x = A\cos 60°$ $A_x = (60.0 \text{ N})\cos 60°$ $A_x = 30.0 \text{ N}$	A_y $A_y = A\sin 300°$ $A_y = (60.0 \text{ N})\sin 60°$ $A_y = 52.0 \text{ N}$
$\vec{B} = 40.0 \text{ N} @ 300°$	B_x $B_x = B\cos 300°$ $B_x = (40.0 \text{ N})\cos 300°$ $B_x = 20.0 \text{ N}$	B_y $B_y = B\sin 300°$ $B_y = (40.0 \text{ N})\sin 300°$ $B_y = -34.6 \text{ N}$
Sum of the components	$\Sigma x = A_x + B_x$ $\Sigma x = 30.0 \text{ N} + 20.0 \text{ N}$ $\Sigma x = 50.0 \text{ N}$	$\Sigma y = A_y + B_y$ $\Sigma y = 52.0 \text{ N} + (-34.6 \text{ N})$ $\Sigma y = 17.4 \text{ N}$

Next, sketch the components of the resultant, $\vec{R}$.

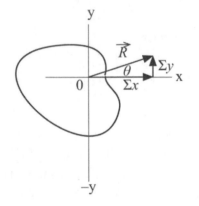

Use the Pythagorean theorem and the inverse tangent to calculate the resultant. Note that both components are positive, placing the resultant in the first quadrant.

$$R = \sqrt{(\Sigma x)^2 + (\Sigma y)^2} = \sqrt{(50.0 \text{ N})^2 + (17.4 \text{ N})^2} = 52.9 \text{ N}$$

$$\theta = \tan^{-1}\left|\frac{\Sigma y}{\Sigma x}\right| = \tan^{-1}\left|\frac{17.4 \text{ N}}{50.0 \text{ N}}\right| = 19.2°$$

The resultant force is $\vec{R} = \textbf{52.9 N @ 19.2°}$.

2. Since both components are negative, the instantaneous velocity vector is in the third quadrant. Note that the angle will be in the third quadrant and we have to correct it to standard position. Use the Pythagorean theorem to calculate the magnitude of the instantaneous velocity vector. Remember that a negative number squared yields a positive square.

$$v = \sqrt{v_x^2 + v_y^2} = \sqrt{\left(-500.0 \ \text{m}\!\big/\!\text{s}\right)^2 + \left(-275.0 \ \text{m}\!\big/\!\text{s}\right)^2} = 570.6 \ \text{m}\!\big/\!\text{s}$$

$$\phi = \tan^{-1}\left|\frac{v_y}{v_x}\right| = \tan^{-1}\left|\frac{275.0 \ \text{m}\!\big/\!\text{s}}{500.0 \ \text{m}\!\big/\!\text{s}}\right| = 28.8°$$

In quadrant 3 we add 180° to the angle within the triangle and

$$\theta = \phi + 180° = 28.8° + 180° = 208.8°$$

$$\vec{v} = \mathbf{570.6 \ \text{m}\!\big/\!\text{s} \ @ \ 208.8°}$$

At the very moment the proton is at point Q it is traveling at a 208.8° angle at $570.6 \ \text{m}\!\big/\!\text{s}$.

3. Since we were given the components all we need to do first is to sum the x- and the y-components.

$$\Sigma x = A_x + B_x + C_x = 3.0 \ \text{N} + (-5.0 \ \text{N}) + (-2.0 \ \text{N}) = -4.0 \ \text{N}$$

$$\Sigma y = A_y + B_y + C_y = 2.0 \ \text{N} + (-4.0 \ \text{N}) + 5.0 \ \text{N} = 3.0 \ \text{N}$$

Next, make a sketch and note the quadrant.

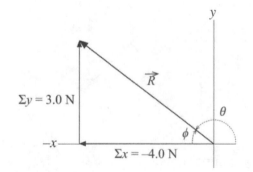

To find the magnitude of the resultant we write the Pythagorean theorem:

$$R = \sqrt{(\Sigma x)^2 + (\Sigma y)^2} = \sqrt{(-4.0 \ \text{N})^2 + (3.0 \ \text{N})^2} = 5.0 \ \text{N}$$

Note that we are dealing with an angle inside a triangle in the second quadrant. To find that angle we use the inverse tangent,

$$\phi = \tan^{-1}\left|\frac{\Sigma y}{\Sigma x}\right| = \tan^{-1}\left|\frac{3.0 \ \text{N}}{-4.0 \ \text{N}}\right| = 36.9°$$

It is conventional to express the angle of $\vec{R}$ in standard position.

$$\theta = 180° - 36.9° = 143.1°$$

The resultant is $\vec{R} = \mathbf{5.0\ N\ @\ 143.1°}$.

4. (a) All four vectors act at the center of mass, which is unique, and since they act at the same point they are concurrent.

(b) Each of the vectors have the same unit, N, the newton, which makes each of them force vectors.

(c) By symmetry the x- and the y-components all subtract, nullifying them. A resultant with zero x-component and zero y-component is zero, $\vec{R} = 0$.

We can verify the conclusion in (c) by solving the problem by inspection. First make a vector diagram.

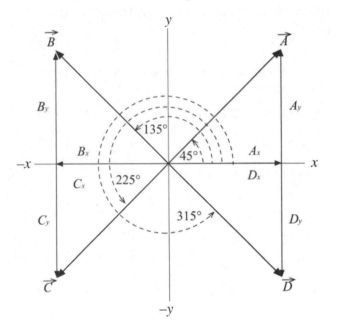

Next we sum the x- and y-components.

$$\Sigma x = A_x \cos\theta_A + B_x \cos\theta_B + C_x \cos\theta_C + D_x \cos\theta_D$$

$$\Sigma x = (120\ \text{N})\cos 45° + (120\ \text{N})\cos 135° +$$
$$(120\ \text{N})\cos 225° + (120\ \text{N})\cos 315° = 0$$

and the y-component

$$\Sigma y = A_y \sin 45° + B_y \sin 135° + C_y \sin 225° + D_y \sin 315°$$

$$\Sigma y = (120\ \text{N})\sin 45° + (120\ \text{N})\sin 135° +$$
$$(120\ \text{N})\sin 225° + (120\ \text{N})\sin 315° = 0$$

Since the components are zero, the resultant is zero.

EQUILIBRIUM

MASS AND INERTIA

(*College Physics* 9th ed. pages 89–91/10th ed. page 91)

Mass is an *intrinsic property* shared by all bodies. It is a measure of the quantity of material present in a body. In our everyday world, the mass of a body is considered to be constant. Mass m is a scalar quantity and its SI unit is the kilogram, kg.

Mass is also a measure of the *inertia* of a body and is not in any way dependent upon gravity. Inertia can be defined as the resistance to any change in the motion of a body. Bodies of small mass have a small inertia and can be moved about rather easily. Very large bodies have a very large inertia and are difficult to move about.

Picture a large truck, a tractor-trailer, having a mass of 18,000 kilograms at rest in neutral with the parking brake released. It sits in a large, empty, flat parking lot. The truck, if weighed at a truck scale would weigh about 40,000 pounds. This truck has quite a large inertia. We have twenty very strong football players get behind the truck and push in unison. Slowly, the truck begins to move. To make it move, the force all the football players simultaneously exert on it overcomes its inertia and now it moves on its own across the parking lot at five miles an hour. Its cab is locked. It is a large moving truck with a large inertia. The question is how do we make it stop? Its inertia must be overcome to bring it to rest.

WEIGHT

(*College Physics* 9th ed. pages 92–93/10th ed. pages 95–96)

Weight and mass are *NOT* the same thing. Weight, $\vec{w}$, is the force of gravitational attraction on a body and is solely dependent upon the strength of a gravitational field. Weight is a vector and its direction is always vertically downward toward the center of the Earth. Think of the center of the Earth as a tiny black hole where all of its mass is concentrated. The weight of a body then is the gravitational force with which the body is pulled toward the center of the Earth.

Mass has another important property. Masses generate *gravitational fields*, $\vec{g}$-fields. Small masses have a small $\vec{g}$-field associated with them and very large masses generate very large gravitational fields. The reason is not fully understood. Compared to you or me, the $\vec{g}$-field of the Earth is huge and extends out a great distance into space. It is the interaction between the $\vec{g}$-fields of the Earth and the moon that brings about the gravitational attraction between them.

The weight of a body on the surface of the Earth is the gravitational attraction the Earth and the body exert on one another. If the body weighs 100 N it means that the gravitational attraction between the body and the Earth is 100 N. We have stated that in our everyday world that mass is a constant. Weight, however, is not.

Assuming that the Earth is homogeneous and is a sphere, at its surface, the $\vec{g}$-field of the Earth has a constant value. For the most part it is constant. The *strength* or *intensity* of the $\vec{g}$-field of the Earth at or within a few kilometers of the surface is

$$\vec{g} = -9.8 \ \text{m}/_{\text{s}^2}$$

The intensity, $\vec{g}$, is a vector and is directed vertically downward toward the center of the Earth. This intensity weakens as you move further from the center of the Earth. In dealing with falling bodies and projectile motion, the intensity is also called the acceleration due to gravity and, within a few kilometers of the surface, has the value

$$\vec{g} = -9.8 \ \text{m}/_{\text{s}^2}$$

Weight, W or w, or the force of gravity, F_g may be defined as the product of the mass of a body and the acceleration due to gravity. Weight is a vector, mass is a scalar, and $\vec{g}$ is a vector.

$$\vec{W} = \vec{w} = \vec{F}_g = m\vec{g}$$

Knowing that weight is a vector and is always directed vertically downward toward the center of the Earth we can write

$$w = mg$$

SAMPLE PROBLEM 1

Determine the weight of a 75.0 kg body at rest on the surface of the Earth.

SOLUTION TO PROBLEM 1

Weight is defined as $w = mg = (75.0 \text{ kg})\left(9.8 \text{ }^{\text{m}}\!\!/\!_{s^2}\right) = \textbf{735.0 N}$

Note the product $(1 \text{ kg})\left(1 \text{ }^{\text{m}}\!\!/\!_{s^2}\right) = 1 \text{ kg} \cdot \text{}^{\text{m}}\!\!/\!_{s^2} = 1 \text{ N}$

AP Tip

Weight is a vector and is expressed in N. Weight is measured on scales and is dependent on location.

SAMPLE PROBLEM 2

A small pickup truck has a weight of 14.7×10^3 N. What is the mass of the truck?

SOLUTION TO PROBLEM 2

The mass of a body is related to weight at or near the surface of the Earth as

$$m = \frac{w}{g} = \frac{\left(14.7 \times 10^3 \text{ N}\right)}{9.8 \text{ }^{\text{m}}\!\!/\!_{s^2}} = \frac{14.7 \times 10^3 \text{ kg} \cdot \text{}^{\text{m}}\!\!/\!_{s^2}}{9.8 \text{ }^{\text{m}}\!\!/\!_{s^2}} = \textbf{1.5} \times \textbf{10}^3 \text{ \textbf{kg}}$$

By definition, 1.0 metric ton = 1.0 MT = 1,000 kg.
We could also have expressed the answer as

$$1.5 \times 10^3 \text{ kg} \times \frac{1.0 \text{ MT}}{1.0 \times 10^3 \text{ kg}} = \textbf{1.5 MT}$$

AP Tip

Mass is a scalar and is expressed in kg. Mass is measured on a balance. Mass in our everyday experience is constant and is independent of location.

SAMPLE PROBLEM 3

If the pickup truck of Problem 2 were placed on the surface of the planet Mars, and knowing that the gravitational intensity for the surface of Mars is $\vec{g}_{Mars} = 3.7 \text{ }^{\text{m}}\!\!/\!_{s^2}$, what is the weight of the truck on the surface of Mars?

SOLUTION TO PROBLEM 3

The weight of the pickup truck on the planet Mars is

$$w_{Mars} = mg_{Mars} = \left(1.5 \times 10^3 \text{ kg}\right)\left(3.7 \text{ }^{\text{m}}\!\!/\!_{s^2}\right) = \textbf{5.6} \times \textbf{10}^3 \text{ \textbf{N}}$$

Mars is a smaller planet with a smaller $\vec{g}$-field. Weight will vary from place to place whereas mass remains constant.

CENTER OF MASS

(*College Physics* 9th ed. pages 241–243/10th ed. pages 246–249)

As we have seen in the first chapter, *simultaneous forces* are forces that are applied to a body at the same time and *concurrent forces* are forces whose lines of action *all* pass through a common point. All regular shaped bodies have a unique point within the body that we call the *center of mass*. We will abbreviate center of mass as c.m. for the remainder of the text. Real bodies all behave as if all their mass is concentrated at the center of mass. Since the Earth behaves as if all its mass were concentrated at its c.m., the $\vec{g}$ -field of the Earth appears to "sink" into its center.

Each and every particle on the Earth has a force acting on it that is common with every other particle and that is its weight. Think of any extended body as being made up of many particles each with a weight vector that points vertically downward to the center of the Earth. It makes no difference as to the shape or size of a body, there exists a unique point where the entire weight may be considered to be concentrated. This point is called the *center of gravity*, c.g., of the body. The c.g. of a regular shaped body such as a cube, uniform sphere, rod, or meterstick is located at the geometrical center of the body. Irregular shaped bodies have centers-of-gravity that may be located outside the material of the body.

The c.m. is identical to the c.g. and the two terms are often used interchangeably. However, the c.m. is preferable in the present context because gravity is not involved. Regular shaped bodies like cubes, spheres, solid disks, and blocks of wood or stone that are homogeneous will have their c.m. at their geometric center. Finding the c.m. of irregular shaped bodies and systems of bodies is a bit complex and will not be considered at this time.

AP Tip

If a single force is applied to the c.m. of a body, purely straight-line motion will occur.

AP Tip

A body is any object and any object is a body. A particle is a tiny body, so small in fact that we can treat it as a point. Under certain conditions we can treat a body as large as the sun as a particle as well as treating a baseball as one, too.

FORCE

(*College Physics* 9th ed. pages 87–88/10th ed. pages 89–90)

In the previous chapter we defined a force as a push or a pull on a body. We also saw how to add up the forces acting on a body: *forces always add as vectors.*

In the world around us, we encounter two classes of force, *contact forces* and *field forces*. In the case of contact forces, the body producing the force actually touches the body being acted upon. With field forces, the force is experienced over a distance such as observed in the case of the force of gravity of the Earth acting on a satellite in Earth orbit.

Gravity is one of the four fundamental forces in nature, and it is the weakest of the four. Gravity is the primary force acting on all astronomical bodies. It is always an attractive force. The force of gravity between two ordinary bodies on the Earth is negligibly small.

On the atomic level physics recognizes that there are four fundamental forces: (1) gravitational, (2) electromagnetic, (3) weak nuclear, and (4) strong nuclear. The contact forces we experience in daily life only appear to be contact forces. Actually, most contact forces are the electromagnetic forces acting as a field force at very small distances.

AP Tip

It is a common practice to treat bodies as a point located at the c.m. of the body and to attach the origin of a frame of reference there.

NEWTON'S FIRST LAW OF MOTION

(*College Physics* 9th ed. pages 88–89/10th ed. pages 90–91)

The part of physics we call mechanics is based on Newton's three Laws of Motion clearly stated for the first time by Sir Isaac Newton (1642–1727) which were published in 1686 in his *Philosophiae Naturalis Principia Mathematica* (The Mathematical Principles of Natural Philosophy).

AP Tip

A major effect of a force is to alter the state of motion of a body.

Newton's first law can be stated as: *A body at rest remains at rest; a body traveling at constant velocity will remain traveling at constant velocity unless an external unbalanced force acts on the body.*

Recall that constant velocity means constant speed in a straight line in a given direction.

We have already seen that the property of a body that allows it to remain at rest or maintain a constant state of motion is called inertia. Newton's first Law is also called the Law of Inertia.

NEWTON'S THIRD LAW OF MOTION

(*College Physics* 9th ed. pages 95–98/10th ed. pages 97–100)

For every force that acts on a body, there is always a reaction force that is equal in magnitude and is opposite in direction. This is a statement of Newton's third law of Motion.

Action-reaction forces act on two different bodies and that means that they do not cancel one another. When two bodies contact one another, the action-reaction forces are called *contact forces*.

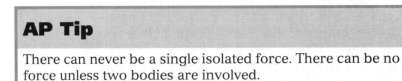

> ## AP Tip
>
> There can never be a single isolated force. There can be no force unless two bodies are involved.

Consider the drawing of a table with a box resting on its surface. The box pushes downward on the tabletop. The tabletop pushes vertically upward on the box. The two forces are an action-reaction pair. Their vector sum is zero.

The table pushed vertically downward on the floor and the floor in return pushes vertically upward on the table. The forces are action-reaction pairs and again, the vector sum is zero.

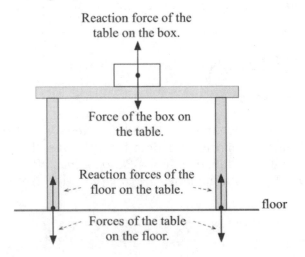

Reaction force of the table on the box.

Force of the box on the table.

Reaction forces of the floor on the table.

floor

Forces of the table on the floor.

CONCURRENT FORCES AND EQUILIBRIUM

(*College Physics* 9th ed. pages 99–101/10th ed. pages 101–103)

If a body is at rest when acted upon by simultaneous and concurrent forces, it is in a state of *static equilibrium*. If a body travels in a straight line with constant velocity when acted on by simultaneous and concurrent forces, it is in a state of *translational equilibrium*. There is no acceleration when a body or a system is in a state of equilibrium. In such a system, the resultant force acting is always zero, $\Sigma \vec{F} = \vec{R} = 0$.

SAMPLE PROBLEM 4

Consider the body shown below. Two concurrent forces, $\vec{F_1} = 20.0$ N at $10.0°$ and $\vec{F_2} = 15.0$ N at $110.0°$, act on the body.

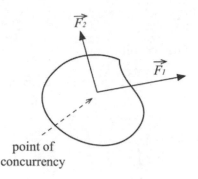

point of
concurrency

(a) By inspection, determine the resultant force, $\vec{R}$, the body experiences.

(b) For a body to be in a state of equilibrium, $\vec{R} = 0$, we can add a force to the system that will place it into a state of equilibrium. We call such a force the *equilibrant*, $\vec{E}$. What equilibrant will place the system into a state of equilibrium?

SOLUTION TO PROBLEM 4

(a) The first thing we do is attach a frame of reference to the point of concurrency. Then we sketch in and identify the x- and y-components.

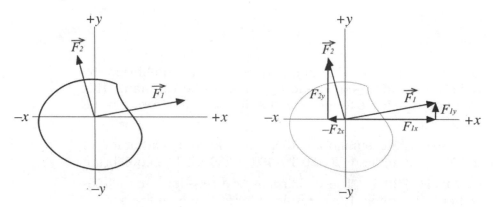

Next, we add the x- and y-components.

$$\Sigma x = F_1 \cos\theta_1 + F_2 \cos\theta_2 = (20.0 \text{ N})(\cos 10.0°) + (15.0 \text{ N})(\cos 110.0°) = 14.57 \text{ N}$$

$$\Sigma y = F_1 \sin\theta_1 + F_2 \sin\theta_2 = (20.0 \text{ N})(\sin 10°) + (15.0 \text{ N})(\sin 110.0°) = 17.57 \text{ N}$$

Recall that the sums of the components are the x- and y-component of the resultant.

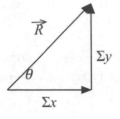

Calculating the magnitude of the resultant:

$$R = \sqrt{(\Sigma x)^2 + (\Sigma y)^2} = \sqrt{(14.57 \text{ N})^2 + (17.57 \text{ N})^2} = \textbf{22.8 N}$$

Finding the angle,

$$\theta = \tan^{-1}\left(\frac{\Sigma y}{\Sigma x}\right) = \tan^{-1}\left(\frac{17.57 \text{ N}}{14.57 \text{ N}}\right) = \textbf{50.3°}$$

The body would move as if a 22.8 N force were pulling it at a 50.3° angle.

(b) The equilibrant E is a force that is equal in magnitude to the resultant but is directed 180° away from the resultant.

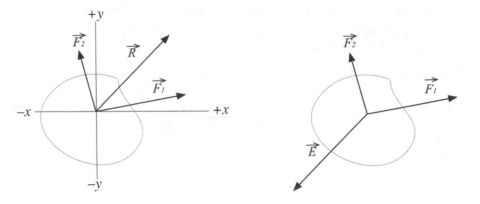

Forces that are not in equilibrium may be put into equilibrium by the addition of a force equal and opposite to the resultant. This equal but opposite force to the resultant of a system of forces is the *equilibrant*.

In this problem, the equilibrant then must have a magnitude of $E = 22.8 \text{ N}$ at an angle of $\theta = 50.3° + 180° = 230.3°$. The equilibrant is $\vec{E} = \textbf{22.8 N @ 230.3°}$. The equilibrant "cancels-out" or nullifies the resultant. Now there is *NO* resultant force acting on the body.

When there is no resultant force, all of the x- and y-components in the system must be zero. This is a statement of the *First Condition for Equilibrium*, $\Sigma x = 0$ and $\Sigma y = 0$. A system is in a state of static equilibrium or in a state of translational equilibrium if and only if the sum of forces acting on the system is zero.

THE NORMAL FORCE

(*College Physics* 9th ed. pages 96–97/10th ed. pages 97–99)

When a body rests on a surface, the surface provides a force on the body in a direction perpendicular to the surface. We call this perpendicular force the *normal force* $\vec{N}$. In this context the word normal means perpendicular.

The origin of the normal force is the interaction between the particles in a solid that act to maintain its shape. Particles are atoms or molecules or ions or some combination of them. Solid-state chemical bonds hold the particles together and are responsible for the normal force.

In most many cases, the normal force is equal to the weight of the body pressing downward on the surface; however, as we will see the normal force can be greater or lesser than the weight of the body.

SAMPLE PROBLEM 5

A wooden crate having a weight of 200.0 N sits at rest on the floor of a storeroom. Determine the normal force exerted on the crate.

SOLUTION TO PROBLEM 5

First we make a free-body or vector diagram of the problem. We attach a frame of reference to the center of mass of the crate. The crate behaves as if all its mass were concentrated there. The normal force originates directly beneath the c.m. at the interface between the undersurface of the crate and the surface of the floor.

In the free-body diagram, we shifted the normal slightly to the left making it completely visible.

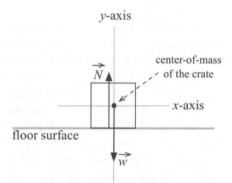

As we pointed out earlier in this chapter as an AP Tip, it is common practice to treat bodies as a point located at the c.m. of the body and to attach the origin of a frame of reference there.

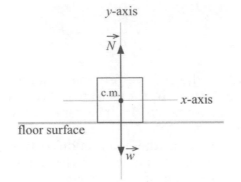

Since the crate is in equilibrium vertically, $\Sigma y = N - w = 0$. Transposing we have $N = w = \mathbf{200.0\ N}$

FRICTION

(*College Physics* 9th ed. pages 105–110/10th ed. pages 108–114)

When the surface of a body slides over the surface of another body, each body exerts a *frictional force,* $\vec{f}$, on the other. This frictional force is parallel or tangent to the contact surfaces. The force on each body is opposite to the direction of its motion or tendency toward motion relative to the other. When a block slides from left to right along a laboratory table, a frictional force acts to the left.

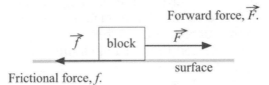

Frictional force may also act when there is no relative motion.

The origin of this type of frictional force is not fully understood. Basically, sliding friction is caused by several factors. Microscopically, surfaces have hills and valleys. The smoother a given surface, the smaller the hills and valleys that cover that surface. As the block slides over the tabletop, the hills and valleys *snag* tending to hold the block back or even prevent it from moving at all. Too, sub-microscopic electrical interactions, *adhesive forces*, between the atoms and molecules of the contact surfaces contribute to the frictional force. The mechanism between the frictional force between a brick and a tabletop and the frictional force between a wooden crate and the surface of a floor will be quite different.

Again, it is common practice to treat bodies as a point located at the c.m. of the body and to attach the origin of a frame of reference there.

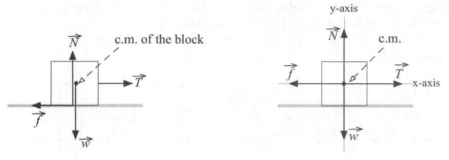

An interesting feature concerning friction forces between contact surfaces is that the frictional force is independent of the contact area. The force of friction depends on two things, one is called the *coefficient of friction*, μ, and the other is the *normal force*, $\vec{N}$, the lower surface exerts on the under surface of the block. We define the maximum value of friction as:

$$\vec{f} = \mu\vec{N}$$

In a state of translational or static equilibrium, $\Sigma\vec{R} = 0$, there is no resultant force. A body in equilibrium is either at rest or moving with constant velocity.

$$\vec{f}_s \le \mu_s\vec{N}$$

Suppose that a cord is attached to the block in the diagram below and the tension, $\vec{T}$, is gradually increased.

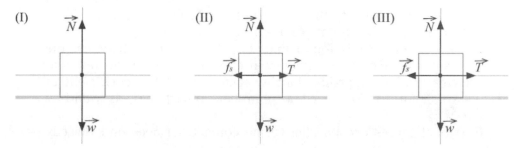

A 100.0 N crate rests on a horizontal floor as in diagram (I) above. The coefficient of static friction between the surfaces is 0.4. What is the maximum static frictional force that can exist between the surfaces? What static frictional force exists?

Note that the only forces acting in the system are the weight of the crate and the normal the floor exerts on the crate. The crate is in equilibrium vertically; the upward force equals the downward force. The floor prevents the crate from moving vertically. Therefore $N = w$.

$$\left(f_s\right)_{max} = \mu_s N = (0.4)(100.0 \text{ N}) = 40.0 \text{ N}$$

Since no horizontal force acts on the crate, no frictional force exists between the crate and floor.

In diagram (II), a rope is attached to the crate and is pulled to the right with a force of $T = 10.0 \text{ N}$. What static frictional force exists? Since the maximum static frictional force that will exist between the surfaces is 40.0 N, a force of 10.0 N to the right is not enough to initiate motion. The crate remains in equilibrium and the force to the right equals the force to the left, the static frictional force is 10.0 N.

In diagram (III), the tension in the rope is 20.0 N making the frictional force 20.0 N.

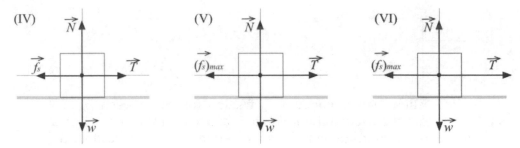

In the above diagram, diagram (IV), the rope is pulled with a force of 30.0 N making the tension in the rope 30.0 N. In equilibrium, all the forces to the right equal the forces to the left and the static frictional force between the surfaces is $T = f_s = 30.0 \text{ N}$.

As T is increased further, a limiting value is reached at which the block breaks away and starts to move.

In diagram (V), a pull of 40.0 N acts on the rope. The maximum static frictional force that can act between the surfaces is $(f_s)_{max} = 40.0 \text{ N}$. The force to the right equals the force to the left placing the crate into a *state of impending motion*. The crate is on the verge of breaking free and moving to the right.

In diagram (VI), the tension in the rope is 50.0 N. The maximum force to the left is 40.0 N. $T + (f_s)_{max} = 50.0 \text{ N} - 40.0 \text{ N} = 10.0 \text{ N} = R$. A resultant of 10.0 N acts to the right since $R > 0$. The system is *NOT* in equilibrium. Note the sign of –40.0 N. Friction acts to the left.

Once in motion, it is found that the frictional force between the contact surfaces decreases. This new frictional force is proportional to the normal and to a proportionality factor called the *coefficient of kinetic or sliding friction*, μ_k. Maximum kinetic friction f_k is found by $\vec{f}_k = \mu_k \vec{N}$.

Frictional forces are parallel to the contact surfaces and directly oppose motion of the surfaces across one another.

AP Tip

The force of static friction is greater than the force of sliding friction for the same materials. In symbols: $\vec{f}_s > \vec{f}_k$ and $\mu_s > \mu_k$.

The coefficient of sliding friction is independent of the velocity. Static and sliding friction are both nearly independent of the contact area.

ROPES SUPPORTING A LOAD

(College Physics 9th ed. pages 100–101/10th ed. pages 102–103)

Consider the following system that is at rest. Since nothing is moving, the system is in a state of static equilibrium. Three ropes come together at the knot. Knots always make a great point to attach a frame of reference. The short rope supports the load of weight, *w*. Rope 1 and rope 2, attached to the ceiling at points A and B, support the entire system. How can we find the tension in the ropes if the load weighs 100 N?

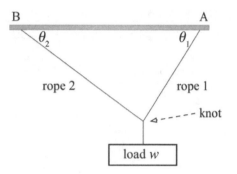

PROBLEM SOLVING STRATEGY

Make a simple sketch showing the system under consideration.

Identify each of the forces acting on the object. The two types of forces that usually act on bodies in equilibrium are *contact forces* and *field forces*. Both must be considered in a free-body diagram. The gravitational attraction exerted on the body by the Earth is *weight* and it does not have a point of contact with the body. Nonetheless, it exerts a real force on the body and must be considered an important factor. The direction of the weight vector, without exception, is always vertically downward toward the center of the Earth.

Next, it is very helpful to redraw the forces making a free-body diagram. In this diagram you reduce the object of interest to a single point. Attach a frame of reference to that point on the free-body diagram.

At the origin of the frame of reference, place each of the force vectors identified in step 2. Place each vector with its tail at the origin.

Resolve each force vector into its *x*- and *y*-components and sketch them in to your diagram. Label each force and its components.

Apply the first condition for equilibrium summing the components along the *x*-axis and the *y*-axis. Write the equations for the first condition for equilibrium, $\Sigma x = 0$ and $\Sigma y = 0$. It is recommended that at first the student constructs and uses a table somewhat as follows.

Finally, solve for the unknown forces.

At first this process appears lengthy, but it is necessary for a clear understanding of a problem.

Force	x-component	y-component
$F_1 @ \theta_1$	$F_1 \cos\theta_1$	$F_1 \sin\theta_1$
$F_2 @ \theta_2$	$F_2 \cos\theta_2$	$F_2 \sin\theta_2$
$F_3 @ \theta_3$	$F_3 \cos\theta_3$	$F_3 \sin\theta_3$
etc.	etc.	etc.
Sum of the components	$\Sigma x = x_1 + x_2 + x_3 + \ldots = 0$	$\Sigma y = y_1 + y_2 + y_3 + \ldots = 0$

SAMPLE PROBLEM 6

In the system shown below, ropes 1 and 2 are attached to the ceiling at angles of 45° and 30° respectively. The system supports a 100 N load. Find the tensions in the ropes.

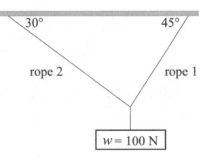

SOLUTION TO PROBLEM 6

First sketch a free-body diagram making the knot the origin of the frame of reference.

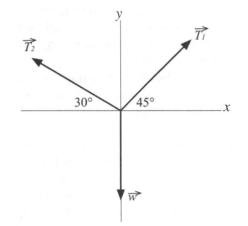

Next, sketch in the x- and y-components of all the vectors and label them.

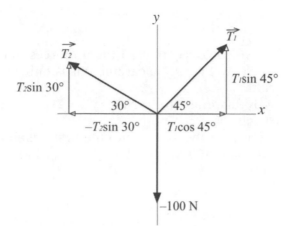

Force	x-component	y-component
T_1	$x_1 = T_1 \cos\theta_1$ $x_1 = T_1 \cos 45°$ $x_1 = 0.7071T_1$	$y_1 = T_1 \sin\theta_1$ $y_1 = T_1 \sin 45°$ $y_1 = 0.7071T_1$
T_2	$x_2 = T_2 \cos\theta_2$ $x_2 = T_2 \cos 150°$ $x_2 = -0.8860T_2$	$y_2 = T_2 \sin\theta_2$ $y_2 = T_2 \sin 150°$ $y_2 = 0.5000T_2$
w	0	−100 N
Component sum	$\Sigma x = x_1 + x_2 = 0$ $0.7071T_1 - 0.8860T_2 = 0$	$\Sigma y = y_1 + y_2 - 100 = 0$ $0.7071T_1 + 0.5000T_2 = 100$

We have developed a set of two simultaneous linear equations containing two unknowns.

(1) $0.7071T_1 - 0.8860T_2 = 0$

(2) $0.7071T_1 + 0.5000T_2 = 100$

Solving equation (1) for T_1 gives $0.7071T_1 = 0.8660T_2$. Substituting this into the second equation yields $0.8660T_2 + 0.5000T_2 = 100$ and $1.3660T_2 = 100$.
Then $T_2 = $ **73.21 N** .
Writing equation (1) $0.7071T_1 - 0.8860T_2 = 0$, and replacing T_2 with 73.21 N, we now have $0.7071T_1 - 0.8660(73.21\text{ N}) = 0$, and

$$T_1 = \frac{0.8660(73.21\text{ N})}{0.7071} = \textbf{89.67 N}$$

There is a second approach to solving the problem that eliminates the need of a force table. In equilibrium we always use the first condition for equilibrium, $\Sigma x = 0$. We could also write that all of the forces to the right equal all of the forces to the left, or $\Sigma x_{right} = \Sigma x_{left}$.

From the above free-body diagram we can write $\Sigma x_{right} = \Sigma x_{left}$ and then $T_1 \cos 45° = T_2 \cos 150°$ which is $0.707 T_1 = 0.866 T_2$. Solving for T_1, $T_1 = \dfrac{0.866 T_2}{0.707}$, we find that $T_1 = 1.225 T_2$.

In equilibrium, $\Sigma y = 0$, or we could say that all the up forces must equal all the down forces, or $\Sigma y_{up} = \Sigma y_{down}$. Be careful, this is only true when a system is in equilibrium.

Returning to the free-body diagram, we write $\Sigma y_{up} = \Sigma y_{down}$ and adding $T_1 \sin 45° + T_2 \sin 150° = 100 \text{ N}$.

We already have a value for T_1. Substituting into the first equation we have $T_1 \sin 45° + T_2 \sin 150° = 100 \text{ N}$ and $(1.225 T_2) \sin 45° + T_2 \sin 150° = 100 \text{ N}$. Solving for T_2,

$$1.366 T_2 = 100$$

$$T_2 = \frac{100}{1.366} = \textbf{73.21 N}$$

$$T_1 = 1.225 T_2 = (1.225)(73.21 \text{ N}) = \textbf{89.67 N}$$

Two-Body System

(*College Physics* 9th ed. pages 109–111/10th ed. pages 111–114)

Sample Problem 7

Consider a block of mass $M = 4.00 \text{ kg}$ at rest on a laboratory tabletop in a state of impending motion. A light cord of negligible mass is attached to M and runs over an ideal pulley to a hanging mass m'. The coefficient of friction for the contact surfaces is $\mu_s = 0.30$. What mass m' is required to place the system in its state of impending motion?

AP Tip

An *ideal pulley* is a one where we ignore any friction within the pulley itself. We also ignore its mass and its radius. An ideal pulley is a first approximation and our present goal is to investigate systems making first approximations. Later in the course, when considering rotational systems, the friction within the pulley, its mass and radius all become important factors.

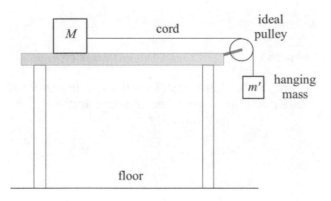

SOLUTION TO PROBLEM 7

The system is in equilibrium and also in a state of impending motion. Just touching the cord or the masses will start the system in motion and it will no longer be at rest or in equilibrium. Make two free-body diagrams, one each for the masses M and m'.

Block M is in equilibrium vertically. The only motion it can have will be along the horizontal. We say that its motion is *constrained*, it can only move horizontally. All the up forces on M will equal all the down forces. The normal force, N, will equal the weight $w = Mg$.

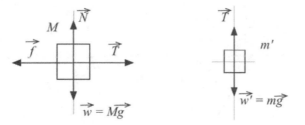

$$N = w = Mg = (4.00 \text{ kg})\left(9.8 \text{ m}/{s^2}\right) = 39.20 \text{ N}$$

Horizontally, all of the forces to the right equal all the forces to the left. The frictional force between the contact surfaces will equal the tension in the rope, $T = f$. The magnitude of the tension T in the rope is everywhere the same. The ideal pulley simply changes the direction of the tension vector.

$$T = f = \mu N = (0.30)(39.20 \text{ N}) = 11.76 \text{ N}$$

The cord attached to the hanging mass supports the mass m'. The sum of all the upward forces acting on m' equals the sum of all the downward forces, or $T = w' = m'g$. Solving for m',

$$m' = \frac{T}{g} = \frac{(11.76 \text{ N})}{\left(9.8 \text{ m}/{s^2}\right)} = \mathbf{1.20 \text{ kg}}$$

Only a 1.20 kg mass will maintain a state of equilibrium and a state of impending motion. A mass greater than 1.20 kg will increase the tension in the cord and will exceed the maximum frictional force between the block and the surface of the laboratory table.

THE INCLINED PLANE

(*College Physics* 9th ed. pages 107–108/10th ed. pages 111–114)

The inclined plane is a simple machine that features a number of excellent learning ideas. Inclined planes are tilted at some angle θ.

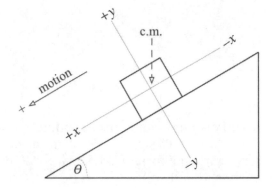

In dealing with inclined planes, we attach our frame of reference to the c.m. of the body and make the x-axis parallel to the surface of the inclined plane and the y-axis perpendicular to that plane. We will also treat motion down the plane as being positive making the x-axis positive down the plane.

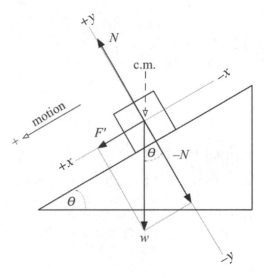

The weight of a body is a force w directed vertically downward. It is useful in analyzing the behavior of a body on an inclined plane to resolve w into vector components in directions parallel and normal to the inclined plane.

The gravitational force on the body is $w = mg$. Resolving w into its two components gives one component parallel to the plane and directed down the plane. This component, F', will be called the *effective weight*, and its value is $F' = mg \sin \theta$. Giving the inclined plane-body system personification, the object on the plane "thinks" its effective weight is its weight. *Effectively*, this is the force that "*pulls*" the body down the inclined plane.

The other component is normal to the plane and has the value $mg\cos\theta$. This component must be balanced by the plane's normal reaction force N. For this reason we could call the y-component, –N, the anti normal. The *normal force* that the inclined plane exerts on the body is $N = mg\cos\theta$. Again being guilty of personification, the inclined plane "thinks" that the anti normal force is the weight of the body.

Earlier, we define the force of friction as $f = \mu N$. On inclined planes the normal is $N = mg\cos\theta$ and we can say that the frictional force a body experienced on an inclined plane is then $f = \mu mg\cos\theta$.

Before we go much further we need to address something about the tilt angle or angle of inclination of an inclined plane. Somewhere between 10° and 20° there is a critical angle where for a given set of surfaces the effective weight of the body equals the maximum static frictional force. Below this angle, friction is greater than the effective weight. Above that angle the effective weight always exceeds friction and there will be motion down the plane. This angle is called the *angle of repose* or simply the *slip angle*. Keep in mind that the slip angle is unique for a given system.

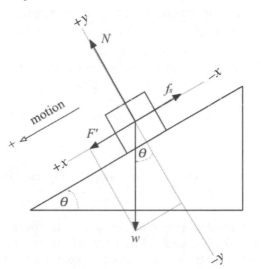

At the slip angle, $F' = \left(f_s\right)_{max}$.

$$mg\sin\theta = \mu_s mg\cos\theta$$

Mass m and g are common to both sides of the equation and divide out leaving us with

$$\sin\theta = \mu_s\cos\theta$$

Solving for the coefficient of static friction gives

$$\mu_s = \frac{\sin\theta}{\cos\theta}$$

The sine of an angle divided by the cosine of the same angle lead to an identity called the tangent function or

$$\mu_s = \frac{\sin\theta}{\cos\theta} = \tan\theta$$

If we know the slip angle, we can find the coefficient of static friction for the surfaces in the problem, or

$$\mu_s = \tan(\text{slip angle})$$

Or the slip angle is the inverse tangent of the coefficient of static friction, or

$$\text{slip angle} = \tan^{-1}\mu_s$$

SAMPLE PROBLEM 8

A 4.0 kg block sits at rest on an inclined plane. The coefficient of static friction for the surfaces is 0.268.

(a) Find the slip angle.

(b) What is the normal force the plane exerts on the block?

(c) What is the effective weight of the block?

SOLUTION TO PROBLEM 8

(a) The block is at rest making it in a state of static equilibrium. To find the slip angle we use slip angle=$\tan^{-1}\mu_s = \tan^{-1}(0.268) = \mathbf{15.0°}$. At all angles below 15.0° there can be no motion on the plane. At angles greater than 15°, friction cannot hold the block at rest and the effective weight "pulls" the block down the plane.

(b) The normal force is $N = mg\cos\theta = (4.0 \text{ kg})\left(9.8 \text{ }^m\!/_{s^2}\right)\cos 15.0° =$

3.8 N

(c) The effective weight is $F' = mg\sin\theta = (4.0 \text{ kg})\left(9.8 \text{ }^m\!/_{s^2}\right)\sin 15.0° =$

10.2 N

In equilibrium on an inclined plane, motion is constrained to the plane. The body can stand still, slide down the plane at constant speed, or be pushed up the plane at constant speed. *All forces down the plane must equal all the forces up the plane.*

We will do one more thing, find the frictional force acting on the block. Remember, the block "wants" to slide down the plane making friction act up the plane. Friction on the plane is

$f = \mu mg\cos\theta = (0.268)(4.0 \text{ kg})\left(9.8 \text{ }^m\!/_{s^2}\right)\cos 15.0° = 10.2 \text{ N}$. Do all

the forces up the plane equal the forces down the plane? Yes.

SAMPLE PROBLEM 9

A 10.0 kg box is lowered down a plane inclined at 30°. The coefficient of friction between the surfaces is 0.25. What push P up and parallel to the plane must be exerted on the box to lower it down the plane at constant speed?

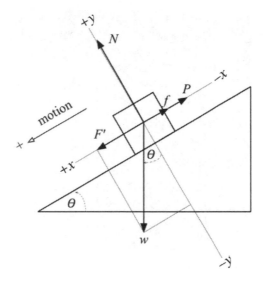

SOLUTION TO PROBLEM 9

Look at the vector diagram given below. Lowering the box at constant speed places the box into a state of equilibrium and all forces acting down the plane must equal all the forces up the plane. Since the box slides down the plane, friction will act up the plane. The box cannot move along the y-axis, so we say its motion is constrained along the y-axis. The inclined plane prevents motion along the y-axis.

forces up the plane = forces down the plane

Therefore, $P + f = F'$ and

$$P = F' - f = mg\sin\theta - \mu mg\cos\theta = mg(\sin\theta - \mu\cos\theta)$$

$$P = mg(\sin\theta - \mu\cos\theta) = (10.0 \text{ kg})\left(9.8 \text{ }^{m}\!/\!_{s^2}\right)(\sin 30° - 0.25\cos 30°) = \textbf{27.8 N}$$

SAMPLE PROBLEM 10

A 100.0 kg crate is pushed up a 35° incline at constant velocity. The coefficient of friction between the underside of the crate and the surface of the incline is 0.44. What push P parallel to the plane is required?

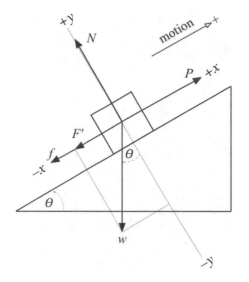

SOLUTION TO PROBLEM 10

Constant velocity implies equilibrium and therefore forces up the plane = forces down the plane. Since motion exists up the plane, friction will act down the plane and we can write

$$P = F' + f = mg\sin\theta + \mu mg\cos\theta = mg\left(\sin\theta + \mu\cos\theta\right)$$

$$P = mg\left(\sin\theta + \mu\cos\theta\right)$$

$$= (100.0 \text{ kg})\left(9.8 \text{ }^{m}\!/_{s^2}\right)\left(\sin 35° + 0.44\cos 35°\right)$$

$$= \mathbf{915.3 \text{ N}}$$

TORQUE

(*College Physics* 9th ed. pages 235–239/10th ed. pages 240–244)

Up to this point we have seen that if all forces acting on a body intersect at a common point and their resultant is zero, the system must be in a state of translational equilibrium. But what happens if a body is acted on by *non-concurrent* forces? Now we have to consider the point of application of each force as well as the magnitude and direction of each force.

Consider a rod of length r that is attached to an external axle about which it can rotate freely. We call that point an *axis of rotation*. As shown below, a force F is applied to the opposite end of the rod. The distance from the axis of rotation to the point of application of the force is called the *moment arm*. Some refer to it as the *lever arm*. This is a "from and to" situation that makes the moment arm a vector, $\vec{r}$.

The applied force, $\vec{F}$, is non-concurrent with the axis of rotation. Non-concurrent forces tend to make bodies and systems rotate. A counterclockwise, CCW, rotation is considered to be a positive rotation (+) and a clockwise, CW, rotation is considered to be a negative rotation (−).

We define the torque $\vec{\tau}$, a vector, exerted by a force on a body as the measure of the effectiveness in turning a body about an axis of rotation. Torque is also called a *moment of force*. Mathematically, torque is defined as

$$\tau = Fr\sin\theta$$

The angle θ is the angle between the moment arm and the applied force. When θ is 90°, when the moment arm and applied force are perpendicular, the $\sin 90° = 1$ and then

$$\tau = Fr$$

When θ is 0°, $\sin 0° = 0$ makes the line of action of the applied force concurrent with the axis of rotation and there is NO torque.

Note that the torque, a vector, is the product of two vectors $\vec{\tau} = \vec{F}\vec{r}$ and this vector equation is written as $\vec{\tau} = \vec{r}\vec{F}$ when working with deeper vector algebra. We will not be dealing with deeper vector algebra however.

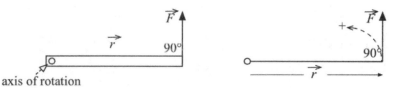

SAMPLE PROBLEM 11

Considering the above drawings. A force of 100.0 N is applied at the end of the rod and at a 90° angle with the rod. Ignore the mass of the rod. If the rod has a length $r = 1.5\ \text{m}$, what is the torque acting on the rod?

SOLUTION TO PROBLEM 11

Note that the force is applied upward making the torque CCW(+). The torque about the axis of rotation is then

$$\tau_0 = Fr = +(100.0\ \text{N})(1.5\ \text{m}) = +\textbf{150.0 N}\cdot\textbf{m}$$

The system will rotate CCW.
The SI unit of torque is the $\text{N}\cdot\text{m}$.

SAMPLE PROBLEM 12

Consider the system illustrated below. A uniform rod, pivoted at one end, is 1.0 m long and weighs 25.0 N. Determine the torque about the axis of rotation.

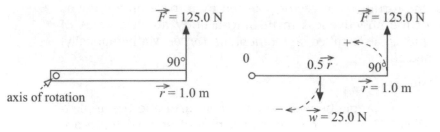

SOLUTION TO PROBLEM 12

Since the rod is uniform, there is the weight of the rod to consider and its weight vector is at the center of mass or $0.5R = 0.5$ m. The weight vector tends to make the system rotate CW (–). The applied force on the system tends to make the system rotate CCW (+). The total torque involved is then

$$\Sigma \tau_0 = \tau_w + \tau_F = -w(0.5r) + Fr = -(25.0 \text{ N})(0.5 \text{ m}) + (125.0 \text{ N})(1.0 \text{ m})$$

$$\Sigma \tau = +112.5 \text{ N} \cdot \text{m}$$

The system will rotate CCW.

SAMPLE PROBLEM 13

A uniform rod, pivoted at one end, has a weight of 30.0 N and a length of 2.0 m. Find the total torque about the axis of rotation if the applied force at the end of the rod is 170.0 N

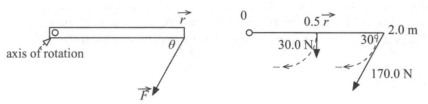

SOLUTION TO PROBLEM 13

Both the weight vector and the applied force tend to make the system rotate CW about the axis of rotation. The total torque is

$$\Sigma \tau_0 = \tau_w + \tau_F$$
$$= -w(0.5r) + (-F)r\sin 30°$$
$$= (-30.0 \text{ N})(0.5 \times 2.0 \text{ m}) + (-170 \text{ N})(2.0 \text{ m})(\sin 30°)$$

$$\Sigma \tau_0 = -200.0 \text{ N} \cdot \text{m}$$

The negative sign implies that the system will rotate CW.

NON-CONCURRENT FORCES AND EQUILIBRIUM

(College Physics 9th ed. pages 240–247/10th ed. pages 245–252)

When there is no resultant torque acting in a system, $\Sigma\tau = 0$, the system is in a state of rotational equilibrium. We have already addressed the first condition for equilibrium where the sums of the *x*- and *y*-components add to zero, $\Sigma x = 0$ and $\Sigma y = 0$. We must now state the second condition for equilibrium and stipulate that there is NO resultant torque in the system or $\Sigma\tau = 0$.

SCAFFOLD MODEL OF ROTATIONAL EQUILIBRIUM

(College Physics 9th ed. pages 240–247/10th ed. pages 870–872)

SAMPLE PROBLEM 14

A uniform meterstick of mass $m = 0.10$ kg is supported at its ends by two cords as shown in the diagram below. A mass $m_1 = 0.80$ kg is suspended from the 20.0 cm mark and a mass $m_2 = 1.10$ kg is suspended at the 60.0 cm mark. The system is in equilibrium. Calculate the tensions in the cords.

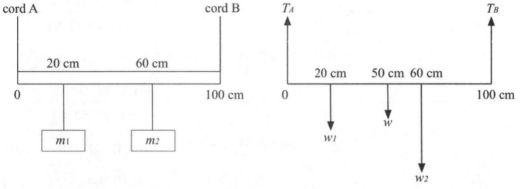

SOLUTION TO PROBLEM 14

Beside the diagram of the system is a vector diagram of the forces involved. The forces are non-concurrent and the system is in a state of rotational equilibrium since non-concurrent forces tend to cause rotation. Both the first and second conditions for equilibrium hold. It is convenient for us to choose the zero, 0, end of the meterstick as our axis of rotation.

Study the vector diagram. There are no *x*-components in the system and the sum is $\Sigma x = 0$.

There are *y*-components. Weight is defined as $w = mg$. Each weight vector is negative since weight vectors always point downward toward the center of the Earth. The tension in each of the cords supporting the meterstick is directed upward and is considered positive.

There are two unknowns in the problem, T_A and T_B, and we can eliminate the twisting effect of one of them by making the left-end of the meterstick the axis of rotation. At the zero-end, our axis of rotation, T_A is concurrent and concurrent forces cannot produce a torque as there is no moment arm.

The system is in rotational equilibrium and $\Sigma y = 0$ or $\Sigma y_{up} = \Sigma y_{down}$.

Then $T_A + T_B = w_1 + w + w_2 = m_1 g + mg + m_2 g$

$$T_A + T_B = (0.80 \text{ kg})\left(9.8 \text{ m}/\text{s}^2\right) + (0.10 \text{ kg})\left(9.8 \text{ m}/\text{s}^2\right) + (1.10 \text{ kg})\left(9.8 \text{ m}/\text{s}^2\right)$$
$$= 19.60 \text{ N}$$

Using the left-end or the 0 of the meterstick as the axis of rotation we sum all torques about the point, or $\Sigma \tau_0 = 0$. In rotational equilibrium we can also write $\Sigma \tau_{CCW} = \Sigma \tau_{CW}$. The tension vector T_B tends to make the system rotate CCW. The weight vectors all tend to make the system rotate CW.

We construct a force table as shown below and substitute in values.

Force	x-component	y-component	Torque about O
T_A	0	T_A	0
T_B	0	T_B	$+T_B r$ $+T_B (1.00 \text{ m})$ $+T_B$
w_1	0	$-m_1 g$ $(-0.80 \text{ kg})\left(9.8 \text{ m}/\text{s}^2\right) -7.84 \text{ N}$	$(-m_1 g)(0.20 \text{ m})$ $(-0.80 \text{ kg})\left(9.8 \text{ m}/\text{s}^2\right)(0.20 \text{ m})$ $-1.57 \text{ N} \cdot \text{m}$
w	0	$-mg$ $(-0.10 \text{ kg})\left(9.8 \text{ m}/\text{s}^2\right) -0.98 \text{ N}$	$(-mg)(0.50 \text{ m})$ $(-0.10 \text{ kg})\left(9.8 \text{ m}/\text{s}^2\right)(0.50 \text{ m})$ $-0.49 \text{ N} \cdot \text{m}$
w_2	0	$-m_2 g$ $(-1.10 \text{ kg})\left(9.8 \text{ m}/\text{s}^2\right)$ -10.80 N	$(-m_2 g)(0.60 \text{ m})$ $(-1.10 \text{ kg})\left(9.8 \text{ m}/\text{s}^2\right)(0.60 \text{ m})$ $-6.48 \text{ N} \cdot \text{m}$
Sum	$\Sigma x = 0$	$\Sigma y = T_A + T_B - 19.6 = 0$ $T_A + T_B = 19.60 \text{ N}$	$\Sigma \tau_0 = +T_B - 8.54 = 0$ $T_B = 8.54 \text{ N}$

Since the system is in rotational equilibrium and,

$\Sigma x = 0$, $\Sigma y = 0$ and $\Sigma \tau_0 = 0$

Adding the torques and solving for the unknown yields

$T_B = \textbf{8.54 N}$

Adding the y-components and solving for the remaining unknown yields

$$T_A = 19.60 \text{ N} - T_B = 19.60 \text{ N} - 8.54 \text{ N} = \textbf{11.06 N}$$

We can do the same problem and eliminate the force table by solving by inspection.

CENTER OF MASS

(*College Physics* 9th ed. pages 241–244/10th ed. pages 246–249)

SAMPLE PROBLEM 15

A uniform meterstick has a weight $w = 4.0 \text{ N}$. A weight of $w_1 = 6.0 \text{ N}$ is attached to the meterstick at the 10 cm mark. Next a second weight $w_2 = 2.0 \text{ N}$ is attached at the 75 cm point and then the entire system is balanced on a *knife edge*. Where is this balance point that is the center of mass of the system?

SOLUTION TO PROBLEM 15

First make a free-body diagram.

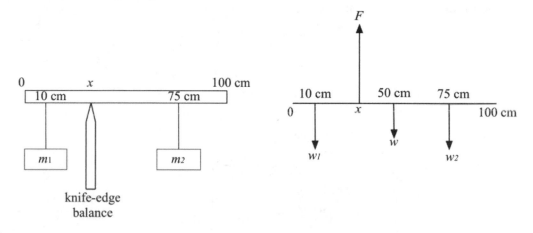

Since the system is balanced at its center of mass, it is in a state of equilibrium. The forces involved are non-concurrent and both conditions for equilibrium apply. There are no horizontal forces. We need only consider the up and down forces and the torques about the balance point.

Since all of the upward forces equal all of the downward forces when in equilibrium, the force F that the knife edge exerts on the system at the center of mass is the normal force N developed in the system and equals the total weight of the system, or

$$N = F = w_1 + w + w_2 = 6.0 \text{ N} + 4.0 \text{ N} + 2.0 \text{ N} = 12.0 \text{ N}$$

Treat the zero, 0, end of the meterstick as the axis of rotation for all of the torques in the system. All the CCW torques in the system equal all the CW torques or

$$Fx = w_1(10 \text{ cm}) + w(50 \text{ cm}) + w_2(75 \text{ cm})$$

We will retain cm and express our answer in cm from the zero end.

$$(12.0 \text{ N})x = (6.0 \text{ N})(10 \text{ cm}) + (4.0 \text{ N})(50 \text{ cm}) + (2.0 \text{ N})(75 \text{ cm})$$

$$x = \frac{410.0 \text{ cm}}{12.0} = \textbf{34.2 cm}$$

The center of mass of the system is at the 34.2 cm point.

THE BOOM CRANE

(*College Physics* 9th ed. pages 244–247/10th ed. pages 249–252)

SAMPLE PROBLEM 16

The uniform *strut* shown in the *boom crane* illustrated below has a weight $w = 100.0$ N and has a length of 3.0 m. A load of 500.0 N is attached to the end of the rigid strut. It is pivoted on the left at the hinge. A support cable of negligible weight is attached to the right end at a 30.0° angle with the horizontal. The crane is motionless. What reactionary force exists in the hinge?

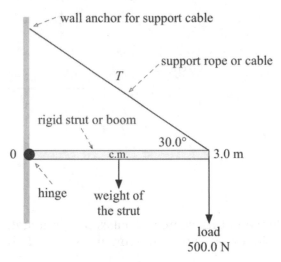

SOLUTION TO PROBLEM 16

Since the strut is uniform, its c.m. is at its center or 1.5 m left of the hinge. The reactionary force R has a horizontal component H and a vertical component V.

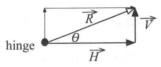

Note that the horizontal component H is the *thrust* generated by the hinge on the system. It is also the *compression* the system exerts on the strut. To find R we need to find H and V.

Next make a free-body diagram.

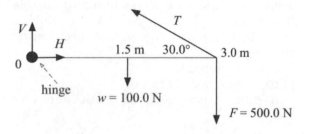

Since the system is motionless it is in a state of equilibrium. The forces are non-concurrent and both conditions for equilibrium will hold.

All the up forces equal all the down forces, or

$$V + T\sin 30.0° = w + F$$

$$V + 0.500T = 100.0 \text{ N} + 500.0 \text{ N}$$

$$V + 0.500T = 600.0$$

All the forces to the right equal all the forces to the left.

$$H = T\cos 30.0°$$

$$H = 0.866T$$

All of the CCW torques equal all the CW torques.

Treating the hinge as the axis of rotation eliminates the twisting effect of both H and V because they are concurrent and concurrent forces cannot produce torque.

$$T(\sin 30°)(3.0 \text{ m}) = (100.0 \text{ N})(1.5 \text{ m}) + (500.0 \text{ N})(3.0 \text{ m})$$

$$(0.500)T(3.0 \text{ m}) = 1650 \text{ N} \cdot \text{m}$$

$$T = \textbf{1100.0 N}$$

From $V + 0.500T = 600.0$,

$$V = 600.0 - 0.500T = 600.0 \text{ N} - 0.500(1100.0 \text{ N}) = \textbf{50.0 N}$$

$$H = 0.866T = 0.866(1100.0 \text{ N}) = \textbf{952.6 N}$$

With both H and V known,

$$R = \sqrt{H^2 + V^2} = \sqrt{(952.6 \text{ N})^2 + (50.0 \text{ N})^2} = 953.9 \text{ N}$$

and

$$\theta = \tan^{-1}\left(\frac{V}{H}\right) = \tan^{-1}\left(\frac{50.0 \text{ N}}{952.6 \text{ N}}\right) = 3.0°$$

$$R = \textbf{952.6 N @ 3.0°}$$

EQUILIBRIUM: STUDENT OBJECTIVES FOR THE AP EXAM

- ■ You should be able to differentiate between mass and weight.
- ■ You should be able to discuss gravitational intensity.

- You should be able to define equilibrium and give examples.
- You should be able to state and apply Newton's first and third laws of motion to equilibrium systems.
- You should be able to relate systems of concurrent forces and the first condition for equilibrium.
- You should be able to define equilibrant.
- You should be able to discuss the normal force.
- You should be able to differentiate between static and kinetic friction.
- You should be able to discuss contact forces and field forces.
- You should be able to define torque and give examples.
- You should be able to relate systems of non-concurrent forces and the First and Second Conditions for Equilibrium.
- You should be able to experimentally find the center of mass of a system.

MULTIPLE-CHOICE QUESTIONS

1. A 25.0 N force applied to a 100.0 N crate moves it at constant velocity on a flat horizontal surface where the coefficient of kinetic friction between the crate and the surface is 0.25.

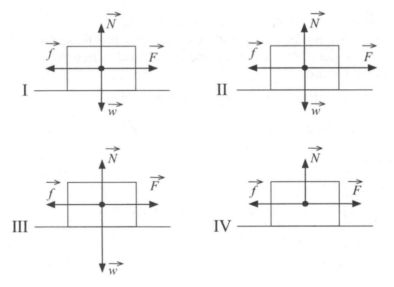

Which of the above illustrations correctly shows the forces acting on the body?
(A) I
(B) II
(C) III
(D) IV

2. A body cannot exert a force on itself. This statement is a direct consequence of Newton's
(A) law of universal gravitation
(B) first law of motion
(C) second law of motion
(D) third law of motion

3. A 500 N crate is moved on a horizontal surface at constant speed by a 120 N force applied at an angle of 40° as shown below.

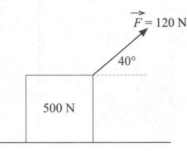

The normal force
(A) acting on the crate is equal to the weight since the normal is the reaction force to the weight of the crate on the surface
(B) is greater than the weight because the object is moving and a force is applied to overcome the frictional force acting on the crate needed to keep the crate in equilibrium
(C) is less than the weight of the crate because the net forces in the y-direction must be zero since the crate is in equilibrium in the y-direction and the 120 N force has a component in the +y direction
(D) is equal to the weight of the crate since the body is in translational equilibrium

4. A 2.00 kg box is placed at the top of a 30° inclined plane as diagrammed below.

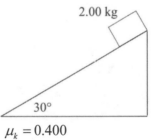

What push P, is required to keep the box moving down the plane at constant speed once the motion has started? The coefficient of kinetic friction, μ_k, is 0.400.
(A) 6.8 N down the plane
(B) 6.8 N up the plane
(C) 3.0 N down the plane
(D) 3.0 N up the plane

5. A 100 N block rests on a horizontal surface where the coefficient of static friction between the block and the surface is 0.64. When a 40 N force is applied to the block the frictional force acting on the block is
(A) 64 N opposite the applied force
(B) 40 N opposite the applied force
(C) 24 N opposite the applied force
(D) 0 since the block is at rest

6. A 300 N weight hangs from three cables as shown below.

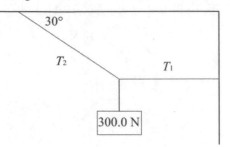

The magnitude of the tension in the horizontal cable T_1 is closest to

(A) 300 N
(B) 450 N
(C) 520 N
(D) 600 N

7. A physics student pulls a wooden crate across a rough horizontal surface with a constant force $\vec{F}$ at constant speed. Which of the following is a correct mathematical relationship for the free-body diagram shown below?

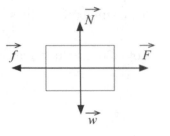

(A) $\vec{F} > \vec{f}$ and $\vec{N} < \vec{w}$
(B) $\vec{F} = \vec{f}$ and $\vec{N} > \vec{w}$
(C) $\vec{F} = \vec{f}$ and $\vec{N} = \vec{w}$
(D) $\vec{F} > \vec{f}$ and $\vec{N} = \vec{w}$

8. A 40.0 kg child stands on a bathroom scale in an elevator that is moving upward at a constant speed of 5.00 m/s. What does the scale read as the elevator moves upward?

(A) 192 N
(B) 240 N
(C) 392 N
(D) 592 N

9. Forces are applied to four different cylinders as is illustrated below.

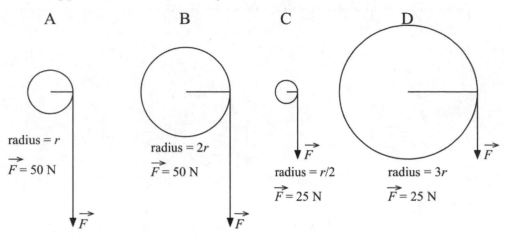

Rank the diagrams for the arrangement that produces the largest torque on the cylinder to the smallest.
(A) $A > B > C > D$
(B) $D > B > A > C$
(C) $B > D > A > C$
(D) $D > B > (A = C)$

10. A uniform meterstick shown below has a mass of 0.100 kg. The pivot is placed at 0.300 m and a 0.200 kg mass is placed at the 0.900 m mark on the meterstick.

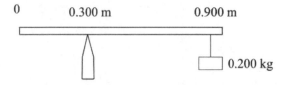

Where should a 0.700 kg mass be placed to bring the system into equilibrium? At the
(A) 0.200 m mark on the meterstick
(B) 0.170 m mark on the meterstick
(C) 0.130 m mark on the meterstick
(D) 0.100 m mark on the meterstick

11. Forces are applied to three fixed pulleys mounted on the same shaft as shown below. The drawing is not to scale.

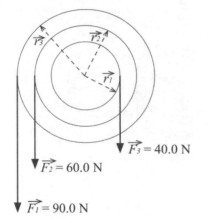

The forces are $\vec{F}_1 = 90.0$ N , $\vec{F}_2 = 60.0$ N and $\vec{F}_3 = 40.0$ N . The radii of the pulleys are $\vec{r}_1 = 0.120$ m , $\vec{r}_2 = 0.100$ m , and $\vec{r}_3 = 0.080$ m . The magnitude of the net torque on the pulley is
(A) 20.0 N·m
(B) 13.6 N·m
(C) 10.8 N·m
(D) 8.00 N·m

12. Two forces are applied to a disk as shown below.

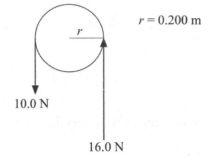

The net torque of the system is
(A) 3.00 N·m counterclockwise
(B) 5.20 N·m counterclockwise
(C) 3.00 N·m clockwise
(D) 5.20 N·m clockwise

13. A force of 75.0 N is applied to a horizontal rod 0.600 m in length at an angle of 30° as shown.

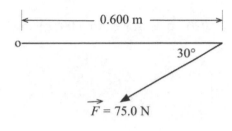

The torque produced by this force is closest to
(A) 22 N·m
(B) 38 N·m
(C) 45 N·m
(D) 90 N·m

Questions 14 to 15

Directions: For each of the questions or incomplete statements below, <u>two</u> of the suggested answers will be correct. For each of these, you must select both correct choices to earn credit. No partial credit can be awarded if only one correct response is selected.

14. A book rests on the top of a level table. The action-reaction pairs are
(A) the force the book exerts on the Earth and the gravitational force exerted by the Earth on the book
(B) the normal force exerted by on the book by the table and the gravitational force exerted by the Earth on the book
(C) the force the book exerts on the table and the normal force exerted on the book by the table
(D) the normal force on the book and the gravitational force exerted by the Earth

15. A body placed on a rough surface experiences a force as shown. Which of the following statements are true?

(A) Friction only exists when there is relative motion between the two surfaces.
(B) Friction only exists when one body tends to slide past another surface because translational equilibrium applies when a stationary body experiences an external force that tries to move the body.
(C) Friction arises from the gravitational force of attraction between the molecules on the two materials. Since friction depends on the normal between the surfaces, a larger gravitational force produces a larger normal.
(D) Friction arises from the electromagnetic force of attraction between the molecules of the two materials that is the same as the bonding holding the materials together.

FREE-RESPONSE PROBLEMS

1. A steel sphere of mass $m = 0.020$ kg is at rest in a 90° groove in a steel track as shown below.

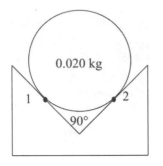

(a) Show the forces acting on the sphere in a free-body diagram. Clearly label and indicate the magnitude and direction of each force.

(b) Determine the normal forces $\vec{N}_1$ and $\vec{N}_2$ acting on the sphere.

2. You are to design an experiment to determine the mass of a meterstick using known masses, a pivot stand, and string in enough detail that another student could duplicate your result.

(a) Explain your procedure and include a schematic diagram of your equipment.

(b) What measurements will you take and how will you use them?

(c) What conditions must be met in order to place the meterstick into a state of rotational equilibrium?

3. A 2.00 kg box slides down an inclined plane at constant speed when the angle of the incline is 30°.

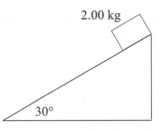

(a) Show the forces acting on the body using the tilted box below. Correctly label the forces.

(b) Write and solve the equation needed to obtain the coefficient of friction between the 2.00 kg box and the surface. Treat down the plane as positive.

(c) Mass is added to the box increasing its total mass to 3.00 kg. As a result, the box will

_____ increase its speed down the plane

_____ decrease its speed down the plane

_____ continue down the plane at constant speed

Explain your answer.

(d) If the box is pushed up the plane at constant speed, the frictional force acting on the box will

_____ increase

_____ decrease

_____ remain the same

Explain your answer.

4. A 6.00 m uniform ladder has a weight of 200.0 N. It rests against a frictionless wall as diagramed below. An 800.0 N painter stands on the ladder with his c.m. 4.00 m from the base.

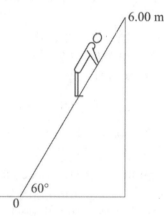

6.00 m

60°

0

(a) Show the forces acting on the ladder.
(b) i.   Write the free-body equation for the force exerted on the ladder by the wall.
    ii. What is the coefficient of static friction acting on the ladder at the base?
(c) Why is it helpful to use the base of the ladder as the point to write the $\Sigma \vec{\tau} = 0$ equation?
(d) The painter finds that he needs to climb higher on the ladder. However, it will slip if the he climbs higher than 4.00 m from the base of the ladder; what could be done so he can climb higher without the ladder slipping?

Answers

MULTIPLE-CHOICE QUESTIONS

1. **A** The 100.0 N body is in translational equilibrium and $\Sigma \vec{F}_x = 0$. The force pulling the crate must equal the frictional force. In the y-direction $\Sigma \vec{F}_y = 0$ means the normal to the surface must be equal and opposite $\vec{w}$, the weight of the body.

    (*College Physics* 9th ed. pages 88, 95–97, 105–106/10th ed. pages 90, 97–100, 108–109)
    (L.O. 3.A.2.1)

2. **D** A body <u>cannot</u> exert a force on itself. Forces always come in pairs. Newton's third law tells us that the action-reaction pair always acts on different objects.

    (*College Physics* 9th ed. pages 95–97/10th ed. pages 97–100)
    (L.O. 3.A.3.2)

3. **C** The body is in translational equilibrium. A free-body diagram shows the direction of the forces. Since the 120 N force acts upward on the crate, the $\Sigma \vec{F}_y = \vec{N} + \vec{F} \sin\theta - \vec{w}$.

    The normal will be less than the weight $\vec{w} = m\vec{g}$.

    (*College Physics* 9th ed. pages 99–100/10th ed. pages 101–103)
    (L.O. 2.B.1.1, 3.A.4.3)

4. **D** The body is in translational equilibrium. The force parallel to the plane is found from solving the $\Sigma \vec{F} = 0$ equation. Since the effective component of the weight is down the plane and friction will be up the plane the difference of the two will give the magnitude of the push as well as indicate the needed direction. Take down the plane as the positive direction.
    $0 = m\vec{g} \sin\theta - \mu_k m\vec{g} \cos\theta \pm \vec{P}$.

    $$(2.00 \text{ kg})\left(9.80 \text{ }^m\!/_{s^2}\right) \sin 30° - 0.400(2.00 \text{ kg})\left(9.80 \text{ }^m\!/_{s^2}\right) \cos 30° \pm \vec{P}$$

    $9.80 \text{ N} - 6.79 \text{ N} \pm \vec{P} = 0$. The push is 3.0 N directed up the plane.

    (*College Physics* 9th ed. pages 99–100/10th ed. pages 101–103)
    (L.O. 2.B.1.1, 3.A.4.3)

5. **B** The block is in equilibrium. In order to start the block moving, the maximum force of static friction must be overcome. The equality, $\vec{f}_{max} = \mu_s \vec{N}$, requires a maximum force of 64 N. The block remains at rest; the first condition of equilibrium applies and $\Sigma \vec{F} = 0$. A 40 N force is applied, thus the frictional force is 40 N.

    (*College Physics* 9th ed. pages 99–100, 105–106/10th ed. pages 101–103)
    (L.O. 2.B.1.1, 2.B.2.1, 3.A.4.3)

6. **C** Drawing a free-body diagram for the system permits you to write

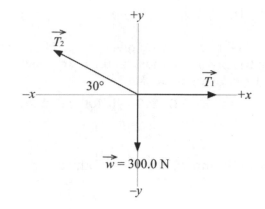

$\vec{F}_y = \vec{T}_2 \sin 30° - \vec{w}$. The tension in $\vec{T}_2 = \dfrac{300.0 \text{ N}}{\sin 30°} = 600.0$ N.

Writing the $\Sigma \vec{F}_x = \vec{T}_1 - \vec{T}_2 \cos 30° = 0$ equation will give the solution for $\vec{T}_1$. The tension in the horizontal cable $\vec{T}_1$ is 520 N.

(*College Physics* 9th ed. pages 99–100/10th ed. pages 101–103, 108–109)
(L.O. 3.A.4.3)

7. **C** Since the crate is moving at constant speed, the free-body diagram shows that $\Sigma \vec{F}_x = 0$, thus the force pulling the crate and the frictional force on the crate are equal and in opposite directions. $\Sigma \vec{F}_y = 0$ also applies, and the normal force must equal the weight of the crate.

(*College Physics* 9th ed. pages 99–100, 105–106/10th ed. pages 101–103, 108–109)
(L.O. 3.B.2.1)

8. **C** The elevator is moving upward at 5.00 m/s, moving at constant speed. There are no net forces acting along the x-direction, only in the y-direction. Newton's first law of motion applies $\Sigma \vec{F}_y = 0$. The bathroom scale will read the weight of the child, 392 N.

(*College Physics* 9th ed. pages 99–100/10th ed. pages 101–103)
(L.O. 3.A.3.1)

9. **C** Torque depends on both the force and the moment arm $\tau = rF \sin \theta$. The correct ranking is $B > D > A > C$.

(*College Physics* 9th ed. pages 239–237/10th ed. pages 241–242)
(L.O. 3.F.1.2, 3.F.1.3)

10. **D** The system is in equilibrium when the clockwise torques are equal to the counterclockwise torques. The moment arm is the distance from where the force is applied to the pivot.

$$(0.100 \text{ kg})\left(9.80 \text{ m}/_{s^2}\right)(0.200 \text{ m}) + (0.200 \text{ kg})\left(9.80 \text{ m}/_{s^2}\right)(0.600 \text{ m})$$

$$= (0.700 \text{ kg})\left(9.80 \text{ m}/_{s^2}\right)r$$

$0.196 \text{ N}\cdot\text{m} + 1.18 \text{ N}\cdot\text{m} = 6.86 \text{ N}\cdot r$. Solving gives $r = 0.200 \text{ m}$. The distance is 0.200 m from the pivot and thus the 0.700 kg mass is located at the 0.100 mark on the meterstick.

(*College Physics* 9th ed. pages 239–237, 240–246/10th ed. pages 241–242, 245–252)
(L.O. 3.F.1.5)

11. **B** In the diagram, $\vec{F}_1 = 90.0 \text{ N}$, and $\vec{F}_2 = 60.0 \text{ N}$ produce counterclockwise rotation.

$\vec{F}_3 = 40.0 \text{ N}$ produces a clockwise rotation.

$$(90.0 \text{ N})(0.120 \text{ m}) + (60.0 \text{ N})(0.100 \text{ m}) - (40.0 \text{ N})(0.080 \text{ m}) = 13.6 \text{ N}\cdot\text{m}$$

(*College Physics* 9th ed. pages 236–237/10th ed. pages 241–242)
(L.O. 3.F.1.1, 3.F.1.2, 3.F.1.5)

12. **B** The two forces applied produce rotation of the disk in the same direction— counterclockwise. Since the moment arm is 0.200 m, the net torque is

$$\Sigma\vec{\tau} = (0.200 \text{ m})(16.0 \text{ N} + 10.0 \text{ N}) = 5.20 \text{ N}\cdot\text{m}.$$

(*College Physics* 9th ed. pages 236–237/10th ed. pages 241–242)
(L.O. 3.F.1.2)

13. **A** The torque on the rod is determined from substitution into $\Sigma\vec{\tau} = (0.600 \text{ m})(75.0 \text{ N})\sin 30° = 22.5 \text{ N}\cdot\text{m}$.

(*College Physics* 9th ed. pages 236–237/10th ed. pages 241–242)
(L.O. 3.F.1.1)

14. **A** and **C** Action reaction pairs have the same magnitude, act in opposite directions, and are always applied to two different objects. The action reaction pairs are A, the book and the Earth that exert equal and opposite forces on each other whose magnitude is given by $F = G\dfrac{M_{Earth}\cdot m_{book}}{r^2}$ and C. The force the book exerts on the table and the normal force exerted on the book by the table's surface are equal. The table exerts an upward force perpendicular to the book.

(*College Physics* 9th ed. pages 92–93, 95–97/10th ed. pages 95–97, 101–103)
(L.O. 3.A.3.3)

15. **B** and **D**. An object that is stationary or moving at constant speed experiences a net force $\Sigma\vec{F} = 0$. The magnitude of the frictional force will equal the applied force. The forces that arise between

two bodies in contact, adhesion between unlike molecules and cohesion between like molecules, are forces of attraction and with surface irregularities are basically responsible for friction. These forces are short-range electromagnetic forces of attraction that are negligible at distances larger than a few atomic diameters.

(*College Physics* 9th ed. pages 99–100, 105–106/10th ed. pages 101–103, 108–109)
(L.O. 3.A.3.4, 3.C.4.1, 3.C.4.2)

FREE-RESPONSE PROBLEMS

1. (a) The diagram of the forces acting between the sphere and the sides of the groove is shown below. The normal force is a reaction to the weight on the sphere on the sides of the groove.

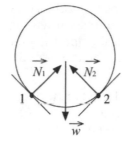

The second diagram indicates the concurrent forces and the angles these force make with respect to the *x* and *y* axis.

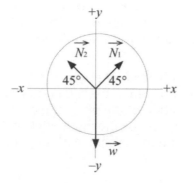

   (b) Due to symmetry, the normal forces are equal in magnitude. The solution for the normal forces is determined by writing the $\Sigma \vec{F} = 0$ equation.

$$\vec{N}_1 \sin 45° + \vec{N}_2 \sin 45° = m\vec{g}$$

$$2\vec{N}_1 \sin 45° = (0.020 \text{ kg})\left(9.80 \text{ m}/_{s^2}\right)$$

$$\vec{N}_1 = \frac{0.196 \text{ N}}{0.707}$$

$$\vec{N}_1 = \vec{N}_2 = \textbf{0.139 N}$$

(*College Physics* 9th ed. pages 88–89, 95–97, 99–101/10th ed. pages 90–91, 97–99, 101–103)
(L.O. 2.B.1.1, 3.A.2.1, 3.A.3.1, 3.A.4.1, 3.A.4.3)

2. (a) By applying the conditions of rotational equilibrium to a meterstick, its mass may be determined.
The schematic of the laboratory equipment is shown below:

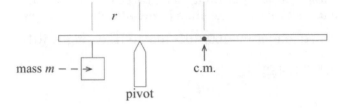

Determine the center of mass for the meterstick by balancing it on the pivot stand and adjusting its position until the meterstick is horizontal. Record the position of the center of mass.

Place the pivot stand at some position other than the center of gravity. Record this position. Using a known mass, bring the meterstick into equilibrium by adjusting the position of the mass. Record both the mass and the moment arm for this known mass.

(Depending on the amount of slotted or hooked masses available, the position can be selected first and the mass can be adjusted to bring the system into equilibrium.)

Repeat this reading at least three times to make sure you have zeroed into the correct mass and its position for equilibrium.

Repeat the experiment for at least 6 new positions for the pivot stand and determine the known mass and its moment arm needed to bring the meterstick into rotational equilibrium again.

(b) Record the position of the pivot stand for each trial. The moment arm for the force applied to the meterstick is the difference between the position of the pivot stand and the applied force. The moment arm for the meterstick is the distance from the pivot stand to the center of mass of the meterstick.

Calculate the mass of the meterstick by writing and solving the summation of the torque equation for each trial.

$$\left(m_{\text{applied mass}}\right)\vec{g}\cdot\vec{r} = m_{\text{meterstick}}\vec{g}\cdot\vec{r}_{\text{meterstick}}.$$

Average the calculated mass for all the trials.

Determine the mass of the meterstick as determined from either a platform balance or an electric scale and compare your experimental value to the one determined from the balance or the scale.

(c) The two conditions that must be met in order to place the meterstick into static equilibrium are: the body must be in translational equilibrium and the body must be in rotational equilibrium.

(*College Physics* 9th ed. pages 240–247/10th ed. pages 245–249)
(L.O. 2.B.1.1, 3.F.1.1, 3.F.1.4, 3.F.1.5)

3. (a) The correct forces on the box are shown below.

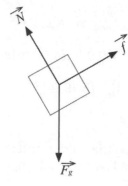

(b) $\Sigma \vec{F} = 0$

$$m\vec{g} \sin\theta = \mu_k m\vec{g} \cos\theta$$

$$(2.00 \text{ kg})\left(9.80 \ \frac{\text{kg}}{\text{m}^2}\right)\sin 30° = \mu_k (2.00 \text{ kg})\left(9.80 \ \frac{\text{kg}}{\text{m}^2}\right)\cos 30°$$

$$\mu_k = \mathbf{0.577}$$

(c) The correct box to check is ___√___ continue down the plane at constant speed.

In the equation in part (b) mass is a common factor in both terms. Changing the mass of the box will not change the speed of the box down the plane.

(d) The correct box to check is ___√___ remain the same.

The frictional force is dependent on the materials in contact and the normal force but not the direction of the motion, since friction is always opposite to the motion or the tendency to move in a direction. The magnitude of the force of friction has the same value up the plane as it does for the box moving down the plane.

(*College Physics* 9th ed. pages 88–89, 95–97, 99–100, 105–107/10th ed. pages 90–91, 98–99, 101–103, 108–109)
(L.O. 3.A.2.1, 3.A.3.1, 3.A.4.2, 3.A.4.3, 3.B.2.1)

4. (a) The free-body diagram for the ladder is shown below.

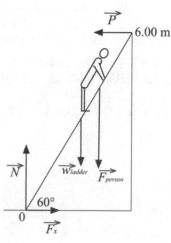

(b) i. $\Sigma \vec{\tau} = 0$

$$-\vec{F}_{ladder} r_{ladder} \sin \theta_{ladder} - \vec{F}_{person} r_{person} \sin \theta_{person} + \vec{F}_{wall} r_{wall} \sin \theta_{wall} = 0$$

$$(200.0 \text{ N})(3.00 \text{ m})\sin 30° + (800.0 \text{ N})(4.00 \text{ m})\sin 30° = \vec{F}_{wall}(6.00 \text{ m})\sin 60°$$

$$300.0 \text{ N} \cdot \text{m} + 1600.0 \text{ N} \cdot \text{m} = \vec{F}_{wall}(5.19 \text{ m})$$

$$\vec{F}_{wall} = \mathbf{366 \text{ N}}$$

ii. The frictional force between the ladder and the ground must equal the force exerted by the wall since the ladder is in translational equilibrium.

The normal force exerted on the ladder by the ground must equal the total forces acting downward, the weight of the ladder, and the weight of the person.

$$f_s = \mu_s N \text{ Solving for } \mu_s = \frac{366 \text{ N}}{1000 \text{ N}} = \mathbf{0.366}$$

The force supplied by the wall will give the solution for the coefficient of static friction between the ladder and the ground. When the painter climbs higher than 4.00 m from the base of the ladder, the push from the wall will increase, increasing the horizontal force at the base of the ladder. This could produce the equality in the static friction $f_s \leq \mu_s N$ where motion impends and the ladder slips.

(c) Because the forces acting at the base, the normal and the horizontal force, are applied at the point of rotation they have no moment arms, therefore they have no torques. The two downward forces, the weight of the ladder, and the weight of the painter produce clockwise torques and the force exerted by the wall produces a counterclockwise torque, which makes writing the equation easier.

(d) Another worker could stand on the base of the ladder, increasing the normal force. An increase in the normal results in an increase in friction that will equal the increased push from the wall as the painter climbs higher on the ladder. You could find a material with a higher coefficient of friction to wrap around the base of the ladder. (Not very practical.)

(*College Physics* 9th ed. pages 95–97, 99–100, 105–107, 236–237, 241–247/10th ed. pages 97–100, 101–103, 108–110, 241–243, 245–252)
(L.O. 3.A.2.1, 3.A.4.2, 3.A.4.3, 3.F.1.1, 3.F.1.2, 3.F.1.3, 3.F.1.5)

3

MOTION

VELOCITY

(*College Physics* 9th ed. pages 25–29/10th ed. pages 26–31)

The location of a particle traveling along the x-axis is described by its x-coordinate. The change in the position of the particle is its *displacement*, Δx. Initially, if the particle is located at position x_0 at time t_0 and at position x at time t, the particle is displaced by $\Delta x = x - x_0$. Recall that displacement is a vector. The elapsed time is $\Delta t = t - t_0$. For motion in one dimension we simply specify the displacement of the x-coordinate of the particle divided by the elapsed time. To the right of the origin, the coordinate is positive and to the left of the origin, the coordinate is negative. As an equation, we define the *average velocity*, $\overline{v}$, as the time rate of change of displacement, or

$$\overline{v} = \frac{x - x_0}{t - t_0} = \frac{\Delta x}{\Delta t}$$

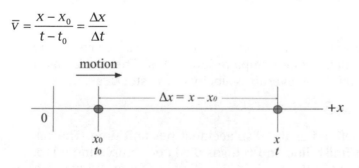

Average velocity is a vector and its SI unit is the $\frac{m}{s}$.

SAMPLE PROBLEM 1

A particle travels along the positive x-axis. Initially, the particle is observed to be located at $x_0 = 2.2$ m to the right of the origin, and

7.0 s later the particle is at $x = 27.4$ m to the right of the origin. What is the average velocity of the particle?

SOLUTION TO PROBLEM 1

The particle initially is located at the 2.2 m position and 7.0 s later it is positioned at the 27.4 m mark. We define average velocity with the equation

$$\overline{v} = \frac{x - x_0}{t - t_0} = \frac{27.4 \text{ m} - 2.2 \text{ m}}{7.0 \text{ s}} = 3.6 \text{ m}/\text{s}$$

Between the two points the particle moves to the right at 3.6 m/s.

If we start the particle at the origin, $x_0 = 0$, and if we start our stopwatches at $t_0 = 0$, then average velocity is

$$\overline{v} = \frac{x}{t}$$

SAMPLE PROBLEM 2

A proton has an average velocity of 4.5×10^6 m/s at 0°. What is the displacement of the proton in time period of 2.0 μs ?

SOLUTION TO PROBLEM 2

Since average velocity is expressed as $\overline{v} = x/t$, then displacement is $x = \overline{v}t$. Substituting we have

$$x = \overline{v}t = \left(4.5 \times 10^6 \text{ m}/\text{s}\right)\left(2.0 \times 10^{-6} \text{ s}\right) = 9.0 \text{ m} @ 0°$$

The proton travels for 2.0 millionth of a second at 4.5 million meters per second. In that time period its displacement is 9.0 meters at 0°.

SAMPLE PROBLEM 3

A stock car is being driven on a circular track. The car starts at the start/finish line and makes one complete lap in 8 s. The track has a radius of 68 m. Determine the average velocity of the stock car.

SOLUTION TO PROBLEM 3

Average velocity is defined as the displacement per unit time. The car leaves from the start/finish line and returns 8 s later completing a lap. Recall that displacement is the straight-line distance from the starting point to the finish point. The displacement is zero. Average velocity cannot be determined.

ACCELERATION

(*College Physics* 9th ed. pages 33–35/10th ed. pages 34–37)

Just as average velocity is the time rate of change of displacement, *average acceleration* is the time rate of change of velocity. As an equation

$$a = \frac{v - v_0}{t - t_0} = \frac{\Delta v}{\Delta t}$$

Constant acceleration mathematically behaves just like average acceleration. Acceleration is a vector that has units of m/s^2 which is read as meters per second per second.

If we again start our observations at $t_0 = 0$, $a = \frac{v - v_0}{t}$ and $v - v_0 = at$, solving for the final velocity yields

$$v = v_0 + at$$

which states that when a particle moving at initial velocity v_0 undergoes an acceleration a for a time interval t, its final velocity is v.

Since the velocity of a particle is increasing or decreasing with time, we can express the average velocity for any time interval as the *arithmetic average* of the initial velocity v_0 and the final velocity v as

$$\overline{v} = \frac{v_0 + v}{2}$$

The average velocity is also $\overline{v} = \frac{x}{t}$. Equating these expressions for average velocity, $\overline{v} = \frac{x}{t} = \frac{v_0 + v}{2}$. Clearing of fractions gives $2x = (v_0 + v)t$. Since $v = v_0 + at$, we can replace final velocity v: $2x = (v_0 + v_0 + at)t = (2v_0 + at)t$. Dividing both sides by 2 yields the displacement of the body

$$x = v_0 t + \frac{1}{2}at^2$$

SAMPLE PROBLEM 4

A body traveling along the positive *x*-axis with an initial velocity of 10.0 m/s is uniformly accelerated to a velocity of 28.0 m/s over a time period of 6.0 seconds.

(a) What constant acceleration does the body experience?

(b) What is the displacement of the body over the 6.0 seconds of acceleration?

SOLUTION TO PROBLEM 4

(a) Since we are seeking acceleration we will use the equation that defines it.

$$a = \frac{v - v_0}{t} = \frac{28.0 \text{ m}/\text{s} - 10.0 \text{ m}/\text{s}}{6.0 \text{ s}} = 3.0 \text{ m}/\text{s}^2$$

Each and every second, the velocity of the body increases by 3.0 m/s.

The displacement of a body while undergoing constant accelerating is

(b) $x = v_0 t + \dfrac{1}{2} a t^2 = \left(10 \text{ m}/\text{s}\right)(6.0 \text{ s}) + (0.5)\left(3.0 \text{ m}/\text{s}^2\right)(6.0 \text{ s})^2 = \mathbf{114 \text{ m}}$

SAMPLE PROBLEM 5

A particle travels along the +x-axis with a velocity of 12 m/s. It is accelerated at 2.5 m/s² for a time period of 15 s. What is the final velocity of the particle?

SOLUTION TO PROBLEM 5

The final velocity is found by

$$v = v_0 + at = 12 \text{ m}/\text{s} + \left(2.5 \text{ m}/\text{s}^2\right)(15 \text{ s}) = \mathbf{50 \text{ m}/\text{s}}$$

We need one more kinematic equation to relate initial velocity, final velocity, acceleration and displacement. Since it is free of time t, we can call it the *time-independent equation*. It is left to the student to derive it.

$$v^2 = v_0^2 + 2ax$$

When the velocity and acceleration of a body are in the same direction, the velocity of the body increases with time. When the velocity and acceleration of the body are in opposite directions, the velocity of the body decreases with time.

KINEMATICS AND GRAPHIC RELATIONSHIPS

(*College Physics* 9th ed. pages 29–36/10th ed. pages 31–38)

A convenient method of determining the displacement from a velocity vs. time graph is simply to find the area under the curve. Consider the following graph. A particle travels with a constant velocity of $v = 5$ m/s. What is the displacement of the particle in the time interval from 1 s to 8 s? The area bound by the time interval is shaded. Its area is that of a rectangle. The area is $A = \text{base} \times \text{height} =$

$(8 \text{ s} - 1 \text{ s})(5 \text{ m/s}) = 35 \text{ m}$. During the time interval between 1 s and 8 s, the particle had a displacement of 35 m.

Consider another approach, constant velocity is expressed as $v = \dfrac{x}{t}$

and the displacement is $x = vt = (5 \text{ m/s})(8 \text{ s} - 1 \text{ s}) = 35 \text{ m}$.

The "curve" is a horizontal line and the slope of a horizontal line is zero. The slope of the curve on a velocity vs. time graph is the acceleration. Since the slope is zero, the particle has an acceleration of zero.

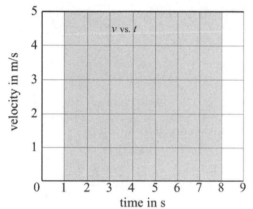

Velocity vs. time graph for constant velocity, showing that the displacement is given by the area beneath the curve.

Consider a body having the velocity vs. time graph given below. Find the displacement of the body over the time interval from 1 s to 6 s.

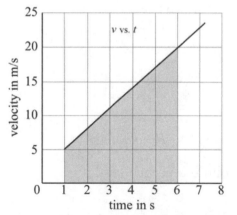

Velocity vs. time graph for uniform acceleration, showing that the displacement is given by the area beneath the curve.

Again, the displacement of the body is the area beneath the velocity vs. time graph. The shaded area under the curve shows the displacement. The shaded area is actually two separate areas, area 1 and area 2. Area 1 is a triangle and its area is

$$A1 = \frac{1}{2}\text{base} \times \text{altitude} = \frac{1}{2}(6 \text{ s} - 1 \text{ s})(20 \text{ m/s} - 5 \text{ m/s}) = 37.5 \text{ m}$$

Area 2 is a rectangle and its area is

$$A2 = \text{base} \times \text{height} = (6 \text{ s} - 1 \text{ s})(5 \text{ m/s}) = 25 \text{ m}$$

The total area is $A1 + A2 = 37.5$ m $+ 25$ m $= 62.5$ m. In the 5 s time interval the body is displaced by 62.5 m.

Note that the shape of the curve is a straight-line sloped up to the right. This means that the velocity of the body is changing; it is accelerating. Since it is sloped up to the right, the body undergoes a positive acceleration. Another feature of a velocity vs. time graph is that we can determine acceleration.

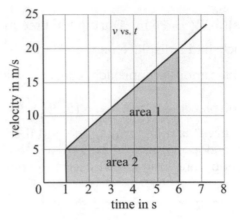

We define the slope of a straight line as

$$slope = \frac{\text{change in the vertical}}{\text{change in the horizontal}}$$

Delta, Δ, is the symbol we use for change. Slope can be defined as

$$m = slope = \frac{\Delta y}{\Delta x}$$

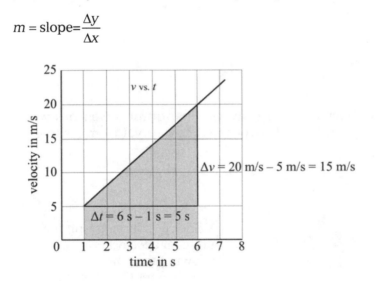

Note that the acceleration process starts at $t = 1$ s. The velocity at this time, the initial velocity, is 5 m/s.

Since we have a graph with the velocity along the vertical and the time along the horizontal we write

$$m = \frac{\Delta v}{\Delta t} = \frac{v - v_0}{t - t_0} = \frac{20 \ m/s - 5 \ m/s}{6 \ s - 1 \ s} = \frac{15 \ m/s}{5 \ s} = 3 \ m/s^2$$

The body is accelerating with a positive 3 m/s^2.

The displacement of a body undergoing acceleration is defined as

$$x = v_0 t + \frac{1}{2}at^2 = \left(5 \ m/s\right)(5 \ s) + \frac{1}{2}\left(3 \ m/s^2\right)(5 \ s)^2 = 62.5 \ m$$

Graphs are pictures framed with a Cartesian coordinate system. Is a graph worth a thousand words?

THE BASIC EQUATIONS OF KINEMATICS

(*College Physics* 9th ed. pages 36–42/10th ed. pages 38–44)

In our study of how things move we require the following five kinematic equations in dealing with motion along the horizontal.

Average velocity $\qquad\qquad \overline{v} = \dfrac{x}{t} = \dfrac{v + v_0}{2}$

Acceleration $\qquad\qquad a = \dfrac{v - v_0}{t}$

Final velocity $\qquad\qquad v = v_0 + at$

Displacement $\qquad\qquad x = v_0 t + \dfrac{1}{2} at^2$

Time-Independent relationship $\qquad v^2 = v_0^2 + 2ax$

We have looked at one-dimensional motion along the *x*-axis. Next, we look at motion along the vertical, the *y*-axis.

Equations with *x* as displacement are specifically for motion along the *x*-axis. We use *y* as displacement along the vertical. To generalize our equations we will use *s* for displacement. Our generalized kinematic equations are then:

Average velocity $\qquad\qquad \overline{v} = \dfrac{s}{t} = \dfrac{v + v_0}{2}$

Acceleration $\qquad\qquad a = \dfrac{v - v_0}{t}$

Final velocity $\qquad\qquad v = v_0 + at$

Displacement $\qquad\qquad s = v_0 t + \dfrac{1}{2} at^2$

Time-Independent relationship $\qquad v^2 = v_0^2 + 2as$

FREE FALL

(*College Physics* 9th ed. pages 43–47/10th ed. pages 44–49)

Much of our understanding about the behavior of falling bodies was developed by Galileo Galilei (1564–1642). He was the first to show that in the absence of air resistance all bodies, regardless of their size or weight, fall to the Earth with the same acceleration. The Earth behaves as if all its mass were concentrated at a single point at the very center of our planet. And again, we call this point the center of mass, c.m. of the Earth. Due to its mass, the Earth generates a *gravitational field* that extends into deep space. Our concern at the moment is the gravitational field within several kilometers of the surface of the Earth. As a first approximation, we treat the gravitational field as uniform with uniform intensity. Fields are vector quantities that have magnitude, a unit, and a direction. The magnitude and unit of the gravitational field is 9.80 m/s^2. The direction is vertically downward.

Note the unit $^m/_{s^2}$ is the same unit as acceleration. The intensity is an acceleration and we call it the *acceleration due to gravity* and we give it its own special symbol, *g*.

$$g = \text{acceleration due to gravity} = -9.80 \ \frac{m}{s^2}$$

The negative sign (–) gives the direction of *g*, vertically downward toward the center of the Earth.

In the gravitational field of the Earth, neglecting air resistance, all compact bodies fall with the same acceleration, *g*, the acceleration due to gravity.

VERTICAL DISPLACEMENT AND VELOCITY

(*College Physics* 9th ed. pages 43–47/10th ed. pages 44–49)

In general, the displacement of a body is $s = v_0 t + \frac{1}{2}at^2$. Treating vertical motion as along the *y*-axis and acceleration as *g* yields the displacement equation for free fall: $y = v_0 t - \frac{1}{2}gt^2$. Modifying $v = v_0 + at$ for the velocity of a body in free fall gives $v = v_0 - gt$. Note that the negative sign for *g* is built into the equations.

In our study of how things move vertically upward or downward, we require the following three free-fall equations.

Vertical displacement	$y = v_0 t - \frac{1}{2}gt^2$
Final velocity	$v = v_0 - gt$
Time-independent relationship	$v^2 = v_0^2 - 2gy$

SAMPLE PROBLEM 6

A person standing at the edge of a cliff drops a brick from rest. The brick impacts the ground 2.4 seconds later.

(a) How far did the brick fall?

(b) What is the velocity of the brick upon impact with the ground?

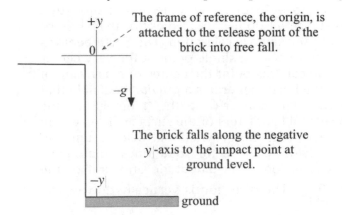

+y

The frame of reference, the origin, is attached to the release point of the brick into free fall.

–g

The brick falls along the negative *y*-axis to the impact point at ground level.

–y

ground

SOLUTION TO PROBLEM 6

(a) The brick is released from rest making $v_0 = 0$. The distance fallen

is $y = v_0 t - \dfrac{1}{2} gt^2 = (0)t - \dfrac{1}{2}\left(9.80\ \dfrac{m}{s^2}\right)(2.4\ s)^2 = \mathbf{-28.22\ m}$

The negative sign implies that the brick has fallen vertically downward from its point of release.

(b) Since $v_0 = 0$, the velocity on impact is:

$v = v_0 - gt = 0 - \left(9.80\ \dfrac{m}{s^2}\right)(2.4\ s) = \mathbf{-23.52\ m/s}$

The negative sign means that the brick is falling vertically downward.

SAMPLE PROBLEM 7

A person standing at the edge of a cliff 30.0 m in height reaches out over the edge and throws a ball vertically upward with a velocity of 12.0 m/s. The ball slows as it rises and reaches a point where it stops momentarily. The ball then falls to the ground just missing the edge of the cliff.

(a) How long is the ball in flight?

(b) How long is the ball in flight if it is thrown vertically downward at 12.0 m/s?

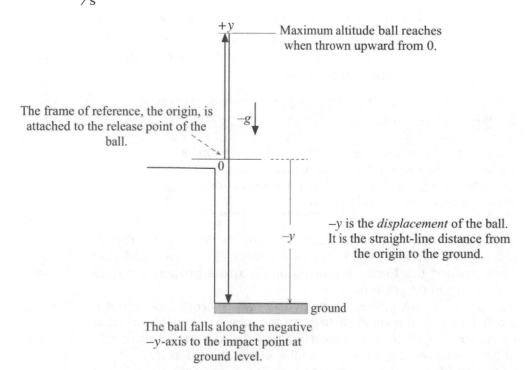

+y ———— Maximum altitude ball reaches when thrown upward from 0.

The frame of reference, the origin, is attached to the release point of the ball.

$-g$

0

−y is the *displacement* of the ball. It is the straight-line distance from the origin to the ground.

−y

ground

The ball falls along the negative −y-axis to the impact point at ground level.

SOLUTION TO PROBLEM 7

(a) The ball ends up 30 m below the origin making its displacement $y = -30$ m. The initial velocity of the ball is $+12.0$ $\frac{m}{s}$ since the ball was thrown vertically upward. Starting with $y = v_0 t - \frac{1}{2}gt^2$ we solve for the time of flight, t. To save time and space we are *not* going to enter the units for each term in this problem. Substituting numbers in,

$$-30 = 12t - \frac{1}{2}(9.8)t^2 = 12t - 4.9t^2.$$

Transposing and rearranging terms gives the $4.9t^2 - 12t - 30 = 0$. Note this is of the form $at^2 + bt + c = 0$, a quadratic equation solvable with the quadratic formula $t = \frac{-b \pm \sqrt{b^2 - 4ac}}{2a}$. Making substitution into the quadratic formula $t = \frac{-(-12) \pm \sqrt{(-12)^2 - 4(4.9)(-30)}}{2(4.9)}$. There are two solutions, $t = 4.0$ s and $t = -1.5$ s. The negative time is not valid. Did the ball leave the hand of the person throwing it upward 1.5 s before it was thrown? Of course not, the correct answer is $\mathbf{t = 4.0\,s}$.

(b) The ball is thrown downward at -12.0 $\frac{m}{s}$. It has a displacement of $y = -30$ m. The quadratic equation that relates these and the time of flight is $4.9t^2 + 12t - 30 = 0$. The quadratic formula once again gives two roots, $t = -4.0$ s and $t = 1.5$ s. Compare these with the ones in part (a). The correct answer is $\mathbf{t = 1.5\,s}$.

AP Tip

Distances above the origin are positive where distances below the origin are negative. Upward velocities are positive and downward velocities are negative. Acceleration in free fall is downward and negative.

When a body is projected vertically upward, its velocity will rapidly diminish until at some point it comes momentarily to rest and then falls back toward the Earth, acquiring again at the ground the same speed it had upon projection.

Study the diagram presented below. A ball is projected vertically upward from ground level at 49.0 $\frac{m}{s}$. Of course we consider the ball to be a compact body and we ignore air resistance. At the end of 1.0 s of flight, it is 44.1 m above the ground traveling upward at 39.2 $\frac{m}{s}$.

At the end of 2.0 s it has a velocity of 29.4 $\frac{m}{s}$ and is now 78.4 m above the ground. Notice the ball is slowing with time and altitude. In all cases it has the same acceleration, $g = -9.8$ $\frac{m}{s^2}$.

At the end of 3.0 s it is 102.9 m above the ground traveling at 19.6 $\frac{m}{s}$.

At t = 4 s it has slowed to 9.8 $\frac{m}{s}$ and is located at 117.8 m above ground level. At the end of 5.0 s the ball reaches a maximum altitude of 122.5 m and for a tiny instant has stopped. Then it begins to fall, accelerating at g as it does.

Note the symmetry in the diagram.

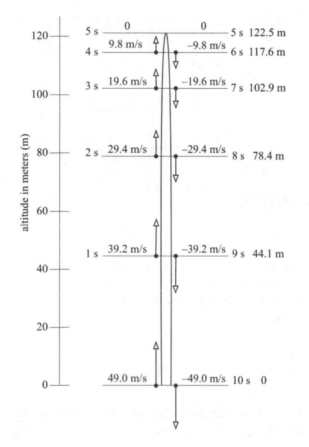

The time it takes to reach the top of its trajectory is equal to the time taken from there to the ground. This implies that the upward motions are just the same as the downward motions, but in reverse.

PROJECTILES

(*College Physics* 9th ed. pages 63–71/10th ed. pages 65–73)

A compact body thrown or projected into 2-D space is called a *projectile*. Its path in flight is called its *trajectory*. As a first approximation, we ignore air resistance and consider projectiles as compact bodies that travel short distances horizontally and vertically. Under these conditions the trajectory is considered *parabolic*.

Let v_0 at θ_0 be the initial velocity of the projectile. Remember that velocity is a vector having both magnitude v and direction θ. We let

y_{max} be the *maximum altitude* reached by the projectile and R or X_{max} be the *maximum range* of the projectile. We make t_T the total time of flight of the projectile.

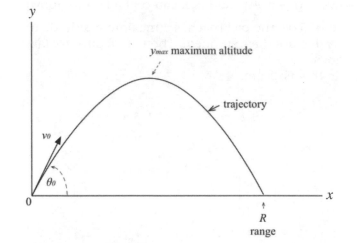

INITIAL VELOCITY COMPONENTS

(*College Physics* 9th ed. pages 63–71/10th ed. pages 65–73)

The initial velocity vector has a set of two components, horizontal v_{0x} and vertical v_{0y}. Components of a vector are mutually perpendicular and form a right triangle with the initial velocity vector. Because of this we can write:

$$\cos\theta_0 = \frac{v_{0x}}{v_0} \text{ and } \sin\theta_0 = \frac{v_{0y}}{v_0}$$

$$v_{0x} = v_0 \cos\theta_0 \quad v_{0y} = v_0 \sin\theta_0$$

Both equations are needed to calculate the horizontal and vertical components of the initial velocity.

SAMPLE PROBLEM 8

A projectile is fired into the air with an initial velocity of $v_0 = 40.0 \text{ m/s}$ at an angle $\theta_0 = 60.0°$. Calculate the initial velocity components.

SOLUTION TO PROBLEM 8

We write

$$v_{0x} = v_0 \cos\theta_0 = \left(40.0 \text{ m/s}\right)\cos 60° = \mathbf{20.0 \text{ m/s}}$$

$$v_{0y} = v_0 \sin\theta_0 = \left(40.0 \text{ m/s}\right)\sin 60° = \mathbf{34.6 \text{ m/s}}$$

INSTANTANEOUS VELOCITY OF A PROJECTILE IN FLIGHT

(*College Physics* 9th ed. pages 63–71/10th ed. pages 65–73)

Ignoring air resistance, the only force acting on the projectile in flight is the force of gravity. The force of gravity is an unbalanced force and causes a vertically downward acceleration, g, where the vertical acceleration, a_y, is $a_y = -g$. There is no horizontal force acting on the projectile and $a_x = 0$.

In general, the kinematic relationship for velocity and acceleration is: $v = v_0 + at$. For the horizontal velocity component, v_x:

$$v_x = v_{0x} + at = v_{0x} + (0)t$$

$$v_x = v_0 \cos\theta_0$$

Note that everywhere along its trajectory, the horizontal component of velocity of the projectile is a constant.

For the vertical velocity component, v_y:

$$v_y = v_{0y} + at = v_{0y} + (-g)t$$

$$v_y = v_0 \sin\theta_0 - gt$$

To find the instantaneous velocity, v, at any point along the trajectory we note that v_x and v_y are mutually perpendicular and that they form a right triangle with v, and:

$$v^2 = v_x^2 + v_y^2$$

Then

$$v = \sqrt{v_x^2 + v_y^2}$$

And the angle of v is found from:

$$\tan\theta = \frac{v_y}{v_x}$$

and

$$\theta = \tan^{-1}\left(\frac{v_y}{v_x}\right)$$

AP Tip

To find the instantaneous velocity of the projectile in flight along its trajectory we must to do <u>four</u> things:

First, find v_x from $v_x = v_0 \cos\theta_0$.

Second, determine v_y using $v_y = v_0 \sin\theta_0 - gt$.

Third, find the magnitude of the instantaneous velocity, v, using $v = \sqrt{v_x^2 + v_y^2}$.

Fourth, find the angle, θ, of the instantaneous velocity vector by $\theta = \tan^{-1}\left(\frac{v_y}{v_x}\right)$.

SAMPLE PROBLEM 9

Considering Sample Problem 8, calculate the instantaneous velocity of the projectile at t = 2.0 s into its flight.

SOLUTION TO PROBLEM 9

To find the instantaneous velocity of the projectile 2.0 s into flight we do four things:

First $v_x = v_0 \cos\theta_0 = \left(40.0 \ \frac{m}{s}\right)\cos 60° = 20.0 \ \frac{m}{s}$

Second $v_y = v_0 \sin\theta_0 - gt = \left(40.0 \ \frac{m}{s}\right)(\sin 60°) - \left(9.8 \ \frac{m}{s^2}\right)(2.0 \ s) = 15.0 \ \frac{m}{s}$

Third $v = \sqrt{v_x^2 + v_y^2} = \sqrt{\left(20.0 \ \frac{m}{s}\right)^2 + \left(15.0 \ \frac{m}{s}\right)^2} = 25.0 \ \frac{m}{s}$

Last $\theta = \tan^{-1}\left(\frac{v_y}{v_x}\right) = \tan^{-1}\left(\frac{15.0 \ \frac{m}{s}}{20.0 \ \frac{m}{s}}\right) = 36.9°$

At t = 2.0 s into its flight, the projectile has a velocity of
$v = \textbf{25.0} \ \frac{m}{s} \ \textbf{@ 36.9°}$

LOCATING A PROJECTILE ALONG ITS TRAJECTORY

(*College Physics* 9th ed. pages 63–71/10th ed. pages 65–73)

The horizontal velocity component of the projectile in flight is a constant $v_x = v_0 \cos\theta_0$ and the horizontal velocity is also equal to the horizontal displacement, x, divided by the time the projectile has been in flight, t, to that point, or $v_x = \frac{x}{t}$.

The horizontal distance the projectile has traveled from its launch point is

$$v_x = \frac{x}{t} = v_0 \cos\theta_0$$

or

$$x = \left(v_0 \cos\theta_0\right)t$$

The vertical distance the projectile has traveled above the plane of launch is

$$y = v_{0y}t - \frac{1}{2}gt^2.$$

From equation (2) $v_{0y} = v_0 \sin\theta_0$. Substitution yields

$$y = \left(v_0 \sin\theta_0\right)t - \frac{1}{2}gt^2$$

> ## AP Tip
>
> To locate the position of a projectile along its trajectory we do <u>two</u> things:
>
> First, determine its distance down range using $x = (v_0 \cos\theta_0)t$.
>
> Second, find its altitude using $y = (v_0 \sin\theta_0)t - \frac{1}{2}gt^2$.

SAMPLE PROBLEM 10

Calculate the position of the projectile of Sample Problem 8 at t = 2.0 s.

SOLUTION TO PROBLEM 10

To locate the projectile 2.0 s into flight we do two things:

First:

$$x = (v_0 \cos\theta_0)t = \left(40.0 \; \frac{m}{s}\right)(\cos 60°)(2.0 \text{ s}) = 40.0 \text{ m}$$

Second:

$$y = (v_0 \sin\theta_0)t - \frac{1}{2}gt^2$$

$$= \left(40.0 \; \frac{m}{s}\right)(\sin 60°)(2.0 \text{ s}) - \frac{1}{2}\left(9.8 \; \frac{m}{s^2}\right)(2.0 \text{ s})^2$$

$$= 49.7 \text{ m}$$

At t = 2.0 s into its flight, the projectile is **40.0 m** down range and is **49.7 m** above the ground.

Notice that both of the above location equations are *parametric* equations with time, t, as the *parameter*. They are both functions of time: $x = f(t)$ and $y = h(t)$. If we wish to express $y = h(x)$ we need to solve $x = (v_0 \cos\theta_0)t$ for t and

$$t = \frac{x}{(v_0 \cos\theta_0)}$$

Substituting for t into $y = (v_0 \sin\theta_0)t - \frac{1}{2}gt^2$:

$$y = (v_0 \sin\theta_0)\left(\frac{x}{v_0 \cos\theta_0}\right) - \frac{g}{2}\left(\frac{x}{v_0 \cos\theta_0}\right)^2$$

In the first term v_0's divide out and $\frac{\sin\theta_0}{\cos\theta_0} = \tan\theta_0$, then we write

$$y = x\tan\theta_0 - \frac{gx^2}{2v_0^2 \cos^2\theta_0}$$

Note that g, v_0 and θ_0 are constants putting the equation into the form

$$y = bx - ax^2$$

which is the equation of an inverted parabola with the projection point being the origin.

SAMPLE PROBLEM 11

Considering the projectile of Sample Problem 8, how far above the ground is the projectile when it has traveled 20.0 m down range?

SOLUTION TO PROBLEM 11

The altitude of the projectile is

$$y = x\tan\theta_0 - \frac{gx^2}{2v_0^2\cos^2\theta_0} = (20.0 \text{ m})(\tan 60°) - \frac{\left(9.8 \text{ }\frac{m}{s^2}\right)(20.0 \text{ m})^2}{2\left(40.0 \text{ }\frac{m}{s}\right)^2(\cos 60°)^2}$$

$$y = 34.64 \text{ m} - \frac{(9.8)(400) \text{ m}}{2(1600)(0.50)^2} = (34.64 - 4.90)\text{m} = \textbf{29.7 m}$$

The projectile will be 29.7 m above the ground when it has traveled 20.0 m down range.

TOTAL TIME OF FLIGHT OF A PROJECTILE

(*College Physics* 9th ed. pages 63–71/10th ed. pages 65–73)

Writing $y = (v_0\sin\theta_0)t - \frac{1}{2}gt^2$, the projectile returns to the ground, $y = 0$, at t_T, the total time of flight.

$$0 = (v_0\sin\theta_0)t_T - \frac{1}{2}gt_T^2$$

Solving for t_T: $gt^2 = 2(v_0\sin\theta_0)t_T$. A t_T on each side divides out, leaving

$$t_T = \frac{2v_0\sin\theta_0}{g}$$

THE RANGE OF A PROJECTILE

(*College Physics* 9th ed. pages 63–71/10th ed. pages 65–73)

The horizontal distance down range a projectile will travel is found from $x = (v_0\cos\theta_0)t$. The projectile will reach maximum distance down range at t_T. Substitution yields:

$$R = x_{max} = (v_0\cos\theta_0)t_T = (v_0\cos\theta_0)\left(\frac{2v_0\sin\theta_0}{g}\right)$$

$$R = v_0^2\left(\frac{2\sin\theta_0\cos\theta_0}{g}\right)$$

To simplify the equation we make use of the trig double angle identity, $2\sin\theta_0\cos\theta_0 = \sin2\theta_0$.

$$R = \frac{v_0^2\sin2\theta_0}{g}$$

Because of the properties of trig functions, sets of complementary angles will give the same range. Projectiles fired at shallow angles spend less time in flight than ones fired at steeper angles. An angle of 45° will give maximum range.

MAXIMUM ALTITUDE OF A PROJECTILE

(*College Physics* 9th ed. pages 63–71/10th ed. pages 65–73)

By symmetry, it takes as long for a projectile to reach maximum altitude, y_{max}, as it does to return to the ground at $y = 0$ and $X = R$. The time, $t_{T/2}$, to reach y_{max} is half of the total time of flight or

$$t_{T/2} = \frac{v_0\sin\theta_0}{g}$$

To find y_{max}, substitute into $y = (v_0\sin\theta_0)t - \frac{1}{2}gt^2$.

$$y_{max} = (v_0\sin\theta_0)t_{T/2} - \frac{1}{2}gt_{T/2}^2 = (v_0\sin\theta_0)\left(\frac{v_0\sin\theta_0}{g}\right) - \frac{1}{2}g\left(\frac{v_0\sin\theta_0}{g}\right)^2$$

$$y_{max} = \frac{v_0^2\sin^2\theta_0}{2g}$$

SAMPLE PROBLEM 12

The projectile of Sample Problem 8 has an initial velocity of $v_0 = 40.0\ \text{m}/_\text{s}$ at an angle $\theta_0 = 60.0°$. Determine

(a) the total time the projectile spends in flight.

(b) the range of the projectile.

(c) the maximum altitude reached by the projectile.

SOLUTION TO PROBLEM 12

(a) total time of flight is

$$t_T = \frac{2v_0\sin\theta_0}{g} = \frac{2\left(40.0\ \text{m}/_\text{s}\right)(\sin60°)}{\left(9.8\ \text{m}/_{\text{s}^2}\right)} = \textbf{7.1 s}$$

(b) range is given by

$$R = \frac{v_0^2 \sin 2\theta_0}{g} = \frac{\left(40.0 \text{ m/s}\right)^2 \sin\left(2 \times 60°\right)}{9.8 \text{ m/s}^2} = \frac{(1600)\sin 120°}{9.8} \text{ m} = 141.4 \text{ m}$$

(c) maximum altitude is

$$y_{max} = \frac{v_0^2 \sin^2 \theta_0}{2g} = \frac{\left(40.0 \text{ m/s}\right)^2 \left(\sin 60°\right)^2}{2\left(9.8 \text{ m/s}^2\right)} = 61.2 \text{ m}$$

MOTION: STUDENT OBJECTIVES FOR THE AP EXAM

- You should be able to define displacement, velocity, time interval and acceleration.
- You should be able to calculate velocity and acceleration from time intervals and displacement.
- You should be able to explain the subsequent motion of a particle that, at one instant, has zero velocity but constant acceleration.
- You should be able to discuss the subsequent motion of a particle that has negative acceleration.
- You should be able to discuss the motion of a particle that, at one instant, has negative velocity but a positive acceleration.
- You should be able to discuss the properties of a velocity vs. time graph.
- You should be able to analyze the motion of a body in free fall.
- You should be able to analyze the motion of a projectile launched into two-dimensional space.

MULTIPLE-CHOICE QUESTIONS

1. A body moves in the x-y plane with some initial velocity v_0, a short time later it has a velocity v_f. Which situation is impossible?
   (A) Velocity and acceleration vectors are parallel.
   (B) Velocity and acceleration vectors are anti-parallel.
   (C) Velocity and acceleration vectors are perpendicular.
   (D) Velocity and acceleration are both constant (nonzero).

2. Six graphs are shown below. Which combination could represent the motion of an object moving in one dimension with a constant nonzero acceleration?

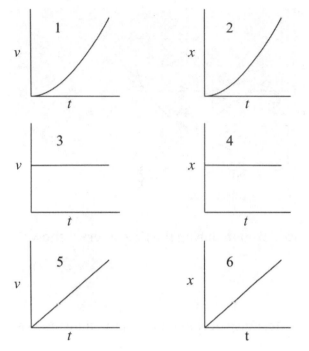

(A) 3 and 6
(B) 1 and 4
(C) 5 and 2
(D) 5 and 6

3. A graph of position as a function of time is shown below. Rank the points A, B, C, and D for the velocity at that point from highest to lowest with negative values below positive values.

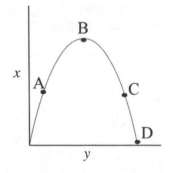

(A) B > A = C > D
(B) A > B > C > D
(C) A = C > B > D
(D) D > A = C > B

Four cars move as indicated on a $v = f(t)$ graph below. Use the graph to answer questions 4 and 5.

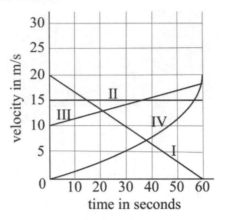

4. Which car has zero acceleration during the time interval shown?
   (A) I
   (B) II
   (C) III
   (D) IV

5. Which car has the greatest displacement during the time interval shown?
   (A) I
   (B) II
   (C) III
   (D) IV

6. A 2.0 kg ball and a 1.0 kg ball are dropped from the roof of a tall building at the same time. If air resistance is neglected, then
   (A) the 2.0 kg ball hits the ground first
   (B) the 1.0 kg ball hits the ground first
   (C) they strike the ground at the same time
   (D) it will depend on the ball with greater radius

7. Three cars travel linearly along the *x*-axis as shown in the graph below.

   At the end of 10.0 s, they have the same

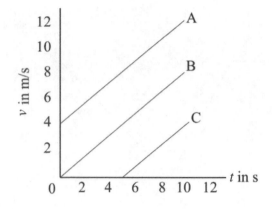

   (A) displacement
   (B) final velocity
   (C) acceleration
   (D) speed

8. A ball is projected upward reaching a maximum height of 10.0 m. Neglecting air resistance, what is the ball's velocity when it returns to its initial height (take downward as negative direction).

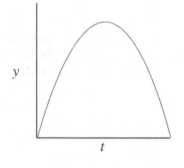

   (A) 0
   (B) 14.0 m/s
   (C) 10.0 m/s
   (D) –14.0 m/s

9. The motion of an object is variable over time as shown in the graph below. Rank the accelerating periods shown from highest acceleration to lowest.

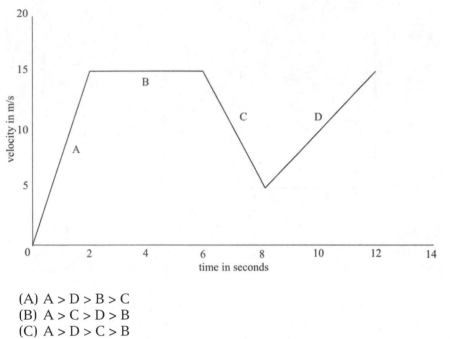

(A) A > D > B > C
(B) A > C > D > B
(C) A > D > C > B
(D) A > C > B > D

10. A body is projected upward with some velocity v_o. At the highest point in its path, which of the following correctly describes the sign of the body's displacement, velocity and acceleration? Ignore air resistance. Take upward as being the positive sense.

	y	v	a
(A)	0	0	0
(B)	+	0	–
(C)	+	+	0
(D)	+	0	–

11. A body is projected horizontally from a table that is 1.0 m above the floor with some initial velocity v_0. Neglecting air resistance, its acceleration after leaving the table is
(A) tangent to the parabolic path of the body
(B) directed vertically downward
(C) directed horizontally
(D) has a horizontal and vertical component

12. Two blocks, $m_A = 1.0$ kg and $m_B = 2.0$ kg, moving parallel to one another slide on the surface of a frictionless table whose height is 1.0 m as illustrated in the diagram below. When the blocks land on the floor which of the following best describes their time of flight and horizontal range?

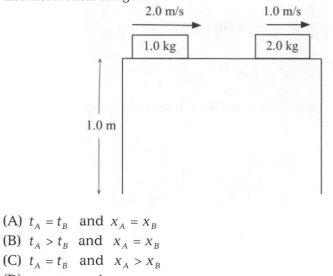

(A) $t_A = t_B$ and $x_A = x_B$
(B) $t_A > t_B$ and $x_A = x_B$
(C) $t_A = t_B$ and $x_A > x_B$
(D) $t_A > t_B$ and $x_A > x_B$

Questions 13 to 15

Directions: For each of the questions or incomplete statements below, <u>two</u> of the suggested answers will be correct. For each of these questions, you must select <u>both</u> correct answers to earn credit. No partial credit will be earned if only one correct answer is selected. Select the two that are best in each case and then enter both of the appropriate answers in the corresponding space on the answer sheet.

13. A particle moves in one dimension as shown on the graph below. The graph indicates that the particle

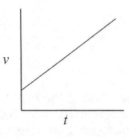

(A) has a constant (non-zero) positive acceleration
(B) has a constant positive velocity
(C) started with some non-zero initial velocity
(D) started with some initial displacement from the origin (0,0)

14. You wish to increase the distance that an object of mass M will travel horizontally when projected from a tall building with some initial horizontal velocity v_0. You can do this by

(A) increasing the height from which it is released
(B) decreasing the height from which it is released
(C) decreasing the mass of the object
(D) increasing the horizontal velocity

15. A student wants to design an experiment to investigate the motion of an object. The experimental equipment they will need for this investigation includes
    (A) a meterstick and a platform balance
    (B) an air-track with glider, timer, and a protractor
    (C) a photogate and a meterstick
    (D) a constant velocity cart, meterstick, and timer

FREE-RESPONSE PROBLEMS

1. A student evaluating the motion of a cart over 1.0 second intervals obtains the following data:

v_{avg}	t
cm/	s
1.3	1.0
2.5	2.0
3.7	3.0
5.1	4.0
6.3	5.0
7.6	6.0

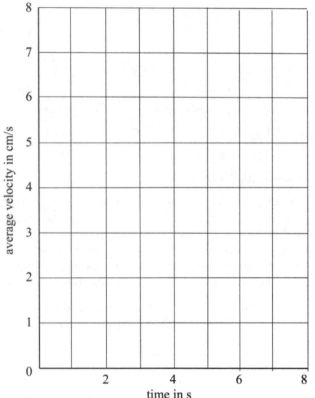

(a) Plot the data on the graph shown on the right.
(b) What does the shape of the best fit curve suggest?
(c) Using the graph, how can you determine the acceleration of the body? Explain your reasoning without calculations, but in enough detail that another student could duplicate your methods and obtain the same results.

2. Two hikers are climbing a hill when one of the hikers tosses a 4.0 kg backpack straight upward with a velocity of + 15.0 m/s. The second hiker, who has run to an outcrop, manages to catch the descending backpack when it was 5.0 m above the elevation of its original release point. (Neglect air resistance.)
   (a) What was the velocity of the backpack when it was caught?
   (b) How long was the backpack in the air?

(c) On the graphs provided, accurately sketch the displacement, velocity, and acceleration of the backpack as a function of time.

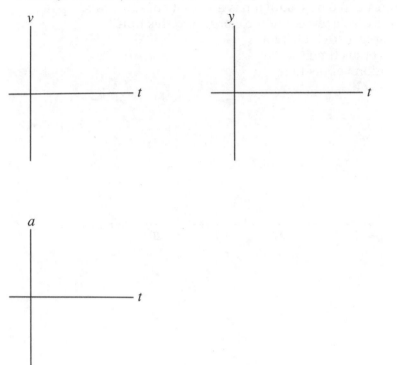

3. (a) A projectile follows the path shown below. Clearly indicate the vectors, drawn to scale, representing v_x, v_y, and a for each of the points shown on the graph.

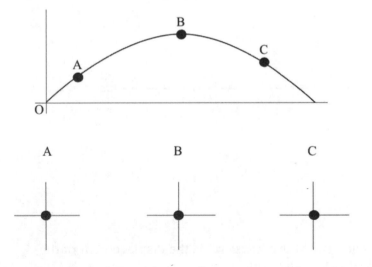

(b) For each of the following, at what angle would you launch the projectile to obtain the
i. greatest range
ii. greatest height
iii. longest time of flight

4. A car initially at rest accelerates at the rate of 4.0 m/s² for 5.0
    seconds. For the next 6.0 seconds, it travels at constant speed, and
    then decelerates at 5.0 m/s² until it has a velocity of –10.0 m/s.
    (a) What is the displacement of the car during this time?
    (b) On the graphs provided, plot
         i. velocity versus time
         ii. acceleration versus time

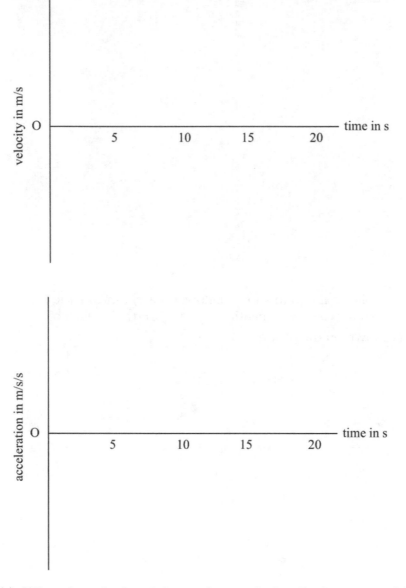

(c) When the velocity of the car is zero, is the displacement of the
     car zero? Justify your answer.

Answers

MULTIPLE-CHOICE QUESTIONS

1. **D** Average acceleration is defined as $\vec{a} = \dfrac{\Delta \vec{v}}{\Delta t}$. The speed, the direction, or both can change. Both cannot remain constant.

    (*College Physics* 9th ed. pages 33–34/10th ed. pages 34–36)
    (L.O. 3.A.1.1)

2. **C** A constant displacement (graph 4) indicates zero values for both velocity and acceleration. In order to have a constant non-zero acceleration, $v = f(t)$, must be linear (graph 5). The displacement graph must be parabolic, $d = f(t^2)$ which is graph 2.

    (*College Physics* 9th ed. pages 27–37/10th ed. pages 28–38)
    (L.O. 3.A.1.1)

3. **B** The graph represents a body that has moved to its highest position in a gravitational field or a body that was initially traveling along the +x–axis, stopped and reversed its direction. Since the question asks to rank for velocity which is a vector having both a magnitude and a direction, points C and D are negative and therefore smaller than the zero value at point B.

    (*College Physics* 9th ed. pages 27, 30, 42, 44 and 46/10th ed. pages 28, 31, 43, 46 and 48)
    (L.O. 3.A.1.1)

4. **B** The slope of a $v = f(t)$ graph is the acceleration of the object. The slope for car B is zero.

    (*College Physics* 9th ed. pages 34–35/10th ed. pages 36–37)
    (L.O. 3.A.1.1)

5. **B** The area under a $v = f(t)$ graph is the displacement of the car.

    The displacement of car I = $\dfrac{1}{2}bh$ which is $\dfrac{1}{2}(20 \text{ } ^m\!/_s)(60 \text{ s}) = 600 \text{ m}$.

    For car II the area is $bh = \left(15 \text{ } ^m\!/_s\right)(60 \text{ s}) = 900$ m. The displacement for car III is

    $\left(10 \text{ } ^m\!/_s\right)(60 \text{ s}) + \dfrac{1}{2}(17.5 \text{ } ^m\!/_s - 10 \text{ } ^m\!/_s)(60 \text{ s}) = 830 \text{ m}$

    For car IV, counting the blocks gives a good value for the displacement. Car IV's displacement is about 450 m.

    (*College Physics* 9th ed. page 42/10th ed. page 43)
    (L.O. 3.A.1.1)

6. **C** Both balls are dropped from rest at the same time. Their acceleration is the gravitational acceleration, $g = -9.80 \text{ } ^m\!/_{s^2}$.

    (*College Physics* 9th ed. pages 42–47/10th ed. pages 44–49)
    (L.O. 3.A.1.1)

7. **C** The cars have different initial velocities and move for different times, but they are parallel to each other and have the same slope, therefore they have the same acceleration.

   (*College Physics* 9th ed. pages 34–35/10th ed. pages 36–37)
   (L.O. 3.A.1.1)

8. **D** The initial velocity of the ball is determined from substitution into $v_f^2 = v_o^2 + 2ax$.

   $0 = v_0^2 + 2(-9.80 \text{ m/s}^2)(10.0 \text{ m})$. The initial velocity is 14.0 m/s. Since the gravitational acceleration is constant, the ball returns to the origin with the same speed, but since it is moving downward, the velocity is -14.0 m/s.

   (*College Physics* 9th ed. pages 43–47/10th ed. pages 44–49)
   (L.O. 3.A.1.1)

9. **A** The slope of the each section of the line is the acceleration for that time period.

   Both **A** and **D** show a positive acceleration. **B** shows a constant velocity and hence no acceleration while **C** indicates a negative acceleration.

   (*College Physics* 9th ed. pages 34–35/10th ed. pages 36–37)
   (L.O. 3.A.1.1)

10. **B** Since air resistance is neglected, the body is under a constant gravitational acceleration, $-g$ for its entire path. At the highest point, y_{max} its velocity is zero; the body will change direction, returning to the ground.

    (*College Physics* 9th ed. pages 43–47/10th ed. pages 44–49)
    (L.O. 3.A.1.1)

11. **B** The body is moving in two dimensions under the action of a gravitational acceleration $a = -g$, which will increase its v_y component of its velocity. Provided air resistance is negligible, the horizontal velocity will not change.

    (*College Physics* 9th ed. pages 63–71/10th ed. pages 65–73)
    (L.O. 3.A.1.1)

12. **C** Both blocks fall the same vertical distance and in the absence of air resistance, the times to fall 1.0 m are the same. Block A has the larger horizontal velocity as they leave the table and knowing $x = v_x t$, block A will travel farther horizontally than block B.

    (*College Physics* 9th ed. pages 63–71/10th ed. pages 65–73)
    (L.O. 3.A.1.1)

13. **A** and **C** The graph of $v = f(t)$ shows the graph is linear, therefore the slope of the line, its acceleration, is positive and constant. The y-intercept of the graph indicates that there is some initial velocity v_0.

    (*College Physics* 9th ed. pages 34–37/10th ed. pages 36–38)
    (L.O. 3.A.1.1)

14. **A** and **D** The range that an object projected into space will travel horizontally is determined $x = v_x t$. Increasing the time it takes to reach the ground or increasing the horizontal velocity will increase the horizontal distance traveled.

    (*College Physics* 9th ed. pages 63–71/10th ed. pages 65–73)
    (L.O. 3.A.1.1)

15. **B** and **D** Since you can elevate the air-track and measure the elevation, the change in the velocity can be determined $\Delta v = v_f - v_0$. The glider starts from rest and using the timer and the built-in distance markings on the air track, you can determine the average velocity, $v_{avg} = \dfrac{v_f - v_0}{2}$ and thus the final velocity v_f.

    A constant velocity cart moves at a set speed. Using the timer and a meter-stick you can determine the constant or average velocity $v_{avg} = \dfrac{d}{t}$.

    (*College Physics* 9th ed. pages 27–30/10th ed. pages 28–31)
    (L.O. 3.A.1.2)

FREE-RESPONSE PROBLEMS

1. Graph with the best fit curve.

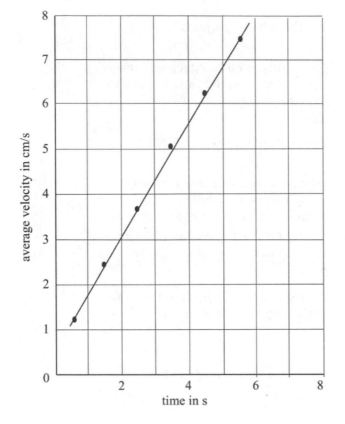

time in s

(a) The graph is v_{avg} versus time. Since the body is uniformly accelerated, the data for the average velocity is the approximate value for the midpoint of the time period. Points should be correctly plotted at the 0.5 s, 1.5 s, 2.5 s, etc. times.

(b) Since the graph is linear, the acceleration is constant.

(c) The acceleration is the change in the velocity divided by the change in time. Since the body starts from rest, the acceleration will be the final velocity divided by the time. Data was obtained for the average velocity that is the sum of the initial velocity and final velocity divided by two. To obtain the correct value for the acceleration, multiply the slope by 2.

(*College Physics* 9th ed. pages 27, 30, 42, 44, and 46/10th ed. pages 28, 31, 43, 46, and 48)
(L.O. 3.A.1.1, 3.A.1.3)

2. (a) The velocity of the backpack when caught by the second hiker is found from

$v_f^2 = v_0^2 - 2gy$. Substitution into the equation

is $v_f^2 = \left(15.0 \ \text{m}/\text{s}\right)^2 - 2(9.80 \ \text{m}/\text{s}^2)(5.00 \ \text{m})$

The final velocity is $-11.3 \ \text{m}/\text{s}$ since the backpack was moving downward when it was caught.

(b) The time the backpack is in the air is determined

from $y = v_0 t - \dfrac{1}{2}gt^2$. Substitution is 5.00 m =

$(15.0 \ \text{m}/\text{s})t - \dfrac{1}{2}(9.80 \ \text{m}/\text{s}^2)(t^2)$. Solving a quadratic equation (without units) will give the times that the backpack is at the 5.00 m position. The longer time is the root for the solution for the backpack on the way down.

$t = \dfrac{-15.0 \pm \sqrt{15.0^2 - 4(-4.90)(-5.00)}}{2(4.90)}$. The times values are 0.38 s (moving upward) and 2.68 s (the time at which the backpack is caught).

An alternate solution is to find the time the backpack rises to y_{max} and add this to the time it takes the backpack to fall back down to 5.00 m.

$v_f = v_0 - gt$. Substitution into the equation

$0 = 15.0 \ \text{m}/\text{s} - 9.80 \ \text{m}/\text{s}^2 (t)$ gives $t = 1.53$ s to y_{max}. Then

$y = -\dfrac{1}{2}gt^2$ (v at y_{max} is zero) yields $-5.00 \ \text{m} = \dfrac{1}{2}(9.80 \ \text{m}/\text{s}^2)(t^2)$

and $t = 1.01$ s. The total time is 1.53 s + 1.01 s = 2.68 s.

(c) Correct graphs are shown below.

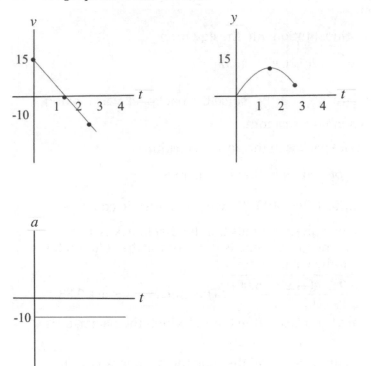

(*College Physics* 9th ed. pages 36–42/10th ed. pages 38–44)
(L.O. 3.A.1.1)

3. (a) The vectors applied to points A, B, and C are shown below.

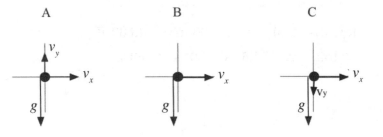

(b) i . 45 °. The greatest range is determined from $R = \dfrac{(V_0)^2 \sin 2\theta}{g}$.

The sin of twice 45° is the sin of 90° or 1.

ii. The angle that gives the greatest height is the angle that has no horizontal component $\theta = 90°$.

iii. The angle that has the longest time of flight is also 90°. Again, there is no horizontal component.

(*College Physics* 9th ed. pages 43–46, 63–66/10th ed. pages 44–49, 65–67)
(L.O. 3.A.1.1)

4. (a) There are three different sections to the trip. The total displacement is the sum of the displacements for each part.

$$x_1 = \frac{1}{2}at^2 \qquad x_1 = \frac{1}{2}(4.0 \, \text{m}/_{\text{s}^2})(5.0 \, \text{s})^2 \qquad x_1 = 50.0 \, \text{m}$$

To find the second displacement, one needs the velocity at the end of the first acceleration. Since the initial velocity is zero $v_f = at$. Substitution is $v_f = (4.0 \, \text{m}/_{\text{s}^2})(5.0 \, \text{s}) = 20 \, \text{m}/_{\text{s}}$,

$x_2 = v_f t$ yields $(20.0 \, \text{m}/_{\text{s}})(6.0 \, \text{s})$ thus $x_2 = 120 \, \text{m}$.

The displacement during the deceleration is obtained from $v_f^2 = v_0^2 + 2ax$.

$$(-10.0 \, \text{m}/_{\text{s}})^2 = (20.0 \, \text{m}/_{\text{s}})^2 + 2(-5.0 \, \text{m}/_{\text{s}^2})x_3. \qquad x_3 = 30 \, \text{m}$$

The total displacement is 50 m + 120 m + 30 m = 200 m.

(b) In order to plot the graphs, the last time period is needed. Solving $v_f = v_0 + at$

$$-10.0 \, \text{m}/_{\text{s}} - 20.0 \, \text{m}/_{\text{s}} - 5.0 \, \text{m}/_{\text{s}^2}(t). \text{ The time for the deceleration}$$

is 6.0 s.

i.

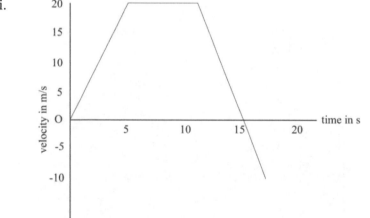

ii.

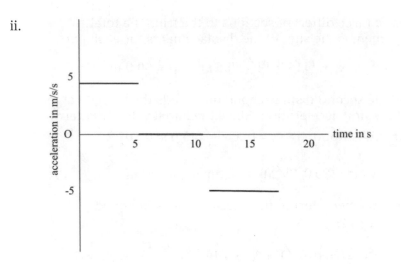

(c) When the velocity is zero, the car begins to reverse direction, but it is 210 m from its origin. 50 m + 120 m + 40 m = 210 m.
(*College Physics* 9th ed. pages 36–42/10th ed. pages 38–44)
(L.O. 3.A.1.1)

4

Dynamics

Newton's Second Law of Motion

(College Physics 9th ed. pages 89–92/10th ed. pages 91–94)

Up to this point we have looked at bodies either at rest or traveling with constant velocity. Such bodies have a resultant force of zero acting on them. What happens when the resultant force is not zero? The answer to this question is contained in Newton's second law, which states that *when the resultant force is not zero the body moves with accelerated motion, and that the acceleration, with a given force, depends on a property of the body known as its mass.*

As we have shown in Chapter 2, the *mass* of a body can be considered to be a measure of the quantity of material that makes up the body. Mass is also considered to be that which causes resistance to change of motion, *inertia*. Mass is a scalar. Mass is measured on a balance.

The part of mechanics that includes the study of motion and the forces that cause the motion is called *dynamics*. Equilibrium treats special cases where the acceleration is zero, and kinematics deals with motion only and not its cause, but dynamics is the study of why motion occurs. In its broadest sense, dynamics includes nearly the whole of mechanics.

We know from experience that a body at rest will never start to move of itself; some other body must exert a push or a pull on it. We also know that a force is required to slow or stop a body that is in motion, and that a sidewise or lateral force must be applied to a body to deviate it from its motion along a straight line. Speeding up, slowing down, or changing direction involve a change in either the magnitude or the direction of the velocity of the body. Every time a body is accelerated an external resultant or unbalanced net force must act on it to produce the acceleration.

Newton's second law takes the equation form $\Sigma \vec{F} = m\vec{a}$. It is a simple equation that states that resultant forces always make a "*ma*".

SAMPLE PROBLEM 1

A 12.0 kg mass is to be accelerated at 4.0 $\frac{m}{s^2}$. What resultant force causes the acceleration?

SOLUTION TO PROBLEM 1

When systems accelerate, there is a resultant or net or unbalanced force causing the acceleration. By Newton's second law,

$$\Sigma F = ma = (12.0 \text{ kg})\left(4.0 \frac{m}{s^2}\right) = \textbf{48.0 N}$$

SAMPLE PROBLEM 2

A mass M is subjected to an unbalanced force of 20.0 N causing it to accelerate from rest to a velocity of 24.0 $\frac{m}{s}$ over a displacement of 10.0 m. Calculate M.

SOLUTION TO PROBLEM 2

The unbalanced force acting on M is $\Sigma F = Ma$ which we can write as $F = Ma$ with the understanding that F also represents the unbalanced force. Since we do not know the time interval involved during the acceleration process, we make use of the time independent equation $v^2 = v_0^2 + 2as$. Since the body starts from rest, the acceleration is $a = \dfrac{v^2}{2s}$. Substituting into $F = Ma$ and solving for M yields $M = \dfrac{2Fs}{v^2}$ and then

$$M = \frac{2(20.0 \text{ N})(10.0 \text{ m})}{\left(24.0 \frac{m}{s}\right)^2} = \textbf{0.69 kg}$$

SAMPLE PROBLEM 3

An 80.0 kg wooden block is pushed to the right across a horizontal surface with a force of 100.0 N. The frictional force between the block and the surface is 12.0 N.

(a) What acceleration does the block experience?

(b) Find the coefficient of sliding friction for the surfaces involved.

SOLUTION TO PROBLEM 3

First we make a free-body diagram.

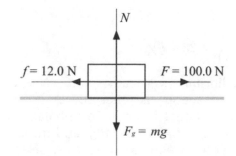

(a) Friction always opposes the motion and is negative. The resultant force, ΣF, is $\Sigma F = F - f = ma$ or $ma = F - f$ and solving for a gives

$$a = \frac{F - f}{m} = \frac{(100.0 \text{ N} - 12.0 \text{ N})}{80 \text{ kg}} = \mathbf{1.1} \frac{\mathbf{m}}{\mathbf{s^2}}$$

(b) To find the coefficient of friction we need the normal force. Vertically, the block is in equilibrium in this problem meaning that all of the upward forces equal all of the downward forces, or

$$N = F_g = mg = (80.0 \text{ kg})\left(9.8 \frac{\text{m}}{\text{s}^2}\right) = 784 \text{ N}$$

By definition the frictional force is $f = \mu N$ and solving for the coefficient gives

$$\mu = \frac{f}{N} = \frac{12.0 \text{ N}}{78.4 \text{ N}} = \mathbf{0.015}$$

Recall that coefficients of friction are dimensionless.

SAMPLE PROBLEM 4

A sports vehicle travels at 50.0 mph on a horizontal, dry section of asphalt highway. If the coefficient of friction between the tires and the surface of the highway is 0.88, what is the minimum stopping distance of the car when the brakes are fully applied? Ignore air resistance.

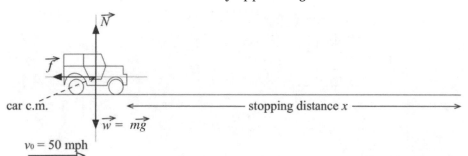

Solution to Problem 4

First, note that the initial speed of the vehicle is expressed in English units: 50.0 mph. Convert to SI:

$$50.0\frac{mi}{h} \times \frac{88\ ^{ft}/_s}{60\ ^{mi}/_h} \times \frac{1\ m}{3.28\ ft} = 22.4\ ^{m}/_s$$

The vehicle is in equilibrium vertically and $N = w = mg$. Horizontally, the only force acting is the force of friction, $f = \mu N = \mu(mg) = -\mu mg$. The frictional force is an unbalanced force and applying Newton's second law: $f = ma = -\mu mg$ and mass divides out on both sides leaving the acceleration as $a = -\mu g$. Acceleration is negative since the vehicle is slowing and the brakes act in the opposite direction to the motion.

The time element is not given in the problem. We know the initial speed, the final speed, and now the acceleration. We require the time independent equation to determine the stopping distance, $x, v^2 = v_0^2 + 2ax$. Since $v = 0$,

$$0 = v_0^2 + 2(-\mu g)x \text{ and } x = \frac{v_0^2}{2\mu g} = \frac{\left(22.4\ ^{m}/_s\right)^2}{2(0.88)\left(9.8\ ^{m}/_{s^2}\right)} = \textbf{29.1 m}$$

Stopping distance is related to the square of the initial speed. The faster a vehicle travels, the greater the distance the vehicle requires to stop. Note that we did not need the mass of the vehicle to find the stopping distance.

ELEVATORS

(*College Physics* 9th ed. pages 103–104/10th ed. pages 106–107)

The basic elevator consists of a mechanism for lifting or lowering, a support cable, and an elevator car. The attachment point for the support cable acts as a knot when making vector or free-body diagrams.

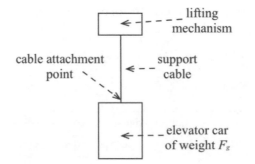

Elevator cars either are being pulled upward or are being lowered by the mechanism and the support cable. Since the car is confined to vertical motion, horizontal motion is not involved in problem work.

SAMPLE PROBLEM 5

Consider an elevator car having a mass of 2000 kg and being accelerated upward at 1.2 $\frac{m}{s^2}$. What tension exists in the support cable?

SOLUTION TO PROBLEM 5

First make a free-body diagram.

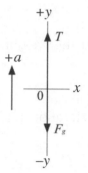

Since the car is accelerating upward, we show the a vector pointing upward and $T > F_g$ in the diagram. Next we write $\Sigma F = T - F_g = ma$. The symbol sigma Σ means to sum but F_g is directed along the $-y$-axis making it negative. Solving for the tension

$$T = ma + mg$$

$$= m(a+g) = (2000 \text{ kg})\left(1.2 \frac{m}{s^2} + 9.8 \frac{m}{s^2}\right)$$

$$= 2.2 \times 10^4 \text{ N}$$

Accelerating upward requires that the tension vector is greater than the weight, $T > F_g$.

SAMPLE PROBLEM 6

Consider an elevator car having a mass of 2000 kg and is being accelerated downward at 1.2 $\frac{m}{s^2}$. What tension exists in the support cable?

SOLUTION TO PROBLEM 6

First make a free-body diagram.

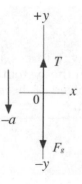

Since the car is accelerating upward, we show the *a* vector pointing downward and $T < F_g$ in the diagram. Next we write $\Sigma F = T - F_g = m(-a)$. F_g is directed along the $-y$-axis making it negative. The acceleration vector is also directed downward making it negative in this case. Solving for the tension

$$T = mg - mg$$
$$= m(g - a)$$
$$= (2000 \text{ kg})\left(9.8 \text{ m}/_{s^2} - 1.2 \text{ m}/_{s^2}\right)$$
$$= 1.7 \times 10^4 \text{ N}$$

Accelerating downward requires that the weight vector is greater than the tension, $T < F_g$.

SAMPLE PROBLEM 7

What is the maximum downward acceleration an elevator car can have?

SOLUTION TO PROBLEM 7

The maximum acceleration is the acceleration due to gravity, *g*. This could only happen if the support cable were detached from the elevator car placing it in free-fall.

SAMPLE PROBLEM 8

What is the tension in the support cable if the 2000.0 kg elevator car is

(a) at rest in the elevator shaft?

(b) moving upward at constant speed?

(c) moving downward at constant speed?

SOLUTION TO PROBLEM 8

In all three cases, the elevator car is NOT accelerating. It is in a state of equilibrium. In such a state, all the upward forces always equal all the downward forces.

$$T = F_g = mg = (2000.0 \text{ kg})\left(9.8 \text{ m}/_{s^2}\right) = 1.96 \times 10^4 \text{ N}$$

AP Tip

When encountering a problem dealing with forces, ask the question: "Is the system accelerating?" If the system accelerates Newton's second law is involved. If there is no acceleration, the system is in equilibrium.

TWO–BODY SYSTEMS

(*College Physics* 9th ed. pages 104, 109–110/10th ed. pages 107, 112–113)

SAMPLE PROBLEM 9

Two wooden blocks, A and B, with masses of $m_A = 4.0$ N and $m_B = 6.0$ kg respectively, are in contact on a frictionless surface. If a horizontal force of $F = 6.0$ N pushes them to the right, what force does m_A exert on m_B?

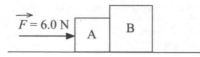

SOLUTION TO PROBLEM 9

Blocks A and B act as a single system of mass $M = m_A + m_B = 4.0$ kg $+ 6.0$ kg $= 10.0$ kg. An unbalanced force $F = 6.0$ N is exerted on the system giving it acceleration

$$a = \frac{F}{M} = \frac{(6.0 \text{ N})}{(10.0 \text{ kg})} = 0.6 \text{ m/s}^2 .$$

Keep in mind that the entire system accelerates at this rate.

Block A pushes into block B with a force F_A.

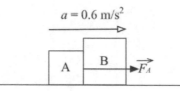

By Newton's second law,

$$F_A = m_B a = (6.0 \text{ kg})\left(0.6 \text{ m/s}^2\right) = \textbf{3.6 N}$$

Note that since F_A is perpendicular to the surface of block B, the force B exerts on A is a normal force, N.

Atwood's machine is a physics laboratory device that is used to experimentally study several areas of physics. One of these areas is dynamics, Newton's second law of motion. The Atwood machine consists of a pulley, an ideal pulley in this case, a cord that passes over the pulley and two masses attached one at each end. The cord is considered massless and ideally does not stretch. Recall that an ideal pulley is one that is frictionless and whose mass and radius are not factors to consider.

SAMPLE PROBLEM 10

Consider the drawing given below of an Atwood's machine. The masses are held at rest and then are released. The mass m_1 falls and m_2 rises. Calculate the acceleration experienced by the system and the tension in the cord.

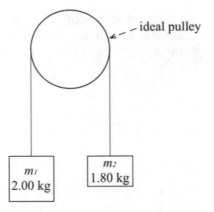

SOLUTION TO PROBLEM 10

First, make a free-body diagram. Since m_1 falls its acceleration is negative. The mass m_2 rises making its acceleration positive.

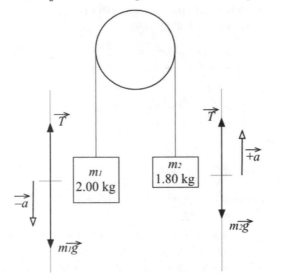

Applying Newton's second law to m_1, $\Sigma F = T - w_1 = T - m_1 g = m_1(-a)$. Solving for T in terms of a, $T = m_1 g - m_1 a$.

Next we apply Newton's second law to m_2, $\Sigma F = T - w_2 = T - m_2 g = m_2 a$. Again solving for T in terms of a, $T = m_2 a + m_2 g$. Since $T = T$, we can write $m_2 a + m_2 g = m_1 g - m_1 a$. Transposing yields $m_1 a + m_2 a = m_1 g - m_2 g$. Factoring: $(m_1 + m_2)a = (m_1 - m_2)g$ and

$$a = \frac{(m_1 - m_2)}{(m_1 + m_2)}g$$

$$= \frac{(2.00 \text{ kg} - 1.80 \text{ kg})}{(2.00 \text{ kg} + 1.80 \text{ kg})}\left(9.8 \frac{m}{s^2}\right)$$

$$= \left(\frac{0.20 \text{ kg}}{3.80 \text{ kg}}\right)\left(9.8 \frac{m}{s^2}\right)$$

$$= 0.52 \frac{m}{s^2}$$

From above,

$$T = m_2 a + m_2 g$$

$$= m_2(a + g) = (1.80 \text{ kg})\left(0.52 \frac{m}{s^2} + 9.8 \frac{m}{s^2}\right)$$

$$= 18.6 \text{ N}$$

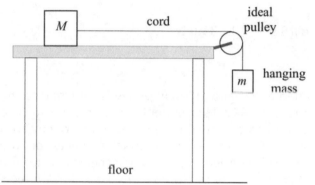

SAMPLE PROBLEM 11

Consider the system shown above. The system is being held in place. Ignoring friction and the mass of the connecting cord, if block M has a mass of 5.0 kg and block m has mass of 12.0 kg, what acceleration will the masses experience when released from rest and what tension will exist in the cord connecting them?

SOLUTION TO PROBLEM 11

First make a free-body diagram for both masses.

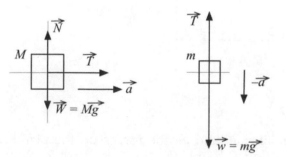

Block M is in equilibrium vertically; however, it is NOT in equilibrium horizontally. It will accelerate to the right with acceleration a.

Since the system is connected with a cord and we are dealing with an ideal pulley, the entire system experiences the same acceleration. The tension in the cord at every point will have the same magnitude. The ideal pulley changes the direction of the acceleration and tension vectors, nothing else.

For block M apply Newton's second law, $\Sigma F = T = Ma$ and for block m, $\Sigma F = T - w = T - mg = ma$ and $T = mg + m(-a) = m(g - a)$.

Since $T = T$, then $Ma = m(g - a) = mg - ma$. Transposing and factoring gives $Ma + ma = a(M + m) = mg$. Solving for the acceleration yields $a = \dfrac{m}{M + m} g$.

$$a = \frac{m}{M + m} g = \frac{12.0 \text{ kg}}{5.0 \text{ kg} + 12.0 \text{ kg}}\left(9.8 \text{ m}\middle/\text{s}^2\right) = 6.9 \text{ m}\middle/\text{s}^2$$

and

$$T = Ma = (5.0 \text{ kg})\left(6.9 \text{ m}\middle/\text{s}^2\right) = 34.6 \text{ N}$$

SAMPLE PROBLEM 12

An inclined plane is angled at 25° and an ideal pulley is attached to the upper end. A block of mass $M = 12.0$ kg is held at rest on the surface of the plane and is attached to a cord that runs over the pulley to a mass m. The coefficient of friction for the contact surfaces on the inclined plane is $\mu = 0.40$. When released, mass M accelerated up the plane at $a = 1.20 \text{ m}\middle/\text{s}^2$. What is mass m? Ignore any stretching effects in the cord and its mass.

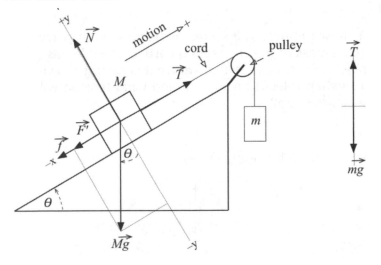

SOLUTION TO PROBLEM 12

The system is not in equilibrium and all the forces up the plane DO NOT equal all the forces down the plane. The force up the plane is greater than the sum of the forces down the plane. Recall that the ideal pulley serves to change the direction of the tension T vector.

Since the block M accelerates up the plane, we apply Newton's second law and write

$$\Sigma F = T - F' - f = Ma \text{ and } T - Mg\sin\theta - \mu Mg\cos\theta = Ma$$

To find the mass at the other end of the string we need the tension in the cord, so we solve for T.

$$T = Mg\sin\theta + \mu Mg\cos\theta + Ma$$

simplifying:

$$T = M\left(g\sin\theta + \mu g\cos\theta + a\right)$$

$$T = 12.0 \text{ kg}\left(9.8 \text{ }^m\!/_{s^2} \times \sin 25° + 0.40 \times 9.8 \text{ }^m\!/_{s^2} \times \cos 25° + 1.20 \text{ }^m\!/_{s^2}\right)$$

$$= 106.7 \text{ N}$$

Mass m is falling and we can write,

$$T - mg = ma$$

Solving for m,

$$m = \frac{T}{(g-a)} = \frac{(106.7 \text{ N})}{\left(9.8 \text{ }^m\!/_{s^2} - 1.2 \text{ }^m\!/_{s^2}\right)} = \textbf{12.4 kg}$$

DYNAMICS: STUDENT OBJECTIVES FOR THE AP EXAM

- You should be able to differentiate between systems in equilibrium and systems not in equilibrium.
- You should be able to explain how a particle can move if no net force is acting on it.
- You should be able to state Newton's second law of motion.
- You should be able to make and discuss free-body diagrams and to use them in problem solutions.
- You should be able to explain the reason for the direction of the force of friction.
- You should be able to define what is meant by an ideal pulley.

MULTIPLE-CHOICE QUESTIONS

1. A 5.00 kg body is supported by a single cord that hangs from the ceiling of a room. The tension in the cord is
   (A) 5.00 kg
   (B) 5.00 N
   (C) 49.0 kg
   (D) 49.0 N

2. A 2.00 kg body is pulled along a rough horizontal surface, $\mu_k = 0.20$, by a 10.0 N force acting at an angle of 40° with the horizontal. Which of the following diagrams correctly illustrates the forces acting on the body?

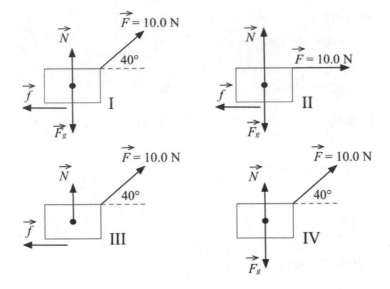

(A) I
(B) II
(C) III
(D) IV

3. Using the information in problem 2, the acceleration of the 2.00 kg body is closest to

(A) 1.85 m/s^2

(B) 2.50 m/s^2

(C) 2.75 m/s^2

(D) 3.80 m/s^2

4. A person stands on a bathroom scale in an elevator moving downward with an acceleration of $\vec{a} = -2.00 \text{ m}/\text{s}^2$. The bathroom scale will read
   (A) the true weight of the person
   (B) a weight larger than the true weight of the person
   (C) a weight smaller than the true weight of the person
   (D) a fractional change in the true weight, but since the true weight is not given, there is no way to determine it

5. A 2.00 kg block is connected to a 1.00 kg block by a massless cord that passes over an ideal pulley as shown in the diagram below. (Neglect frictional forces.)

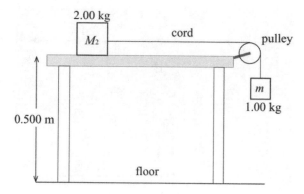

When the 1.00 kg body strikes the floor, the speed of the center of mass of the system is closest to

(A) 3.67 $\frac{m}{s}$

(B) 3.13 $\frac{m}{s}$

(C) 2.21 $\frac{m}{s}$

(D) 1.81 $\frac{m}{s}$

6. The acceleration due to gravity on a certain planet is approximately one-fourth of that on the surface of the Earth. What force is required to accelerate a 25.0 kg mass on the surface of the planet?
(A) one-fourth of the force required on the surface of the Earth
(B) the same as the force required on the surface of the Earth
(C) three-fourths of the force required on the surface of the Earth
(D) four times the force required on the surface of the Earth

7. Two blocks are pushed across a frictionless surface by a constant horizontal force as shown in the diagram below.

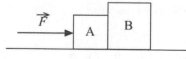

The mass of block A is m and the mass of block B is $2m$. If the blocks remain in contact as they move across the surface, block B experiences a net force of

(A) $\frac{2}{3}\vec{F}$

(B) $\vec{F}$

(C) $\frac{3}{2}\vec{F}$

(D) $2\vec{F}$

8. Two forces are applied to a body initially at rest on a frictionless surface as shown below. Rank the diagrams for the largest acceleration of the blocks to the least.

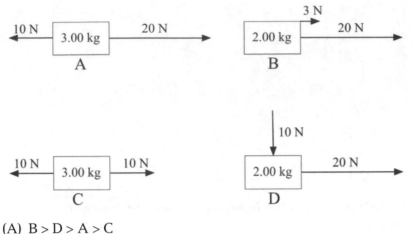

(A) B > D > A > C
(B) B > (A = C) > D
(C) C > A > B > D
(D) C > B > A > D

9. Two bodies connected by a massless rod as shown in the diagram are moving with some velocity to the right on a frictionless surface.

An external force is applied to the bodies as shown:

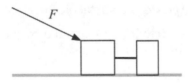

The applied force will
(A) have no effect on the velocity of center of mass of the system since it is only applied to the larger body
(B) increase the velocity of the center of mass of the system since it will provide an acceleration to the system
(C) only change the velocity of the larger body
(D) maintain the initial velocity as a constant since forces would have to be applied to both bodies in order to increase the velocity of the center of mass

10. A 20.0 N force is applied to the bodies in the diagram shown below. Consider the contact surfaces to be frictionless and ignore air resistance.

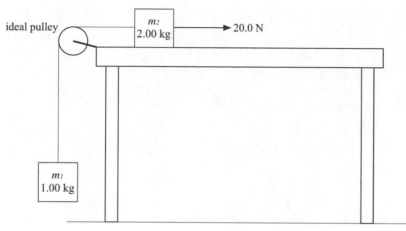

The magnitude of the acceleration of the masses indicates

(A) $\vec{a}_{2\,kg} > \vec{a}_{1\,kg}$

(B) $\vec{a}_{2\,kg} < \vec{a}_{1\,kg}$

(C) $\vec{a}_{2\,kg} = \vec{a}_{1\,kg}$

(D) the only acceleration is $\vec{a}_{2\,kg}$

11. A 1.80 kg body experiences a force acting on it for 5.00 s. The graph representing the velocity of the body vs. time is given below.

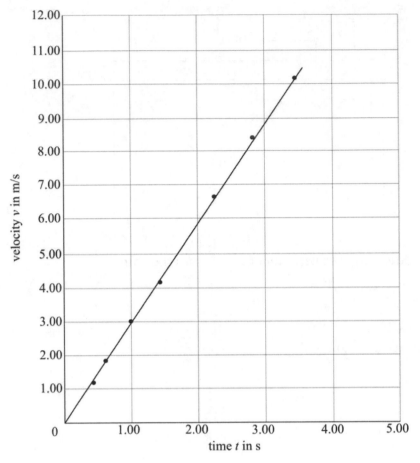

What was the magnitude of the force?

(A) 5.40 N

(B) 3.00 N

(C) 1.50 N

(D) 0.600 N

12. A body weighing 49 N is lifted by a cord as shown in the diagram below. What acceleration does the body experience?

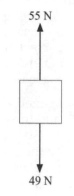

55 N

49 N

The acceleration of the body is

(A) 6.0 $\frac{m}{s^2}$

(B) 5.0 $\frac{m}{s^2}$

(C) 1.2 $\frac{m}{s^2}$

(D) 0.83 $\frac{m}{s^2}$

13. A diagram showing the forces acting in a system is illustrated below. Consider the pulley to be an ideal pulley. Ignore friction and air resistance.

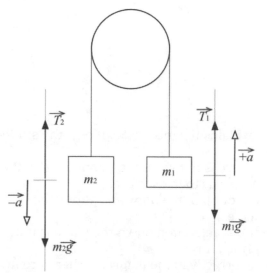

Which of the four choices gives the correct mathematical expression for the representation of the system?

(A) $\vec{T_2} - \vec{T_1} = (m)\vec{a}$

(B) $\vec{T_2} - \vec{T_1} = (m_1 + m_2)\vec{a}$

(C) $m_2\vec{g} - m_1\vec{g} = (m_1 - m_2)\vec{a}$

(D) $m_2\vec{g} - m_1\vec{g} = (m_1 + m_2)\vec{a}$

Questions 14 to 15

Directions: For each of the questions or incomplete statements below, two of the suggested answers will be correct. For each of these questions, you must select both correct answers to earn credit. No partial credit will be earned if only one correct answer is selected. Select the two that are best in each case and then enter both of the appropriate answers in the corresponding space on the answer sheet.

14. A 2.00 kg body accelerates down a 30° inclined plane where the coefficient of friction between the body and the plane is small. Increasing the
    (A) angle of the inclined plane makes with the horizontal will increase the effective weight down the plane and thus the acceleration down the plane will increase
    (B) mass of the body will increase the acceleration since it increases the effective weight down the plane
    (C) angle will have no effect on the acceleration down the plane since it will not change the net force on the body
    (D) mass will not change the acceleration

15. A student makes a free-body diagram of an object accelerating down an inclined plane as shown below.

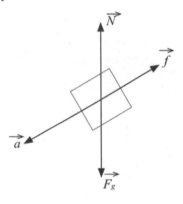

    Which of the following explains the mistake(s), if any, the student made in the diagram?
    (A) The normal to the surface is not vertical and opposite to the weight, but is perpendicular to the surface.
    (B) Friction opposes the motion of the body and should be directed down the plane.
    (C) An arrow showing the acceleration down the plane is incorrect since acceleration is not a force.
    (D) All forces are shown correctly in the diagram. There are no mistakes.

FREE-RESPONSE PROBLEMS

1. In a laboratory experiment the acceleration of a small cart is measured by the separation of dots burned at regular intervals onto a paraffin-coated tape. Weights are transferred from the small cart that is connected by a massless cord to a weight hanger that passes over a frictionless pulley. The surface is considered

frictionless, thus the weight at the end of the cord is the resultant force on the system. Students obtained the following data:

$\vec{F}$ (N)	$\vec{a}$ $\left(\dfrac{m}{s^2}\right)$
1.60	1.00
2.30	1.50
4.00	2.50
4.75	3.00
5.50	3.50
6.50	4.50
7.25	5.50
8.00	6.50

(a) Plot the graph of force versus acceleration on the grid below.

(b) What is the slope of the graph and its significance?

(c) Why did students in this experiment transfer weights from the small cart to the weight hanger attached to the cord? Explain your answer using the correct scientific terms.

2. A 1.50 kg block is placed at the top of a 38° inclined plane and released. The block accelerates down the plane at 3.80 $\dfrac{m}{s^2}$.

(a) Draw the forces acting on the block as it moves down the plane.

(b) Write the equation to determine the coefficient of friction between the block and the plane as the block accelerates down the plane. Calculate the coefficient of friction.

(c) Some time later, the block is pushed up the plane by a push *P*, of 16.0 N applied to the body and directed upward and parallel to the plane. The friction acting between the plane and the 1.50 kg block is

_____ greater than the friction acting when the block accelerated down in the plane.

_____ less than the friction acting when the block accelerated down in the plane.

_____ same as the friction acting when the block accelerated down in the plane.

Justify your answer.

3. Two metal guide rails for a 450 kg mine elevator each exert a constant frictional force of 110.0 N on the elevator car when it is moving upward with an acceleration of 2.50 $\frac{m}{s^2}$ as shown in the diagram below. Attached to the lower right side of the cable lifting the elevator is a counterweight of mass *M*. The pulley is an ideal pulley.

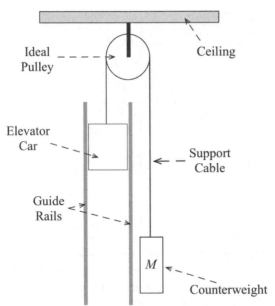

(a) What is the direction of the net force on the elevator car? Justify your answer.
(b) On the elevator cage represented below, sketch and clearly label all forces acting on the elevator during its motion.

(c) What is the tension in the supporting cable when the elevator is accelerating as described?
(d) Explain using the correct scientific terms and without writing a mathematical equation how you would determine the mass *M*

of the counterweight needed to give the elevator cage the described acceleration.

4. When you and your lab partners enter the physics classroom, your teacher has laboratory equipment on the tables and asks you determine what, if any, relationship exists between a constant force and a variable mass.
   (a) Design a laboratory experiment in enough detail that another student could duplicate your results and reach the same conclusion(s) about your inquiry lab.
   (b) Make a sketch of your equipment, and correctly label each part of the sketch.
   (c) What measurements will you take and how will you use them to answer you experimental question?
   (d) Another group of students obtained data to plot the graph below. How does this graph answer the experimental question?

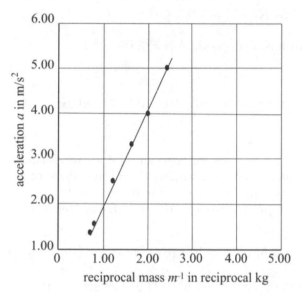

Answers

MULTIPLE-CHOICE QUESTIONS

1. **D** The gravitational force is the tension in the cord. $F_g = mg$. The

   tension is $F_g = 5.00 \text{ kg} \left(9.80 \ \dfrac{\text{m}}{\text{s}^2} \right) = 49.0 \text{ N}$

   (*College Physics* 9th ed. pages 89–92/10th ed. pages 92–93)
   (L.O. 2.B.1.1)

2. **A** The 10.0 N force has two components, $F_x = F \cos\theta$ which will give a force in the +x direction. The vertical component $F_y = F \sin\theta$ is used in determining the normal force. Since the applied force is

upward, the normal force will be smaller than the weight by this value. A coefficient of friction is given in the question; therefore a frictional force will act opposite to the motion of the body.
(*College Physics* 9th ed. pages 98–102, 107–108/10th ed. pages 100–105, 110–111)
(L.O. 2.A.2.1)

3. **B** $\Sigma F = F_x - f = ma$ applies to the problem.

    $F_x = F\cos\theta = 10.0\ \text{N}\cos 40° = 7.66\ \text{N}$.

    The friction is determined from $f = \mu_k N$. The solution to the $\Sigma F_y = 0$ equation will give the normal force.

    $\Sigma F_y = 0 = N + F\sin\theta - mg$. The normal is

    $2.00\ \text{kg}\left(9.80\ \text{m}/_{\text{s}^2}\right) - 10.0\ \text{N}\sin 40°$. Solving gives the value for the normal as $19.6\ \text{N} - 6.43\ \text{N} = 13.2\ \text{N}$. Then the frictional force is $f = 0.20(13.2\ \text{N}) = 2.64\ \text{N}$.

    Finally the acceleration is $7.66\ \text{N} - 2.64\ \text{N} = (2.00\ \text{kg})a$.

    $a = 2.51\ \text{m}/_{\text{s}^2}$

    (*College Physics* 9th ed. pages 98–102, 107–108/10th ed. pages 100–105, 110–111)
    (L.O. 3.B.1.3)

4. **C** The elevator is moving downward with a negative acceleration; the tension in the cable is therefore smaller than the weight of the person. The apparent weight is less than the true weight.
    (*College Physics* 9th ed. pages 101–105/10th ed. pages 104–107)
    (L.O. 3. B.1.1)

5. **D** Newton's second law applies to this problem. $F_g = (m_1 + m_2)a$.

    $1.00\ \text{kg}\left(9.80\ \text{m}/_{\text{s}^2}\right) = (1.00\ \text{kg} + 2.00\ \text{kg})a$. The acceleration is

    $a = 3.67\ \text{m}/_{\text{s}^2}$.

    The absolute value of the velocity of the center of mass of the system, its speed, is found from $v_f^2 = +2ay$. Substitution

    $v_f^2 = +2\left(-3.67\ \text{m}/_{\text{s}^2}\right)(-0.500\ \text{m})\quad v_f = -1.81\ \text{m}/_{\text{s}}$.

    (*College Physics* 9th ed. pages 101–105/10th ed. pages 104–107)
    (L.O. 3.A.3.1)

6. **B** The weight of the body is one fourth of its weight on the surface of the Earth, but its mass has not changed. $F = ma$ applies; the force is the same as on the surface of the Earth.
    (*College Physics* 9th ed. page 93/10th ed. pages 104–107)
    (L.O. 3.B.1.4)

7. **A** Newton's second law $F = ma$ applies. The acceleration of the system $F = 3ma$ is $a = \dfrac{F}{3m}$. Block B experiences a force that is $F' = 2m(a) = 2m\left(\dfrac{F}{3m}\right) = \dfrac{2}{3}(F)$

   (*College Physics* 9th ed. pages 98–103/10th ed. pages 104–107)
   (L.O. 3.A.1.1)

8. **A** Forces that act parallel to each other as in diagram B will produce the largest net force. Any force applied perpendicular to the direction of motion on the frictionless surface as in diagram D will not change the acceleration of the body. In diagram A, the net force on the body is 10 N in the direction of motion and in diagram C, the net force is zero.
   (*College Physics* 9th ed. pages 98–103/10th ed. pages 104–107)
   (L.O. 3.A.3.1)

9. **B** The acceleration and hence the velocity of the center of mass is related to the net external force. The motion of the system is the same as if it were a point mass M acted upon by the ΣF_{ext}. This is then, $\Sigma F_{ext} = M_{total} a_{cm}$. Therefore the velocity increases.
   (*College Physics* 9th ed. pages 98–103/10th ed. pages 104 107)
   (L.O. 4.A.3.2)

10. **C** Newton's second law applies $F = ma$. Expanding this equation gives $F - \left(m_{1\ kg}\right)g = \left(m_{1\ kg} + m_{2\ kg}\right)a$

    $$20.0 \text{ N} - (1.00 \text{ kg})9.80 \text{ m}/_{s^2} = (2.00 \text{ kg} + 1.00 \text{ kg})a .$$

    Both bodies will have the same acceleration.
    (*College Physics* 9th ed. pages 98–103/10th ed. pages 104–107)
    (L.O. 3.B.1.4)

11. **A** The slope of the velocity as a function of time graph will give the acceleration of the body $a = \dfrac{\left(9.00 \text{ m}/_s - 3.00 \text{ m}/_s\right)}{(3.00 \text{ s} - 1.00 \text{ s})} = 3.00 \text{ m}/_{s^2}$. Then using $\Sigma F = ma$, the force acting on the body is
    $\Sigma F = 1.80 \text{ kg}\left(3.00 \text{ m}/_{s^2}\right) = 5.40 \text{ N}$

    (*College Physics* 9th ed. pages 98–103/10th ed. pages 104–107)
    (L.O. 3.B.1.2, 3.B.1.3)

12. **C** The acceleration of the system is determined from $T - mg = ma$. The weight of the body is shown, not the mass. The mass is found from $49 \text{ N} = m\left(9.80 \text{ m}/_{s^2}\right)$. $m = 5.0 \text{ kg}$.

    Then $56 \text{ N} - 49 \text{ N} = (5.0 \text{ kg})a$ and $a = 1.2 \text{ m}/_{s^2}$
    (*College Physics* 9th ed. pages 98–103/10th ed. pages 104–107)
    (L.O. 3.B.1.3)

13. **D** Newton's second law applies $\Sigma F = ma$. Since the tension on either side of the rope is the same, the tension does not enter into

the correct solution. The correct substitution is

$$m_2g - m_1g = (m_1 + m_2)a.$$

(*College Physics* 9th ed. pages 98–103/10th ed. pages 104–107)
(L.O. 3.B.1.3)

14. **A** and **D** Increasing the angle of the incline increases the effective weight down the plane and thus the acceleration. Since Newton's second law applies, $\Sigma F = ma = mg \sin\theta - \mu_f mg \cos\theta$ increasing the angle increases the value for the $\sin\theta$ while decreasing the $\cos\theta$. Increasing the mass will not change the acceleration since it is a common factor in all three terms of the equation. $ma = mg \sin\theta - \mu_f mg \cos\theta$.
(*College Physics* 9th ed. pages 98–103, 107–108/10th ed. pages 104–107, 110)
(L.O. 3.A.1.1)

15. **A** and **C** The normal to the surface is a perpendicular force exerted on the body by the plane in response of the $\Sigma F_y = 0$ equation. The normal must cancel the y-component of the gravitational force relative to the plane. Acceleration is not a force. What causes the acceleration down the plane is the x-component of the gravitational force minus the frictional force up the plane. $ma = mg \sin\theta - \mu_f mg \cos\theta$.
(*College Physics* 9th ed. pages 98–103, 107–108/10th ed. pages 104–107, 110)
(L.O. 3.B.2.1)

FREE-RESPONSE PROBLEMS

1. (a) The graph of force versus acceleration is shown below.

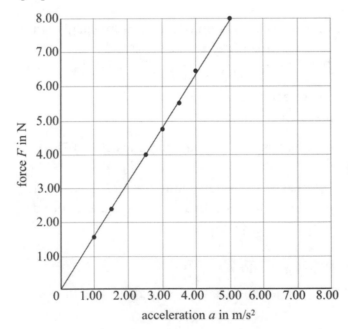

(b) The slope of the line is the total mass in the system. $\Sigma F = ma$

$$m = \frac{(8.00 \text{ N} - 1.60 \text{ N})}{\left(5.00 \text{ m}\!/\!_{s^2} - 1.00 \text{ m}\!/\!_{s^2}\right)} = \mathbf{1.60 \text{ kg}}$$

(c) Students transferred mass from the cart to the mass hanger in order to keep the total mass in the experiment a constant. In the absence of frictional forces, the only net force acting on the cart is the weight on the weight hanger since $F_g = mg$. If mass does not vary in the experiment, the acceleration is directly proportional to the net unbalanced force acting on the constant mass. $F \propto a$.

(*College Physics* 9th ed. pages 101–105/10th ed. pages 104–107)
(L.O. 2.B.1.1, 4.A.2.2)

2. (a) The correct force diagram is shown below.

(b) The block is in equilibrium in the y direction since it is neither lifting off the incline nor sinking into it. $\Sigma F_y = N - F_g \cos\theta$. The normal is the reaction force applied by the plane to what it perceives as the "weight" of the block. $N = mg \cos\theta$.

The motion of the block is down the plane. $\Sigma F_{net} = F_{effective} - f$.
Since the effective force down the plane is given by
$F_{effective} = mg \sin\theta$, then substitution into $\Sigma F_{net} = F_{effective} - f$ is

$$(1.50 \text{kg})\left(3.80 \text{ m}\!/\!_{s^2}\right) = (1.50 \text{ kg})\left(9.80 \text{ m}\!/\!_{s^2}\right)\sin 38° - \mu_k (1.50 \text{ kg})\left(9.80 \text{ m}\!/\!_{s^2}\right)\cos 38°$$

$$5.70 \text{ N} = 9.05 \text{ N} - \mu_k (11.6 \text{ N})$$

$$\mu_k = \mathbf{0.289}$$

(c) The correct line checked is __√__ same as the friction acting when the block accelerated down in the plane. Frictional forces act parallel to the bodies in contact and are opposite the direction of motion. Since a push is applied to the block to send it up the plane, the friction will be down the plane. (Checking to see that it moves up the plane, write the $\Sigma F_{net} = F_{effective} + f$ equation. $\Sigma F_{net} = 9.05 \text{ N} + 3.35 \text{ N} = 12.4 \text{ N}$. Since the applied force is 16.0 N, the block will accelerate up the plane.)

(*College Physics* 9th ed. pages 101–105, 107–108/10th ed. pages 104–107, 110–111)
(L.O. 2.B.1.1, 3.A.2.1, 3.A.4.3, 3.B.1.3, 3.B.2.1)

3. (a) Since the cage is moving upward with an acceleration of
2.50 $\frac{m}{s^2}$, the net force on the cage is upward.

(b) The forces on the cage are shown below; since both rails exert frictional forces, acting downward they must be included in the diagram as well as the normal forces exerted on the two guide rails. The last two forces are the tension in the cable and the weight of the cage.

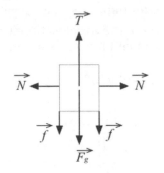

(c) Because the mass of the counterweight is unknown, the solution is $T_{cable} - 2f - mg = ma$. Substitution into the equation

is $T_{cable} - 2(110.0 \text{ N}) - (450.0 \text{ kg})\left(9.80 \ \frac{m}{s^2}\right) = (450.0 \text{ kg})\left(2.50 \ \frac{m}{s^2}\right)$

$\vec{T}_{cable} = \textbf{5760 N}$

(d) Since the force on the counterweight is in the y direction, applying Newton's second law will give the mass of the counterweight. The upward tension in the cable minus the weight of the counterweight will give the net force on the counterweight. Then the mass M can be calculated by dividing the net force by the acceleration of the system.

(*College Physics* 9th ed. pages 101–105, 107–108/10th ed. pages 104–107, 110–111)

(L.O. 2.B.1.1, 3.A.2.1, 3.A.4.3, 3. B.1.1, 3.B.1.3, 3.B.1.4, 3.B.2.1)

4. (a) What relationship exists between a constant force and a variable mass?

A known force will be applied to a body that is free to move by passing a cord connected to the body over an ideal pulley to a weight hanger at the other end of the cord.

Using a platform balance, determine the mass of the body.

Connect the body via the cord to the known force on the weight hanger.

Using a meterstick, measure the distance between two motion sensors.

Calculate the acceleration of the body using $v_f^2 = v_0^2 + 2ax$.

Repeat the observation for at least three readings, taking the average of the readings and recording this average.

Increase the mass of the glider by attaching an additional mass to the glider, then record the new mass. Using the same force on the weight hanger, determine the acceleration of the new mass.

(b) Several possible pieces of equipment could be used.

    i.   An airtrack is the best choice of equipment if it is available since it has very low friction between the track and the glider.

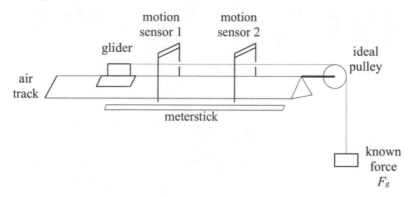

    ii. The equipment can be set up on a lab table, but friction between the body and the known <u>net</u> force will have to be measured for each trial. The frictional force, $f_k = \mu_k N$ will increase with additional weight on the block since the normal force increases. Once adjusting for the increase in friction, the acceleration of the body can be measured for the known <u>net</u> force.

(c) Measurements taken in the experiment include the known weight, and the mass for each trial.

The motion sensors will record the velocity of the glider as it passes through the sensor. The separation of the motion sensors will be needed to determine the acceleration using $v_f^2 = v_0^2 + 2ax$.

Knowing the acceleration will permit a calculation of the product of the mass and the acceleration. If the force calculations are equal to the known force, then experimentally we can write the acceleration is directly proportional to the force and inversely proportional to the mass.

(d) The slope of the acceleration as a function of the reciprocal of the mass will give the value of the known net force. Increasing the mass results in a decrease in acceleration when a constant force is applied.

(*College Physics* 9th ed. pages 101–105, 107–108/10th ed. pages 104–107, 110–111)

(L.O. 1.C.1.1, 2.B.1.1, 3.A.1.2, 3.B.1.3, 3.B.1.4, 3.B.2.1)

5

WORK, ENERGY, AND POWER

WORK

(College Physics 9th ed. pages 124–129/10th ed. pages 127–132)

The term *work* is restricted in physics to cases in which there is a force and a displacement along the line of the force. When a force F moves a body through a displacement s and the directions of these two vectors are not the same, the work W is defined as

$$W = Fs\cos\theta$$

where θ is the angle between the direction of the force and that of the displacement. In the special case where the force has the same direction as the displacement, $\cos 0° = 1$, the work done is simply $W = Fs$. Even though work is the product of two vector quantities, it itself is a scalar quantity. When two vector quantities are multiplied to produce a scalar quantity the operation is called *scalar multiplication* of two vectors. The magnitude of a scalar multiplication always involves a cosine function. The unit of work in the SI is the newton-meter that is called the *joule,* J.

$$1\,\text{J} = 1\,\text{N}\cdot\text{m} = 1\,\frac{\text{kg}\cdot\text{m}^2}{\text{s}^2}$$

This unit is named for the British physicist James Prescott Joule (1818–1889) whose experimental investigations greatly contributed to the acceptance of the relationship between heat and work.

169

SAMPLE PROBLEM 1

A wooden box is pulled at constant speed across a horizontal floor by a rope that makes an angle of 20° with the floor. The tension in the rope is 120.0 N. Ignoring friction, what work is done displacing the box 4.6 m horizontally?

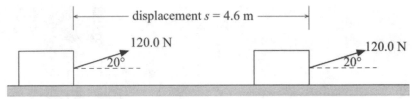

SOLUTION TO PROBLEM 1

The force vector makes an angle of 20° with respect to the displacement; therefore the work done is

$$W = Fs\cos\theta = (120.0 \text{ N})(4.6 \text{ m})(\cos 20°) = \textbf{518.7 J}.$$

AP Tip

The work done on a body is always done by some agent.

SAMPLE PROBLEM 2

A 600.0 N force is developed in the braking system of a car to bring it to rest over a horizontal distance of 80.0 m. What work is done by the braking system?

SOLUTION TO PROBLEM 2

The force developed by the brakes acts in the exact opposite direction to the displacement making $\theta = 180°$ and the $\cos 180° = -1$. Notice that the brake system is the *agent* doing the work on the car. The work done will be negative.

$$W = Fs\cos\theta$$
$$= (600.0 \text{ N})(80.0 \text{ m})(\cos 180°)$$
$$= (600.0 \text{ N})(80.0 \text{ m})(-1)$$

$$= \textbf{-48.0 kJ}$$

THE ELECTRON VOLT

(*College Physics* 9th ed. page 559/10th ed. pages 569–570)

There is another unit of work we need to introduce. It is a unit used in addressing certain work and energy relationships in atomic, molecular, and nuclear physics. This unit is called the *electron volt, eV,* and we define it as

$$1 \text{ eV} = 1.602 \times 10^{-19} \text{ J}$$

The electron volt is a tiny unit but quite important in dealing with the work involved in moving electron and protons through electrical and magnetic fields.

SAMPLE PROBLEM 3

A minimum of 13.6 eV of work is required to remove an electron from a hydrogen atom. What is this amount of work expressed in joules?

SOLUTION TO PROBLEM 3

We will use the value $1 \text{ eV} = 1.602 \times 10^{-19} \text{ J}$ as a conversion factor.

$13.6 \text{ eV} \times \dfrac{1.602 \times 10^{-19} \text{ J}}{1 \text{ eV}} = \mathbf{2.18 \times 10^{-18} \text{ J}}$ is required to separate an electron from a hydrogen atom. Note that in the division, eV divides out leaving J as the unit of work.

SAMPLE PROBLEM 4

In a battery that is in operation, the chemical agents of the battery do an average of $2.4 \times 10^{-19} \text{ J}$ of work transporting an electron to the negative terminal. In eV, how much work is this?

SOLUTION TO PROBLEM 4

As in the previous sample problem treat $1 \text{ eV} = 1.602 \times 10^{-19} \text{ J}$ as a conversion factor. $2.4 \times 10^{-19} \text{ J} \times \dfrac{1 \text{ eV}}{1.602 \times 10^{-19} \text{ J}} = \mathbf{1.5 \, eV}$. As we will see later in the course, volts in a roundabout way are related to work in batteries and electrical fields.

KINETIC ENERGY

(*College Physics* 9th ed. pages 129–132/10th ed. pages 132–135)

In physics we say that anything that has *energy* has the capacity to do work. Energy, *E*, exists in many forms and can be transformed from one form to another. At present we are making a study of a branch of physics we call *mechanics,* and for now, our primary interest is *mechanical energy.* When we consider energy in our study of mechanics we primarily make reference to three forms:

1. Kinetic energy, *K*

2. Potential energy, *U*

3. Total mechanical energy, $E = K + U$

As we saw at an earlier point in our study of physics, the expression *kinetic* makes reference to motion. All moving bodies have *kinetic energy.* Bodies that are at rest do not have kinetic energy. To give a body motion requires an unbalanced force and that force causes an acceleration. Consider the following diagram where a body of mass m is acted upon by a force F that results in a horizontal displacement s. The work done is defined as $W = Fs\cos\theta$. Note that in the diagram both the force vector and the displacement vector are parallel. This means that the angle between F and s is $0°$ and the cosine of $0°$, $\cos 0° = 1$, is 1. Then $W = Fs\cos\theta$ takes the form $W = Fs$.

This is *always* the case when F and s have the same direction.

AP Tip

When the force and displacement vectors are parallel, the $\cos 0° = 1$ making the work done on a body $W = Fs$.

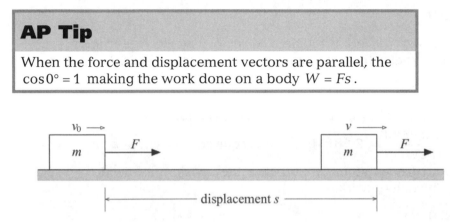

From Newton's second law, the resultant force $F = ma$. The body is accelerated from some initial velocity, v_0, to some final velocity, v, over some displacement, s. The work done is $W = Fs$ where $F = ma$, and then $W = mas$.

Although Newton's laws of motion provide a very powerful method of attack on problems in mechanics, they do not give the only one. In problems where time is not specifically mentioned, the concept of energy provides another approach. We have no idea how long the acceleration will take and we did not bother to define the time period involved. This means that in order to continue we need to use the time-independent equation $v^2 = v_0^2 + 2as$. If the body starts from rest we set $v_0 = 0$. Then we write $v^2 = 2as$. Solving for the product of a and s yields $as = \dfrac{v^2}{2}$. Substituting into $W = mas$ gives $W = m\left(\dfrac{v^2}{2}\right)$, or better yet $W = \dfrac{1}{2}mv^2$.

The work done accelerating a body from rest to some velocity, v, is then determin7ed by $W = \dfrac{1}{2}mv^2$. The work done to accelerate a body to some velocity, v, is called the *kinetic energy, K,* of the body.

$$K = \frac{1}{2}mv^2$$

AP Tip

The work done by some agent on a body to give it speed v equals the kinetic energy of that body.

Sample Problem 5

A 0.03 kg bullet is fired horizontally from a rifle giving it a muzzle velocity of 300.0 $\frac{m}{s}$. The rifle barrel has a length of 75.0 cm.

(a) What is the kinetic energy of the bullet as it exits the muzzle of the rifle?

(b) What work is done on the bullet by the expanding gases as it travels the length of the barrel?

(c) What acceleration does the bullet experience while in the barrel?

(d) How long does the bullet spend in the rifle barrel?

(e) Ignoring air resistance, how much work will the bullet do when striking a thick tree trunk 100 m from the rifle?

Solution to Problem 5

(a) The kinetic energy of the bullet is

$$K = \frac{1}{2}mv^2 = \frac{1}{2}(0.03 \text{ kg})\left(300.0 \ \frac{m}{s}\right)^2 = \textbf{1.35 kJ}$$

(b) The expanding hot gases drive the bullet the length of the barrel. The gases are the agent doing work on the bullet. The work done to give the bullet a kinetic energy of **1.35 kJ** is the same, **1.35 kJ**.

(c) The work done on the bullet is $W = Fs$. The force exerted on the bullet by the gases is $F = \dfrac{W}{s} = ma$. The acceleration of the bullet is then

$$a = \frac{W}{ms} = \frac{1.35 \times 10^3 \text{ J}}{(0.03 \text{ kg})(0.75 \text{ m})} = \textbf{60} \times \textbf{10}^3 \ \frac{\textbf{m}}{\textbf{s}^2}$$

(d) Acceleration is defined by $a = \dfrac{v - v_0}{t} = \dfrac{v - 0}{t}$. The time period is

$$t = \frac{v}{a} = \frac{\left(300.0 \ \frac{m}{s}\right)}{\left(60 \times 10^3 \ \frac{m}{s^2}\right)} = \textbf{5.0 ms}$$

(e) Since the bullet has 1.35 kJ of kinetic energy it will do **1.35 kJ** of work when it hits the tree trunk in coming to rest.

Like work, kinetic energy is a scalar quantity and is measured in the same units as work.

> ### AP Tip
>
> Unlike work, kinetic energy is never negative.
>
> If the body has some initial speed, v_0, other than zero, then its final kinetic energy is
>
> $$K = \frac{1}{2}mv^2 - \frac{1}{2}mv_0^2$$
>
> Note that the above equation may also be written as
>
> $$\Delta K = \frac{1}{2}mv^2 - \frac{1}{2}mv_0^2 = K - K_0$$
>
> The quantity ΔK is the change in kinetic energy.

THE WORK-KINETIC ENERGY THEOREM

(*College Physics* 9th ed. pages 129–132/10th ed. pages 132–135)

If the body in the above diagram has some initial velocity other than zero, $v^2 = v_0^2 + 2as$ and solving for the product of acceleration and displacement, as, gives $as = \dfrac{v^2 - v_0^2}{2}$ and substituting into $W = mas$ yields: $W = m\left(\dfrac{v^2 - v_0^2}{2}\right) = \dfrac{1}{2}mv^2 - \dfrac{1}{2}mv_0^2$. We call this relationship the *work-kinetic energy theorem*.

The work done on a moving system changes the kinetic energy of that system.

In Sample Problem 5(e) the question is "Ignoring air resistance, how much work will the bullet do when striking a thick tree trunk 100 m away from the rifle?" Since air resistance was ignored the bullet strikes the tree trunk with a speed equivalent to the muzzle velocity, 300.0 $\frac{m}{s}$. The bullet hits the tree trunk and penetrates it to some depth before coming to rest. The tree trunk is the agent stopping the bullet and the work done is found by the work-kinetic energy theorem, or

$$W = \Delta K = K - K_0$$
$$= \frac{1}{2}mv^2 - \frac{1}{2}mv_0^2$$
$$= \frac{1}{2}m(0)^2 - \frac{1}{2}(0.03 \text{ kg})\left(300.0 \tfrac{m}{s}\right)^2$$
$$= -1.35 \text{ kJ}$$

The work the tree trunk does on the bullet is negative. The tree trunk stops the bullet. It takes kinetic energy away.

POTENTIAL ENERGY

(*College Physics* 9th ed. pages 132–134/10th ed. pages 135–138)

Consider lifting a body initially at rest from the floor. In lifting the body, work is done against gravity. Lifting the body with some constant vertical velocity implies that the body is in translational equilibrium and the lifting force, F, equals to the weight, w, of the body.

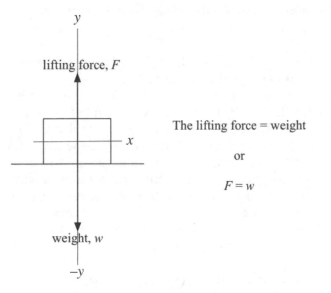

The lifting force = weight

or

$$F = w$$

If a body weighs 98 N, a minimal lifting force of 98 N is used to assure the body is lifted with constant velocity. If a lifting force greater than 98 N is used, the body accelerates upward since a resultant upward force is then acting.

Consider a body, of mass m, being lifted through a vertical displacement, y, with a constant velocity.

At times we use h to represent this vertical distance. In either case work is done against gravity lifting the mass. The lifter is the *agent doing the work*, and the *agent does work against* gravity. Work is defined as $W = Fs\cos\theta$. Here, the displacement is y (or h) and it is directed vertically upward. The lifting force is F and it is also directed vertically upward. These vectors are parallel and that means the cos 0° = 1 and $W = Fs = Fy = wy$ since the lifting force $F = w = mg$. In doing work against gravity, the work is: $W = mgy = mgh$.

When the mass is lifted to a position above floor or ground level, the mass is then in a position where it can do work. It can fall! Any mass that is in a position where it can do work is said to have *potential energy, U*, or more specifically, *gravitational potential energy, U*. The body has been given gravitational potential energy or

$$U = mgy = mgh$$

The joule, J, is the SI unit of potential energy.

Gravitational fields, like the one generated by the mass of the earth, have a very special property that relates to *conservation*. Gravitational force is called a *conservative force*, and this makes potential energy conservative. What does this mean? Well, we're going to have to show you as we go along with our study of work and energy.

When we deal with potential energy, we need to establish a rule. We define the ground as having zero potential energy. For reasons we will explore later, we will state that the work done in a conservative field, work done by conservative forces like gravity, is defined as

$$W_g = -\Delta U$$

The work done in lifting a mass in the earth's gravitational field is equal to the negative change in potential energy. This is written as

$$\Delta U = U - U_0$$

Where the change in potential energy, ΔU, is the difference between the final state, U, of the mass and the initial state, U_0.

The major feature of a conservative field, like the earth's gravitational field, is that the work done in moving a mass is totally independent of the path taken from the ground to the final position. The change in potential energy, the work done, is only dependent on the vertical displacement. We say that in general a force is conservative if the work done by that force acting on a body moving between two points is independent of the path the body takes between the points. A conservative force has the property that the **total work** done by the conservative force is zero when the body moves around any closed path and returns to its initial position.

THE LAW OF CONSERVATION OF MECHANICAL ENERGY

(*College Physics* 9th ed. pages 145–147/10th ed. pages 148–150)

In a conservative field, the total energy is always a constant. This means that the total initial energy in a closed system before an event will always equal the total final energy in that same system after the event. Or symbolically

$$\Sigma E_0 = \Sigma E$$

where $\Sigma E_0 = K_0 + U_0$ and $\Sigma E = K + U$ which means that

$$K_0 + U_0 = K + U$$

We call this mathematical statement the *law of conservation of mechanical energy*.

SAMPLE PROBLEM 6

Consider the following diagram where a crate of mass m is held at rest at point A. The crate is released and slides along the frictionless curved surface to point B. What is the velocity of the crate when it reaches point B?

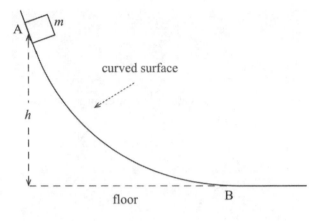

SOLUTION TO PROBLEM 6

Since friction is ignored, the system is a conservative system. The total energy at point A is equal to the total energy at point B, or

$$K_0 + U_0 = K + U$$

At point A, initially the crate is at rest and its kinetic energy is zero. The initial gravitational potential energy at A is $U_0 = mgh$. At ground-level the gravitational potential energy becomes zero and the kinetic energy of the crate is $K = \frac{1}{2}mv_B^2$. Writing $K_0 + U_0 = K + U$ and substituting gives $0 + mgh = \frac{1}{2}mv_B^2 + 0$. Solving for v_B yields $v_B = \sqrt{2gh}$.

THE HOOKEAN SPRING AS A CONSERVATIVE SYSTEM

(*College Physics* 9th ed. pages 140–145/10th ed. pages 143–148)

Springs obey a rather simple law discovered by Robert Hook in the eighteenth century. Hook's law states that the force of restitution acting in a spring is directly proportional to the amount of stretching or compressing. Or

$$F = -kx$$

The negative sign (–) reminds us that F is a force of restitution, k is the spring constant unique to a given spring, and x is the amount of stretching or the amount of compression in the spring. Stretch a spring within reason or compress it and it wants to return to its original shape. The free end of a spring in the relaxed position is called the *equilibrium position*.

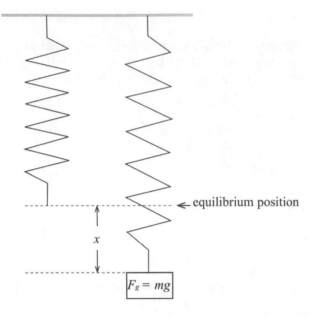

equilibrium position

The work required to stretch a Hookean spring is found by

$$W = \frac{1}{2}kx^2$$

The force of restitution in Hookean springs is conservative. Since the work done by a conservative force equals the change in potential energy, the elastic potential energy, U_s, a stretched or compressed spring is determined by

$$U_s = \frac{1}{2}kx^2$$

SAMPLE PROBLEM 7

A spring is attached to a rod as shown above. The spring has a length of 0.22 m. A 0.44 kg mass is attached to the free end of the spring, stretching it to a new length of 0.28 m.

(a) What is the spring constant of the spring?

(b) How much work was done on the spring elongating it?

SOLUTION TO PROBLEM 7

(a) The spring is stretched by $x = x_{loaded} - x_{releaxed} = 0.28 \text{ m} - 0.22 \text{ m} = 0.06 \text{ m}$. The stretching force is the weight of the load attached to the spring $F = F_g = mg = (0.44 \text{ kg})\left(9.8 \text{ m}/_{s^2}\right) = 4.31 \text{ N}$. Hooke's law is $F = kx$ and $k = \dfrac{F}{x} = \dfrac{4.31 \text{ N}}{0.06 \text{ m}} = \textbf{71.87 N}/_{\textbf{m}}$.

(b) The work done is $W = \dfrac{1}{2}kx^2 = \dfrac{1}{2}\left(71.87 \text{ N}/_{\text{m}}\right)(0.06 \text{ m})^2 = \textbf{0.13 J}$.

NON–CONSERVATIVE FORCES

(College Physics 9th ed. pages 128, 131–132/10th ed. pages 131, 134–136)

A force is non-conservative if the work done by the force on a body moving between two points depends on the path taken. Friction, *f*, is such a force. Friction is *degrading force* since it takes away kinetic energy and converts it to another energy form, *thermal energy, Q.* Thermal energy or heat is a wasteful energy form, a dissipative form, and it cannot be recovered into the mechanical system. Heat escapes into the environment of the system, warming it.

The work, W_{nc}, done by all non-conservative forces in a system equals the change in the total mechanical energy of the system.

$$-W_{nc} = \Delta K + \Delta U$$

or

$$-W_{nc} = (K + U) - (K_0 + U_0).$$

SAMPLE PROBLEM 8

A 2.00 kg block of wood slides across a horizontal floor with an initial velocity of 0.40 $^{m}/_{s}$ and comes to rest after sliding 1.20 m. Using energy considerations, calculate the average frictional force acting on the block.

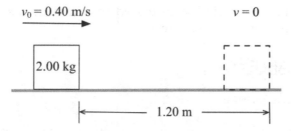

SOLUTION TO PROBLEM 8

The block moves along the horizontal making the change in gravitational potential energy zero.

Since friction brings the block to rest, this is a non–conservative system and $-W_{nc} = \Delta K + \Delta U = K - K_0 + 0$. The final kinetic energy is zero since the block comes to rest and $-W_{nc} = -fx = -K_0 = -\frac{1}{2}mv_0^2$. The average frictional force is

$$f = \frac{mv_0^2}{2x} = \frac{(2.00 \text{ kg})(0.40 \text{ }^{m}/_{s})^2}{2(1.20 \text{ m})} = \textbf{0.13 N}$$

WORK DONE BY A CONSTANT FORCE

(College Physics 9th ed. pages 124–125/10th ed. pages 128–129)

Lifting a mass m through a vertical displacement h is an example of work done by a *constant force*. In this simple case, we can write $F = $ constant and the work done by the lifting agent is $W = Fh$.

If we draw a graph with the force F plotted along the vertical axis and the distance h through which the force acts, we get a straight horizontal line as shown in the graph below.

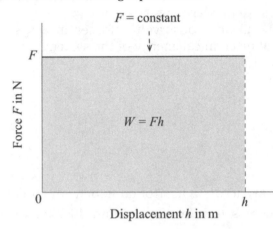

For any given F and h, the work done is simply equal to the shaded area in the graph. This idea that *the area under a curve can represent work done* is extremely useful. It can be extended to practical cases where the force may not be constant, but varies.

WORK DONE BY A VARIABLE FORCE

(College Physics 9th ed. pages 152–154/10th ed. pages 155–157)

Up to this point in the treatment of work done and energy expended, we have assumed that an applied force is constant at all points along the path over which it acts. As we will see later, there are numerous situations where a force is far from being constant. One such case is in the stretching of a spring. The spring shown below is elongated through a displacement x by a horizontal force F. Data is collected and a F vs. x graph is plotted. The stretching force is not a constant; it varies with displacement.

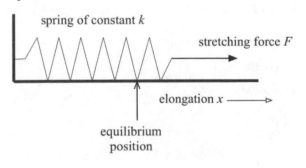

The curve is the straight, inclined line that is shown below. The interpretation of the graphical result is that of a direct proportionality between F and x. The curve passes through the origin and we can write

$$F = kx$$

This result is Hooke's Law!

Before we do anything else, we need to find the slope of the curve. The slope is the spring constant, k. Earlier, when we were making a study of motion, we define slope as

$$\text{slope} = \frac{\text{change in the vertical}}{\text{change in the horizontal}}$$

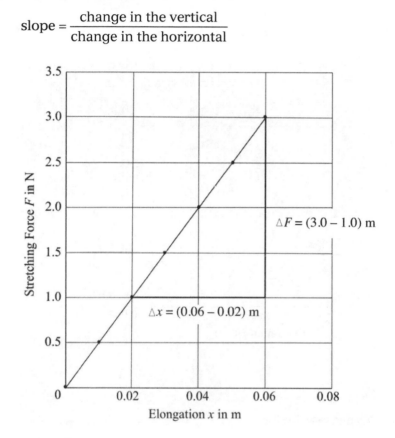

and we can write

$$\text{slope} = k = \frac{\Delta F}{\Delta x} = \frac{F - F_0}{x - x_0} = \frac{3.0 \text{ N} - 1.0 \text{ N}}{0.06 \text{ m} - 0.02 \text{ m}} = 50.0 \text{ }^{N}\!/_{m}$$

We said above that the area beneath a F vs. x graph is the work done by the force F. Note in the following graph that the shaded area represents the work done in stretching the spring by 0.06 m.

Recall that the area bounded by a triangle, which is the work done by the variable force, is one-half the base multiplied by the height, or

$$\text{area} = W = \frac{1}{2}(x)(F) \text{ and since } F = kx, \text{ then } W = \frac{1}{2}(x)(kx) \text{ or}$$

$$W = \frac{1}{2}kx^2$$

The work done in stretching the spring by 0.06 m is then

$$W = \frac{1}{2}kx^2 = \frac{1}{2}\left(50.0\ {N}\!/\!{m}\right)\left(0.06\ m\right)^2 = 0.09\ J$$

Or taking one-half the base times the height,

$$\text{area} = \frac{1}{2}\left(0.06\ m\right)\left(3.0\ N\right) = 0.09\ J$$

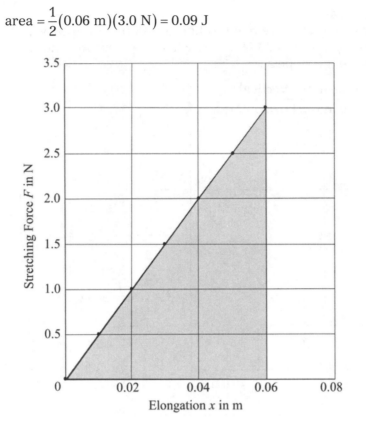

POWER

(*College Physics* 9th ed. pages 147–152/10th ed. pages 150–155)

We define power as the work done by some agent per unit time.

$$P = \frac{W}{t}$$

Power, like work, is a scalar quantity. In the SI, the unit of power is the watt (W), and we define 1 W as

$$1.00\ W = 1.00\ \frac{J}{s}$$

Sometimes, the kilowatt, kW, is more advantageous to use and 1 kW = 1000 W.

The English system unit of power is the horsepower, hp, and it is defined as

$$1\ hp = 0.746\ kW = 746\ W.$$

Power may also be expressed as the product of the average force acting on the body and the average speed of a body:

$$P = Fv$$

SAMPLE PROBLEM 9

An 1100 kg car accelerates from 5.0 $\frac{m}{s}$ to a speed of 25.0 $\frac{m}{s}$ in a time interval of 6.0 s. Ignoring frictional losses, what average horsepower must the drive train produce to cause this acceleration?

SOLUTION TO PROBLEM 9

The work done in accelerating the car is

$$W = \Delta K = K - K_0 = \frac{1}{2}mv^2 - \frac{1}{2}mv_0^2 = \frac{1}{2}m\left(v^2 - v_0^2\right).$$

Power is defined as

$$P = \frac{W}{t}$$

$$= \frac{m\left(v^2 - v_0^2\right)}{2t} = \frac{(1100 \text{ kg})\left[\left(25.0 \ \frac{m}{s}\right)^2 - \left(5.0 \ \frac{m}{s}\right)^2\right]}{2(6.0 \text{ s})}.$$

$$= 55.0 \text{ kW}$$

Converting to hp,

$$55.0 \times 10^3 \text{ W} \times \frac{1 \text{ hp}}{746 \text{ W}} = \textbf{73.7 hp}.$$

SAMPLE PROBLEM 10

A 1.50 hp electric motor at a construction site can vertically lift a load at the rate of 0.10 $\frac{m}{s}$. What maximum mass of building materials can it lift at this constant speed?

SOLUTION TO PROBLEM 10

The horsepower output of the electric motor is

$$1.50 \text{ hp} \times \frac{746 \text{ W}}{1.00 \text{ hp}} = 1.12 \times 10^3 \text{ W}.$$

In 1.0 s, the load mg is lifted a vertical distance of 0.10 m. The work done in 1.0 s is $W = mgh$.

By definition, $P = \dfrac{W}{t} = \dfrac{mgh}{t}$. Solving for m yields

$$m = \frac{Pt}{gh} = \frac{\left(1.12 \times 10^3 \text{ W}\right)(1.0 \text{ s})}{\left(9.8 \ \frac{m}{s^2}\right)(0.10 \text{ m})} = \textbf{1.14} \times \textbf{10}^3 \textbf{ kg}$$

WORK, ENERGY, AND POWER: STUDENT OBJECTIVES FOR THE AP EXAM

- You should be able to define work.
- You should be able to define energy.
- You should be able to differentiate between total mechanical energy, kinetic energy, and gravitational potential energy.
- You should be able to state the work–kinetic energy theorem.
- You should be able to state the law of conservation of mechanical energy.
- You should be able to calculate the work done in stretching a spring.
- You should be able to explain why friction is called a dissipative force.
- You should be able to explain what will happen to the kinetic energy of a body if the net work done on it is negative.

MULTIPLE-CHOICE QUESTIONS

1. A 4.00 kg block moving with a velocity of 1.5 m/s on a flat horizontal surface enters a region where the coefficient of friction has increased. The kinetic energy of the block will
   (A) increase as the block enters the region
   (B) decrease as the block enters the region
   (C) remain constant in the region
   (D) decrease then increase as the block leaves the region

2. A 5.00 kg body is lifted vertically a distance of 1.20 m and then carried a horizontal distance of 4.00 m. The work done by gravity on the body is
   (A) –245 J
   (B) –196 J
   (C) –58.8 J
   (D) –24.0 J

3. A block moves from point A to B to C and back to A along the path shown.

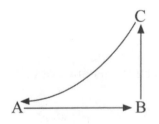

   The path is conservative if the
   (A) final kinetic energy is the same as the initial kinetic energy
   (B) final gravitational potential energy is the same as the initial gravitational potential energy
   (C) the loss of gravitational potential energy will equal the loss in kinetic energy
   (D) the sum of the total mechanical energy remains the same

4. A body experiences a variable force applied over a displacement of
    8.00 m as shown in the graph. What is the change in the kinetic
    energy as the body moves through the displacement of 8.00 m?

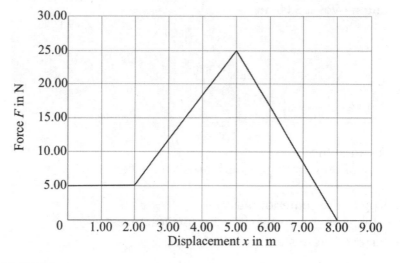

(A) 67.5 J
(B) 92.5 J
(C) 130. J
(D) 160. J

5. A 2.00 kg block slides on a frictionless horizontal surface with a
    velocity of 1.60 m/s when it strikes the massless bumper on a
    spring attached to a wall as shown below.

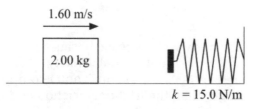

The maximum increase in the internal potential energy of the
massless bumper and spring is
(A) 5.12 J
(B) 3.20 J
(C) 2.56 J
(D) 1.60 J

6. Two blocks, $m_1 = 1.00$ kg and $m_2 = 2.00$ kg, are connected by a massless 0.60 m long rod. The system is moving horizontally with a velocity of 1.50 m/s. A force of 20.0 N, as shown below, is applied to the system and moves it 3.00 m.

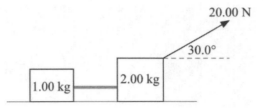

This force will change the
(A) kinetic energy of only m_2 since it is closest to the center of mass
(B) kinetic energy of the center of mass
(C) kinetic energy of only m_1 since it is the smallest mass
(D) internal energy of the system

7. A body moving along a horizontal surface with an initial velocity of 1.50 m/s is acted upon by the two forces shown below.

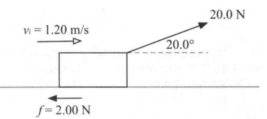

(A) The kinetic energy of the body will decrease because a frictional force acts on it, reducing its initial velocity.
(B) The kinetic energy increases because the horizontal component of the 20.0 N force is larger than the frictional friction and in the same direction as the initial velocity.
(C) The kinetic energy is constant since the two forces acting on the body change neither the respective magnitude nor the direction of the initial velocity.
(D) It cannot be determined since the mass of the body is not indicated in the question.

8. A 4.00 kg block is attached to a horizontal spring that has s spring constant $k = 15.0 \frac{N}{m}$. The block is pushed to the left compressing the spring by 8.00 cm. The block is then released from rest. Determine the maximum velocity of the block as its center of mass passes through the equilibrium position. (Ignore friction)

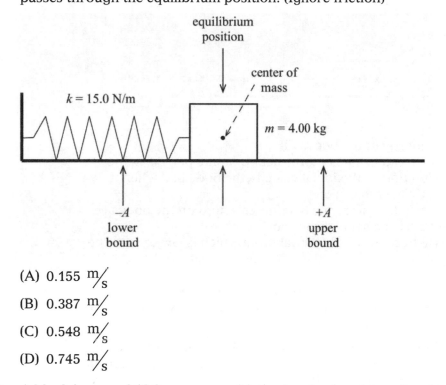

(A) 0.155 $\frac{m}{s}$

(B) 0.387 $\frac{m}{s}$

(C) 0.548 $\frac{m}{s}$

(D) 0.745 $\frac{m}{s}$

9. A block is moved 12.0 m across a frictionless horizontal surface by a constant force of 30.0 N that acts at some angle θ less than 90° to the horizontal. If θ changes, what happens to the kinetic energy of the block?
   (A) It remains the same since the force and the displacement remain the same.
   (B) The kinetic energy will increase if θ increases toward 90°.
   (C) The kinetic energy will decrease if θ decreases toward 0°.
   (D) The kinetic energy will increase only if you increase the force or the displacement as you change the angle.

10. A 3.00 kg body is pushed in the +x direction by a force as shown below. The velocity of the body is 1.80 m/s when it enters a rough region where the coefficient of friction between the body and the surface is $\mu_k = 0.200$.

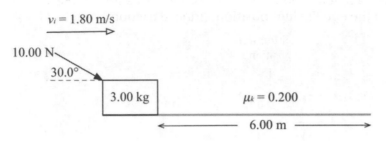

The kinetic energy of the body will

(A) increase because the net force acting on the body is in the same direction as the initial velocity the body had when it entered the rough region

(B) remain constant since the two forces acting on the body are applied over the same displacement

(C) decrease because the frictional force which is larger than the 10.0 N force is acting in the direction opposite to the body's initial velocity

(D) decrease because the net force acting on the body is in the opposite direction of the initial velocity the body had when it entered the rough region

11. A 5.00 kg block with an initial velocity of 10.0 m/s is projected up a rough 30° incline. When the center of mass of the block has been elevated by 3.00 m, its velocity is 4.00 m/s.

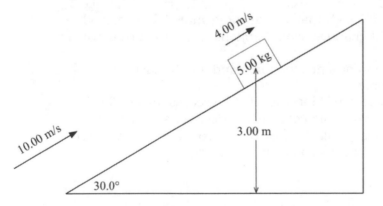

Which of the following best describes the work done by the frictional force?

(A) –250. J

(B) –147. J

(C) –63.0 J

(D) –40.0 J

12. Two masses, $m_1 = 2.00 \text{ kg}$ and $m_1 = 1.00 \text{ kg}$, are connected to a massless string that passes over a frictionless pulley.

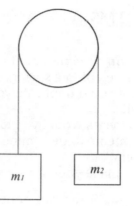

The speed of the two masses after the larger mass has descended 1.50 m to the floor is
(A) $v_1 > v_2$
(B) $v_2 > v_1$
(C) $v_1 = v_2$
(D) $v_2 = 2v_1$

13. A 2.50 kg body slides across a frictionless tabletop that is 1.20 m above the floor with a speed of 1.50 m/s. Relative to the tabletop, the energy associated with the body is
(A) only kinetic energy
(B) only gravitational potential energy
(C) the sum of the kinetic and the gravitational potential energy
(D) the difference between the kinetic energy and the gravitational potential energy

Questions 14 to 15

Directions: For each of the questions or incomplete statements below, two of the suggested answers will be correct. For each of these questions, you must select both correct choices to earn credit. No partial credit will be earned if only one correct answer is selected. Select the two that are best in each case and then enter both of the appropriate answers in the corresponding space on the answer sheet.

14. The work done by the frictional force in question 11 goes into the system as
(A) internal energy of the particles that compose the block and the incline as increased vibratory energy
(B) non-recoverable energy
(C) energy that leaves the system entirely
(D) some form of energy that is completely recoverable

15. Two balls of the same mass are released from a height h. The first ball is dropped from rest and the second ball is thrown vertically downward with some initial velocity v_0. Just before the balls reach the ground,
(A) both balls have the same gravitational potential energy
(B) both balls have the same kinetic energy
(C) the ball that was thrown downward has the greater total energy
(D) the ball that was dropped has the greater total energy since it spends more time in the air

FREE-RESPONSE PROBLEMS

1. (a) You are to design an experiment to determine the amount of work done in stretching a spring. Provide enough detail so that another student could duplicate your experiment and obtain the same results.
    (b) What measurements would you take and how would you use these measurements to determine the amount of work done in your experiment?
    (c) Suppose you replace your spring with one whose spring constant $k_2 = \dfrac{1}{2}k_1$. The work done in stretching the spring will

    _____ increase

    _____ decrease

    _____ remain constant

    Justify your answer without calculations.
    (d) Another student plots the following graph from data obtained in his experiment.

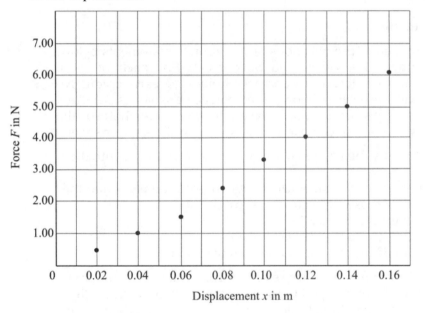

    i.   What does the plotted data indicate about the spring constant for their experiment?
    ii. Will the spring return to its original un-stretched position when the load is removed?

    Explain your answer.

2. A small heavy block of mass m as shown in the diagram rests on top of a smooth curved track whose lowest end is a height h_2 above a horizontal floor. When released from a height h_1 above the table, the block moves down the track and leaves the table horizontally striking the floor a distance D from the base of the table.

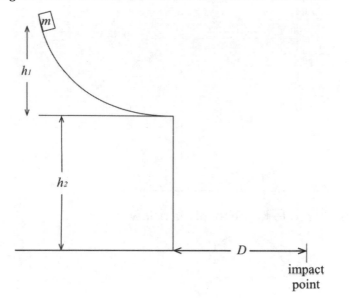

(a) Explain, without calculations, how you would determine the horizontal velocity of the block as it leaves the table.

(b) Explain, without calculations, how you would determine the horizontal distance D that the block travels before it strikes the floor.

(c) How will reducing the mass of the block change the distance D?

_____ Reducing the mass will increase D.

_____ Reducing the mass will decrease D.

_____ Reducing the mass will not change D.

Justify your answer.

3. (a) A 2.00 kg block M_2 is pulled across a frictionless surface by a 1.00 kg mass m_1 as shown in the figure (a) below. Determine the velocity of the system when the 1.00 kg mass has descended to the floor.

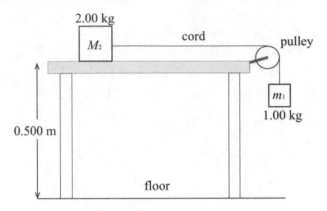

(b) The system is altered to figure (b) given below.

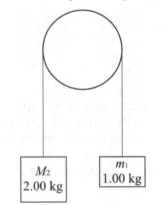

The velocity of the system will

_____ increase

_____ decrease

_____ not change

Justify your answer.

4. A 0.500 kg block slides on a frictionless curved track that is 1.50 m in height. It slides 2.00 m on a straight track where the coefficient of kinetic friction μ_k is 0.100 before striking a spring with a spring constant of 100.0 N/m.

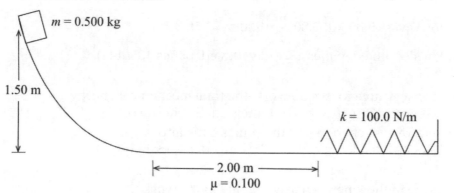

(a) Find the maximum compression of the spring.
(b) The mass rebounds returning up the curved ramp. Determine the rebound height.
(c) Complete the bar charts shown below for the energies associated with the mass.

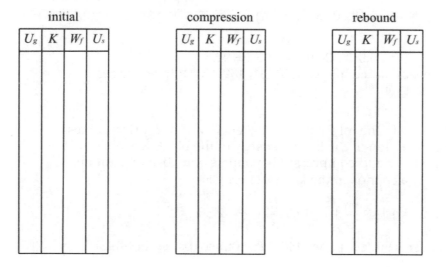

Answers

MULTIPLE-CHOICE QUESTIONS

1. **B** The kinetic energy of the block will decrease. Frictional forces act opposite to the motion of a body and will do negative work on the block. Increasing the coefficient of friction will increase the frictional force.
(*College Physics* 9th ed. pages 128–132/10th ed. pages 131–135)
(L.O. 3.E.1.2)

2. **C** Gravity, a force that acts at a distance, does negative work on the 5.00 kg body as it is lifted 1.20 m in the gravitational field. It does no work on the body as it is carried horizontally 4.00 m since the force is perpendicular to the displacement. $W_g = -mgh$.

    Substitution gives $-5.00 \text{ kg} \left(9.80 \ \frac{m}{s^2} \right) 1.20 \text{ m} = -58.8 \text{ J}$

    (*College Physics* 9th ed. pages 132–139/10th ed. pages 135–141)
    (L.O. 5.B.5.5)

3. **D** If only conservative forces do work, the total mechanical energy will be conserved. $K_0 + U_0 = K + U$ Either kinetic energy or potential energy can change, but the sum is constant.
    (*College Physics* 9th ed. pages 131–137/10th ed. pages 134–140)
    (L.O. 4.C.1.1, 4.C.1.2)

4. **B** The change in the kinetic energy is equal to the work done $W = \Delta K$.

    The work done is the area under the force-displacement graph.

    $$5.00 \text{ N}(5.00 \text{ m} - 0 \text{ m}) + \frac{1}{2}(25.00 \text{ N} - 5.00 \text{ N})(5.00 \text{ m} - 2.00 \text{ m})$$

    $$+ \frac{1}{2}(25.0 \text{ N} - 0 \text{ N})(8.00 \text{ m} - 5.00 \text{ m})$$

    The work done is 25.0 J + 30.0 J + 37.5 J = 92.5 J.
    (*College Physics* 9th ed. pages 129–131, 152–154/10th ed. pages 132–134, 155–157)
    (L.O. 3.F.1.4)

5. **C** The increase in the internal potential energy of the spring comes from the conversion of the kinetic energy of the block when it strikes the spring and compresses beyond its equilibrium position. $\Delta K = -\Delta U_s$ The change in the kinetic energy is

    $$\Delta K = -\frac{1}{2}(2.00 \text{ kg}) \left(\left(0 \ \frac{m}{s} \right)^2 - \left(1.60 \ \frac{m}{s} \right)^2 \right) = -2.56 \text{ J}$$

    (*College Physics* 9th ed. pages 140–145/10th ed. pages 143–148)
    (L.O. 5.B.3.3)

6. **B** The center of mass is the point in the body or a system of objects where the mass of the objects appears to be concentrated. A force applied to the center of mass will accelerate the system and change its velocity and hence its kinetic energy.
    (*College Physics* 9th ed. page 151/10th ed. page 154)
    (L.O. 4.C.2.2)

7. **B** The net force acting on the body is in the direction of the initial velocity of the body. The work of the net force will increase the velocity and thus the kinetic energy of the body.
    (*College Physics* 9th ed. pages 128–132/10th ed. pages 131–135)
    (L.O. 3.E.1.2)

8. **A** The internal energy of the spring is converted into kinetic energy of the block. The maximum velocity of the block occurs when the spring has a displacement from the equilibrium position

of $x = 0$. $U_s = \Delta K$, solving the energy equation

gives $\dfrac{1}{2}kx^2 = \dfrac{1}{2}mv^2$.

Thus $\dfrac{1}{2}\left(15.0 \text{ N}/_{\text{m}}\right)(0.080 \text{ m})^2 = \dfrac{1}{2}(4.00 \text{ kg})v^2$. The velocity is

$\pm 0.155 \text{ m}/_{\text{s}}$.

(*College Physics* 9th ed. pages 140–145/10th ed. pages 143–148)
(L.O. 5.B.4.2)

9. **C** The work done in moving a body by a given force is

$W = \left|\vec{F}\right|(\cos\theta)d$. Increasing the angle decreases the horizontal

component of the force acting in the direction of the displacement
since the maximum value of the cosine of 0° is 1 and the minimum
value of the cosine is 0 when the angle is 90°. This increase of the
angle will decrease the amount of work done by the force
compared to the original force over the 12.00 m displacement.
(*College Physics* 9th ed. pages 124–129/10th ed. pages 128–132)
(L.O. 3.E.1.1)

10. **A** The 10.0 N force acting downward at an angle of 30° has two
components. The horizontal component of the force
is $F_x = 10.0 \text{ N}\cos 30° = 8.66 \text{ N}$. Since the 10.0 N force pushes
downward on the body it increases the normal force exerted on
the body by the surface. $N = F_y + F_g$. The normal is therefore

$N = 10.0 \text{ N }(\sin 30°) + (3.00 \text{ kg})\left(9.80 \text{ m}/_{\text{s}^2}\right) = 34.4 \text{ N}$. The net force

acting on the body is $\Sigma F_x = 8.66 \text{ N} - 0.200(34.4 \text{ N}) =$

$8.66 \text{ N} - 6.88 \text{ N} = 1.78 \text{ N}$. The net force is in the direction of the
initial velocity and the kinetic energy will increase $\Sigma F_x \cdot x = \Delta K$.
The kinetic energy will increase by 10.7 J.
(*College Physics* 9th ed. pages 128–132/10th ed. pages 131–135)
(L.O. 3.E.1.3)

11. **C** Conservation of energy applies. $K_0 + U_0 = K + U + W_f$. The initial
gravitational potential energy is zero since the base of the incline is
the reference point for this problem.

$$\dfrac{1}{2}(5.00 \text{ kg})\left(10.0 \text{ m}/_{\text{s}^2}\right)^2 - \dfrac{1}{2}(5.00 \text{ kg})\left(4.00 \text{ m}/_{\text{s}^2}\right)^2$$

$$-(5.00 \text{ kg})\left(9.80 \text{ m}/_{\text{s}^2}\right)(3.00 \text{ m}) = W_f$$

$250. \text{ J} - 40. \text{ J} - 147. \text{ J} = W_f$. Since friction acts opposite to the
displacement of the body, the work done by friction is negative.
The answer is −63.0 J .
(*College Physics* 9th ed. pages 129–131/10th ed. pages 132–134)
(L.O. 4.C.1.1)

12. **C** Conservation of energy must occur. The change in the gravitational potential energy is equal to the change in the kinetic energy in the system.

$$2.00 \text{ kg}\left(9.80 \text{ }^{m}/_{s^2}\right)(1.50 \text{ m}) - 1.00 \text{ kg}\left(9.80 \text{ }^{m}/_{s^2}\right)(1.50 \text{ m})$$

$$= \frac{1}{2}(2.00 \text{ kg} + 1.00 \text{ kg})v^2 \text{ ,}$$

the speed of each body is $3.13 \text{ }^{m}/_{s}$.

(*College Physics* 9th ed. pages 129–131/10th ed. pages 132–134)
(L.O. 3.E.1.4, 5.B.4.2)

13. **A** Since the reference position is the tabletop, the body has no gravitational potential energy; it possesses only kinetic energy.
(*College Physics* 9th ed. pages 129–130, 132/10th ed. pages 132–133, 135)
(L.O. 5.B.1.1)

14. **A** and **C** Work done by a non-conservative force either leaves the system for the surrounding environment or stays in the system in some form of an increase in internal energy which is vibratory energy that could show up as thermal energy or sound.
(*College Physics* 9th ed. pages 145–146/10th ed. pages 148–149)
(L.O. 4.C.1.1, 4.C.1.2, 5.B.3.3, 5.B.4.1)

15. **A** and **C** Since they are released from the same height, they have the same gravitational potential energy. The ball that was projected downward with some initial velocity v_0 has initial kinetic energy. When they reach the ground, the body that was thrown downward has the greatest total energy. $K_0 + U_0 = K$.
(*College Physics* 9th ed. pages 131–137/10th ed. pages 135–140)
(L.O. 4.C.1.1, 5.B.4.2)

FREE-RESPONSE PROBLEMS

1. The work done in stretching a spring is the area under the curve of a force vs. displacement graph.

   (a) Measure the length of the spring.

   Hang the spring from a hook collar attached to a support.

   Add a mass to the free end of the spring and measure the elongation.

   Continue adding masses, one at a time, making sure that the spring does not oscillate, and

   Record the elongation of the spring. Repeat until you have a minimum of 6–8 readings.

(b) The measurements taken will be the mass in kg added to the spring and the force in N that each of the masses exert converted from $F_g = mg$.

The elongation of the spring measured in cm will be converted into m units for each mass added to the spring.
A graph of force as a function of elongation will be plotted from the data that was recorded. The graph is linear if the spring obeys Hooke's law $F = -kx$. The slope of the line is the spring constant k measured in N/m and the area under the curve is the work done on the spring.

(c) The correct line checked is *increased*. If the spring constant is reduced such that $k_2 = \frac{1}{2}k_1$ forces applied to the spring will increase the elongation, therefore increasing the work done.

(d) i. The graph indicates that the spring constant is not uniform over the graph.
    ii. There are two possible answers:
        No, the spring will not return to its initial position when the forces are removed. The spring is distorted.
        Yes, because the fact that the spring is non Hookean does not mean the spring will not return to its original position. Unloading data is not given.
(*College Physics* 9th ed. pages 135–138/10th ed. pages 138–141)
(L.O. 5.B.5.1, 5.B.5.2)

2. (a) By applying conservation of energy between the highest point and the table top, we can find the horizontal velocity of the block when it leaves the table. Since the track is smooth, there is no energy "lost" to friction and the change in the gravitational potential energy of the Earth-block system will equal its gain in kinetic energy. Since mass is a common factor in the equation, the horizontal velocity will be the square root of twice the acceleration due to gravity times the height h_1.

   (b) The body leaves the table with a constant horizontal velocity. The distance traveled will be the horizontal velocity times the time to reach the floor. Since the body leaves the table with no vertical velocity, falling a distance h_2, the time for it to drop is found from taking the square root of twice the height, h_2, divided by the acceleration due to gravity.

   (c) The mass of the body was eliminated in the conservation of energy equation. Changing the mass will not change the distance D.
(*College Physics* 9th ed. pages 135–138/10th ed. pages 138–141)
(L.O. 4.C.1.1, 5.B.4.2, 5.B.5.4)

3. (a) Conservation of energy applies to the problem. Since the surface is frictionless the gravitational potential energy of the Earth falling weight will be converted into the kinetic energy of both bodies as the falling weight drops to the floor.

$$m_1 gh = \frac{1}{2}(m_1 + M_2)v^2 .$$

Substitution gives

$$(1.00 \text{ kg})\left(9.8 \text{ m}/_{s^2}\right)(0.500 \text{ m}) = \frac{1}{2}(1.00 \text{ kg} + 2.00 \text{ kg})v^2$$

$$v = 1.81 \text{ m}/_{s} .$$

(b) Correct line checked is the velocity will *not change*.
When the arrangement is changed to figure (b), conservation of energy still applies to the problem.

$$M_2 gh - m_1 gh = \frac{1}{2}(m_1 + M_2)v^2 .$$

The result is the same velocity,

$$v = 1.81 \text{ m}/_{s} .$$

(*College Physics* 9th ed. pages 135–138/10th ed. pages 138–141)
(L.O. 4.C.1.1, 5.B.4.2, 5.B.5.4)

4. (a) The maximum compressions of the spring is determined from conservation of energy, $E = E_0 - W_f$

$$U_{g0} + U_{s0} + K_0 - W_f = U_g + U_s + K$$

$$mgh + 0 + 0 - \mu_k mgx = 0 + \frac{1}{2}kx^2 + 0$$

$$(0.500 \text{ kg})\left(9.80 \text{ m}/_{s^2}\right)(1.50 \text{ m}) - (0.100)(0.500 \text{ kg})\left(9.80 \text{ m}/_{s^2}\right)(2.00 \text{ m})$$

$$= \frac{1}{2}\left(100.0 \text{ N}/_{m}\right)(x^2)$$

$$x = 0.356 \text{ m}$$

(b) After compression, conservation of energy still applies.

$$U_{g0} + U_{s0} + K_0 - W_f = U_g + U_s + K$$

$$0 + \frac{1}{2}kx^2 + 0 - W_f = mgh + 0 + 0$$

$$\frac{1}{2}\left(100.0 \text{ N}/_{m}\right)(0.356 \text{ m})^2 - 0.100(0.500 \text{ kg})\left(9.8 \text{ m}/_{s^2}\right)(2.00 \text{ m})$$

$$= 0.500 \text{ kg}\left(9.8 \text{ m}/_{s^2}\right)h$$

$$h = 1.10 \text{ m}$$

(c)

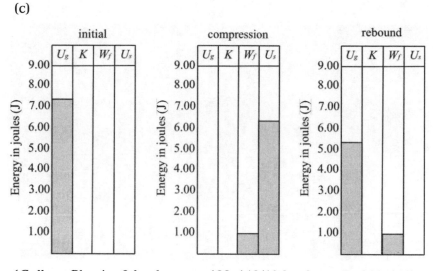

(*College Physics* 9th ed. pages 138–146/10th ed. pages 141–148)
(L.O. 4.C.1.1, 4.C.1.2, 5.B.3.1, 5.B.3.2, 5.B.4.2, 5.B.5.4)

6

Momentum, Impulse, and Collisions

Linear Momentum

(*College Physics* 9th ed. pages 167–169/10th ed. pages 170–172)

Linear momentum, or simply momentum, $\vec{p}$, is a characteristic of a moving body. It is a vector quantity with magnitude and direction. It is defined as the product of the mass, m, of the body and its velocity, $\vec{v}$.

$$\vec{p} = m\vec{v}$$

The SI unit of momentum is $kg \cdot \dfrac{m}{s}$.

All moving bodies have two properties, (1) momentum and (2) kinetic energy. Stationary bodies do not have these properties.

Sample Problem 1

(a) Find the momentum of a proton, $m_p = 1.67 \times 10^{-27}$ kg, that has been accelerated to a velocity of 4.50×10^6 m/s in a particle accelerator.

(b) What work, in eV, was done by the particle accelerator in giving its momentum?

SOLUTION TO PROBLEM 1

(a) Momentum is $p = mv$ and

$$p = \left(1.673 \times 10^{-27} \text{ kg}\right)\left(4.50 \times 10^{6} \text{ m}/_{s}\right) = 7.53 \times 10^{-21} \text{ kg} \cdot \text{m}/_{s}$$

(b) The work done by the accelerator is the kinetic energy of the proton

$$W = K = \frac{1}{2}mv^2$$

$$W = \frac{1}{2}\left(1.673 \times 10^{-27} \text{ kg}\right)\left(4.5 \times 10^{6} \text{ m}/_{s}\right)^2$$

$$= 1.69 \times 10^{-14} \text{ J} \times \frac{1 \text{ eV}}{1.60 \times 10^{-19} \text{ J}}$$

$$= 1.06 \times 10^{5} \text{ eV}$$

SAMPLE PROBLEM 2

Derive an expression relating momentum, p, and kinetic energy, K, as $p = f(K)$.

SOLUTION TO PROBLEM 2

$K = \frac{1}{2}mv^2$ and $K = \frac{1}{2}(mv)v$ then $K = \frac{1}{2}pv$. Solving for p yields $p = \dfrac{2K}{v}$. Use the data from Sample Problem 1 and determine the momentum of the proton from its kinetic energy.

$$p = \frac{2K}{v} = \frac{2\left(1.69 \times 10^{-14} \text{ J}\right)}{\left(4.50 \times 10^{6} \text{ m}/_{s}\right)} = 7.53 \times 10^{-21} \text{ kg} \cdot \text{m}/_{s}$$

IMPULSE

(*College Physics* 9th ed. pages 167–169/10th ed. pages 170–172)

Consider when a golf ball is struck with a golf club. The club is in contact with the golf ball for a very short time interval, Δt. During this time interval, a very large force is exerted on the ball; this force varies with time in a very complex manner that is difficult to determine. Forces of this kind are called *impulsive forces*. Initially, the golf ball is at rest. Over the time interval Δt the ball is accelerated and separates from the club with some velocity, v.

We define *impulse*, J, as a vector quantity equal to the product of the force, $\vec{F}$, and the time interval, Δt over which it acts. The direction of the impulse is the same as that of the force.

$$\vec{J} = \vec{F}\Delta t$$

The unit of impulse is the $\text{N} \cdot \text{s}$.

Impulse causes change in momentum, and we can write $\vec{J} = \Delta\vec{p}$, or

$$\vec{F}\Delta t = m\Delta\vec{v}$$

With every momentum change there is an impulse.

SAMPLE PROBLEM 3

A 1100 kg car traveling at 10 m/s collides with a concrete barrier and comes to rest in 0.9 second.

(a) What force does the barrier exert on the car?

(b) What acceleration does the car experience?

SOLUTION TO PROBLEM 3

(a) The car undergoes a momentum change that is caused by impulse, $m\Delta v = F\Delta t$. Since we are seeking the force we solve for F

$$F = \frac{m\Delta v}{\Delta t} = \frac{m(v - v_0)}{\Delta t} = \frac{(1100 \text{ kg})\left(0 - 10 \text{ }^m\!/_s\right)}{(0.9 \text{ s})} = \textbf{-12.2} \times \textbf{10}^3 \textbf{ N}$$

(b) Unbalanced forces cause accelerations: $F = ma$. The acceleration is

$$a = \frac{F}{m} = \frac{-12.2 \times 10^3 \text{ N}}{1100 \text{ kg}} = \textbf{-11.1 }^m\!/_{s^2}$$

We could have also found the acceleration from

$$a = \frac{v - v_0}{t} = \frac{0 - 10 \text{ }^m\!/_s}{0.9 \text{ s}} = \textbf{-11.1 }^m\!/_{s^2}$$

AP Tip

The area beneath an F vs. Δt graph for a collision is the impulse generated during the collision.

SAMPLE PROBLEM 4

A cue ball traveling the +x-axis makes a *head-on* collision with a pool ball. The force developed over time period t in the collision is shown in the graph below. From the graph, determine the impulse generated in the collision.

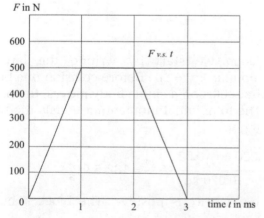

SOLUTION TO PROBLEM 4

The impulse $J = F\Delta t$ is the area under the curve that consists of two triangles and a rectangle.

$$J = A = \frac{1}{2}(base)(altitude) + (base)(altitude) + \frac{1}{2}(base)(altitude)$$

$$J = \frac{1}{2}(1.00 \times 10^{-3}\ s)(500\ N) + (1.00 \times 10^{-3}\ s)(500\ N) + \frac{1}{2}(1.00 \times 10^{-3}\ s)(500\ N)$$

$$= 1.00\ N \cdot s$$

The direction is to the right.

LAW OF CONSERVATION OF LINEAR MOMENTUM

(College Physics 9th ed. pages 172–175/10th ed. pages 176–179)

In a closed system with no external forces acting, the total initial momentum, $\Sigma \vec{p}_0$ of the system is always equal to the total final momentum, $\Sigma \vec{p}$ of the system. This is a statement of one of the most important principals in all of physics, the *Law of Conservation of Linear Momentum*. Or

$$\Sigma \vec{p}_0 = \Sigma \vec{p}$$

SAMPLE PROBLEM 5

A 20 gram projectile is shot horizontally into a stationary 7 kg block of wood and becomes imbedded in it. Immediately after impact the block is observed to move to the right with a velocity of 0.52 m/s. Determine the initial velocity of the projectile.

$m = 0.020$ kg

$M = 7.000$ kg
$V_0 = 0$

COLLISION EVENT

$M + m = 7.020$ kg

SOLUTION TO PROBLEM 5

Anytime we have a collision we start by writing the law of conservation of linear momentum: $\Sigma p_0 = \Sigma p$. Before collision one body is moving, the projectile. After collision a single body moves, the block with the imbedded bullet. The total initial momentum equals the total final $mv_0 = (M + m)V$. Solving for V,

$$v_0 = \frac{(M + m)V}{m} = \frac{(7.020\ kg)(0.52\ m/s)}{(0.020\ kg)} = 182.5\ m/s$$

Note that the sign of the velocity is positive. The block + bullet combination moves to the right.

COLLISIONS

(*College Physics* 9th ed. pages 175–176/10th ed. pages 179–180)

When two bodies strike one another, a *collision* occurs, in which case the net external force is zero. During a collision an impulse is generated that produces momentum change. There will always be a momentum change and the law of conservation of linear momentum always holds true.

Consider two non-rotating spherical bodies traveling to the right in such a way that the centers of mass, c.m., travel along the *x*-axis as diagramed below. Let *v*'s represent initial velocities and *u*'s represent final velocities.

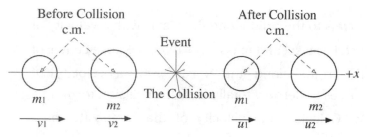

The bodies collide and then separate after collision with their centers of mass, c.m., continuing along the *x*-axis. Such a collision is called a one-dimensional collision or a head-on collision. Initially, two bodies are in linear motion and after the event, the collision, two bodies are in linear motion.

Any collision that is not a perfectly elastic collision is called inelastic. In all inelastic collisions there is a disappearance of kinetic energy during the collision process. A major portion of the lost kinetic energy is transformed into thermal energy—heat. The best way to account for the thermal energy loss in collisions is by means of an empirical quantity that we call the *coefficient of restitution, ε*. We define the coefficient of restitution as the ratio of the relative rate of separation after collision to the relative rate of approach before collision

$$\varepsilon = \frac{\text{relative rate of separation}}{\text{relative rate of approach}}$$

or

$$\varepsilon = \frac{u_2 - u_1}{v_1 - v_2}$$

Of course *v*'s represent initial velocities of the colliding bodies and *u*'s represent all final velocities.

The coefficient of restitution will have values ranging from $0 \le \varepsilon \le 1$. The lower the value of ε the more thermal energy that is generated in the collision. In the case where $\varepsilon = 0$, the collision is a totally inelastic collision and the bodies merge into a single composite body. This type of collision is called a *totally inelastic collision*. In a perfectly elastic collision, the relative rate of separation equals the relative rate of approach and $\varepsilon = 1$. When $0 < \varepsilon < 1$, the collision is a *partially elastic collision* where the bodies collide and separate and their shapes are somewhat altered in the collision process.

THE TOTALLY INELASTIC COLLISION

(*College Physics* 9th ed. pages 176–179/10th ed. pages 180–183)

In the totally inelastic collision the coefficient of restitution is zero, $\varepsilon = 0$, the initial kinetic energy is always greater than the final kinetic energy, $\Sigma K_0 > \Sigma K$, and the total initial momentum is always equal to the final momentum, $\Sigma p_0 = \Sigma p$. The law of conservation of linear momentum is always our starting point.

SAMPLE PROBLEM 6

A 4.0 kg mass, m_1 travels to the right along the *x*-axis with a velocity of $v_1 = 10.0 \frac{m}{s}$. It overtakes a second mass $m_2 = 6.0$ kg whose center of mass travels to the right along the x-axis with a velocity of $v_2 = 4.0 \frac{m}{s}$. The masses undergo a totally inelastic collision forming a composite mass, *M*. Calculate the velocity of the composite mass immediately after collision.

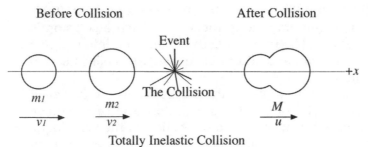

Totally Inelastic Collision

SOLUTION TO PROBLEM 6

As stated above, the starting point is the law of conservation of linear momentum: $\Sigma p_0 = \Sigma p$. Before the collision, two bodies are moving. In the collision process the bodies merge forming a single body. We write $m_1 v_1 + m_2 v_2 = Mu$. Next we solve for the final velocity, u, and substitute the known values.

$$u = \frac{m_1 v_1 + m_2 v_2}{M} = \frac{(4.0 \text{ kg})(10.0 \text{ m/s}) + (6.0 \text{ kg})(4.0 \text{ m/s})}{(10.0 \text{ kg})}$$

$$= 6.4 \frac{m}{s}$$

In a totally inelastic collision, kinetic energy is not conserved and $\Sigma K_0 > \Sigma K$. Calculating both K_0 and K

$$\Sigma K_0 = \frac{1}{2} m_1 v_1^2 + \frac{1}{2} m_2 v_2^2$$

$$= \frac{1}{2}(4.0 \text{ kg})(10.0 \text{ m/s})^2 + \frac{1}{2}(6.0 \text{ kg})(4.0 \text{ m/s})^2 = 248.0 \text{ J}$$

$$\Sigma K = \frac{1}{2}Mu^2 = \frac{1}{2}(10.0 \text{ kg})(6.4 \text{ m/s})^2 = \textbf{204.8 J}$$

By the work-kinetic energy theorem

$$W = \Delta K = \Sigma K - \Sigma K_0 = 204.8 \text{ J} - 248.0 \text{ J} = \textbf{-43.2 J}$$

During the collision, work is done merging the bodies and thermal energy is developed in the merged mass, M. Sound, acoustical energy is produced.

THE PARTIALLY ELASTIC COLLISION

(College Physics 9th ed. pages 179–182/10th ed. pages 183–185)

SAMPLE PROBLEM 7

A 4.0 kg mass, m_1, travels to the right along the x-axis with a velocity of $v_1 = 10.0$ m/s. It overtakes a second mass $m_2 = 6.0$ kg whose center of mass travels to the right along the x-axis with a velocity of $v_2 = 4.0$ m/s. The masses undergo a partially perfectly elastic collision where the coefficient of restitution for the interacting bodies is $\varepsilon = 0.75$. Calculate the velocity of the masses m_1 and m_2 immediately after collision.

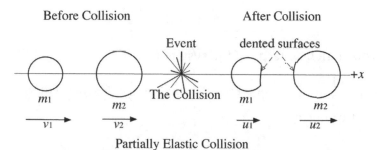

Partially Elastic Collision

SOLUTION TO PROBLEM 7

First we can write the law of conservation of linear momentum: $\Sigma p_0 = \Sigma p$ and $m_1v_1 + m_2v_2 = m_1u_1 + m_2u_2$

Substituting without units

$$(4.0)(10.0) + (6.0)(4.0) = 4.0u_1 + 6.0u_2$$

Solving for u_1 and u_2 we write equation (1)

$$4.0u_1 + 6.0u_2 = 64.0 \qquad\qquad (1)$$

From the definition of the coefficient of restitution, $\varepsilon = \dfrac{u_2 - u_1}{v_1 - v_2}$,

and we can write

$$u_2 - u_1 = \varepsilon(v_1 - v_2)$$

Substituting without units

$$u_2 - u_1 = 0.75(10.0 - 4.0) = 4.5$$

Solving for u_1 and u_2 we write equation (2) as

$$u_1 - u_2 = -4.5 \qquad (2)$$

Equations (1) and (2) constitute a pair of simultaneous linear equations.

$$4.0u_1 + 6.0u_2 = 64.0 \qquad (1)$$

$$u_1 - u_2 = -4.5 \qquad (2)$$

Solving them algebraically we multiply equation (2) by 6

$$4.0u_1 + 6.0u_2 = 64.0$$

$$6.0u_1 - 6.0u_2 = -27.0$$

Adding

$$10.0u_1 = 37.0$$

Dividing both sides by 10 yields

$$u_1 = 3.7\,\frac{\text{m}}{\text{s}}$$

Substituting into equation (1)

$$(4.0)(3.7) + 6.0u_2 = 64.0$$

Solving for u_2

$$u_2 = 8.2\,\frac{\text{m}}{\text{s}}$$

The total initial total kinetic energy of the system is

$$\Sigma K_0 = \frac{1}{2}m_1v_1^2 + \frac{1}{2}m_2v_2^2 = \frac{1}{2}(4.0\text{ kg})(10.0\text{ m/s})^2 + \frac{1}{2}(6.0\text{ kg})(4.0\text{ m/s})^2 = \textbf{248.0 J}$$

The final total kinetic energy is

$$\Sigma K = \frac{1}{2}m_1u_1^2 + \frac{1}{2}m_2u_2^2$$

$$= \frac{1}{2}(4.0\text{ kg})(3.7\text{ m/s})^2 + \frac{1}{2}(6.0\text{ kg})(8.2\text{ m/s})^2 = \textbf{229.1 J}$$

By the work-kinetic energy theorem

$$W = \Delta K = \Sigma K - \Sigma K_0 = 229.1\text{ J} - 248.0\text{ J} = \textbf{--18.9 J}$$

THE PERFECTLY ELASTIC COLLISION

(*College Physics* 9th ed. pages 179–182/10th ed. pages 183–185)

In this perfectly elastic collisions, the quantity of energy before and after the event is unaltered. No energy is lost during this collision process. Such a collision is called a perfectly elastic collision.

In nature very few collisions are perfectly elastic. Neutrons and mono-atomic molecules such as helium approximate perfectly elastic collisions. Colliding ivory billiard balls come within several percent of being perfectly elastic. Other than the formality of deriving the equations of a perfectly elastic head-on collision, mathematical analysis of these collisions are actually approximations.

Let's look at a head-on perfectly elastic collision.

In perfectly elastic collisions, as in all collisions, the law of conservation of linear momentum, $\Sigma p_0 = \Sigma p$, always holds true and kinetic energy is also conserved, $\Sigma K_0 = \Sigma K$. It is only in the perfectly elastic collision that $\Sigma K_0 = \Sigma K$ holds true. For a perfectly elastic collision we define the coefficient of restitution, $\varepsilon = 1$.

$$u_1 = \frac{(m_1 - m_2)}{(m_1 + m_2)} v_1 + \frac{2m_2}{(m_1 + m_2)} v_2$$

$$u_2 = v_1 - v_2 + u_1$$

$$u_2 = \frac{2m_1}{(m_1 + m_2)} v_1 + \frac{(m_2 - m_1)}{(m_1 + m_2)} v_2$$

SAMPLE PROBLEM 8

A 4.0 kg mass, m_1, travels to the right along the x-axis with a velocity of $v_1 = 10.0$ m/s. It overtakes a second mass $m_2 = 6.0$ kg whose center of mass travels to the right along the axis with a velocity of $v_2 = 4.0$ m/s. The masses undergo a perfectly elastic collision. Calculate the velocity of the masses m_1 and m_2 immediately after collision.

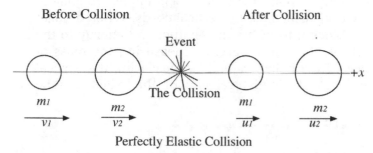

Perfectly Elastic Collision

SOLUTION TO PROBLEM 8

In all collisions the law of conservation of linear momentum always holds true and in a perfectly elastic collision kinetic energy is also conserved. From both of these laws we derive the following equations that only hold for perfectly elastic collisions.

The velocity of mass m_1 immediately after collision is found by using

$$u_1 = \left(\frac{m_1 - m_2}{m_1 + m_2}\right) v_1 + \left(\frac{2m_2}{m_1 + m_2}\right) v_2$$

$$u_1 = \left(\frac{4.0 \text{ kg} - 6.0 \text{ kg}}{10 \text{ kg}}\right)\left(10.0 \frac{m}{s}\right) + \left(\frac{12 \text{ kg}}{10 \text{ kg}}\right)\left(4.0 \frac{m}{s}\right) = 2.8 \frac{m}{s}$$

$$u_2 = \left(\frac{2m_1}{m_1 + m_2}\right) v_1 + \left(\frac{m_2 - m_1}{m_1 + m_2}\right) v_2$$

$$u_2 = \left(\frac{8.0 \text{ kg}}{10.0 \text{ kg}}\right)\left(10.0 \frac{m}{s}\right) + \left(\frac{2.0 \text{ kg}}{10.0 \text{ kg}}\right)\left(4.0 \frac{m}{s}\right) = 8.8 \frac{m}{s}$$

Calculating the total initial kinetic energy, ΣK_0

$$\Sigma K_0 = \frac{1}{2}m_1v_1^2 + \frac{1}{2}m_2v_2^2$$

$$\Sigma K_0 = \frac{1}{2}(4.0 \text{ kg})(10.0 \text{ m/s})^2 + \frac{1}{2}(6.0 \text{ kg})(4.0 \text{ m/s})^2 = \textbf{248.0 J}$$

Calculating the total finial kinetic energy, ΣK

$$\Sigma K = \frac{1}{2}m_1u_1^2 + \frac{1}{2}m_2u_2^2$$

$$\Sigma K = \frac{1}{2}(4.0 \text{ kg})(2.8 \text{ m/s})^2 + \frac{1}{2}(6.0 \text{ kg})(8.8 \text{ m/s})^2 = \textbf{248.0 J}$$

$\Sigma K_0 = \Sigma K$ and the collision is perfectly elastic.

BALLISTIC PENDULUM

(*College Physics* 9th ed. pages 178–179/10th ed. pages 182–183)

A ballistic pendulum is a device that is used to measure the velocities of small projectiles such as bullets. Ballistic pendulums in general consist of a block of wood suspended by vertical cords. When a bullet is fired into the wood block it transfers momentum and energy to the block causing it to swing through an arc. By measuring the mass of the block, M, the mass of the bullet, m, and by measuring the vertical elevation, h, of the block the initial velocity of the bullet can be determined.

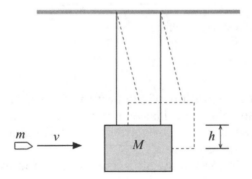

SAMPLE PROBLEM 9

Consider the above diagram. A 10 g bullet is fired into the stationary 3990 g block of a ballistic pendulum. The bullet is captured in the block elevating it vertically by 0.03 m.

(a) What is the velocity, V, of the block-bullet system just after impact?

(b) What is the velocity of the bullet prior to impact with the block?

SOLUTION TO PROBLEM 9

(a) Mechanical energy is conserved from the time the bullet impacts the block through its 0.03 m rise. Writing the law of conservation of mechanical:

$E_0 = E$ and at the moment just after impact:

$$\frac{1}{2}(m+M)V^2 = (m+M)gh.$$ Solving for V:

$$V = \sqrt{2gh} = \sqrt{2\left(9.8 \text{ m}/_{s^2}\right)(0.03 \text{ m})} = 0.77 \text{ m}/_s$$

(b) On impact, $\Sigma p_0 = \Sigma p$ and $mv = (m+M)V$. Solving for the initial velocity of the bullet, v:

$$v = \frac{(m+M)V}{m} = \frac{(4.00 \text{ kg})\left(0.77 \text{ m}/_s\right)}{(0.01 \text{ kg})} = 308 \text{ m}/_s$$

CENTER OF MASS

(*College Physics* 9th ed. pages 151, 241–243/10th ed. pages 154, 246–248)

The *center of mass*, c.m., of a system is the point, either inside or outside the system, where the system can be balanced in a uniform gravitational field. All bodies and all system behave as if all of their masses were concentrated at the c.m.

In two-dimensional space the center of mass of a system composed of i particles can be located from the coordinates of the c.m.

$$X_{c.m.} = \frac{\Sigma x_i m_i}{\Sigma m_i} \text{ and } y_{c.m.} = \frac{\Sigma y_i m_i}{\Sigma m_i}$$

In a uniform gravitational field, the center of mass and the center of gravity coincide.

SAMPLE PROBLEM 10

Determine the center of mass for the following system.

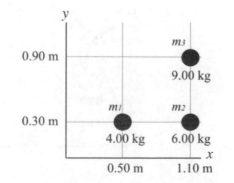

SOLUTION TO PROBLEM 10

The x-coordinate of the c.m.

$$x_{c.m.} = \frac{\Sigma x_i m_i}{\Sigma m_i}$$

$$= \frac{(0.50 \text{ m})(4.00 \text{ kg}) + (1.100 \text{ m})(6.00 \text{ kg}) + (1.10 \text{ m})(9.00 \text{ kg})}{4.00 \text{ kg} + 6.00 \text{ kg} + 9.00 \text{ kg}}$$

$$= \mathbf{0.97 \text{ m}}$$

$$y_{c.m.} = \frac{\Sigma y_i m_i}{\Sigma m_i}$$

$$= \frac{(0.30 \text{ m})(4.00 \text{ kg}) + (0.30 \text{ m})(6.00 \text{ kg}) + (0.90 \text{ m})(9.00 \text{ kg})}{4.00 \text{ kg} + 6.00 \text{ kg} + 9.00 \text{ kg}}$$

$$= \mathbf{0.58 \text{ m}}$$

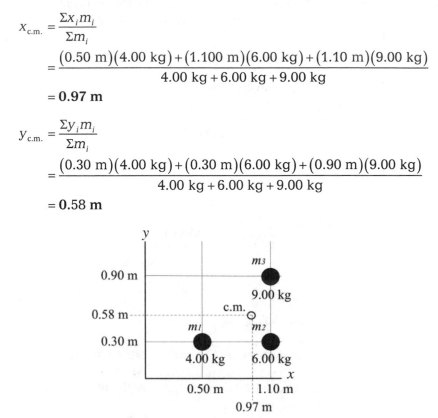

Consider an artillery shell fired from a cannon. Ignoring air resistance, the shell, actually the center of mass of the shell, follows a parabolic trajectory that is a function of the elevation angle and the initial velocity of the shell. At a point along the trajectory, as shown in the diagram below, the shell explodes into eight fragments.

The *cluster* of fragments form a cloud about the center of mass. The beauty of the law of conservation of linear momentum is that the c.m. follows the original trajectory of the shell.

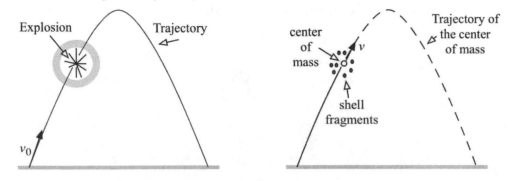

The total momentum remains constant since no external forces act on the shell. The kinetic energy, however, increases because the shell fragments receive additional kinetic energy from the explosion.

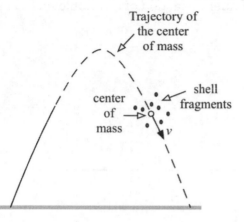

Once one or more of the fragments impacts the ground, the center of mass of the system changes, and the trajectory shifts.

MOMENTUM, IMPULSE, AND COLLISION: STUDENT OBJECTIVES FOR THE AP EXAM

- You should know how to determine the value of the average impulsive force if you know the change in the velocity of a body and the duration of the impulse.
- You should be able to explain how a system of two particles can have a total momentum of zero when both particles are moving.
- You should know the relationship between the coefficient of restitution and the total kinetic energy before and after a collision between two particles.
- You should know how to locate the c.m. for a system of particles.

MULTIPLE-CHOICE QUESTIONS

1. A 2.00 kg body moves under the action of a variable force as shown in the graph below.

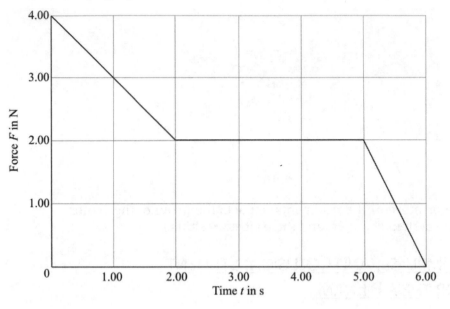

What is the change in the momentum of the body after 6.00 s?
(A) 7.00 N·s
(B) 10.0 N·s
(C) 12.0 N·s
(D) 13.0 N·s

2. A small rocket explodes into two fragments of equal mass at the highest point in its trajectory as shown:

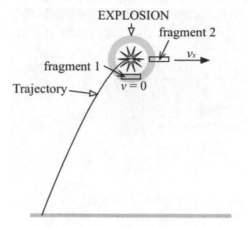

EXPLOSION

The first fragment has zero velocity and drops as a falling body. The second fragment moves with horizontal velocity $\vec{v}_x$ after the explosion. After the two fragments have hit the ground, the center of mass of the system will be located

(A) at the position of fragment 1 as it falls since the only force acting on it as it falls is the force of gravity

(B) at the position of fragment 2 since all of the velocity $\vec{v}_x$ remains with this fragment

(C) midway between the two equal massed fragments and located at the position where the rocket would have landed if there had been no explosion

(D) between the two equal massed fragments but closer to the landing position of the second fragment since it moved with all the velocity $\vec{v}_x$ after the explosion

3. Two students $m_1 = 60.0$ kg and $m_2 = 50.0$ kg push off one another on frictionless ice exerting forces on each other in four possible diagrams as shown below. F_{12} represents the force student 1 applies to student 2 and F_{21} represents the force student 2 applies to student 1.

I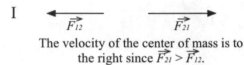
$\vec{F}_{12}$ $\vec{F}_{21}$

The velocity of the center of mass is to the right since $\vec{F}_{21} > \vec{F}_{12}$.

II
$\vec{F}_{12}$ $\vec{F}_{21}$

The velocity of the center of mass is to the left since $\vec{F}_{12} > \vec{F}_{21}$.

III
$\vec{F}_{12}$ $\vec{F}_{21}$

The velocity of the center of mass is constant since $\vec{F}_{12} = \vec{F}_{21}$.

IV
$\vec{F}_{12}$ $\vec{F}_{21}$

The velocity of the center of mass is to the left since both forces are to the left.

Which answer best represents this scenario?
(A) I
(B) II
(C) III
(D) IV

4. A 20.0 g pellet is fired into a 1.50 kg block hanging by a vertical cord from the ceiling.

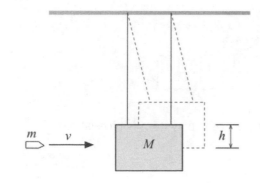

After the collision the center of mass of the system rises 15.0 cm from its initial position.

The initial velocity of the pellet is
(A) 106 m/s
(B) 130 m/s
(C) 147 m/s
(D) 223 m/s

5. A body moving in the positive x-direction experiences a variable force as shown in the force versus time graph below.

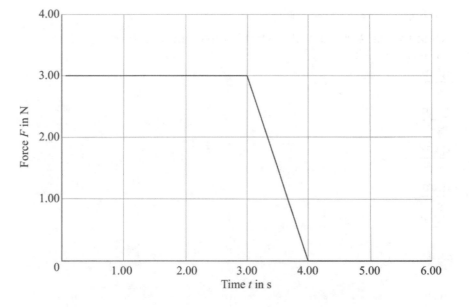

The momentum of the system will
(A) increase since a variable but positive force acts on the body as shown by the area under the force–time graph
(B) decrease since the force applied to the body drops to zero as shown in the graph
(C) increase from 1.00 s to 3.00 s, then decrease from 3.00 s to 4.00 s as shown in the force–time graph
(D) will be undetermined since the mass of the body is not included in the problem

6. As shown in the figure below, a 20.0 N force applied at an angle of 30° with the horizontal acts on the system for 10.0 s. The surface is flat and frictionless.

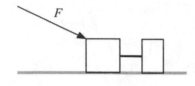

The change in the momentum of the system is closest to
(A) 200 N·s
(B) 173 N·s
(C) 150 N·s
(D) 100 N·s

7. Students performed a collision experiment measuring the recoil of two bodies, $m_1 = 4.00$ kg and $m_2 = 2.00$ kg. Part of their data is shown below for the 4.00 kg body.

x (m)	t (s)
0.05	0.10
0.10	0.20
0.15	0.30
0.20	0.40
0.25	0.50
0.30	0.60

Using the data for the 4.00 kg body, what is the change in the momentum of the 2.00 kg body?

(A) $6.0 \dfrac{\text{kg} \cdot \text{m}}{\text{s}}$

(B) $3.0 \dfrac{\text{kg} \cdot \text{m}}{\text{s}}$

(C) $2.0 \dfrac{\text{kg} \cdot \text{m}}{\text{s}}$

(D) $1.0 \dfrac{\text{kg} \cdot \text{m}}{\text{s}}$

8. Two blocks of 0.500 kg and 1.00 kg on a flat horizontal surface are pushed together against a compressed spring and then released. When released, the 1.00 kg block moves to the right and the 0.500 kg block moves to the left.

   Data for the blocks at 0.100 s intervals is shown below.

v (m/s) for 1.00 kg	v (m/s) for 0.500 kg
1.20	2.40
1.00	2.20
0.81	2.00
0.61	1.82
0.42	1.62
0.21	1.42

   Evaluation of the data shows that
   (A) momentum was not conserved in the recoil since the velocities were not constant after the recoil
   (B) momentum was conserved in the initial recoil of the two blocks, but frictional forces acting on the bodies reduced their speeds due to a frictional impulse
   (C) momentum was conserved because momentum was transferred to the spring, increasing the internal energy and momentum of the molecules in the spring
   (D) momentum may have been conserved, but without additional information about the spring, it can not be determined

9. Two blocks slide on a horizontal frictionless surface and collide as diagrammed below.

   The velocity and the kinetic energy for the 1.00 kg block are best answered by which of the following choices?

	$v_{1.00\ kg}$ (m/s)	$K_{1.00\ kg}$ (J)	Type of Collision
(A)	1.50	1.50	perfectly elastic
(B)	2.00	2.00	perfectly elastic
(C)	1.50	1.50	perfectly inelastic
(D)	2.00	2.00	perfectly inelastic

10. A 2.00 kg cart moves in a straight line on a flat frictionless surface under the action of a variable force for 6.00 s. The graph of the velocity as a function of time is shown below.

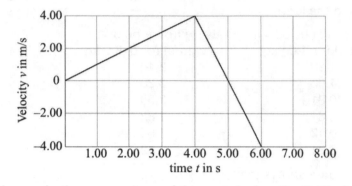

The change in the momentum of the cart during the 6.00 s interval is

(A) −16.0 N·s
(B) −8.00 N·s
(C) 8.00 N·s
(D) 16.0 N·s

11. A graph of the impulse on the 2.00 kg cart in problem 10 is best shown in which of the following graphs?

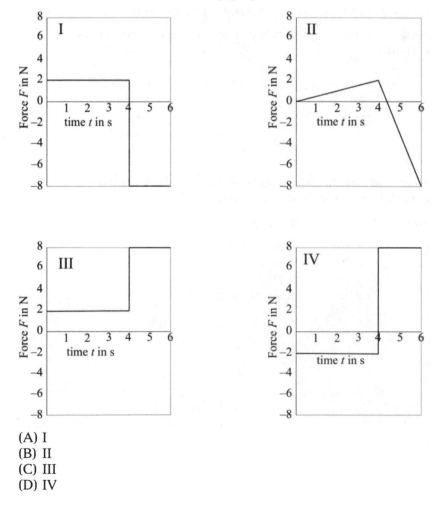

(A) I
(B) II
(C) III
(D) IV

12. A projectile of mass M at the apex of its flight explodes into three fragments whose mass and velocity are shown in the illustration below.

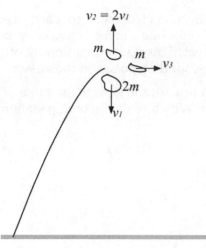

What was the velocity of the projectile just before exploding?

(A) $2v_1$

(B) $\dfrac{v_3}{4}$

(C) $\dfrac{v_3}{3}$

(D) $\dfrac{v_2}{3}$

13. Rank the 4 blocks shown below for their change in momentum from the largest change to the smallest change. Each block is in motion for 10.0 s.

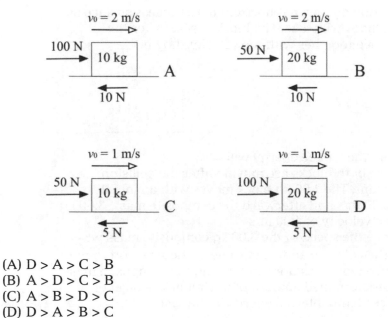

(A) D > A > C > B

(B) A > D > C > B

(C) A > B > D > C

(D) D > A > B > C

Questions 14 to 15

Directions: For each of the questions or incomplete statements below, two of the suggested answers will be correct. For each of these questions, you must select both correct choices to earn credit. No partial credit will be earned if only one correct answer is selected. Select the two that are best in each case and then enter both of the appropriate answers in the corresponding space on the answer sheet.

14. A 0.30 kg sphere is projected toward the floor at an angle of 60° with the horizontal as shown. Which of the following statements are correct?

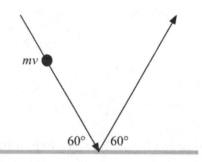

(A) Momentum is not conserved because the force between the sphere and the floor changes the vertical component of the velocity causing it to rebound at the same angle.
(B) Momentum is conserved because the force between the sphere and the floor changes the horizontal component of the sphere so that it rebounds at the same angle.
(C) Kinetic energy is conserved since it has the same speed after the impact with the floor as it did before the impact.
(D) Kinetic energy is not conserved since the velocity changed from downward and negative to upward and positive.

15. A 1.00 kg block moving on a flat horizontal frictionless surface as shown below collides with a 2.00 kg block at rest. After the collision, they move together with the velocity shown.

After the collision, the kinetic energy will
(A) increase since both blocks are moving after the collision
(B) remain constant. The 1.00 kg block moves with an initial velocity of 3.00 m/s and afterward the composite mass, 3.00 kg, moves with a velocity of 1.00 m/s
(C) decrease since the speed of the 3.00 kg composite mass was reduced in the collision and kinetic energy depends on v^2 not v
(D) decrease since work was done in forming the composite mass and some undetermined amount of the initial kinetic energy was transferred into internal energy in the system

FREE-RESPONSE PROBLEMS

1. The series of objects shown below have been constructed by bending uniform, heavy gauge wire. Locate the center of mass of each by using symmetry and graphical methods as opposed to using mathematical equations. Explain your reasoning.

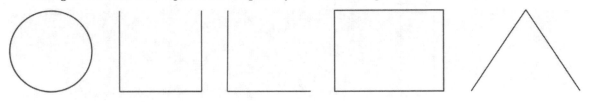

2. A 2.00 kg body, m_A, is attached to a cord. In the diagram below, the distance, L, from the attachment point of the cord to the center of mass of m_A is 1.20 m. A second mass, $m_B = 1.00 \text{ kg}$, is attached to a second cord with the same dimensions. Mass m_B is displaced by 60.0° with the vertical and is then released from rest.

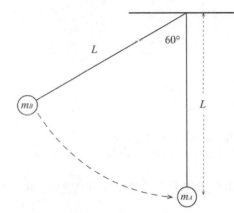

(a) Using a diagram show how you will determine the height, h, that m_B drops before its collision with the stationary mass, m_A.

(b) If the collision of the bodies is totally inelastic, what is the speed immediately after collision?

(c) Explain how you would determine the maximum vertical displacement of the composite mass after collision.

3. As shown below, a 0.030 kg projectile moving with a velocity of 300.0 m/s strikes a 2.00 kg block at rest on a post. The projectile passes through the block emerging on the other side with a velocity of 100.0 m/s.

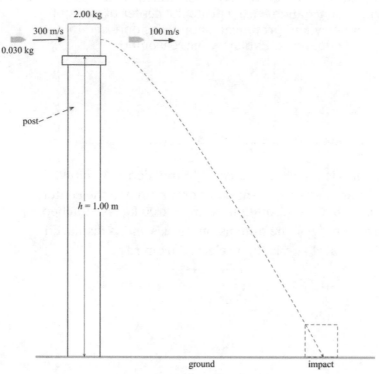

(a) What is the velocity of the block after the impact?
(b) How far from the base of the post will the block be when it impacts the ground?
(c) What is the fractional change in the kinetic energy of the block and the projectile?
(d) What are three possible reasons for the fractional change in the kinetic energy?

4. A firecracker shot into the air at some angle θ relative to the horizontal explodes into several fragments at the apex of its trajectory. (Ignore air resistance)
(a) Is momentum conserved (i) before the explosion? (ii) after the explosion?
Justify your answers.
(b) What is the path of the center of mass?

Answers

MULTIPLE-CHOICE QUESTIONS

1. **D** The change in the momentum is the area under the graph of force versus time. This is $\frac{1}{2}bh + bh + \frac{1}{2}bh$. Substitution into the sum of the areas gives

   $$\frac{1}{2}(4.00 \text{ N} - 2.00 \text{ N})(2.00 \text{ s}) + 2.00 \text{ N}(5.00 \text{ s} - 0) +$$

   $$\frac{1}{2}(2.00 \text{ N} - 0)(1.00 \text{ s}) = 13.0 \text{ N} \cdot \text{s}.$$

   (*College Physics* 9th ed. pages 168–169/10th ed. pages 171–172)
   (L.O. 4.B.2.1)

2. **C** The center of mass of the system is located at the position where the projectile would have landed if it had not exploded. The explosion supplied an internal force only; no external force was applied in the horizontal direction. (The gravitational force was applied to the fragments, and hence the center of mass to change the vertical velocity; in the absence of friction this results in the same vertical velocity.) In the horizontal direction momentum is conserved. $MV_x = \frac{M}{2}(0) + \frac{M}{2}(2v_x)$. The second fragment will move horizontally a distance of $d = 2v_x(t)$. The center of mass is at the midpoint between the two fragments.
   (*College Physics* 9th ed. pages 151, 241–243/10th ed. pages 154, 246–248)
   (L.O. 4.A.1.1)

3. **C** Action–reaction forces apply to the students as they push off each other on frictionless ice. These forces are equal in magnitude and opposite in direction. There will be no change in the center of mass of the system. As the students recoil, the velocity of the center of mass will remain in its original position between the two students and since the students were initially at rest, the velocity of the center of mass will be constant—zero.
   (*College Physics* 9th ed. pages 174–175, 241–243/10th ed. pages 177–178, 246–248)
   (L.O. 5.D.3.1)

4. **B** The collision is inelastic. Kinetic energy is not conserved in the collision, but after the collision, the initial kinetic energy of the block and the pellet is converted into gravitational potential energy of the system. $U_i + K_i = U_f + K_f$

   $$\frac{1}{2}(m + M)V^2 = (m + M)gh.$$

   Since the mass is a common factor, substitution gives
   $V^2 = 2\left(9.80 \text{ m}/\text{s}^2\right)(0.150 \text{ m})$ and the velocity of the center of mass

of the system is 1.71 $\frac{m}{s}$. Solving for momentum $mv = (m + M)V$.
The velocity of the pellet is

$$v = \frac{(0.020 \text{ kg} + 1.50 \text{ kg})}{0.020 \text{ kg}} \left(1.71 \frac{m}{s}\right) = 130 \frac{m}{s}.$$

(*College Physics* 9th ed. pages 176–179/10th ed. pages 180–182)
(L.O. 5.D.2.5)

5. **A** The change in momentum is given as the area under the force–time graph. The force is variable, but always positive; thus the momentum will increase.
(*College Physics* 9th ed. pages 169, 172–173/10th ed. pages 172, 175, 177)
(L.O. 4.B.2.2)

6. **B** Since the surface is frictionless, the net force acting on the system is $F = 20.0 \text{ N}(\cos 30°) = 17.3 \text{ N}$. The change in the momentum is given by $Ft = \Delta p$. The change in the momentum is 173 N·s.
(*College Physics* 9th ed. pages 168–169/10th ed. pages 170–171)
(L.O. 4.B.2.1)

7. **C** The velocity is determined from the change in x divided by the change in t. The velocity is $\frac{0.30 \text{ m} - 0.10 \text{ m}}{0.60 \text{ s} - 0.20 \text{ s}} = 0.50 \frac{m}{s}$. The momentum of the 4.00 kg body is 2.0 $\frac{kg \cdot m}{s}$. Since momentum is conserved, the momentum of the 2.00 kg body is also 2.0 $\frac{kg \cdot m}{s}$.
(*College Physics* 9th ed. pages 29–31, 167–169/10th ed. pages 31–33, 170–172)
(L.O. 4.B.1.1)

8. **B** Momentum is conserved. After the initial recoil, both blocks move on a surface where friction acts. Friction applies an impulse to the blocks reducing their momentum as indicated with the velocities in the data chart.
(*College Physics* 9th ed. pages 168–169/10th ed. pages 170–172)
(L.O. 5.D.2.4)

9. **B** Conservation of momentum $\vec{p}_i = \vec{p}_f$ will give the velocity of the 1.00 kg body after the collision.

$$\left(2.00 \text{ kg}\right)\left(1.50 \frac{m}{s}\right) = \left(2.00 \text{ kg}\right)\left(0.500 \frac{m}{s}\right) + \left(1.00 \text{ kg}\right)v.$$

The velocity of the 1.00 kg body is 2.00 $\frac{m}{s}$. The kinetic energy is found from

$$\frac{1}{2}\left(2.00 \text{ kg}\right)\left(1.50 \frac{m}{s}\right)^2$$

$$= \frac{1}{2}\left(2.00 \text{ kg}\right)\left(0.500 \frac{m}{s}\right)^2 + \frac{1}{2}\left(1.00 \text{ kg}\right)\left(2.00 \frac{m}{s}\right)^2$$

$$2.25 \text{ J} = 0.25 \text{ J} + 2.00 \text{ J}.$$

The kinetic energy of the 1.00 kg body is 2.00 J and since the initial kinetic energy equals the final kinetic energy, the collision is elastic.
(*College Physics* 9th ed. pages 179–181/10th ed. pages 183–185)
(L.O. 5.D.1.5)

10. **B** The change in momentum is $m\Delta v$ which is

$$(2.00\ \text{kg})\left(-4.00\ \tfrac{m}{s} - 0\ \tfrac{m}{s}\right) = -8.00\ \text{N}\cdot\text{s}.$$

(*College Physics* 9th ed. pages 168, 172–173/10th ed. pages 172, 175, 177)
(L.O. 3.D.2.1)

11. **A** The shape of the graph can be determined from either $F\Delta t = m\Delta v$ or by taking the slope of the velocity–time graph $a = \dfrac{\Delta v}{\Delta t}$ and then using $\Sigma F = ma$. In the first method,

$$F(4.00\ \text{s}) = 2.00\ \text{kg}\left(4.00\ \tfrac{m}{s} - 0\right) = 2.00\ \text{N}.$$

The next section of the graph

$$F(1.00\ \text{s}) = 2.00\ \text{kg}\left(0 - 4.00\ \tfrac{m}{s}\right) = -8.00\ \text{N}$$

and the last section is

$$F(1.00\ \text{s}) = 2.00\ \text{kg}\left(-4.00\ \tfrac{m}{s} - 0\right) = -8.00\ \text{N}.$$

Using the slope requires taking the slope of the line from t = 0.00 s to 4.00 s and the line from 4.00 s to 6.00 s and this gives from 0.00 s to 4.00 s

$$a = \frac{4.00\ \tfrac{m}{s} - 0}{4.00\ \text{s}} = 1.00\ \tfrac{m}{s^2}\ \text{then using}$$

$$\Sigma F = 2.00\ \text{kg}\left(1.00\ \tfrac{m}{s^2}\right) = 2.00\ \text{N}.$$

Then the slope of the line from 4.00 s to 6.00 s

$$a = \frac{\left(-4.00\ \tfrac{m}{s} - 4.00\ \tfrac{m}{s}\right)}{2.00\ \text{s}} = -4.00\ \tfrac{m}{s^2}\ \text{and}$$

$$\Sigma F = 2.00\ \text{kg}\left(-4.00\ \tfrac{m}{s^2}\right) = -8.00\ \text{N}.$$

(*College Physics* 9th ed. pages 34–35, 89, 168, 172–173/10th ed. pages 36, 92, 172, 175, 177)
(L.O. 4.B.1.2)

12. **B** The momentum has v_x and v_y components; looking at the information in the illustration, the change in the momentum $\Delta p_y = 0$ since $m(2v_1) - (2m)v_1 = 0$. The solution arises from $\Delta p_x = 0$. $MV = mv_3$ and since $M = m + 2m + m = 4m$, the initial velocity of the projectile is $V = \dfrac{mv_3}{4m} = \dfrac{v_3}{4}$.
(*College Physics* 9th ed. pages 167–169/10th ed. pages 167–169)
(L.O. 3.D.2.1)

13. **A** Since the ranking asks for the change in the momentum, neither the mass nor the initial velocity is needed for the ranking. $F\Delta t = \Delta p$.
The forces are applied for the same amount of time; thus the largest net force will produce the largest change in the momentum.
(*College Physics* 9th ed. pages 167–169/10th ed. pages 167–169)
(L.O. 3.D.1.1)

14. **A** and **C** In the collision with the floor, the force the floor applies is upward; it changes the vertical component of the initial velocity from $-\vec{v}_y$ to $+\vec{v}_y$ as

$$\left|\vec{F}_y\right|\Delta t = \left(mv\sin 60° - (-mv\sin 60°)\right) = 2mv\sin 60°$$

and makes no change to the $+\vec{v}_x$ component. The sphere leaves the floor at the same angle with the horizontal and thus the same speed and therefore momentum is not conserved here. Since the magnitude of the velocity components remained the same, the kinetic energy, which is a scalar, is conserved.
(*College Physics* 9th ed. pages 168–169/10th ed. pages 171–172)
(L.O. 5.D.1.1)

15. **C** and **D** The collision was inelastic. Momentum is conserved in the collision but not kinetic energy. Kinetic energy after the collision depends on $\frac{1}{2}(m_1 + m_2)V^2$ not on v. (Not part of the question, but these values can be calculated. The initial kinetic energy was 4.5 J and the final kinetic energy was 1.5 J.)
(*College Physics* 9th ed. pages 168–169/10th ed. pages 171–172)
(L.O. 5.D.2.3)

FREE-RESPONSE PROBLEMS

1. The center of mass of a uniform segment is located at its midpoint. Symmetry and graphical methods are shown with the dotted lines and the intersection of the dotted lines locates the c.m. of the shape.

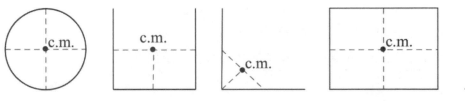 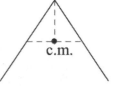

(*College Physics* 9th ed. pages 151, 241–243/10th ed. pages 154, 246–248)
(L.O. 1.A.5.2)

2. (a) The mass m_B was displaced through an angle of 60° forming a right triangle of altitude $L - h$ and hypotenuse L. The vertical drop h can then be found by writing $\cos 60° = \dfrac{L-h}{L}$ $L - h = L \cos 60°$ and then h becomes $h = L - L \cos 60° = L(1 - \cos 60°)$.

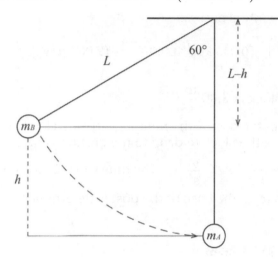

(b) By using the law of conservation of energy, the velocity of m_B can be determined just before the collision.

$U_0 + K_0 = U + K$

$m_B g h + 0 = 0 + \dfrac{1}{2} m_B v_B^2$ and $v_B^2 = 2gh$

From part (a), $h = L(1 - \cos 60°) = (1.20 \text{ m})(1 - \cos 60°) = 0.60 \text{ m}$

Solving for v: $v = \sqrt{2\left(9.80 \text{ m}/_{\text{s}^2}\right)(0.60 \text{ m})} = \textbf{3.43 m}/_\textbf{s}$

The law of conservation of linear momentum will allow us to calculate the velocity of the composite mass after collision.

$m_B v_B = (m_A + m_B)u$

Solving for the final velocity, u:

$u = \dfrac{m_B v_B}{(m_A + m_B)} = \dfrac{(1.00 \text{ kg})\left(3.43 \text{ m}/_\text{s}\right)}{3.00 \text{ kg}} = \textbf{1.14 m}/_\textbf{s}$.

(c) After collision, use the law of conservation of mechanical energy to find the height, H, the center of mass of the composite mass is elevated. The final gravitational potential energy of the system is related to the initial kinetic energy by total initial energy of the system = total final energy of the system

Before collision is the kinetic energy of m_B and after collision the system has only gravitational potential energy when the system comes to rest.

$\dfrac{1}{2} m_B v_B^2 = (m_A + m_B)gH$

And then, $H = \dfrac{m_B v_B^2}{2(m_A + m_B)g}$

(*College Physics* 9th ed. pages 89–92, 98–105, 175–178/10th ed. pages 91–92, 100–107, 179–183)
(L.O. 3.A.1.1, 4.C.1.1, 5.A. 2.1, 5.B 4.2, 5.D.1.5)

3. (a) Conservation of momentum occurs.

$$(0.030 \text{ kg})\left(300.0 \ \frac{m}{s}\right) = (0.030 \text{ kg})\left(100.0 \ \frac{m}{s}\right) + (2.00 \text{ kg})V_{block} .$$

The velocity of the block is **3.00** $\dfrac{m}{s}$.

(b) The block drops from the post with an initial vertical velocity of zero. The time it takes the block to drop to the ground is given by $y = \dfrac{1}{2}gt^2$. $-1.00 \text{ m} = \dfrac{1}{2}\left(-9.80 \ \dfrac{m}{s^2}\right)t^2$. The time $t = 0.452$ s. The distance the block is from the base of the post is determined from $x = v_x t$.

$$x = \left(3.00 \ \frac{m}{s}\right)(0.452 \text{ s}) = \textbf{1.36 m}$$

(c) The fractional change in the kinetic energy is

$$\frac{1}{2}(0.030 \text{ kg})\left(300.0 \ \frac{m}{s}\right)^2 \neq \frac{1}{2}(0.030 \text{ kg})\left(100.0 \ \frac{m}{s}\right)^2 + \frac{1}{2}(2.00 \text{ kg})\left(3.00 \ \frac{m}{s}\right)^2$$

$13.5 \times 10^2 \text{ J} \neq 1.50 \times 10^2 + 9.00 \text{ J}$.

$\dfrac{159 \text{ J}}{13.5 \times 10^2 \text{ J}} = 0.118$ or 11.8% of the initial kinetic energy remains in the system.

(d) Possible explanations for the reduction in the kinetic energy include
   ▪ The projectile did work on the block as it bored through the block.
   ▪ The projectile transferred kinetic energy to the block giving it a horizontal velocity of 3.00 m/s.
   ▪ The internal energy of the block and the surrounding air are increased.
   ▪ Energy was transferred to the surroundings in the production of sound and heat energy.

(*College Physics* 9th ed. pages 63–71, 145–146, 175–178/10th ed. pages, 65–73, 148–149, 179–183)
(L.O. 5.B.3.1, 5.B.4.1, 5.D.1.5, 5.D.2.3)

4. (a) i. As the firecracker rises, the horizontal component v_x of its initial velocity is constant and p_x is also constant. The vertical component v_y changes because the motion of the firecracker is opposite to the direction of the gravitational force acting on it; thus p_y reduces. The gravitational force applies an impulse that decreases the vertical component. $F_g \Delta t = m \Delta v_y$.

ii. At the instant the firecracker explodes into several fragments no external forces act on the system (the explosion is caused by an internal chemical process) so the initial momentum at the instant before explosion is equal to the final momentum just after the explosion.

(b) In the absence of friction, the center of mass of the system follows the parabolic path the firecracker would have followed if it had not exploded. The explosion supplied an internal force only; no external force was applied to the center of mass of the system in the explosion. The gravitational force will be applied to the fragments, and hence the center of mass, to change the vertical velocity in the downward part of the trajectory. In the absence of friction, this causes the fragments to have the same vertical speed when they return the origin. The horizontal velocity is constant.

(*College Physics* 9th ed. pages 63–71, 151, 167–174, 242/10th ed. pages 65–73, 154, 170–179, 247–248)

(L.O. 3.D.1.1, 5.D.3.1)

7

CIRCULAR MOTION AND ROTATIONAL MOTION

ANGULAR MOTION

(*College Physics* 9th ed. pages 198–199/10th ed. page 203)

In our everyday world, angles are commonly measured and expressed in degrees, where one full turn or one complete *revolution* is 360°. In the study of physics, a more suitable unit, the *radian*, rad, is used.

$$\text{angle in radians} = \frac{\text{arc length}}{\text{radius}}$$

$$\theta = \frac{s}{r}$$

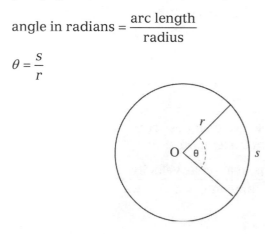

Since the circumference of a circle of radius r is $2\pi r$, there are 2π rad in one complete revolution, rev.

$$1 \text{ rev} = 360° = 2\pi \text{ rad}$$

and

$$1 \text{ rad} = 57.3°$$

AP Tip

All counterclockwise (CCW) rotations are considered positive and all clockwise (CW) rotations are negative.

ANGULAR VELOCITY

(*College Physics* 9th ed. pages 199–200/10th ed. pages 204–205)

The *angular velocity*, ω, defines how rapidly a body is turning or spinning or rotating about an axis.

$$\text{angular velocity} = \frac{\text{angular displacement}}{\text{time}}$$

$$\omega = \frac{\theta}{t}$$

Angular velocity, ω, is expressed in radians per second, rad/s.

$$1\,\frac{\text{rev}}{\text{s}} = 2\pi\frac{\text{rad}}{\text{s}}$$

The linear velocity, v, of a particle that travels in a circle of radius r with uniform angular velocity, ω, is related by

linear velocity = angular velocity × radius of the circle

or

$$v = \omega r$$

The time required to make one complete revolution is the period, T, and

$$T = \frac{2\pi}{\omega}$$

Since $f = \frac{1}{T}$, the angular frequency, ω, is $\omega = 2\pi f$.

ANGULAR ACCELERATION

(*College Physics* 9th ed. page 201/10th ed. pages 205–206)

A rotating body whose angular velocity changes from ω_0 to ω in a time interval t undergoes an *angular acceleration,* α.

$$\text{angular acceleration} = \frac{\text{change in angular velocity}}{\text{time interval}}$$

or

$$\alpha = \frac{\omega - \omega_0}{t}$$

The unit for angular acceleration is the rad/s^2. If the angular velocity increases, ω and α have the same sign. If the angular velocity decreases, ω and α will have opposite signs.

In the study of linear motion we found that when a body undergoes uniform acceleration over a time interval, its final velocity is $v = v_0 + at$. In rotational motion, the final angular velocity for a rotating body will be

$$\omega = \omega_0 + \alpha t$$

The linear displacement of an accelerating body is $x = v_0 t + \dfrac{1}{2}at^2$. The angular displacement is found by

$$\theta = \omega_0 t + \frac{1}{2}\alpha t^2$$

The time independent kinematic equation is $v^2 = v_0^2 + 2ax$ and its counterpart in rotational kinematics is

$$\omega^2 = \omega_0^2 + 2\alpha\theta$$

SAMPLE PROBLEM 1

A wheel of radius $r = 0.30$ m spins at the rate of 900 rpm.

(a) What is the angular velocity of all points on the wheel?

(b) If the wheel slows uniformly to 60 rpm in 15 s, what angular acceleration does the wheel experience?

SOLUTION TO PROBLEM 1

(a) 900 rpm = 900 revolutions per minute. To find the angular velocity we need to convert revolutions into radians and minutes into seconds.

$$\omega = 900 \ \frac{\text{rev}}{\text{min}} \times \frac{2\pi \ \text{rad}}{1 \ \text{rev}} \times \frac{1 \ \text{min}}{60 \ \text{s}} = \textbf{94.2} \ \frac{\textbf{rad}}{\textbf{s}}$$

(b) First we need to find the final angular and every point on the wheel has the same angular velocity:

$$\omega = 60 \ \frac{\text{rev}}{\text{min}} \times \frac{2\pi \ \text{rad}}{1 \ \text{rev}} \times \frac{1 \ \text{min}}{60 \ \text{s}} = 6.28 \ \frac{\text{rad}}{\text{s}} \ .$$

Define angular acceleration and set the initial angular velocity as ω_0.

$$\alpha = \frac{\omega - \omega_0}{t} = \frac{6.28 \ \frac{\text{rad}}{\text{s}} - 94.2 \ \frac{\text{rad}}{\text{s}}}{15 \ \text{s}} = \textbf{-5.9} \ \frac{\textbf{rad}}{\textbf{s}^2}$$

SAMPLE PROBLEM 2

A small pulley attached to the shaft of an electric motor has a radius $r = 0.05$ m and is turning at $\omega_0 = 5 \ \frac{\text{rad}}{\text{s}}$ and speeds up to $\omega = 8 \ \frac{\text{rad}}{\text{s}}$ in 2.5 s.

(a) What acceleration does the pulley experience?

(b) What is the angular displacement during this time period?

(c) How many revolutions, n, is this?

SOLUTION TO PROBLEM 2

(a) Both the initial and final angular velocities are in rad/s. Then

$$\alpha = \frac{\omega - \omega_0}{t} = \frac{8 \ \text{rad}/\text{s} - 5 \ \text{rad}/\text{s}}{2.5 \ \text{s}} = 1.2 \ \text{rad}/\text{s}^2$$

(b) Since we know the time period,

$$\theta = \omega_0 t + \frac{1}{2}\alpha t^2 = \left(5 \ \frac{\text{rad}}{\text{s}}\right)(2.5 \ \text{s}) + \frac{1}{2}\left(1.2 \ \frac{\text{rad}}{\text{s}^2}\right)(2.5 \ \text{s})^2 = 16.2 \ \text{rad}$$

(c) To find the number of revolutions, n, we use a conversion factor:

$$n = 16.2 \ \text{rad} \times \frac{1 \ \text{rev}}{2\pi \ \text{rad}} = 2.6 \ \text{rev}$$

ANGULAR AND TANGENTIAL RELATIONSHIPS

(*College Physics* 9th ed. pages 203–206/10th ed. pages 208–211)

When a wheel of radius, r, rotates about its axis, a point on the rim of the wheel can be described in terms of the *circumferential* distance, s, it has moved, its tangential speed, v, and its tangential acceleration, a. These quantities are related to the angular displacement, θ, angular velocity, ω, and the angular acceleration, α, by the following relationships:

$$s = \theta r \qquad v = \omega r \qquad a = \alpha r$$

SAMPLE PROBLEM 3

A bicycle wheel mounted on a test frame has a diameter of 1.2 m and spins at the rate of 4.0 rad/s.

(a) What is the linear or tangent speed of a particle on the circumference of the wheel?

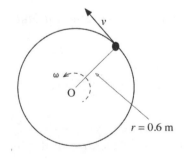

$r = 0.6 \ \text{m}$

(b) What is the linear or tangent speed of a particle 0.3 m from the center of the wheel?

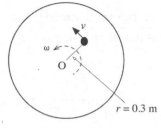

$r = 0.3$ m

SOLUTION TO PROBLEM 3

(a) The relationship between the angular velocity of a wheel and the linear velocity at any point on the wheel is

$$v = \omega r = \left(4.0 \ \frac{rad}{s}\right)(0.6 \ m) = \textbf{2.4 } \frac{\textbf{m}}{\textbf{s}}$$

If the particle were free to leave the circumference of the wheel, it would fly off in a straight-line tangent to the circumference at $2.4 \ \frac{m}{s}$.

(b) The linear speed at 0.3 m from the center of the wheel is

$$v = \omega r = \left(4.0 \ \frac{rad}{s}\right)(0.3 \ m) = \textbf{1.2 } \frac{\textbf{m}}{\textbf{s}}$$

Notice that radians have no dimensions and are therefore dropped out in arriving at the linear speed.

CENTRIPETAL ACCELERATION

(*College Physics* 9th ed. pages 207–208/10th ed. pages 211–213)

When a body is moving in a circular path with constant speed, its velocity is constantly changing because the direction of the tangential velocity is constantly changing. It is for this reason the body experiences a constant acceleration. The acceleration produces a change in direction but not in speed. Therefore the acceleration must always be at right angles to the motion, since any component in the direction of the motion would produce a change in speed. The acceleration is always directed toward the center of the circle. Such an acceleration is called a *centripetal acceleration*. Centripetal means *center-seeking*.

> ## AP Tip
>
> Any body that travels along a curved path always experiences a centripetal acceleration.

Centripetal acceleration, a_c, is determined from the radius of curvature of the path and the speed as

$$\text{centripetal acceleration} = \frac{(\text{tangential speed})^2}{\text{radius of circular path}}$$

$$a_c = \frac{v^2}{r}$$

The SI units of centripetal acceleration are m/s^2, the same as any other acceleration.

CENTRIPETAL FORCE

(*College Physics* 9th ed. pages 209–214/10th ed. pages 214–219)

According to Newton's second law of motion, any object experiencing acceleration by an unbalanced force, then the force is proportional to the acceleration and the direction of the acceleration. The unbalanced force that causes centripetal acceleration is called *centripetal force* and is directed toward the center of curvature.

> ## AP Tip
>
> A body moving with uniform speed in a circle is not in equilibrium.

Centripetal force is

$$F_c = ma_c = \frac{mv^2}{r} = m\omega^2 r$$

The SI unit of centripetal force, as with all forces, is the newton, N.

Any body moving in a curved path *always* experiences centripetal force. Some agent supplies the centripetal force. A ball tied to a string that is twirled overhead in a flat circle experiences centripetal force; so does the diesel engine rounding a curve on railroad tracks; so does the Earth in its orbit about the Sun. The tension in the string is the agent that supplies the centripetal force on the ball. The rails provide centripetal force to the diesel engine. The force of gravity is the agent providing the centripetal force on the Earth.

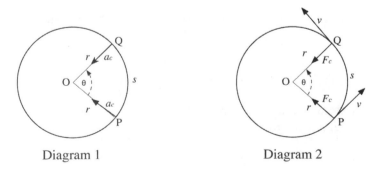

Diagram 1   Diagram 2

In Diagram 1, a particle, as seen from above, travels with uniform speed v counterclockwise in a horizontal circle of radius r. As it moves from point P to point Q it undergoes an angular displacement θ and subtends an arc length s. Regardless of its location, the particle experiences a centripetal acceleration a_c directed along the radius toward the center of the circle, O.

In Diagram 2, the particle experiences a centripetal force F_c directed along the radius to the center of the circle. At point P the particle experiences a tangential velocity v. A tangent of course touches a curve at one point and one point only. Note the direction of the tangential velocity at point Q. The speed remains the same but the direction changes. The tangential velocity vector is always perpendicular to the centripetal acceleration vector and the centripetal force vector.

If the centripetal force were suddenly removed at point Q, no outside force acts on the particle and it obeys Newton's first law of motion and flies away in a straight line with speed v at some direction.

SAMPLE PROBLEM 4

A 2000-kg car rounds a flat curve of radius 60 m with a velocity of 9 m/s.

(a) What centripetal force acts on the car?

(b) What agent provides the centripetal force?

SOLUTION TO PROBLEM 4

(a) Centripetal force:

$$F_c = \frac{mv^2}{r} = \frac{(2000 \text{ kg})(9 \text{ m/s})^2}{60 \text{ m}} = 2.7 \times 10^3 \text{ N}$$

(b) The agent providing the force is the friction between road surface and the tires.

SAMPLE PROBLEM 5

A 500-g wooden ball is attached to a piece of string rated with a maximum tension of 8 N. The ball is tied to a 1 m piece of the string and is whirled overhear in a horizontal circle. What maximum speed can the ball have?

SOLUTION TO PROBLEM 5

The centripetal force cannot exceed 8 N. Since $F_c = \dfrac{mv^2}{r}$, then

$$v^2 = \frac{F_c r}{m} \text{ and taking the square root of both sides gives}$$

$$v = \sqrt{\frac{F_c r}{m}} = \sqrt{\frac{(8 \text{ N})(1 \text{ m})}{0.5 \text{ kg}}} = 4 \text{ m/s}$$

MOMENT OF INERTIA

(College Physics 9th ed. page 251/10th ed. page 257)

All rotating bodies have a property called a *moment of inertia*. The moment of inertia, *I*, of a body is a measure of the rotational inertia of the body. It depends upon the size, shape and mass distribution of the body with respect to an axis of rotation. Moment of inertia is a scalar quantity with units of $kg \cdot m^2$. The moments of inertia of several bodies are given below. In most cases, the equations are derived by using the calculus.

Object	Moment of Inertia	Shape
Hoop of mass M and radius R. The axis of rotation is through the geometric center.	$I = MR^2$	
Solid disk of mass M and radius R. The axis of rotation is through the geometric center.	$I = \dfrac{1}{2} MR^2$	
Solid cylinder of mass M and radius R. The axis of rotation is through the geometric center.	$I = \dfrac{1}{2} MR^2$	
Solid sphere of mass M and radius R. The axis of rotation is through the center of mass.	$I = \dfrac{2}{5} MR^2$	
Hollow sphere of mass M and radius R. The axis of rotation is through the center of mass.	$I = \dfrac{2}{3} MR^2$	
Thin rod of mass M and length L. The axis of rotation is through the center of mass and is perpendicular to the length.	$I = \dfrac{1}{12} ML^2$	

SAMPLE PROBLEM 6

Determine the moment of inertia about an axis through the center of a 25 kg solid sphere whose diameter is 0.30 m.

SOLUTION TO PROBLEM 6

Since the diameter is given as 0.30 m, the radius is 0.15 m. Write the equation for the moment of inertia of a solid sphere and make substitution

$$I = \frac{2}{5}MR^2 = 0.4(25 \text{ kg})(0.15 \text{ m})^2 = \textbf{0.23 kg} \cdot \textbf{m}^2$$

THE PARALLEL-AXIS THEOREM

(*College Physics* 9th ed. pages 249–250/10th ed. pages 255–256)

There are times when it is desirable to find the moment of inertia of a body about an axis other than its common geometric axis. To do so we make use of the *parallel axis theorem*. Let the moment of inertia of an object through its center of mass be I_c. The moment of inertia through any other axis parallel to the first is given by

$$I = I_c + Md^2$$

where M is the total mass of the object and d is the distance between the two parallel axes. Essentially, we are adding Md^2 to the moment of inertia through the center of mass of the body.

SAMPLE PROBLEM 7

A thin, uniform rod of length L and mass M rotates about an axis perpendicular to and through the center of the rod. Find the moment of inertia if the rod rotates about an axis at the end of the rod.

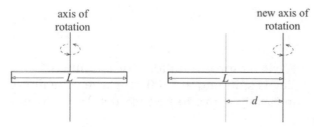

SOLUTION TO PROBLEM 7

The moment of inertia through the center of mass of a long, thin rod is $\frac{1}{12}MR^2$. The radius of rotation is $R = L$ and the moment of inertia about an axis at the end of the rod is $I = I_c + Md^2$. The distance from the original axis of rotation to the new one is $d = \frac{L}{2}$. Making substitution

$$I = I_c + Md^2 = \frac{1}{12}ML^2 + M\left(\frac{L}{2}\right)^2 = \frac{1}{12}ML^2 + \frac{1}{4}ML^2 = \frac{4}{12}ML^2$$

$$I = \frac{1}{3}ML^2$$

TORQUE AS THE AGENT OF ROTATION

(*College Physics* 9th ed. pages 247–248/10th ed. pages 252–254)

The expression *moment of force* and the word *torque* are synonymous, and are used interchangeably. We know that a force is necessary to change the motion of a body, that is, to produce an acceleration. If the rotation of a body about an axis is to be changed, torque τ about that axis must be applied. Recall that a torque tends to cause rotation. Unbalanced torque causes angular acceleration. The angular acceleration produced by a given torque depends upon the mass as well as the *distribution of mass* with respect to the axis, the moment of inertia.

Torque = moment of inertia x angular acceleration

A resultant torque, $\vec{\tau}$, acting on a rigid body of moment of inertia, I, about an axis, produces an angular acceleration, $\vec{\alpha}$.

$$\vec{\tau} = I\vec{\alpha}$$

Torque is a vector quantity. Bodies rotating counterclockwise have a positive (+) torque and clockwise rotations are negative (–).

Earlier we defined torque as the product of the force $\vec{F}$ applied at a distance $\vec{R}$ from the axis of rotation. Recall that we called $\vec{R}$ the moment arm. When $\vec{F}$ and $\vec{R}$ are perpendicular

$$\vec{\tau} = \vec{R}\vec{F} \text{ and } I\alpha = RF$$

When $\vec{F}$ and $\vec{R}$ are not perpendicular,

$$\vec{\tau} = \vec{R}\vec{F}\sin\theta$$

SAMPLE PROBLEM 8

A pulley attached to an electric motor is a uniform disk of mass 1.2 kg and radius 0.12 m. The pulley is spinning at 1200 rpm when the motor is turned off. The pulley uniformly slows to rest in 40 s. What torque brings the pulley to rest?

SOLUTION TO PROBLEM 8

First we need to determine the angular acceleration.

$$\omega_0 = 1200 \text{ rev/min} \times 1 \text{ min/60 s} \times 2\pi \text{ rad/1 rev} = 126 \text{ rad/s}$$

$$\text{Angular acceleration } \alpha = \frac{\omega - \omega_0}{t} = \frac{0 - 126 \text{ rad/s}}{40 \text{ s}} = -3.2 \text{ rad/s}^2$$

The required torque is $\tau = I\alpha$ and $I = \frac{1}{2}MR^2$. Combining equations

$$\tau = \frac{1}{2}\alpha MR^2 = (0.5)\left(-3.2 \frac{\text{rad}}{\text{s}^2}\right)(1.2 \text{ kg})(0.12 \text{ m})^2 = -0.028 \text{ N} \cdot \text{m}$$

The negative sign appears because the force must be directed opposite to the direction of rotation of the pulley.

SAMPLE PROBLEM 9

A 0.6 kg mass, as shown in the diagram below, hangs at rest from the end of a cord wrapped several times around a pulley of 0.15 m radius. When released from rest, the mass falls 2.2 m in 6.0 s. Determine the moment of inertia of the pulley. Ignore the mass of the cord, friction, and air resistance.

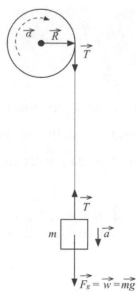

SOLUTION TO PROBLEM 9

The torque acting on the pulley is $\vec{\tau} = I\vec{\alpha}$ and the force acting on the mass is $\vec{F} = m\vec{a}$. Next we find the acceleration a of the system. We know the vertical drop from rest and the time it takes for the drop, $y = -2.2$ m and $t = 6$ s. Recall that

$$y = v_0 t + \frac{1}{2}at^2 = 0 + \frac{1}{2}at^2$$

Solving for a, $a = \dfrac{2y}{t^2} = \dfrac{2(-2.2 \text{ m})}{(6 \text{ s})^2} = -0.12 \text{ m}\big/_{\text{s}^2}$

The negative sign implies that m is accelerating downward.

The angular acceleration, α, of the pulley is related to a by $a = \alpha R$ and then

$$\alpha = \frac{a}{R} = \frac{\left(-0.12 \text{ m}\big/_{\text{s}^2}\right)}{0.15 \text{ m}} = -0.8 \text{ rad}\big/_{\text{s}^2}$$

The negative sign means the pulley accelerates in the clockwise direction.

From Newton's second law, the unbalanced force acting on mass m is $\vec{F}_{net} m\vec{a}$ and $T - mg = ma$. Solving for T,

$$T = ma + mg = m(a + g) = (0.6 \text{ kg})\left(-0.12 \text{ m}\big/_{\text{s}^2} + 9.8 \text{ m}\big/_{\text{s}^2}\right) = 5.8 \text{ N}$$

Now we write $\tau = I\alpha$ for the pulley.

$$\tau = RF = RT = Ia$$

Solving for I,

$$I = \frac{RT}{\alpha} = \frac{(0.15\ \text{m})(-5.8\ \text{N})}{\left(-0.8\ \text{rad}\middle/\text{s}^2\right)} = \textbf{1.1 kg} \cdot \textbf{m}^2$$

ROTATIONAL ENERGY

(*College Physics* 9th ed. pages 254–256/10th ed. pages 259–262)

All moving bodies have kinetic energy. Rotating bodies have what we call *rotational kinetic energy*, K_{rot}, and we define it as $K_{rot} = \frac{1}{2}I\omega^2$. Rotational kinetic energy is a scalar and has the J as its unit.

SAMPLE PROBLEM 10

A 12 kg solid steel disk has a radius of 0.06 meter. The disk spins with a velocity of 10 $\text{rad}\middle/\text{s}$. What is the rotational kinetic energy of the disk?

SOLUTION TO PROBLEM 10

First, write the moment of inertia of the disk. A solid disk has $I = \frac{1}{2}MR^2$. Substitute this expression into $K_{rot} = \frac{1}{2}I\omega^2$.

$$K_{rot} = \frac{1}{2}I\omega^2$$

$$= \frac{1}{2}\left(\frac{1}{2}MR^2\right)\omega^2$$

$$= \frac{1}{4}MR^2\omega^2$$

$$= (0.25)(12\ \text{kg})(0.06\ \text{m})^2\left(10\ \frac{\text{rad}}{\text{s}}\right)^2$$

$$K_{rot} = \textbf{1.08 J}$$

Notice how we combined equations in this problem.

Consider the following problem. To this point we have ignored the mass and radius of pulleys. We have reached the point where we can treat them more realistically.

SAMPLE PROBLEM 11

A mass M is free to slide without friction across a horizontal tabletop. This mass is connected by a light string to a mass m that hangs over the edge of the table. The connecting string passes over a frictionless pulley in the shape of a disk with radius R and mass m_p. Find the velocity of the falling mass as it strikes the floor. The mass m, starting from rest, falls a distance h to the floor.

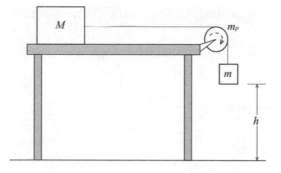

SOLUTION TO PROBLEM 11

The potential energy of the falling mass is converted into kinetic energy of all three masses. The kinetic energy of the pulley is due to its rotation. Because the pulley is a disk, its moment of inertia is $I = \frac{1}{2}m_pR^2$. Since frictionless forces are ignored, we use the conservation of mechanical energy. The gravitational potential energy of mass m is going to change into the kinetic energy due to translation of both masses plus the kinetic energy due to the rotation of the pulley. From the conservation of mechanical theorem we write

$$U_0 + K_0 = U + K$$

$$mgh + 0 = 0 + \frac{1}{2}mv^2 + \frac{1}{2}Mv^2 + \frac{1}{2}I\omega^2$$

Here, v is the translational velocity of the blocks and ω is the rotational velocity of the pulley. At any instant M does not change height, only m appears in the gravitational potential energy term. Provided the string does not slip over the pulley, the tangential velocity of the edge of the pulley is also v. Thus, we can write $v = \omega R$ and substitute $\omega = v/R$. Making substitutions,

$$mgh = \frac{1}{2}mv^2 + \frac{1}{2}Mv^2 + \frac{1}{2}\left(\frac{1}{2}m_pR^2\right)\left(\frac{v}{R}\right)^2$$

Solving for v yields

$$v = \sqrt{\frac{2mgh}{m + M + {m_p}/{2}}}$$

Bodies can have *rolling motion*. They can be traveling along the horizontal and be rolling at the same time. Such bodies will have both rotational motion as well as linear motion. The total kinetic energy of such a body is

$$K_{total} = K_{rot} + K = \frac{1}{2}I\omega^2 + \frac{1}{2}Mv^2$$

SAMPLE PROBLEM 12

A solid sphere of mass 10 kg rolls without slipping across a horizontal surface at 15 m/s and rolls up an inclined plane tilted at 30°. If friction losses are negligible, at what height, h, above the floor will the ball come to rest?

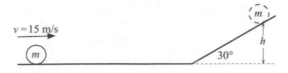

SOLUTION TO PROBLEM 12

The rotational and translational kinetic energies of the rolling sphere at the bottom of the incline will be totally changed into gravitational potential energy when it stops. Again we employ the law of conservation of mechanical energy. With friction being ignored, we write $U_0 + K_0 = U + K$ and

$$0 + K_{rot} + K = mgh + 0 + 0$$

$$\frac{1}{2} I\omega^2 + \frac{1}{2} mv^2 = mgh$$

The moment of inertia of the solid sphere is $I = \frac{2}{5} mR^2$ and the linear velocity of the sphere at its periphery is $v = \omega R$. Solving for angular velocity we get $\omega = v/R$. Substituting

$$\frac{1}{2}\left(\frac{2}{5} mR^2\right)\left(\frac{v}{R}\right)^2 + \frac{1}{2} mv^2 = mgh$$

Note that the mass of the sphere is common to both sides and divides out. The R^2 terms likewise divide out. Solving for h,

$$\frac{1}{5} v^2 + \frac{1}{2} v^2 = gh$$

And,

$$h = \frac{0.7v^2}{g} = \frac{0.7\left(15 \text{ m}/_\text{s}\right)^2}{9.8 \text{ m}/_{\text{s}^2}} = \textbf{16 m}$$

Notice that the mass m, radius R and the angular velocity ω did not enter into the calculations.

ROTATIONAL WORK AND POWER

(*College Physics* 9th ed. pages 254–256/10th ed. pages 260–262)

At an earlier time we defined work as the product of a displacement and the component of the force in the direction of the displacement. The rotational analogy is that *rotational work* is defined as the product of an angular displacement and the torque causing the rotation.

$$W = \tau\theta$$

Mechanical energy developed in machines is usually transmitted in the form of rotational work. Engine output is expressed in terms of the rate at which rotational work is done. The rate at which work is done is called power, P.

$$P = \frac{W}{t} = \frac{\tau\theta}{t}$$

Since average angular speed, $\bar{\omega}$, is θ/t, then power output is also expressed as

$$P = \tau\bar{\omega}$$

Work and power are both scalars. The unit of rotational work is the J and power is the W.

SAMPLE PROBLEM 13

A wheel, initially at rest, has a moment of inertia of $3.2\ \text{kg} \cdot \text{m}^2$ and is attached to a 1.0 kW electric motor. (a) What is the angular speed developed in the wheel 10 s after the motor is turned on? (b) What torque is developed by the motor?

SOLUTION TO PROBLEM 13

(a) The work done by the motor in 10 s $= K_{rot}$ of the wheel after 10 s

$$W = Pt = \frac{1}{2}I\omega^2$$

Solving for ω

$$\omega = \sqrt{\frac{2Pt}{I}}\sqrt{\frac{2\left(1000\ \text{J}/\text{s}\right)(10\ \text{s})}{3.2\ \text{kg}\cdot\text{m}^2}} = \mathbf{79\ rad/s}$$

(b) Torque is $\tau = I\alpha = I\left(\dfrac{\omega - \omega_0}{t}\right) = \left(3.2\ \text{kg}\cdot\text{m}^2\right)\left(\dfrac{79\ \text{rad}/\text{s} - 0}{10\ \text{s}}\right) = \mathbf{25\ N\cdot m}$

ANGULAR MOMENTUM

(*College Physics* 9th ed. pages 257–261/10th ed. pages 262–267)

Any rigid body that rotates has *angular momentum*, $\vec{L}$, and its angular momentum is $\vec{L} = I\vec{\omega}$. Bodies that travel along a curved path also have angular momentum about a given point $\vec{L} = m\vec{v}\vec{r}$.
The unit of angular momentum is the $kg \cdot m^2 / s$.

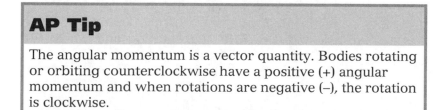

AP Tip

The angular momentum is a vector quantity. Bodies rotating or orbiting counterclockwise have a positive (+) angular momentum and when rotations are negative (–), the rotation is clockwise.

Angular acceleration is defined as the time rate of change angular velocity. Torque then, may be defined as the product of the moment of inertia and the time rate of angular velocity or

$$\vec{\tau} = I\vec{\alpha} = I\frac{\Delta\vec{\omega}}{\Delta t}$$

Multiplying both sides of the equation by Δt gives $\vec{\tau}\Delta t = I\Delta\vec{\omega}$. The quantity $\vec{\tau}\Delta t$ is called angular impulse and $I\Delta\vec{\omega}$ is the change in the angular momentum, $\Delta\vec{L}$. Just as linear impulse changes linear momentum, angular impulse changes angular momentum.

$$\vec{\tau}\Delta t = I\Delta\vec{\omega} = \Delta\vec{L}$$

SAMPLE PROBLEM 14

A hollow sphere having a mass of 4 kg and a radius of 4 cm is set into motion about an axis through the center. If the sphere has an angular speed of 20 rad/s, what is its angular momentum?

SOLUTION TO PROBLEM 14

The moment of inertia of a hollow sphere is $\frac{2}{3}MR^2$. Its angular momentum is

$$L = I\omega$$

$$= \left(\frac{2}{3}MR^2\right)\omega^2$$

$$= \frac{2(4\text{ kg})(0.04\text{ m})^2\left(20\text{ }\text{rad}/\text{s}\right)^2}{3}$$

$$= 1.7\text{ kg}\cdot\frac{\text{m}^2}{\text{s}}$$

SAMPLE PROBLEM 15

A grinding wheel mounted on the shaft of an electric motor is initially at rest. The wheel has a mass of 8 kg and a radius of 0.12 m. Twenty seconds after the motor was turned on, the grinding wheel reached its maximum speed of 1800 rpm. What was the torque developed?

SOLUTION TO PROBLEM 15

First, we convert 1800 rpm to rad/s.

$$\omega = 1800\text{ rpm} \times \frac{1\text{ min}}{60\text{ s}} \times \frac{2\pi\text{ rad}}{1\text{ rev}} = 188.5\text{ }\text{rad}/\text{s}$$

Since the wheel starts from rest, $\omega_0 = 0$. Next, we write $\vec{\tau}\Delta t = I\Delta\vec{\omega}$.

The grinding wheel is a solid disk and $I = \frac{1}{2}MR^2$. Substituting and solving for the torque,

$$\tau = \frac{I\Delta\omega}{\Delta t}$$

$$= \frac{\frac{1}{2}MR^2(\omega-\omega_0)}{t} = \frac{(0.5)(8\text{ kg})(0.12\text{ m})^2\left(188.5\ \frac{\text{rad}}{\text{s}}-0\right)}{(20\text{ s})}$$

$$= \mathbf{0.5\ N\cdot m}$$

THE LAW OF CONSERVATION OF ANGULAR MOMENTUM

(*College Physics* 9th ed. pages 257–261/10th ed. pages 262–267)

If no external torque acts on a body, the angular momentum of a body rotating about a fixed axis is constant.

In a system where there is no external torque, the total angular momentum before any event is always equal to the total angular momentum after the event. We call this statement the *law of conservation of angular momentum*.

$$\Sigma\vec{L} = \Sigma\vec{L}_0$$

$$I_0\omega_0 = I\omega$$

SAMPLE PROBLEM 16

A neutron star is formed when a star, such as our Sun, collapses in on itself. Before collapse, the mass of the star is M_0 and its radius R_0. After collapse, the neutron star has mass M_0 and radius $\left(1\times10^{-5}\right)R_0$. The mass does not change but the radius shrinks by a factor of one hundred thousand. Before collapse, the star rotated at 1 revolution every 25 days. Determine the rotation rate of the neutron star in rev/s.

SOLUTION TO PROBLEM 16

Angular momentum must be conserved and the total angular momentum before collapse must equal the total angular momentum after collapse. We write the law of conservation of angular momentum $I_0\omega_0 = I\omega$.

$$\frac{1}{2}M_0R_0^2\omega_0 = \frac{1}{2}M_0\left(1\times10^{-5}R_0\right)^2\omega$$

Note that the one-half, M_0 and R_0^2 appear on both side of the equation and divide out.

$$\omega = \frac{\omega_0}{\left(1\times10^{-5}\right)^2} = \frac{\dfrac{1\text{ rev}}{25\text{ d}}\times\dfrac{1\text{ d}}{24\text{ h}}\times\dfrac{1\text{ h}}{3600\text{ s}}}{\left(1\times10^{-10}\right)} = \mathbf{4630}\ \frac{\text{rev}}{\text{s}}$$

It is important to keep in mind that it is $I\omega$, the product of the moment of inertia and the angular velocity that is conserved, and not the angular velocity ω. In many situations, internal rearrangement of the masses of a system may change its moment of inertia. When that happens the angular velocity changes even though no external torque is applied to the system.

A figure skater starts a pirouette in a crouch, rotating on the toe of one skate with the other leg and both arms extended. She then slowly rises, pulling the extended leg and arms to her body, thus reducing her moment of inertia about the axis of rotation. As she does so, her angular velocity increases substantially.

The torque due to friction between the ice skate and ice is quite small. As a result, the angular momentum remains nearly constant.

CIRCULAR MOTION AND ROTATIONAL MOTION: STUDENT OBJECTIVES FOR THE AP EXAM

- You should be able to discuss why a particle moving in a horizontal circle at constant speed experiences a centripetal acceleration and a centripetal force.
- You should be able to explain the relationship between angular and linear descriptions of rotational motion.
- You should be able to explain how to locate experimentally the c.m. of a flat body of irregular shape.
- You should explain the meaning of the term moment of inertia.
- You should be able to explain why an ice skater spins faster when she pulls her arms in toward her body than when she extends her arms.

MULTIPLE-CHOICE QUESTIONS

1. A cylinder is rotating clockwise about a frictionless axle when two forces are applied to the rim of the cylinder as shown below.

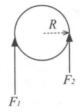

The cylinder will rotate with
(A) increasing angular speed in the clockwise direction since
$$\left|\vec{F_1}\right| > \left|\vec{F_2}\right|$$
(B) decreasing angular speed in the clockwise direction since the net force acting on the cylinder is $\left|\vec{F}_{net}\right| = \left|\vec{F_1}\right| - \left|\vec{F_2}\right|$
(C) decreasing angular speed in the clockwise direction since
$$\left|\vec{\tau_1}\right| > \left|\vec{\tau_2}\right|$$
(D) increasing angular speed in the clockwise direction since
$$\left|\vec{\tau_1}\right| > \left|\vec{\tau_2}\right|$$

2. A graph of the torque applied to a cylinder as a function of time is show below.

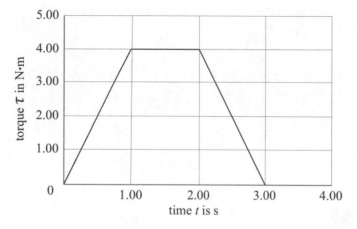

The change in the angular momentum of the cylinder is

(A) 8.0 $\dfrac{\text{kg} \cdot \text{m}}{\text{s}}$

(B) 6.0 $\dfrac{\text{kg} \cdot \text{m}}{\text{s}}$

(C) 4.0 $\dfrac{\text{kg} \cdot \text{m}}{\text{s}}$

(D) 2.0 $\dfrac{\text{kg} \cdot \text{m}}{\text{s}}$

3. A disk with a moment of inertia I_1 is rotating with an angular velocity of ω_0 when a small lump of clay drops onto the edge of the disk. The angular velocity of the disk will
   (A) increase because the falling clay strikes the disk with an initial kinetic energy which will be given to the disk, increasing its rotational speed
   (B) decrease because the lump of clay with no initial angular velocity makes an inelastic collision with the disk causing the composite mass to slow
   (C) remain constant since the mass of the disk is much larger than the lump of clay
   (D) increases as the small lump of clay makes contact with the disk, but will decrease as the lump of clay spreads out on the disk

4. A plate with a moment of inertia of $0.300 \ kg \cdot m^2$ which is initially at rest experiences two torques applied to the rim of the plate as shown in the diagram below for 10.0 s.

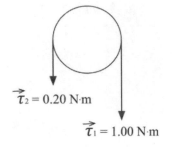

$$\vec{\tau}_2 = 0.20 \ N \cdot m$$

$$\vec{\tau}_1 = 1.00 \ N \cdot m$$

The change in the angular momentum of the plate is

(A) $10.0 \ \dfrac{kg \cdot m^2}{s}$

(B) $8.00 \ \dfrac{kg \cdot m^2}{s}$

(C) $5.00 \ \dfrac{kg \cdot m^2}{s}$

(D) $3.00 \ \dfrac{kg \cdot m^2}{s}$

5. Various forces are applied to 4 identical rods as shown below. Rank the forces for the greatest change in the angular velocity to the least change in angular velocity.

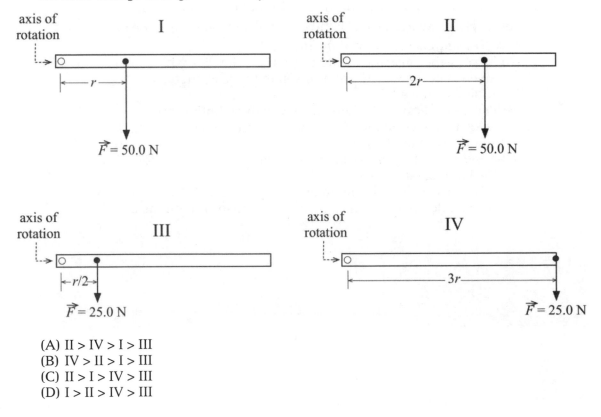

(A) II > IV > I > III
(B) IV > II > I > III
(C) II > I > IV > III
(D) I > II > IV > III

6. A skater with a moment of inertia of 2.40 kg·m² rotating with an angular velocity ω_0 pulls her arms in toward her body, changing her moment of inertia to 1.50 kg·m².
    (A) Because angular momentum is conserved, her angular speed will increase; her kinetic energy will also increase because she does work in moving her arms closer to her body.
    (B) Only her angular speed will increase since conservation of angular momentum applies.
    (C) Her angular speed and kinetic energy will increase because the force applied by her arms in bringing them closer to her body provides a torque, increasing her angular momentum and thus her kinetic energy.
    (D) Her angular speed and her rotational kinetic energy will remain the same since no net torque was applied to the system.

7. A counterclockwise rotating platform, with a diameter of 1.00 m and shown in the diagram below, slows from 4.00 rad/s to 2.00 rad/s in 1.00 s.

   Which of the acceleration vectors shown best illustrates the magnitude and the direction of the acceleration of the point on the rim when its angular velocity is 2.00 rad/s?

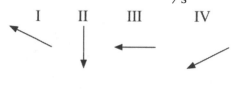

    (A) I
    (B) II
    (C) III
    (D) IV

8. A satellite moving in an elliptical orbit around the Earth is shown in the diagram below. Which statement best describes the torque on the satellite about the Earth while in orbit?

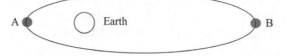

    (A) The torque on the satellite is greatest at point B because it is farthest from the Earth at that point and a larger torque is needed to cause it to move in toward perigee.
    (B) The torque on the satellite is greatest at point A since the satellite is at perigee.
    (C) The torque at A is larger than the torque at point B since the angular velocity at A is greater than the angular velocity at point B.
    (D) The torque at A and B are both zero since angular momentum in the system is conserved.

9. In problem 8 consider the satellite to be a GPS satellite. At closest approach, perigee, its distance from the center of the Earth is 20,200 km and its orbital velocity is 13,900 km/h . At apogee, its distance is 26,560 km. What is its orbital velocity at this position?
   (A) 10,570 km/h
   (B) 12,500 km/h
   (C) 13,900 km/h
   (D) 18,280 km/h

10. Various forces are exerted on 4 identical cylinders as shown. Rank the cylinders for the greatest change in angular velocity to the smallest change.

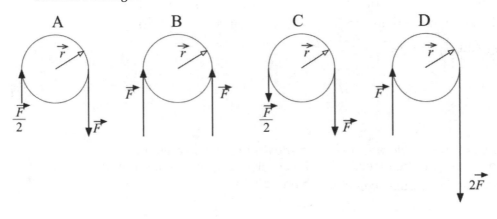

   (A) $D > A > C > B$
   (B) $D > (A = C) > B$
   (C) $B > C > A > D$
   (D) $(A = C) > D > B$

11. A 60.0 kg student stands on the outer rim of a merry-go-round at a playground that has a moment of inertia of 500.0 $kg \cdot m^2$. The initial angular velocity of the merry-go-round is 3.00 rad/s when the student is 2.50 m from the center. What is the angular velocity of the system when the student walks to a position that is 1.50 m from the center of the merry-go-round? (The student may be considered as a point mass with a moment of inertia given by $I = mr^2$.)
   (A) 1.77 rad/s
   (B) 4.13 rad/s
   (C) 5.25 rad/s
   (D) 8.33 rad/s

12. A hockey puck is attached to a string that passes through a hole in a frictionless table and is initially moving in a circle of radius r. A student slowly increases the force on the opposite end of the string beneath the hole in the table keeping that portion of the string vertical. As a result,

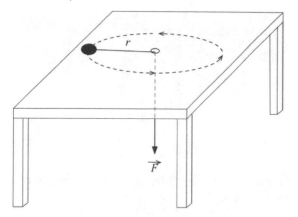

(A) the angular momentum of the puck is conserved and the kinetic energy of the puck increases
(B) angular momentum is conserved and kinetic energy decreases
(C) kinetic energy is conserved and angular momentum increases
(D) kinetic energy is conserved and angular momentum decreases

13. A disk rotating with some initial angular velocity ω_0 was engaged by a second smaller disk that dropped vertically onto the larger rotating disk, reducing the speed of the system to ω_f. To bring the system back to its initial angular velocity will require
(A) a force applied in the direction of rotation for a period of time
(B) a torque applied in the direction of rotation for a period of time
(C) an angular impulse opposite to the direction of rotation
(D) a linear impulse opposite to the direction of rotation

14. A comet is in an elliptical orbit around the Sun. Rank the positions shown for the largest centripetal force acting on the comet to the least.

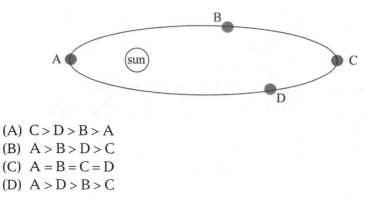

(A) $C > D > B > A$
(B) $A > B > D > C$
(C) $A = B = C = D$
(D) $A > D > B > C$

15. A small block slides without friction through a loop-the-loop as shown in the diagram below.

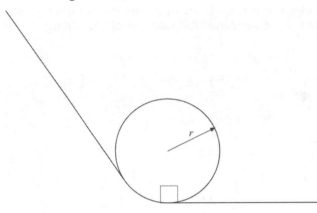

Which of the force diagrams best illustrates the forces on the block at the bottom of the loop-the-loop?

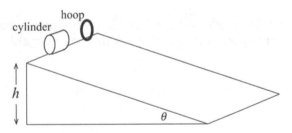

(A) I
(B) II
(C) III
(D) IV

FREE-RESPONSE PROBLEMS

1. A cylinder and a hoop are released from rest at the top of a long inclined plane and roll down the plane without slipping.

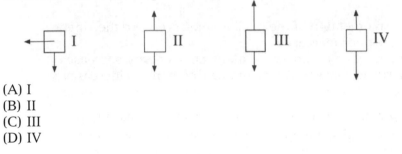

(a) Which of the two objects reaches the bottom of the inclined plane first?

_____ The hoop

_____ The cylinder

_____ They both reach the bottom at the same time.

Justify your answer without a mathematical solution.

(b) Since the objects roll without slipping

_____ the friction acting on them is up the plane

_____ the friction acting on them is down the pane

_____ there is no friction since they roll without slipping

(c) If the mass of each is doubled and the radius of each is reduced by half, how does this affect the velocity when the objects reach the end of the incline?
Justify your answer with a mathematical solution in enough detail to answer your question. You do not have to solve for the velocity at the bottom of the incline.

2. Your teacher has set up an Atwood's machine in the room and tells your laboratory group to design an experiment to determine the change in the angular momentum of the cylinder.

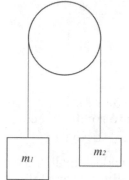

(a) Design an experiment to determine the change in the angular momentum of the cylinder in sufficient detail that another student could duplicate your experiment and obtain the same result.
(b) What measurements will you take and how will you use them to determine the change in the angular momentum?
(c) If you plot a graph, what will you plot and how will this help you answer your experimental question?
(d) Another group of students obtained data to produce the following graph. What information can you obtain from the analysis of this graph?

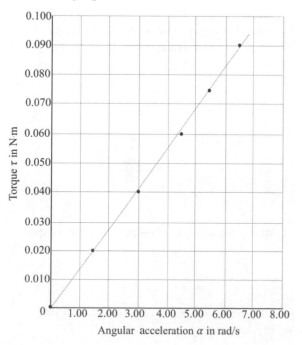

3. A small disk, mass $M = 1.00$ kg, slides on a flat frictionless table connected by a massless rod 0.500 m long that is attached by a ring to a pin in the table.

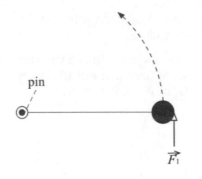

A force applied tangentially to the disk for a short period of time and then removed causes the disk to rotate in a counterclockwise direction with a tangential velocity $v_t = 2.00$ m/s.

(a) Shortly after the force is removed, a small piece of modeling clay, $m = 0.100$ kg drops onto the center of the disk. The velocity of the disk will

——— increase

——— decrease

——— remain constant

Justify your answer in a well-written statement using the correct scientific terms.

(b) Write, but do not solve, the mathematical equation related to your answer. Include all steps needed to show your final answer. (Both the disk and the modeling clay may be considered to be point masses $I = mr^2$ for this part of the question.)

(c) Some time after the modeling clay has fallen on the disk, a second force is applied to the system as shown.

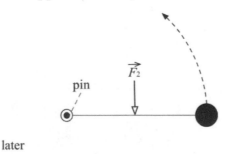

later

When the force is initially applied, the velocity of the system will

——— increase

——— decrease

——— remain constant

Justify your answer in a well-written statement using the correct scientific terms.

4. A large wheel and axle, as shown in the diagram below, experiences two forces

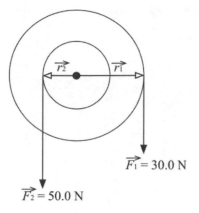

$\vec{F_1}$ = 30.00 N is applied to the outer radius $\vec{r_1}$ = 0.500 m and

$\vec{F_2}$ = 50.0 N is applied to the inner radius $\vec{r_2}$ = 0.250 m .

(a) The net torque acting on the wheel and axle produces

_____ clockwise rotation

_____ counterclockwise rotation

_____ no rotation

Justify your answer.

(b) Several students wanted to experimentally determine the moment of inertia of the wheel and axle. They attached a weight hanger to the cord wrapped around the outer rim of the wheel and axle shown above and measured the distance from the bottom of the outer wheel to the floor. Keeping this distance constant in their experiment, they used an electronic timer to measure the time it took various masses to descend to the floor. The torque was then calculated for each descending mass to produce the data below.

Torque $(N \cdot m)$	Time (s)
1.00	5.00
2.00	4.00
2.75	3.50
3.25	3.00
3.75	2.50
4.50	2.00
5.00	1.50
5.50	1.00

Using the data, plot a graph of the net torque versus time graph. How would you use this graph to determine the change in the angular momentum of the wheel and axle?

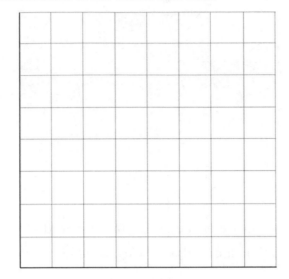

Answers

MULTIPLE-CHOICE

1. **D** The net torque on the system is $|\vec{\tau}_{net}| = |\vec{\tau}_1 \cdot r| - |\vec{\tau}_2 \cdot r|$. The cylinder will increase its angular speed in the clockwise direction because $|\vec{\tau}_1| > |\vec{\tau}_2|$.
    (*College Physics* 9th ed. pages 236–239/10th ed. pages 241–244)
    (L.O. 3.F.2.1)

2. **A** The change is the angular momentum ΔL is the area under a torque as a function of time graph. The total area is $\frac{1}{2}bh + bh + \frac{1}{2}bh$. The area is

    $$\frac{1}{2}(4.0 \text{ N} \cdot \text{m})(1.0 \text{ s}) + (4.0 \text{ N} \cdot \text{m})(1.0 \text{ s}) + \frac{1}{2}(4.0 \text{ N} \cdot \text{m})(1.0 \text{ s})$$

    $$= 8.0 \, \frac{\text{kg} \cdot \text{m}}{\text{s}}.$$

    (*College Physics* 9th ed. pages 257–261/10th ed. pages 262–267)
    (L.O. 3.F.3.2)

3. **B** This is an inelastic collision. The small lump of clay has no initial angular velocity, but when it strikes the disk, conservation of momentum applies.

    $$\left(I_{disk}\right)\left(\omega_{disk}\right) = \left(I_{disk} + I_{clay}\right)\left(\omega_f\right).$$

    (*College Physics* 9th ed. pages 257–261/10th ed. pages 262–267)
    (L.O. 3.F.3.1)

4. **B** The change in the angular momentum is given by $\vec{\tau}_{net} = \dfrac{\Delta L}{t}$. The net torque is $1.00 \text{ N} \cdot \text{m} - 0.200 \text{ N} \cdot \text{m} = 0.800 \text{ N} \cdot \text{m}$. Thus the change in the angular momentum is $\Delta L = (0.800 \text{ N} \cdot \text{m})(10.0 \text{ s}) =$ $8.00 \text{ N} \cdot \text{m} \cdot \text{s}$. The answer is also expressed as $8.00 \dfrac{\text{kg} \cdot \text{m}^2}{\text{s}}$.

   (*College Physics* 9th ed. pages 257–261/10th ed. pages 262–267) (L.O. 4.D.3.1)

5. **A** $\tau = rF \sin\theta$ and $\tau = I\alpha$ apply. The greatest change in the angular velocity is produced by the torque that produces the largest angular acceleration. Since the rods are identical and hinged at the left end, their moment of inertia is the same, $I = \dfrac{1}{3}mL^2$.

   (*College Physics* 9th ed. pages 236–239/10th ed. pages 241–244) (L.O. 3.F.2.1)

6. **A** Conservation of angular momentum applies, thus her speed will increase since she moved her arms closer to her body, reducing her moment of inertia, which results in an increase in angular velocity. Work must be done in order to bring her arms closer to her body. This results in an increase in rotational kinetic energy. (*College Physics* 9th ed. pages 257–261/10th ed. pages 262–267) (L.O. 5.E.1.1)

7. **D** The angular acceleration of the platform is found from $\omega_f = \omega_0 + \alpha t$. Substituting into the equation gives $2.00 \text{ rad}/\text{s} = 4.00 \text{ rad}/\text{s} + \alpha(1.00 \text{ s}) = -2.00 \text{ rad}/\text{s}^2$. The platform is initially rotating counterclockwise, and thus the tangential acceleration of the point is $a_t = \alpha r = 2.00 \text{ rad}/\text{s}^2 (0.500 \text{ m}) = 1.00 \text{ m}/\text{s}^2$ pointing downward (clockwise direction). The centripetal acceleration is $a_c = v^2/r = \omega^2 r$. $a_c = (2.00 \text{ rad}/\text{s})^2 (0.50 \text{ m}) = 2.00 \text{ rad}/\text{s}^2$, and inward. The resultant acceleration is $a = \sqrt{(a_c^2 + a_t^2)} = 2.24 \text{ rad}/\text{s}^2$ pointing downward and to the left into the third quadrant.

   (*College Physics* 9th ed. pages 202–204/10th ed. pages 207–209) (L.O. 3.B.1.3, 3.B.2.1)

8. **D** There is no torque applied to the system; therefore, angular momentum is conserved. (*College Physics* 9th ed. pages 257–260/10th ed. pages 262–266) (L.O. 5.E.1.1)

9. **A** Conservation of angular momentum applies. $I_p \omega_p = I_a \omega_a$. The GPS satellite may be considered as a point mass at this distance and its moment of inertia is $I = mr^2$. The orbital velocity is $v = \omega r$, therefore $mr_p^2 \left(\dfrac{v_p}{r_p} \right) = mr_a^2 \left(\dfrac{v_a}{r_a} \right) = v_p r_p = v_a r_a$.

$$(20\ 200\ \text{km})\left(13\ 900\ \tfrac{\text{km}}{\text{h}}\right) = (26\ 560\ \text{km}) v_a$$

giving the orbital speed at apogee as $10\ 570\ \tfrac{\text{km}}{\text{h}}$.

(*College Physics* 9th ed. pages 236–239/10th ed. pages 241–244)
(L.O. 5.E.1.2)

10. **A** The net torque on the cylinders is determined by $\tau = rF \sin \theta$ and how the applied force will cause the cylinder to rotate either clockwise or counterclockwise. In the case of B the net torque on the cylinder is zero since equal torques cause opposite and balanced rotation and either the cylinder is at rest or rotating at constant speed. D will cause the largest change in speed since the net torque is $\Sigma \tau = 3rF$ followed by A and then C.
(*College Physics* 9th ed. pages 236–239/10th ed. pages 241–244)
(L.O. 3.F.2.1)

11. **B** Conservation of angular momentum is required to solve this question. The correct equation is $\left(I_{\text{platform}} + I_{\text{child}_0} \right) \omega_0 = \left(I_{\text{platform}} + I_{\text{child} f} \right) \omega_f$. The initial moment of inertia of the child considered as a point mass is found by substituting into $I = mr^2$. Then $I_{\text{child}_0} = 60.0\ \text{kg} (2.50\ \text{m})^2 = 375.0\ \text{kg} \cdot \text{m}^2$. The final moment of inertia of the child is $I_{\text{child}_0} = 60.0\ \text{kg} (1.50\ \text{m})^2 = 135.0\ \text{kg} \cdot \text{m}^2$ Substitution into the first equation given by $\left(I_{\text{platform}} + I_{\text{child}_0} \right) \omega_0 = \left(I_{\text{platform}} + I_{\text{child} f} \right) \omega_f$ is

$$\left(500.0\ \text{kg} \cdot \text{m}^2 + 375.0\ \text{kg} \cdot \text{m}^2 \right) 3.00\ \tfrac{\text{rad}}{\text{s}}$$
$$= \left(500.0\ \text{kg} \cdot \text{m}^2 + 135.0\ \text{kg} \cdot \text{m}^2 \right) \omega_f$$
$$= 4.13\ \tfrac{\text{rad}}{\text{s}}.$$

(*College Physics* 9th ed. pages 257–260/10th ed. pages 262–266)
(L.O. 5.E.1.2)

12. **A** As the student pulls the cord through the table, the radius decreases, but since no torque is applied to the hockey puck, conservation of angular momentum applies $L_0 = L_f$. As the puck moves closer to the hole, its moment of inertia decreases since r decreases. The kinetic energy will also increase since

$$K_{\text{rotation}} = \frac{1}{2} I \omega^2$$

(*College Physics* 9th ed. pages 257–260/10th ed. pages 262–266)
(L.O. 5.E.1.1)

13. **B** The interaction was an inelastic collision. To return the system to its original angular velocity, a torque must be applied to the rotating disk. $\Sigma \tau = \dfrac{\Delta L}{\Delta t}$

(*College Physics* 9th ed. pages 257–260/10th ed. pages 262–263)
(L.O. 4.D.1.1)

14. **B** The centripetal force $F_c = m\dfrac{v^2}{r}$ arises from the gravitational force between the Sun and the comet. The force is greater at point A since this position is closest to the Sun.

Since the orbit is elliptical and not circular, the force will vary in magnitude, so answer C is not a choice. Correct ranking is A > B > D > C.
(*College Physics* 9th ed. pages 209–214/10th ed. pages 214–219)
(L.O. 3.A.3.4)

15. **C** The small block is in circular motion and the centripetal force acting on it is directed into the center of the circle. At the lowest point, the normal force acting on the body is equal to the sum of the centripetal force and the gravitational force. Thus diagram III best illustrates the size of the normal force and the gravitational force.
(*College Physics* 9th ed. pages 209–214/10th ed. pages 214–219)
(L.O. 3.A.2.1)

FREE-RESPONSE PROBLEMS

1. (a) The correct line checked is __√__ the cylinder.
   Justification
   Two possible answers:

   The cylinder has a smaller moment of inertia $I = \dfrac{1}{2}mr^2$. More of the gravitational potential energy will be transferred into translational kinetic energy and less into rotational kinetic energy and the cylinder will reach the bottom with the higher linear velocity.
   The hoop, because its mass is concentrated on the rim, has a larger moment of inertia $I = mr^2$. More of the gravitational potential energy will be transferred into rotational kinetic energy and less into translational kinetic energy and the hoop will reach the bottom with the lower linear velocity.

   (b) The correct line checked is __√__ the friction acting on them is up the plane.
   To cause either object to roll down the plane, the friction must provide the torque on the outer surface at the contact point with the plane. This causes rotation of the object in a clockwise direction as it rolls down the plane.

(c) Changing the mass and the radius of either or both objects will not change the linear velocity as they roll down the plane.

$$U_0 + K_{0_T} + K_{0_i} = U_f + K_{f_T} + K_{f_R}$$

$$mgh = \frac{1}{2}mv^2 + \frac{1}{2}I\omega^2$$

Then knowing the moment of inertia and $v = \omega r$, substitution into a solution for the cylinder $mgh = \frac{1}{2}mv^2 + \frac{1}{2}\left(\frac{1}{2}mr^2\right)\frac{v^2}{r^2}$.

The mass m and the radius r are common factors in all terms and can be eliminated, yielding $gh = \frac{1}{2}v^2 + \frac{1}{2}\left(\frac{1}{2}\right)v^2$. The

solution for the hoop proceeds in the same manner.
(*College Physics* 9th ed. pages 250–251, 254–255/10th ed. pages 256–257, 259–261)
(L.O. 4.C.1.1, 4.C.1.2, 5.A.2.1)

2. (a) The net torque acting on the cylinder for a period of time will give the change in the angular momentum of the cylinder.
Measure and record the radius of the cylinder.
Measure and record the distance from the descending mass attached to the cord wrapped around the cylinder to the floor so that the height will be constant in the experiment.
Balance the system with sufficient weight $F_g = w = mg$ on the

mass hangers so that the weights will rise and descend at constant speed. The difference, if any, will indicate the frictional force on the system.
Increase the weight on the descending mass hanger so that the system will accelerate. Record this force.
Measure the time needed for the descending weight to reach the floor. Repeat the observation at least three times.
Increase the force on the descending mass hanger, making at least three observations for this force. Record the force and the time for each descent. Record the average time, making sure that the times were consistent.
Repeat the above step for 5 to 8 additional readings.

(b) Since we determined the net force acting on the system in part (a), we can calculate each torque and the net torque acting on

the system. Each torque is determined by $|\vec{\tau}| = \vec{r}|\vec{F}|\sin\theta$ and the

net torque acting on the system is. $\Sigma|\vec{\tau}| = |\vec{\tau}_2| - |\vec{\tau}_1|$.

Use the data to plot a graph of $\Sigma|\vec{\tau}|$ as a function of time.

(c) The plot of $\Sigma|\vec{\tau}|$ as a function of time will give a linear graph.

The area under the curve is the change in the angular

momentum $\Delta\vec{L}$.

(d) This plot of $|\vec{\tau}|$ versus $\vec{\alpha}$ is linear and the slope of this line will

determine the moment of inertia of the system. Since the angular acceleration is given, if you knew the time of the descent, you could determine the change in the angular velocity. Then the change in the angular momentum could be found $\Delta L = I \Delta \omega$.

(*College Physics* 9th ed. pages 236–237, 261–264/10th ed. pages 241–242, 262–264)
(L.O. 4.D.1.1, 4.D.1.2, 4.D.2.2, 4.D.3.1, 4.D.3.1)

3. (a) Correct line checked ___√___ decrease.
   The small piece of putty makes an inelastic collision with the disk. It has a moment of inertia that must be added to the moment of inertia of the disk. Since there is an increase in the moment of inertia there must be a corresponding decrease in the velocity.

   (b) Solution $\vec{L}_0 = \vec{L}_f$

   $$I_0 \omega_0 = I_f \omega_f$$

   The moment of inertia of a point mass is given as $I = mr^2$

   $$Mr^2 \omega_0 = (M + m) r^2 \omega_f$$

   The angular velocity is related to the linear velocity by $\omega = \dfrac{V_t}{r}$

   Then

   $$Mr^2 \frac{V_0}{r} = (M + m) r^2 \frac{V_f}{r}$$

   and finally

   $$Mrv_0 = (M + m) rv_f$$

   (c) Correct line checked ___√___ decrease
   The force produces a torque that is opposite to the rotation of the system causing it to slow. (If the force was applied long enough it might cause the system to stop and perhaps change direction of rotation.)

   (*College Physics* 9th ed. pages 257–261/10th ed. pages 262–265)
   (L.O. 3.F.2.1, 3.F.3.1, 3.F.3.2, 4.D.3.1)

4. (a) Correct line checked is _____√___ clockwise rotation
   The net torque acting on the system is negative.
   The solution gives:

   $$\Sigma \vec{\tau} = (50.0 \text{ N})(0.250 \text{ m}) - 30.0(0.500 \text{ m})$$
   $$= 12.5 \text{ N} \cdot \text{m} - 15.0 \text{ N} \cdot \text{m}$$
   $$= -2.50 \text{ N} \cdot \text{m}$$

(b) The correct graph is shown below.

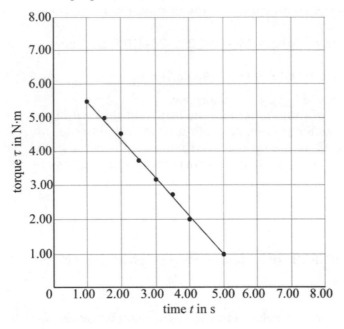

The area beneath the curve will give the change in the angular momentum of the system.

(*College Physics* 9th ed. pages 236–239, 257–260/10th ed. pages 241–244, 262–266)

(L.O. 4.D.1.1, 4.D.3.1)

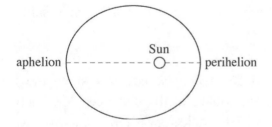

8

Gravitation

Kepler's Laws of Planetary Motion

(*College Physics* 9th ed. pages 221–224/10th ed. pages 226–229)

Over a three-year span from 1599 to 1601, Johannes Kepler (1571–1630) worked with the noted Danish astronomer Tycho Brahe (1546–1601). Brahe had amassed over twenty-five years of carefully measured observations of the planets, moon, and stars. Keep in mind that the telescope was invented in 1608. The quality and accuracy of the observations led Kepler to develop his three laws of planetary motion.

Kepler's first law (1609): *The planets move in elliptical orbits with the Sun at one of the foci.*

At its most fundamental, the first law shows that planets trace out elliptical orbits with the Sun at one of the focal points. Nothing occupies the other focal point. The *eccentricities* of the planetary orbits are so small that they can almost be considered circles.

When a planet is at its most distant point from the Sun, the position is called *aphelion*. At its closest approach the planet is at *perihelion*. Helion comes from the ancient Greek and it means Sun. For Earth orbit, it is *apogee* and *perigee*. For moon or lunar orbit it is *apolune* and *perilune*.

267

Kepler's second law (1609): *The straight line joining the Sun and any planet sweeps out equal areas, A, in equal intervals of time, T.*

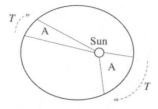

The first law gives all possible positions of a planet, but no time indications. The second law implies that the velocity of the planet in its orbit decreases with increasing distance to the Sun. A planet moves faster when at *perihelion,* and slower at *aphelion.* The second law gives the time dependence critical to predicting planetary positions.

Kepler's third law (1619): *The ratio of the square of the period, T, of one full orbit about the Sun and the cube of the radius, R, of the orbit is a constant.*

Mathematically, the third law can be expressed as $\dfrac{T^2}{R^3} = \text{constant}$.

The constant can be deduced from other considerations and then

$$\frac{T^2}{R^3} = \frac{4\pi^2}{GM}$$

G is a constant we will encounter in the next section. M is the mass of the central body and T is the period or time of one complete orbit.

NEWTON'S UNIVERSAL LAW OF GRAVITATION

(*College Physics* 9th ed. pages 214–217/10th ed. pages 219–222)

It is often said incorrectly that Newton discovered gravity. What Newton actually discovered was the universal law of gravitation.

Basically, he wrote, *every particle in the universe attracts every other particle with a force that is directly proportional to their masses and is inversely proportional to the inverse square of the distance between them,* or

$$\vec{F} \propto \frac{m_1 m_2}{R^2}$$

To make the proportionality an equation we introduce the constant, G, and call it the *universal gravitational constant.* The universal law of gravitation is then written:

$$\vec{F} = G\frac{m_1 m_2}{R^2}$$

The relationship is called an *inverse square law* since the force drops off as the inverse of the square of the distance, $\dfrac{1}{R^2}$, between interacting bodies, m_1 and m_2. It was not until 1798 when the English experimentalist Henry Cavendish (1731–1810) first measured the universal gravitational constant, G. In terms of today's values it is

$$G = 6.67 \times 10^{-11} \ \text{N} \cdot \text{m}^2 \big/ \text{kg}^2$$

Gravity is one of the four fundamental forces in nature. It is the weakest of the four. Gravity is the primary force acting on astronomical bodies. It is always an attractive force. The force of gravity between two ordinary bodies on the Earth is negligibly small.

There is much about gravity we do not completely understand. All bodies of mass m generate a gravitational field, a **g**-field. A small mass generates a tiny field and an enormous body, such as a planet, generates an enormous field. It is the interaction of these **g**-fields that is the gravitational force of attraction. All bodies have a center of mass, c.m. A symmetrical body such as a sphere has its c.m. at its very center. All bodies behave as if all their mass were concentrated at the c.m. The **g**-field converges into the center of mass. The **g**-field intensity, $\vec{g}$, is a vector. It has magnitude and direction.

SAMPLE PROBLEM 1

Spent uranium is a very dense material. A cubic foot of it would weigh over 1200 pounds. What gravitational attraction would exist between two identical 100 kg spheres of spent uranium? The spheres are positioned so that their centers of mass are 3.0 m apart.

SOLUTION TO PROBLEM 1

The gravitational force is

$$F = \frac{Gm_1 m_2}{R^2} = G\left(\frac{m}{R}\right)^2$$

$$= \left(6.67 \times 10^{-11} \text{ N} \cdot \text{m}^2 \Big/ \text{kg}^2\right)\left(\frac{100 \text{ kg}}{3.0 \text{ m}}\right)^2$$

$$= 7.4 \times 10^{-8} \text{ N}$$

This gravitational force is on the order of the force an amoeba generates pushing off the surface of a tiny grain of sand in a few drops of water.

THE ACCELERATION DUE TO GRAVITY

(*College Physics* 9th ed. pages 216–217/10th ed. pages 221–222)

The gravitational force acting on a body is its weight, $\vec{w} = m\vec{g}$. Since weight is gravitational force we can write

$$F = w = G\frac{mM}{R^2} = m\left(\frac{GM}{R^2}\right)$$

Assuming any planet or moon as being spherical and of uniform or homogenous composition, the acceleration due to gravity at the surface is then

$$\vec{g}_P = G\frac{M_P}{R_P^2}$$

$\vec{g}_p$ is the acceleration due to gravity on the surface of the planet, M_p the mass of the planet and R_p the planet radius. Think of it as the distance from the c.m. of the planet to the surface.

SAMPLE PROBLEM 2

The planet Mars has a mass of 6.387×10^{23} kg and a radius of 3.332×10^6 m. To two decimal places, determine the acceleration due to gravity for the surface of Mars assuming that it is spherical and homogeneous. The mass of Mars is 6.386×10^{24} kg and its radius is 3.332×10^6 m.

SOLUTION TO PROBLEM 2

For the surface of Mars:

$$g_{Mars} = G \frac{M_{Mars}}{R_{Mars}^2}$$

$$= \frac{\left(6.673 \times 10^{-11} \ ^{N \cdot m^2}\!/_{kg^2}\right)\left(6.387 \times 10^{23} \ kg\right)}{\left(3.332 \times 10^6 \ m\right)^2}$$

$$= 3.83 \ ^m\!/_{s^2}$$

Mars is considerably less massive and has a smaller radius than the Earth. At its surface it has 39% of the acceleration due to gravity as the Earth.

SAMPLE PROBLEM 3

On the surface of the Earth a 100 kg body has a weight $w = mg = \left(100 \ kg\right)\left(9.8 \ ^m\!/_{s^2}\right) = 980 \ N$. What is the weight of this body on the surface of Mars?

SOLUTION TO PROBLEM 3

From the above problem $g_{Mars} = 3.83 \ ^m\!/_{s^2}$ and the weight on the surface of Mars is

$$w_{Mars} = mg_{Mars} = \left(100 \ kg\right)\left(3.83 \ ^m\!/_{s^2}\right) = 383 \ N$$

SAMPLE PROBLEM 4

Assume that the moon moves about the Earth in circular orbit having a radius of 3.846×10^8 m. The period of revolution of the moon is 27.32 days.

(a) What is the centripetal acceleration of the moon in its orbit?

(b) Knowing the Earth has a mass of 5.97×10^{24} kg, what is the acceleration due to gravity at any point along the orbit of the moon? Express the answer as a decimal value.

SOLUTION TO PROBLEM 4

(a) Convert the period, T, into seconds.

$$27.32 \ day \times \frac{8.64 \times 10^4 \ s}{1 \ day} = 2.36 \times 10^6 \ s$$

Next find the orbital speed of the moon:

$$v = \frac{C}{T} = \frac{2\pi R}{T} = \frac{2\pi\left(3.846\times10^8 \text{ m}\right)}{\left(2.36\times10^6 \text{ s}\right)} = 1.02\times10^3 \text{ }^m\!/\!_s$$

The centripetal acceleration experienced by the moon is $a_c = \frac{v^2}{R}$

and $a_c = \frac{\left(1.02\times10^3 \text{ }^m\!/\!_s\right)^2}{\left(3.846\times10^8 \text{ m}\right)} = 0.0027 \text{ }^m\!/\!_{s^2}$

(b) The acceleration due to gravity at a point 3.846×10^8 m from the center of the Earth:

$$g = G\frac{M_{Earth}}{R^2}$$

$$= \frac{\left(6.73\times10^{-11} \text{ N}\cdot m^2\!/\!_{s^2}\right)\left(5.97\times10^{24} \text{ kg}\right)}{\left(3.846\times10^8 \text{ m}\right)^2}$$

$$= 0.0027 \text{ }^m\!/\!_{s^2}$$

In Newton's earliest investigation into gravitation he suspected that gravity was an inverse square law. In terms of the SI, which did not exist at the time of Newton, he knew the distance between the moon and Earth was 60 Earth radii. He reasoned, as we did above, that the centripetal acceleration at the moon's orbit was $0.0027 \text{ }^m\!/\!_{s^2}$. Then taking g for the surface of the Earth and dividing by the square

$$\frac{9.8 \text{ }^m\!/\!_{s^2}}{60^2} = \frac{9.8 \text{ }^m\!/\!_{s^2}}{3600} = 0.0027 \text{ }^m\!/\!_{s^2}$$

This was all the proof Newton needed to know he was correct. Universal gravitation was an inverse square law.

CIRCULAR ORBIT SPEED

(*College Physics* 9th ed. pages 217–220/10th ed. pages 222–225)

When a space vehicle is launched atop a rocket from the surface of the Earth to orbit, the initial liftoff direction is vertically upward. As the rocket gains altitude, control jets and fins slowly make it turn toward a horizontal trajectory. At the proper point, the satellite separates from the rocket. With too low of an initial speed, the vehicle will follow a nearly parabolic trajectory and will strike the Earth. With just the right speed, the satellite will follow a circular orbit of radius R. We call this speed *the circular orbit speed*. At higher speed the satellite will go into an elliptical orbit or will completely escape the Earth.

A satellite in a circular orbit about a central body of mass M and orbiting a distance R from the center of mass of the body will have an orbital speed given by

$$v = \sqrt{\frac{GM}{R}}$$

The equation holds for any satellite moving in a circular orbit around any astronomical body. The general equations for a satellite moving in elliptical orbits are rather complicated and will not be considered here.

SAMPLE PROBLEM 5

A 500 kg satellite is placed into a circular orbit 300 km above the surface of the Earth.

(a) What is its orbital speed?

(b) What is its orbital period, T?

SOLUTION TO PROBLEM 5

(a) The orbital speed is independent of the mass of the orbiting satellite. The radius of the orbit, R, is the distance from the center of the c.m. of the Earth to the c.m. of the satellite:

$$R = R_E + h = 6{,}378 \text{ km} + 300 \text{ km} = 6{,}678 \text{ km} \times \frac{1{,}000 \text{ m}}{1 \text{ km}} = 6.678 \times 10^6 \text{ m}$$

$$V_{orbit} = \sqrt{\frac{GM_{Earth}}{R}}$$

$$= \sqrt{\frac{\left(6.67 \times 10^{-11} \text{ N} \cdot \text{m}^2 \Big/ \text{kg}^2\right)\left(5.97 \times 10^{24} \text{ kg}\right)}{\left(6.678 \times 10^6 \text{ m}\right)}}$$

$$= 7.72 \times 10^3 \text{ m} \Big/ \text{s}$$

(b) By definition, speed is defined as $v = \dfrac{s}{T}$. The distance traveled in one orbit is $s = C = 2\pi R$. The period then is

$$T = \frac{2\pi R}{v} = \frac{2\pi\left(6.678 \times 10^6 \text{ m}\right)}{7.72 \times 10^3 \text{ m} \Big/ \text{s}} = 5.43 \times 10^3 \text{ s} = 90.6 \text{ min}$$

(b) Alternative solution: Using Kepler's third law $\dfrac{T^2}{R^3} = \dfrac{4\pi^2}{GM}$ and solving for T

$$T = \sqrt{\dfrac{4\pi^2 R^3}{GM_E}} = 2\pi R \sqrt{\dfrac{R}{GM}}$$

$$= 2\pi\left(6.678\times 10^6 \text{ m}\right)\sqrt{\dfrac{\left(6.678\times 10^6 \text{ m}\right)}{G\left(5.97\times 10^{24} \text{ kg}\right)}}$$

$$= 5.43\times 10^3 \text{ s} = \mathbf{90.6 \ min}$$

Note that in (b) and (b) alternative solutions both use the same equation but were approached differently.

SAMPLE PROBLEM 6

A weather satellite circles the Earth in a *geosynchronous orbit* with a period of exactly 1 day. In this way the satellite is always over the same spot all the time. Find the altitude of a geosynchronous orbit.

SOLUTION TO PROBLEM 6

A satellite moving in a circular orbit of radius R covers a distance of $2\pi R$ in a time period T. First, convert 1 day into seconds, $1 \text{ d} = (24 \text{ h})(60 \text{ min}/1 \text{ h})(60 \text{ s}/1 \text{ min}) = 8.64\times 10^4 \text{ s}$. Next write Kepler's third law $T^2 = \left(\dfrac{4\pi^2}{GM_E}\right)R^3$. Solving for R gives

$$R = \sqrt[3]{\dfrac{GMT^2}{4\pi^2}}$$

$$= \sqrt[3]{\dfrac{\left(6.672\times 10^{-11} \ {}^{\text{N}\cdot\text{m}^2}\!\big/\!{}_{\text{kg}^2}\right)\left(5.97\times 10^{24} \text{ kg}\right)\left(8.64\times 10^4 \text{ s}\right)^2}{4\pi^2}}$$

$$R = 4.23\times 10^7 \text{ m}$$

Next we subtract the radius of the Earth to find the altitude, h.

$$h = 4.23\times 10^7 \text{ m} - 0.64\times 10^7 \text{ m} = \mathbf{3.59\times 10^7 \ m}$$

The satellite orbits at 22,310 miles above the surface of the Earth.

ESCAPE VELOCITY

(*College Physics* 9th ed. page 220/10th ed. page 225)

For a space vehicle to escape from the gravitational field of the Earth and never return, it must be launched with a velocity greater than that required to place it into Earth's orbit. The minimum *escape velocity* from the surface of any planet or moon is

$$v_{escape} = \sqrt{\dfrac{2GM}{R}}$$

The escape velocity of a space vehicle is independent of the mass m of the vehicle.

SAMPLE PROBLEM 7

Find the escape velocity from the surface of the Earth required to send a 1000 kg space probe into the depths of outer space.

SOLUTION TO PROBLEM 7

Escape velocity is independent of the mass of the space probe being launched. The escape velocity is

$$V_{escape} = \sqrt{\frac{2GM_{Earth}}{R_{Earth}}}$$

$$= \sqrt{2\frac{\left(6.67\times10^{-11}\,\text{N}\cdot\text{m}^2\!\Big/\text{kg}^2\right)\left(5.97\times10^{24}\,\text{kg}\right)}{\left(6.378\times10^6\,\text{m}\right)}}$$

$$= 1.12\times10^4\,\text{m}\!\Big/\text{s}$$

The above equation can be modified for the Earth, and the escape velocity from the Earth's surface takes the form

$$v = \sqrt{2gR_E}$$

ANGULAR MOMENTUM

(*College Physics* 9th ed. page 222/10th ed. page 227)

Planets move in curved paths and therefore have angular momentum $\vec{L} = M_{planet}\vec{v}R$. When the net force acting on the system is zero, there is no change in angular momentum, L, and angular momentum is conserved. As a planet gets closer to the Sun it must orbit faster in order to maintain constant angular momentum. The mass of the planets is constant. So the law of conservation of angular momentum requires that the product vR remains constant. This is another way of expressing Kepler's second law.

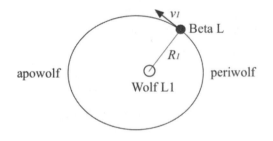

SAMPLE PROBLEM 8

An Earth-size planet named Beta L circles the star Wolf L1. When Beta L is at a distance $R_1 = 1.50\times10^{11}$ m from Wolf L1, it is observed to have an orbital speed of 30.0×10^3 m$\big/$s. What is the orbital speed of Beta L at periwolf ($R_p = 1.00\times10^{10}$ m) and apowolf (3.40×10^{11} m)?

SOLUTION TO PROBLEM 8

The law of conservation for the planet is $\Sigma L_0 = \Sigma L$ and $M_{planet}v_1R_1 = M_{planet}v_{peri}R_{peri}$. Note the mass of the planet appears on both sides of the equation and will divide out. To find the orbital speed at periwolf we now write

$$V_{peri} = \frac{v_1R_1}{R_{peri}} = \frac{\left(30.0\times10^3 \text{ m/s}\right)\left(1.5\times10^{11} \text{ m}\right)}{\left(1.00\times10^{10} \text{ m}\right)} = 450\times10^3 \text{ m/s}$$

For apowolf

$$V_{apo} = \frac{v_1R_1}{R_{apo}} = \frac{\left(30.0\times10^3 \text{ m/s}\right)\left(1.5\times10^{11} \text{ m}\right)}{\left(3.4\times10^{11} \text{ m}\right)} = 13.2\times10^3 \text{ m/s}$$

GRAVITATIONAL POTENTIAL ENERGY

(*College Physics* 9th ed. pages 219–219/10th ed. pages 222–224)

Since gravity is a conservative force, we can define a potential energy associated with it. Recall that the work done, W, in lifting a mass, m, from one point to another in the **g**-field of the Earth equals the gain in the potential energy, U. Work is only done against gravity when the displacement is radial. Moving a body sideways requires no work. There is no vertical displacement.

Recall that the word arbitrary is associated with a choice. We must choose where we start and where we finish. If we choose $U = 0$ at $R = \infty$, then the *gravitational potential energy* is

$$U = -\frac{GmM}{R}$$

SAMPLE PROBLEM 9

A 2,000 kg satellite that is 0.23×10^6 m above the surface of the Earth is in a circular orbit. Calculate the potential energy of the satellite.

SOLUTION TO PROBLEM 9

We need the distance from the center of the Earth to the satellite.

$$R = h + R_E = 0.23\times10^6 \text{ m} + 6.4\times10^6 \text{ m} = 6.63\times10^6 \text{ m}$$

Next, we define the potential energy

$$U = -\frac{GmM}{R}$$

$$= -\frac{\left(6.672\times10^{-11} \text{ N}\cdot\text{m}^2/\text{kg}^2\right)\left(2\times10^3 \text{ kg}\right)\left(5.97\times10^{24} \text{ kg}\right)}{6.63\times10^6 \text{ m}}$$

$$U = -1.21\times10^{11} \text{ J}$$

WEIGHTLESSNESS

(*College Physics* 9th ed. page 210/10th ed. page 215)

Astronauts orbiting the Earth in an artificial satellite feel *apparent weightlessness*. This is similar to the sensation experienced by a person in a freely falling elevator. When the elevator accelerates downward with uniform acceleration *a*, the apparent weight of the person in the elevator is $w = m(g - a)$. When the elevator accelerates downward, the passenger feels lighter.

If the elevator is in *free fall*, the downward acceleration is $a = g$, and $w = m(g - g) = 0$. Thus, a person feels apparent weightlessness in a freely falling elevator.

A satellite is in a continuous state of free fall. Although the force of gravity acts on the satellite, an astronaut inside experiences apparent weightlessness.

GRAVITATION: STUDENT OBJECTIVES FOR THE AP EXAM

- ▤ You should be able to explain the differences between mass and weight.
- ▤ You should be able to state Newton's universal law of gravitation.
- ▤ You should be able to calculate gravitational forces between two bodies.
- ▤ You should be able to determine the orbital speed and angular momentum of a satellite in a circular orbit.
- ▤ You should understand the concept of weightlessness.
- ▤ You should be able to explain why the moon does not crash into the Earth despite the large gravitational force acting on it.

MULTIPLE-CHOICE QUESTIONS

1. A radius vector, *r*, is a straight line that runs from the center of mass of one body to the center of mass of a second body, as in the diagram below depicting the Earth and a satellite. The radius vector changes length as the satellite moves toward perigee (closest distance to the Earth) because of gravitational forces between the Earth and the satellite.

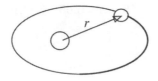

The velocity of the center of mass as the satellite approaches perigee will
(A) increase
(B) decrease
(C) remain constant
(D) be zero

2. A 10.0 kg body is lifted 2.00 m above the surface of the Earth. The work done by the gravitational force is
   (A) –20.0 J
   (B) 20.0 J
   (C) –196 J
   (D) 196 J

3. The Earth moves in an elliptical orbit around the sun as shown in the diagram below.

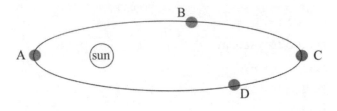

   Rank the positions for the force acting on the Earth due to the sun from highest to lowest.
   (A) A > C > B > D
   (B) A > B > D > C
   (C) C > D > B > A
   (D) C > A > D > B

4. A body is moved from one isoline of equal gravitational potential energy to another as shown in the illustration below. Rank the positions of gravitational potential energy per unit mass from the greatest to the least.

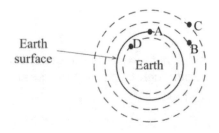

   (A) A > B > C > D
   (B) D > A > B > C
   (C) C > B > A > D
   (D) D > C > B > A

5. If you could place an object at the center of the Earth, which of the following statements would be true for the object at that location?
   (A) The mass and the weight of the object would be the same as the values on the surface of the Earth.
   (B) The mass would be zero and the weight would be the same as on the surface.
   (C) The mass and the weight would both be zero.
   (D) The weight would be zero and the mass would be the same as the value on the surface of the Earth.

6. Three spheres $m_1 = 10.0 \text{ kg}$, $m_2 = 20.0 \text{ kg}$ and $m_3 = 30.0 \text{ kg}$ are located along the x-axis as shown below. What is the resultant force on M_2 due to the other two spheres?

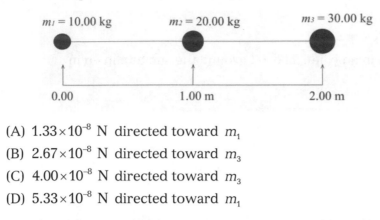

$m_1 = 10.00 \text{ kg}$ $m_2 = 20.00 \text{ kg}$ $m_3 = 30.00 \text{ kg}$

0.00   1.00 m   2.00 m

(A) 1.33×10^{-8} N directed toward m_1

(B) 2.67×10^{-8} N directed toward m_3

(C) 4.00×10^{-8} N directed toward m_3

(D) 5.33×10^{-8} N directed toward m_1

7. The gravitational force between two point masses A and B is $\vec{F}$ when they are r meters apart. When the mass of A is increased by a factor of 4, the mass of B is halved and the distance of separation is increased by a factor of three, what is the new force acting between them?

(A) $\dfrac{2}{9}\vec{F}_1$

(B) $\dfrac{2}{3}\vec{F}_1$

(C) $2\vec{F}_1$

(D) $3\vec{F}_1$

8. Which of the following graphs best represents the gravitational force as a function of distance between two point masses m_1 and m_2 as they are moved farther apart?

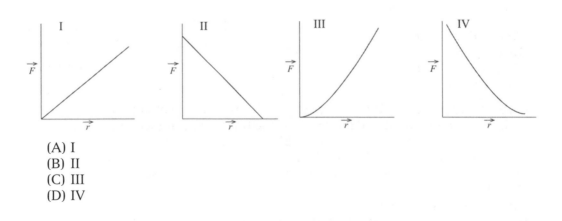

(A) I

(B) II

(C) III

(D) IV

9. A satellite is in circular motion a distance of $3R_E$ above the surface of the Earth. The acceleration experienced by the satellite at that location is closest to

   (A) 9.8 m/s^2

   (B) 1.1 m/s^2

   (C) 0.61 m/s^2

   (D) 0

10. What is the change in the gravitational potential energy of the Earth satellite system when a 20,000 kg satellite is boosted from a distance of $2R_E$ to a distance of $3R_E$ above the surface of the Earth?

    (A) $-1.03 \times 10^{11}\,\text{J}$

    (B) $1.03 \times 10^{11}\,\text{J}$

    (C) $-2.08 \times 10^{11}\,\text{J}$

    (D) $2.08 \times 10^{11}\,\text{J}$

11. What is the gravitational acceleration on the surface of a planet that has three times the mass and twice the radius of the Earth?

    (A) $\dfrac{3}{4}g$

    (B) g

    (C) $\dfrac{4}{3}g$

    (D) $2g$

12. A small moon is in a circular orbit around its planet as shown below.

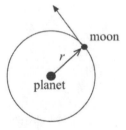

    Which of the vectors displayed below gives the correct direction for the velocity and the acceleration of the moon at the point indicated in its orbit?

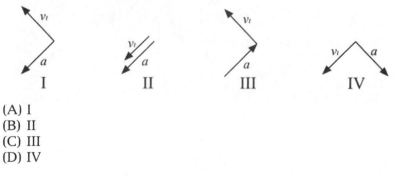

    (A) I
    (B) II
    (C) III
    (D) IV

13. A 600 N astronaut travels from the Earth to the moon. The mass of the astronaut as measured on the moon is
    (A) zero
    (B) 1/6 of the mass of the astronaut on the Earth
    (C) equal to the mass of the astronaut on the Earth
    (D) 6 times the mass of the astronaut on the Earth

14. Two satellites of different masses are in the same circular orbit around Earth. Which of the following statements is correct?
    (A) The magnitude of the gravitational force is the same for both satellites since they are in the same orbit, and both satellites have the same period.
    (B) The magnitude of the gravitational force is zero for the smaller satellite because it in the same orbit as the larger satellite. Thus the gravitational force exerted on the larger satellite gives it a larger period.
    (C) The magnitude of the gravitational force depends on the masses of the satellites, and the orbital periods are the same.
    (D) The magnitude of the gravitational force is zero for both satellites, and they have the same period.

15. Which of the illustrations show the correct relationship between the gravitational field strength vectors and the isolines of gravitational potential energy per unit mass?

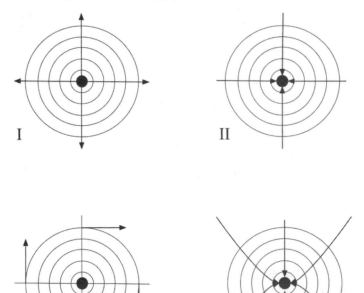

    (A) I
    (B) II
    (C) III
    (D) IV

FREE-RESPONSE PROBLEMS

1. (a) Design an experiment to measure the gravitational mass and the inertial mass of a body and distinguish between the two parts of the experiment in enough detail that another student could duplicate your experiment and obtain the same results.
   (b) What measurements will you take, and how will you utilize these measurements in the experiment?
   (c) If you plot a graph(s), what will you plot and how will you use the information obtained from the graph in your analysis of the experiment(s)?

2. (a) A satellite moves around a central body as shown below.

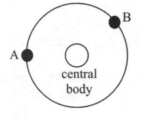

   The force on the satellite is
   _____ greatest at point A
   _____ greatest at point B
   _____ the same at points A and B
   Justify your answer without a mathematical solution.

   (b) If the orbit is changed to the diagram below, then the force on the satellite is

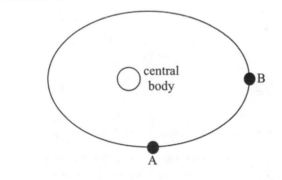

   _____ greater at point A
   _____ greater at point B
   _____ the same at points A and B
   Justify your answer without a mathematical solution.

(c) The orbit is now changed to the diagram below

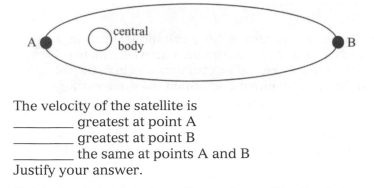

The velocity of the satellite is
_____ greatest at point A
_____ greatest at point B
_____ the same at points A and B
Justify your answer.

3. A 100.0 kg body is taken from the surface of the Earth to a satellite in orbit at an altitude of 1.50 R_E above the surface of the Earth.
   (a) Determine the weight of the body on the surface of the Earth.
   (b) Determine the weight of the body at the altitude 1.50 R_E above the surface of the Earth.
   (c) What is the fractional change in the weight of the body?
   (d) What is the fractional change in the mass of the body?

4. A 2000.0 kg satellite is inserted into an orbit 7.00×10^6 m above the surface of the Earth.
   (a) What is the gravitational force exerted between the satellite and the Earth?
   (b) Determine the orbital velocity of the satellite in this orbit.
   (c) What is the change in the potential energy and the work done by the force of gravity in lifting the satellite to an orbit that is 12.0×10^6 m above the surface of the Earth?

Answers

Multiple-Choice Questions

1. **A** The external force applied to the satellite from $F = G\dfrac{m_s M_E}{r^2}$

   increases as the satellite moves inward toward the Earth. Since $\Sigma F = ma$, the satellite in its elliptical path increases in speed. There is an increase the velocity of the center of mass as the satellite approaches perigee.
   (*College Physics* 9th ed. pages 214–217/10th ed. pages 246–248)
   (L.O. 4.A.3.1)

2. **C** The work done is the negative of the change in the gravitational potential energy of the Earth-object (10.0 kg body) system.
   (*College Physics* 9th ed. pages 217–219/10th ed. pages 246–248)
   (L.O. 5.B.5.5)

3. **B** The force acting between the Earth and the Sun is given by

   $F = G\dfrac{M_s M_E}{r^2}$. When the Earth is closest to the Sun, the

gravitational force is the greatest; at aphelion, the farthest point in the orbit, the force is the least. The correct ranking is A >B > D > C.
(*College Physics* 9th ed. pages 214–217/10th ed. pages 246–248)
(L.O. 3.A.4.2)

4. **C** Gravitational potential energy is measured to a reference point. The surface of the Earth is set at zero gravitational potential energy. Point D is shown below the surface of the Earth and therefore is negative. The isoline showing a position farthest from the surface has the greatest gravitational potential energy per unit mass.
(*College Physics* 9th ed. pages 217–219/10th ed. pages 246–248)
(L.O. 5.B.5.5)

5. **D** Mass is the measure of inertia of the body; the mass will not change as we move the body from location to location. The weight of the body is determined by $F = w = mg$ and if the body is located at the center of the Earth it will experience equal pulls in all directions, making the net gravitational force on it $\Sigma F = 0$ and thus both its acceleration and weight will be zero.
(*College Physics* 9th ed. pages 214–217/10th ed. pages 246–248)
(L.O. 2.B.1.1)

6. **B** The net force on M_2 is the vector sum of the forces between M_2 and the other two spheres.

$$F_{12} = \left(6.67 \times 10^{-11}\ \frac{N \cdot m^2}{kg^2}\right)\left(\frac{10.0\ kg \cdot 20.0\ kg}{(1.00\ m)^2}\right) = 1.33 \times 10^{-8}\ N \text{ directed}$$

toward M_1. The force between M_2 and M_3 is

$$F_{23} = \left(6.67 \times 10^{-11}\ \frac{N \cdot m^2}{kg^2}\right)\left(\frac{20.0\ kg \cdot 30.0\ kg}{(1.00\ m)^2}\right) = 4.00 \times 10^{-8}\ N \text{ directed}$$

toward M_3.

The net force is $2.67 \times 10^{-8}\ N$ directed toward M_3.
(*College Physics* 9th ed. pages 214–217/10th ed. pages 246–248)
(L.O. 3.C.1.1)

7. **A** The original force between the two bodies is $F = G\dfrac{M_A M_B}{r^2}$. The

new force is $F_2 = G\dfrac{4M_A\left(\frac{1}{2}M_B\right)}{(3r)^2}$ Setting up a ratio of $\dfrac{F_1}{F_2} =$

$\dfrac{9r^2}{4M_A\left(\frac{1}{2}M_B\right)} \cdot \dfrac{M_A M_B}{r^2}$ and solving for the new force gives $\dfrac{2}{9}F_1$.

(*College Physics* 9th ed. pages 214–217/10th ed. pages 246–248)
(L.O. 3.C.1.1)

8. **D** The force between two point masses is an inverse square law. Increasing the distance by a factor of 2 reduces the force by one-fourth, increasing r by a factor 3 drops the force to one ninth of its initial value.
(*College Physics* 9th ed. pages 214–217/10th ed. pages 246–248)
(L.O. 3.C.1.1)

9. **C** The acceleration due to gravity at the location of $4R_E$ from the center of the Earth is given by

$$\vec{g} = \left(6.67 \times 10^{-11} \ \frac{\text{N} \cdot \text{m}^2}{\text{kg}^2}\right)\left(\frac{5.98 \times 10^{24} \ \text{kg}}{\left(4 \cdot 6.38 \times 10^6 \ \text{m}\right)^2}\right) = 0.61 \ \frac{\text{m}}{\text{s}^2} \ .$$

(*College Physics* 9th ed. pages 214–217/10th ed. pages 246–247)
(L.O. 2.B.2.1)

10. **B** The change in the altitude of the satellite is measured as the distance $3R_E$ from the center of the Earth to $4R_E$ from the center of the Earth. Substitution into the equation

$$PE_{4R_E} - PE_{3R_E} = -GM_E m_s \left(\frac{1}{4R_E} - \frac{1}{3R_E}\right)$$

$$PE_{4R_E} - PE_{3R_E} =$$
$$-\left(6.67 \times 10^{-11} \ \frac{\text{N} \cdot \text{m}^2}{\text{kg}^2}\right)\left(5.98 \times 10^{24} \ \text{kg}\right)\left(2.00 \times 10^4 \ \text{kg}\right)\left(\frac{1}{4\left(6.38 \times 10^6 \ \text{m}\right)} - \frac{1}{3\left(6.38 \times 10^6 \ \text{m}\right)}\right)$$

$$PE_{4R_E} - PE_{3R_E} = -7.98 \times 10^{18} \left(3.94 \times 10^{-8} - 5.23 \times 10^{-8}\right) \text{J} =$$
$$1.03 \times 10^{11} \ \text{J}$$

(*College Physics* 9th ed. pages 217–219/10th ed. pages 246–247)
(L.O. 5.B.5.5)

11. **A** The acceleration due to gravity on the planet can be determined from the ratio of the acceleration in terms of "g" to the acceleration g on the surface of the Earth.

$$\frac{g_{planet}}{g_{Earth}} = \frac{G\left(\dfrac{3M}{(2R)^2}\right)}{G\left(\dfrac{M}{R^2}\right)} = \frac{\left(\dfrac{3}{4}\right)}{\left(\dfrac{1}{1}\right)} = \frac{3}{4}g$$

(*College Physics* 9th ed. pages 214–216/10th ed. pages 246–247)
(L.O. 2.B.2.1)

12. **A** The acceleration of the moon is directed along the radial line connecting the centers of mass of the moon and the planet, toward the planet. The velocity of the moon is tangential to its orbit.
(*College Physics* 9th ed. pages 214–216/10th ed. pages 246–247)
(L.O. 3.B.2.1)

13. **C** The mass of the astronaut is the same as the mass on Earth. The lunar value for g_{moon} as determined from $g_{moon} = G\dfrac{M_{moon}}{r_{moon}^2}$ gives

$$g_{moon} = 6.67 \times 10^{-11} \, \frac{N \cdot m^2}{kg^2} \frac{\left(7.36 \times 10^{22} \, kg\right)}{\left(1.74 \times 10^6 \, m^2\right)} \qquad g_{moon} = 1.62 \, \frac{m}{s^2} \, . \, \text{The}$$

weight of the astronaut is 1/6 of the weight on Earth.
(*College Physics* 9th ed. pages 214–217/10th ed. pages 246–247)
(L.O. 2.B.2.1, 2.B.2.2)

14. **C** Newton's law of gravitation $F = G\dfrac{M_s M_E}{r^2}$ shows that the force
is dependent on the product of the masses. Thus the satellite of
larger mass will experience the larger force. Kepler's third law also
applies. $T^2 = \dfrac{4\pi^2}{GM} r^3$ indicates that the periods are the same since
they are in the same orbit.
(*College Physics* 9th ed. pages 214–217, 221–224/10th ed. pages
246–247)
(L.O. 3.A.3.4, 3.A.4.1)

15. **B** The direction of the gravitational field strength vector
(acceleration) is into the center of mass of the body creating the
field. The isolines of gravitational potential energy are
perpendicular to the direction of the gravitational field strength
vector. Work is done in moving a body in a gravitational field
between two isolines. No work is done when the mass is moved
along an isoline.
(*College Physics* 9th ed. pages 214–217/10th ed. pages 246–247)
(L.O. 5.B.5.4)

FREE-RESPONSE PROBLEMS

1. The experimental question has two parts, inertial mass and
gravitational mass.
(a) A body that experiences a net unbalanced force will accelerate.
The inertia of the body is the ratio of $F\!/\!_a$ and is a constant.

Using a known force that is applied to a body, determine its
acceleration. Keep increasing the known force, and determine
the acceleration for each trial.

(b) The laboratory setup might look like this or some other
variation of a known force that produces acceleration of a
body.

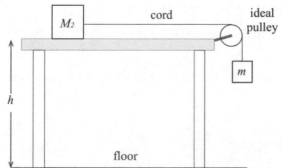

© 2015 Cengage Learning. All Rights Reserved. May not be copied, scanned, or duplicated, in whole or in part, except for use as permitted in a license distributed
with a certain product or service or otherwise on a password-protected website for classroom use.

Adjust the system so that the system moves with constant velocity. This is the force needed to overcome friction between the mass on the table and the table. Measure the height of the table and record. Add known weights to the weight hanger and record this force in newtons. Determine the time for the hanging weight to reach the floor. From the height of the table, and the time, the acceleration can be determined from

$$y = \frac{1}{2}at^2 .$$

(c) Plot a graph of F verses a. Since the graph is linear, the slope of the line will be the inertial mass in kg.

Gravitational mass can be determined by comparing the weight of a body from a spring scale using Hooke's law.

The inertial mass and the gravitational mass can be compared. They are proportional and independent of each other.
(*College Physics* 9th ed. pages 214–217/10th ed. pages 246–248)
(L.O. 1.C.1.1, 1.C.3.1, 2.B 1.1)

2. (a) Correct line checked is _____√_____ the same at points **A** and **B**.

   The orbit is circular and the radius is constant; thus the force is constant.

   (b) Correct line checked is ___√___ greatest at point **A**.

   The orbit is now elliptical, and the radius will vary from point to point. The satellite is closer to the central body at point **A**; therefore the force is greater at **A** than at **B**.

   (c) Correct line checked is ___√___ greatest at point **A**. The force on the body $F = G\dfrac{M \cdot m}{r^2}$ produces a larger centripetal

   force $F = \dfrac{m \cdot v^2}{r_A}$ at point **A** since the distance from the central

   body is much smaller at **A** than at **B**.
   (*College Physics* 9th ed. pages 207–210, 214–217/10th ed. pages 211–215, 219–222)
   (L.O. 3.B.1.1, 3.C.1.2)

3. (a) The weight of the body on the surface of the Earth is determined from $F = w = mg$. On the surface of the Earth, the

   weight is $100.0 \text{ kg}\left(9.80 \text{ m}\middle/\text{s}^2\right) = 980.0 \text{ N}$.

   (b) At the elevation of 1.50 R_E, the 100.0 kg body is 2.50 R_E from the center of the Earth.

   At that location the acceleration due to gravity is determined

   from $g = G\dfrac{M_E}{r_E^2}$

Substitution into the equation gives

$$g = \left(6.67 \times 10^{-11} \ \frac{N \cdot m^2}{kg^2}\right) \frac{5.98 \times 10^{24} \ kg}{\left(1.60 \times 10^7 \ m\right)^2} = \mathbf{1.56 \ m/s^2}$$

(c) The weight of the body at that location

$$W_{2.50 \ R_E} = 100.0 \ kg\left(1.56 \ m/s^2\right) = \mathbf{156.0 \ N} \ .$$

The fractional change is determined by comparing the value of **g** at the two locations. Thus there is a **84.1% loss of weight** at that height.

(d) The mass of the body is constant. It is **100.0 kg** both on the surface of the Earth and at the elevation of 1.5 R_E above the surface of the Earth.

(*College Physics* 9th ed. pages 214–217/10th ed. pages 219–222)
(L.O. 2.B.1.1, 2.B.2.1)

4. (a) The gravitational force acting between the Earth and the satellite is determined from

$$F = G\frac{M \cdot m}{r^2} \ . \quad \text{Substitution into the equation is}$$

$$\vec{F} = \left(6.67 \times 10^{-11} \ \frac{N \cdot m^2}{kg^2}\right)\left(\frac{5.98 \times 10^{24} \ kg \cdot 2000 \ kg}{\left(6.38 \times 10^6 \ m + 7.00 \times 10^6 \ m\right)^2}\right)$$

The force is **4450 N**.

(b) The orbital velocity is determined from $F_g = F_c$. Substitution into the centripetal force equation, $\vec{F} = \frac{m \cdot v^2}{r}$, will give the orbital velocity $4450 \ N = \frac{2000.0 \ kg \cdot v^2}{1.34 \times 10^7 \ m}$

The velocity $v = \sqrt{\frac{5.96 \times 10^{10} \ N \cdot m}{2000.0 \ kg}}$, thus $v = \mathbf{5.46 \times 10^3 \ \frac{m}{s}}$

(c) The change in the gravitational potential energy is $\Delta U = -\frac{GM_E m}{r_f} - \left(-\frac{GM_E m}{r_f}\right)$

$$\Delta U = -GM_E m\left(-\frac{1}{r_f} + \frac{1}{r_i}\right)$$

$$\Delta U = 7.98 \times 10^{17} \ N \cdot m^2 \left(-\frac{1}{1.84 \times 10^7 \ m} + \frac{1}{1.34 \times 10^7 \ m}\right)$$

The change in the potential energy of the satellite is 1.62×10^{10} J.

The work done by the gravitational force is $-\Delta U = \mathbf{-1.62 \times 10^{10} \ J}$.

(*College Physics* 9th ed. pages 214–219/10th ed. pages 219–224)
(L.O. 3.B.1.4, 3.C.1.1, 3.C.1.2, 4.C.1.1, 5.B.4.2)

9

OSCILLATORY MOTION

PERIODIC MOTION

(College Physics 9th ed. pages 437–439/10th ed. pages 445–447)

To this point we have studied three types of motion. The simplest is that of a body in translatory equilibrium, a motion consisting of constant speed in an unchanging direction. The second type of motion that is produced by the action of a constant force parallel to the direction of motion is that in which the direction is constant and the speed increases uniformly. Projectile motion is an example of these two types of motion. The third type of motion is uniform circular motion that is produced by a centripetal force of constant magnitude directed inward along the radius of the circular path of the moving body.

There is one common and important type of nonuniformly accelerated motion that can be analyzed rather simply. We call this motion *periodic* or *oscillatory* motion.

Oscillatory motion is quite important in many areas of physics. It is the to-and-fro or vibrating motion of bodies stretched or bent from their normal positions and then released. Such a body moves back and forth along a fixed path, repeating over and over a fixed set of motions and returning to each position and velocity after a definite period of time. Besides being called oscillatory, or periodic, motion, it is also called *harmonic* motion. This motion is caused by varying forces and hence the body experiences varying accelerations.

Consider a block of mass m at rest on a frictionless surface. The block is attached to a spring of elastic constant k that is fastened to a rigid wall. The mass is pulled to the right and is released from rest. The center of mass of the block oscillates between two amplitude positions,

+A and –A. The motion of the oscillating mass is bounded by these two points, +A and –A.

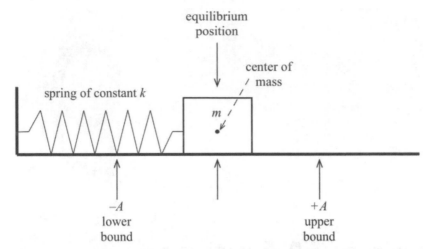

The spring exerts a restoring force on the block that tends to pull or push it back to its initial position, the *equilibrium position*. This force, Hooke's law, is proportional to the displacement x but opposite in direction to the displacement.

$F = -kx$

When the block is released, the restoring force, which is the net force, produces an acceleration a:

$F = ma = -kx$

$$a = -\frac{k}{m}x$$

The acceleration a is proportional to the displacement x but opposite in direction.

As the block slides toward its equilibrium position, its speed increases but the force, and consequently the acceleration, decreases until it becomes zero when the block reaches the equilibrium position. Because of its momentum, the block continues past the equilibrium position, but at once a retarding force comes into being which increases until the block reaches the amplitude position –A, where it stops momentarily and begins its return trip. At all times during this motion the net force, and hence the acceleration, is proportional to the displacement and directed toward the equilibrium position.

This type of oscillatory motion, when the acceleration is proportional to the displacement and is always directed toward the equilibrium position, is called *simple harmonic motion*, SHM. Simple harmonic motion is always motion along a straight line, the acceleration and velocity constantly changing as the oscillating block moves through its series of positions.

AP Tip

A body can only be in simple harmonic motion when there is a force of restitution.

AMPLITUDE, PERIOD, AND FREQUENCY

(College Physics 9th ed. pages 438–439/10th ed. pages 446–447)

The *amplitude, A,* of oscillatory motion is the maximum displacement from the equilibrium position. $\pm A$ are the boundaries of the motion. Amplitude is expressed in meters, m.

The *period, T,* of an oscillating body is the time for a complete to-and-fro motion, or a complete oscillation. Period is expressed in seconds, s.

The *frequency, f,* of the oscillatory motion is the number of complete oscillations per second. The frequency is defined as the reciprocal of the period

$$f = \frac{1}{T}$$

Frequency is expressed in hertz, Hz and $1\ Hz = \frac{1}{s} = s^{-1}$.

The *angular frequency,* ω, is defined as

$$\omega = 2\pi f = \frac{2\pi}{T}$$

and it is expressed in $\frac{rad}{s}$. It is also expressed in Hz and

$1\ Hz = 1\frac{rad}{s} = s^{-1}$.

LOCATION OF A HARMONIC OSCILLATOR

(College Physics 9th ed. page 449/10th ed. page 457)

When an oscillator like the block on a frictionless surface that is connected to a spring is pulled to the right, aligning its center of mass to the amplitude position $+A$ and is then released from rest, it undergoes SHM. At any time *t* after it is released its position *x* is found by using

$$x = A\cos \omega t$$

Note that the equation is a cosine function. The graph of the cosine function starts at $+A$ and oscillates through $-A$ back to $+A$ for a complete cycle or oscillation.

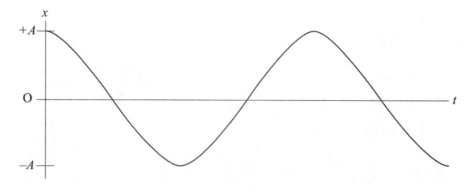

If the oscillator is given a shove left or right at $+A$ to begin the motion the situation becomes complex and will not be handled here.

THE ACCELERATION OF A HARMONIC OSCILLATOR

(*College Physics* 9th ed. pages 449–450/10th ed. pages 457–458)

Above you saw that the acceleration of the oscillator is a function of position, $a = f(x)$ or $a = -\dfrac{k}{m}x$. The acceleration of the oscillator is also given by

$$a = -\omega^2 x$$

The maximum acceleration, a_{max}, occurs at the amplitude positions, $a_{max} \propto \pm A$ and is expressed as

$$a_{max} = -\omega^2 A$$

Since $a = -\dfrac{k}{m}x$ and $a = -\omega^2 x$ then $\omega^2 = \dfrac{k}{m}$ and taking the square root of both sides yields

$$\omega = \sqrt{\dfrac{k}{m}}$$

Frequency can now be expressed as

$$f = \dfrac{1}{2\pi}\sqrt{\dfrac{k}{m}}$$

And the period is

$$T = 2\pi\sqrt{\dfrac{m}{k}}$$

SAMPLE PROBLEM 1

A 0.40 kg mass is attached to a vertical spring of $k = 10.0 \; \text{N}\!/\!\text{m}$. The mass is displaced 0.04 m vertically downward from equilibrium and is released from rest. The mass executes SHM. Neglecting friction and air resistance, find

(a) the angular frequency

(b) the period of motion

(c) the maximum acceleration experienced by the mass

SOLUTION TO PROBLEM 1

(a) The angular frequency is

$$\omega = \sqrt{\dfrac{k}{m}} = \sqrt{\dfrac{10.0 \; \text{N}\!/\!\text{m}}{0.40 \; \text{m}}} = \sqrt{25 \; 1\!/\!\text{s}^2} = 5.0 \; \dfrac{\text{rad}}{\text{s}}$$

(b) The period of the oscillator is

$$T = \frac{2\pi}{\omega} = \frac{2\pi \ \text{rad}}{5.0 \ \text{rad}/\text{s}} = \textbf{1.26 s}$$

(c) The maximum acceleration is

$$a_{max} = -\omega^2 A = -\left(25.0 \ \text{rad}^2/\text{s}^2\right)(0.04 \ \text{m}) = -\textbf{1.00} \ \frac{\textbf{m}}{\textbf{s}^2}$$

THE ENERGY OF A HARMONIC OSCILLATOR

(College Physics 9th ed. pages 441–445/10th ed. pages 449–453)

The total energy, E, of a mechanical system is the sum of its kinetic energy, K, and potential energy, U, or $E = K + U$.

The kinetic energy is zero at the amplitude positions since the body is momentarily at rest. The kinetic energy is always zero at $\pm A$. At the equilibrium position, $x = 0$, the kinetic energy of the body is a maximum and is $K = \frac{1}{2}mv^2$.

The elastic potential energy, $U = \frac{1}{2}kx^2$, of the system is zero at the equilibrium position since $x = 0$. At the amplitude positions U is a maximum.

The total energy of a simple harmonic oscillator is

$$E = \frac{1}{2}kA^2$$

Without proof, the velocity of the oscillator at any position, x, is given by

$$v = \pm\omega\sqrt{A^2 - x^2}$$

Therefore

$$v_{max} = \pm\vec{\omega}A$$

SAMPLE PROBLEM 2

A 0.50 kg block is connected to a horizontal spring, $k = 20.0 \ \text{N}/\text{m}$. The block is pulled to the right and then released from rest where it begins to oscillate on a horizontal, frictionless surface with amplitude 0.03 m. Analyze the motion of the block.

SOLUTION TO PROBLEM 2

The spring exerts a force on the block and that force, Hooke's law, is a force of restitution making the motion simple harmonic.

The acceleration is zero at equilibrium. Maximum acceleration occurs at $\pm A$.

$$a_{max} = \pm\omega^2 A = \pm\frac{k}{m} \ \text{since} \ \omega = \sqrt{\frac{k}{m}}$$

$$a_{max} = \pm\left(\frac{20 \text{ N}/\text{m}}{0.5 \text{ kg}}\right)(0.03 \text{ m}) = \pm 1.20 \frac{\text{m}}{\text{s}^2}$$

Maximum velocity occurs at equilibrium where $x = 0$.

$$V_{max} = \pm\omega A = \pm\sqrt{\frac{k}{m}}A = \pm\sqrt{\frac{20.0 \text{ N}/\text{m}}{0.5 \text{ kg}}}(0.03 \text{ m}) = \pm 0.19 \frac{\text{m}}{\text{s}}$$

The total energy of the system is found by

$$E = \frac{1}{2}kA^2 = \frac{1}{2}(20.0 \text{ N}/\text{m})(0.03 \text{ m})^2 = 0.009 \text{ J}$$

The angular frequency is related to frequency of vibration or oscillation by

$$\omega = 2\pi f \text{ and then } f = \frac{\omega}{2\pi} = \frac{1}{2\pi}\sqrt{\frac{k}{m}} = \frac{1}{2\pi}\sqrt{\frac{20.0 \text{ N}/\text{m}}{0.5 \text{ kg}}} = 1.007 \text{ Hz}$$

Period is the reciprocal of the frequency of vibration.

$$T = \frac{1}{f} = \frac{1}{1.007 \text{ s}^{-1}} = 0.993 \text{ s}$$

The angular frequency $\omega = \sqrt{\frac{k}{m}}$ will allow us to write the position equation of the oscillator.

$$\omega = \sqrt{\frac{k}{m}} = \sqrt{\frac{20.0 \text{ N}/\text{m}}{0.5 \text{ kg}}} = 6.325 \frac{\text{rad}}{\text{s}}$$

Since the equation of motion is $x = A\cos\omega t$, then $x = 0.03\cos(6.325t)$

SAMPLE PROBLEM 3

Consider the system analysis above.

(a) Determine the velocity of the block when its displacement is 0.02 m and it is moving to the right.

(b) Find the acceleration of the block when its displacement is 0.02 m and it is moving to the right.

(c) What are the kinetic energy, elastic potential energy, and total energy of the oscillator when it is at the 0.02 m position to the right of equilibrium?

SOLUTION TO PROBLEM 3

(a) $v = \pm\omega\sqrt{A^2 - x^2} = \pm(6.325 \text{ s}^{-1})\sqrt{(0.03 \text{ m})^2 - (0.02 \text{ m})^2} = \pm 0.141 \frac{\text{m}}{\text{s}}$

Since the block travels to the right, the velocity is positive and

$v = 0.141 \frac{\text{m}}{\text{s}}$

(b) $a = \pm\omega^2 x = \pm(6.325 \text{ s}^{-1})^2 (0.02 \text{ m}) = \pm 0.800 \dfrac{\text{m}}{\text{s}^2}$

Since the block moves right, the elastic force acts in the opposite direction, slowing it. Thus $a = -\mathbf{0.800} \dfrac{\mathbf{m}}{\mathbf{s}^2}$.

(c) Kinetic energy: $K = \dfrac{1}{2}mv^2 = \dfrac{1}{2}(0.50 \text{ kg})\left(0.141 \dfrac{\text{m}}{\text{s}}\right)^2 = \mathbf{0.005 \text{ J}}$

Potential energy: $U = \dfrac{1}{2}kx^2 = \dfrac{1}{2}\left(20.0 \text{ N}/_{\text{m}}\right)(0.02 \text{ m})^2 = \mathbf{0.004 \text{ J}}$

Total energy: $E = K + U = 0.005 \text{ J} + 0.004 \text{ J} = \mathbf{0.009 \text{ J}}$

THE SIMPLE PENDULUM

(*College Physics* 9th ed. pages 451–454/10th ed. pages 460–462)

A simple pendulum is an idealized body that consists of a light, inextensible cord, one end of which is attached to a fixed support O, and a small mass, called a *pendulum bob*, which is attached to the other end. When at rest the bob hangs at the equilibrium position. When pulled aside to the amplitude position and released from rest, it travels an arc length x through the equilibrium position to the amplitude position on the other side. If the arc length is made very small so that it approximates a straight line, the motion of the pendulum is simple harmonic.

Simple Pendulum

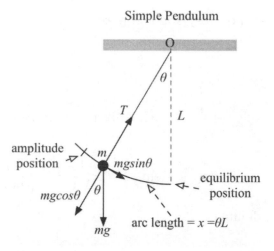

The forces acting on the bob are its weight, *mg*, and the tension, *T*, in the cord. Resolve the weight vector, *mg*, into a radial component, $mg\cos\theta$, and a tangential component, $mg\sin\theta$. The radial component along with the tension T supply the centripetal acceleration that keeps the bob moving along a circular arc. The tangential component is the restoring force acting on the bob tending to return it to the equilibrium position. The force of restitution is:

$F = -mg\sin\theta$

Notice that the force of restitution is proportional to $\sin\theta$ and not the angular displacement, θ. For very small angles, $1° < \theta < 6°$, the sine of the angle in degrees is about equal to the angle expressed in radians. See the table that follows. The displacement along the arc is $x = \theta L$, and for small angles this is nearly straight-line motion.

The relationship between degrees and radians can be written as $1° \times \dfrac{\pi\ \text{rad}}{180°}$.

Define deviation as $\Delta = \left|\sin\theta - \theta(\text{ in radians})\right|$

Define percent deviation as $\%\Delta = \dfrac{\Delta \times 100\%}{\sin\theta}$

Degrees and Radians Table for Small Angles

angle θ	$\sin\theta$	θ in radians	deviation Δ	% deviation
1°	0.01745	0.01745	0	0
2°	0.03490	0.03491	0.00001	0.03%
3°	0.05234	0.05236	0.00002	0.04%
4°	0.06976	0.06981	0.00005	0.06%
5°	0.08716	0.08727	0.00011	0.13%
10°	0.17365	0.17453	0.00088	0.50%

The arc length, x, is related to the length, L, of the pendulum by $x = \theta L$ and from this $\theta = \dfrac{x}{L}$. For very small angles $\sin\theta \approx \theta$, we can write

$$F = -mg\sin\theta = -mg\theta = -mg\frac{x}{L}$$

Rearranging terms yields $F = -\left(\dfrac{mg}{L}\right)x$ which is a form of Hooke's law, $F = -kx$.

Define $k = \dfrac{mg}{L}$. For an oscillating system, $T = 2\pi\sqrt{\dfrac{m}{k}} = 2\pi\sqrt{\dfrac{m}{mg/L}}$.

The period for a simple pendulum is

$$T = 2\pi\sqrt{\frac{L}{g}}$$

AP Tip

The period of the simple pendulum is independent of the mass of the pendulum bob.

SAMPLE PROBLEM 4

Calculate the length of a simple pendulum with a period of 4.00 seconds.

SOLUTION TO PROBLEM 4

By definition $T = 2\pi\sqrt{\dfrac{L}{g}}$ and solving for the length yields

$$L = \frac{T^2 g}{4\pi^2} = \frac{(4.00\ \text{s})^2 \left(9.80\ \text{m}/\text{s}^2\right)}{4\pi^2} = \textbf{3.97 m}$$

SAMPLE PROBLEM 5

Find an expression for the angular frequency of a simple pendulum.

SOLUTION TO PROBLEM 5

Period is $T = 2\pi\sqrt{\dfrac{L}{g}}$ and frequency is defined as $f = \dfrac{1}{T}$.

For the simple pendulum

$f = \dfrac{1}{2\pi\sqrt{\dfrac{L}{g}}} = \dfrac{1}{2\pi}\sqrt{\dfrac{g}{L}}$. Cross-multiplying yields $2\pi f = \sqrt{\dfrac{g}{L}}$.

Angular frequency is defined by $\omega = 2\pi f$, the angular frequency of the simple pendulum is then $\omega = \sqrt{\dfrac{g}{L}}$.

OSCILLATORY MOTION: STUDENT OBJECTIVES FOR THE AP EXAM

- You should understand the relationship between the angular frequency, the ordinary frequency, and the period of an oscillator.
- You should be able to define the term simple harmonic motion.
- You should be able to explain the relationship between the kinetic, potential, and total energies for a harmonic oscillator.
- You should be able to explain the source of the restoring force for the simple pendulum.
- You should be able to analyze the motion of a system in simple harmonic motion.

MULTIPLE-CHOICE QUESTIONS

1. A body of mass m, attached to an ideal spring whose spring
    constant is k, is set into motion on a horizontal frictionless surface
    with an amplitude of vibration of A. Which of the following
    statements is correct?
    (A) Increasing the amplitude of vibration by a factor of 2 will
        increase the period of vibration since the mass has to travel a
        greater distance in making a complete vibration.
    (B) Increasing the mass on the spring by a factor of 2 will keep the
        amplitude the same, but will change the period of the motion
        by a factor of $\sqrt{2}$.
    (C) Increasing the spring constant k by a factor of 2 will increase
        the amplitude by a factor of $\sqrt{2}$ but will not change the period
        of vibration.
    (D) Increasing the spring constant by a factor of 2 will increase
        both the amplitude and period of motion by a factor of the $\sqrt{2}$.

2. A mass of 0.20 kg is attached to a spring whose spring constant is
    $k = 25.0 \text{ N}/\text{m}$. The spring is compressed 0.40 m on the frictionless
    surface, as shown below, and then released from rest.

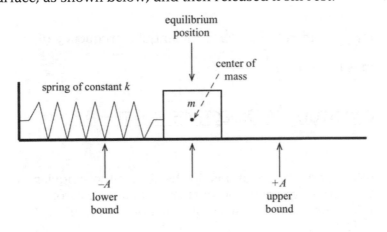

    As the mass moves through the equilibrium position, its kinetic
    energy is
    (A) 0.20 J
    (B) 0.50 J
    (C) 2.0 J
    (D) 5.0 J

3. Several simple pendulums are shown in the diagram below. Each pendulum is set into motion by releasing the masses from the same angle with the vertical.

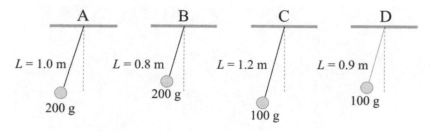

Rank the pendulums from the pendulum having the highest frequency to the one with the lowest frequency.
(A) A > B > C > D
(B) A > C > D > B
(C) B > A > D > C
(D) B > D > A > C

4. A block of mass $m = 0.250$ kg is attached to a spring, $k = 20.0$ $\frac{N}{m}$ and is undergoing simple harmonic motion SHM on a frictionless surface. The mass oscillates under the action of an elastic restoring force. Determine the acceleration of the mass when its displacement is -0.150 m .
(A) 12.0 $\frac{m}{s^2}$
(B) -12.0 $\frac{m}{s^2}$
(C) 5.0 $\frac{m}{s^2}$
(D) -5.0 $\frac{m}{s^2}$

5. A body attached to a spring oscillates on a frictionless horizontal surface. A graph of the amplitude as a function of time is shown below.

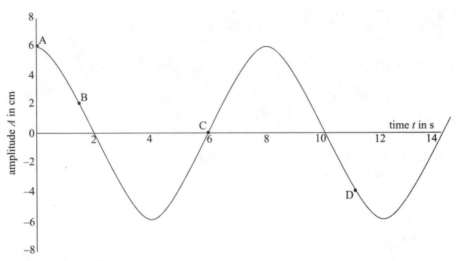

Rank the internal energy of the spring from largest to smallest for the points shown in the graph.
(A) $A > D > B > C$
(B) $A > B > C > D$
(C) $A = C > D > B$
(D) $A > B > D > C$

6. A simple pendulum of mass m and length L on the surface of the Earth oscillates with a period T. The pendulum is moved to a location a distance r_E above the surface of the Earth and replaced with a mass of $2m$ while keeping its length as L. Its new period is
(A) $T_2 = T_1$
(B) $T_2 = \sqrt{2}T_1$
(C) $T_2 = 2T_1$
(D) $T_2 = 4T_1$

7. A variable force acts on a mass attached to a spring on a frictionless horizontal surface elongating the spring as shown in the graph below.

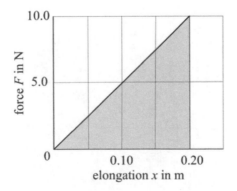

When the spring is set into SHM the maximum internal energy in the spring is

(A) 0.20 J at the maximum amplitude $\pm A$

(B) 0.20 J at the equilibrium

(C) 1.0 J at the maximum amplitude $\pm A$

(D) 1.0 J at the equilibrium

8. A spring supported vertically from a clamp is elongated 0.100 m when a 0.200 kg body is hung on the free end. If this mass is replaced by a 0.400 kg body and set into simple harmonic motion, SHM, what is the period of vibration?

(A) 0.634 s

(B) 0.897 s

(C) 1.10 s

(D) 1.58 s

9. Several students perform an experiment using a 0.150 kg pendulum bob attached to a string and obtain the following data:

Length of the string (m)	Time for 50.0 vibrations (s)
1.40	119
1.20	110
1.00	99.9
0.90	95.0
0.70	83.9
0.50	70.9

They want to determine an experimental value for the acceleration due to the gravitational force in the classroom using information from the slope of the line. In order to do this, they should plot the data using which of the graphs shown below?

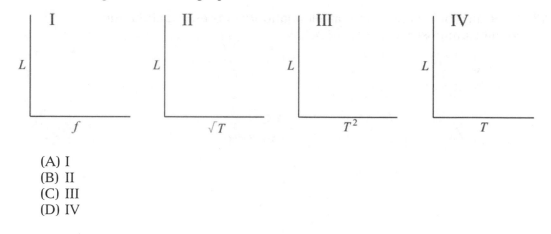

(A) I

(B) II

(C) III

(D) IV

10. A 0.300 kg block attached to a spring moves on a flat frictionless surface under the action of an elastic restoring force. The spring constant for the spring is 25.0 $\frac{N}{m}$. Which of the following statements is correct?
    (A) The force acting on the spring is proportional to the displacement of the spring and is directed to the equilibrium position; therefore, the acceleration is variable and points to the equilibrium position as the displacement changes.
    (B) The force acting on the spring is inversely proportional to the displacement of the spring and is directed to the equilibrium position; therefore, the acceleration is variable and points to the equilibrium position.
    (C) The force is constant; the block moves with constant acceleration in the direction of the elastic restoring force.
    (D) Since the force points to the equilibrium and is proportional to the displacement, the magnitude of the acceleration is variable, but will point toward the maximum displacement.

11. A mass on a spring oscillates between $x = \pm A$. The elastic potential energy graph as a function of time is best shown in which of the graphs shown below?

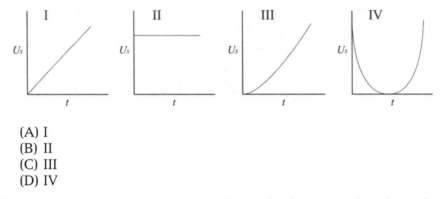

    (A) I
    (B) II
    (C) III
    (D) IV

12. A certain spring undergoes an elongation/compression about the equilibrium position as shown below.

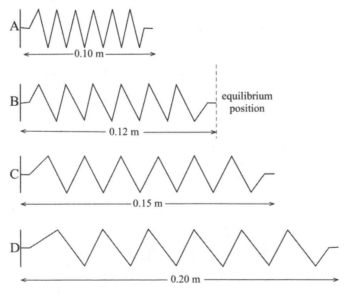

Rank the positions of the system from the one that has the most elastic potential energy to the one that has the least.
(A) D > C > A > B
(B) A > B > C > D
(C) D > C > B > A
(D) B > A > C > D

13. The simple harmonic motion of a 2.00 kg mass oscillating on a spring of spring constant k is shown in the graph below.

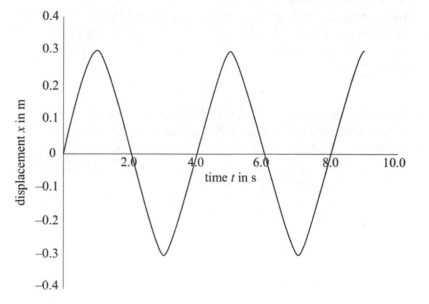

What is the value of the spring constant in N/m?

(A) $\dfrac{4}{\pi}$

(B) $\dfrac{\pi^2}{2}$

(C) $\dfrac{8}{\pi^2}$

(D) $\dfrac{\pi^2}{4}$

14. An object swings on the end of a cord as a simple pendulum with period T. Another object oscillates up and down on the end of a vertical spring, also with period T. If the masses of both objects are doubled, what are the new values for the periods?

	Pendulum	Mass on the Spring
(A)	$\dfrac{T}{\sqrt{2}}$	$T\sqrt{2}$
(B)	T	$T\sqrt{2}$
(C)	$T\sqrt{2}$	$\dfrac{T}{\sqrt{2}}$
(D)	T	T

15. A student observes that the motion of a body of mass, m, attached to a spring of constant k_i, moving on a horizontal frictionless surface has a maximum velocity v_i as it passes through the equilibrium position. If the student replaces the spring with another spring with a spring constant of $4k_i$ the maximum velocity of the mass will
    (A) increase by a factor of 4 while keeping the same amplitude
    (B) remain the same but the amplitude will increase by a factor of 2
    (C) increase by a factor of 2 while keeping the same amplitude
    (D) remain the same but the amplitude will increase by a factor of 4

FREE-RESPONSE PROBLEMS

1. A 0.60 kg body oscillates on a horizontal frictionless surface as a simple harmonic oscillator attached to a spring with a constant k as shown in the graph below.

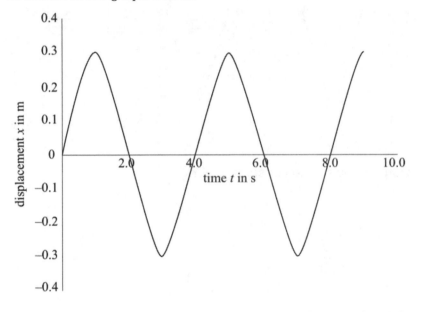

   (a) Determine the amplitude of vibration for this body. Explain your answer.
   (b) What is the period of motion of the spring-mass system? Explain how you determined your answer.
   (c) Determine the spring constant k for the system.

(d) Sketch the velocity of the mass on the graph below for at least two cycles of motion.

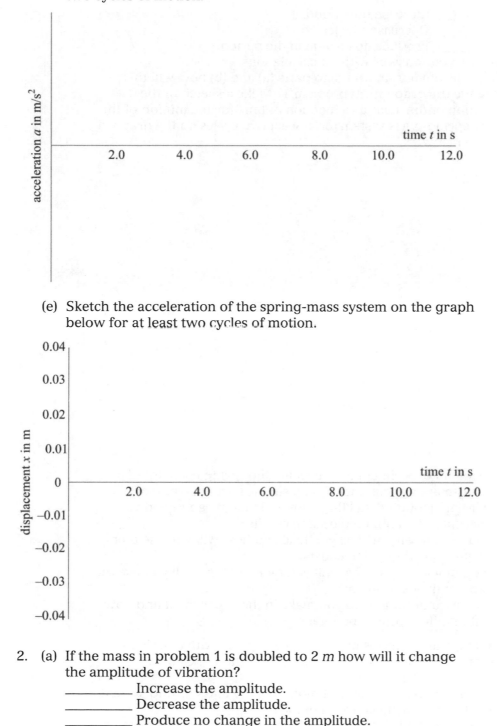

(e) Sketch the acceleration of the spring-mass system on the graph below for at least two cycles of motion.

2. (a) If the mass in problem 1 is doubled to 2 m how will it change the amplitude of vibration?

_____ Increase the amplitude.

_____ Decrease the amplitude.

_____ Produce no change in the amplitude.

Justify your answer.

(b) If the mass in problem 1 is doubled to $2m$ how will it change the period of vibration?

_____ Increase the period.

_____ Decrease the period.

_____ Produce no change in the period.

Justify your answer without calculations.

(c) In terms of your answer(s) to parts (a) and (b) how will this change the graph from problem 1? Make a sketch of the position of the mass as a function of time for the motion of the new spring-mass system for at least two cycles on the graph given below.

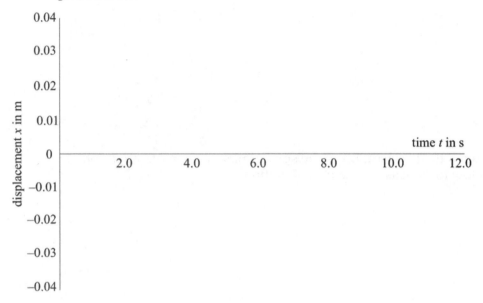

3. (a) Design an experiment to determine the spring constant of a spring-mass system undergoing simple harmonic motion (SHM) in enough detail that another student can repeat your experiment and obtain the same results.

(b) What measurements will you take and how will you use them to determine the spring constant?

(c) If you plot a graph, what will you plot and how will you use the graph in the experiment?

(d) What assumption(s) did you make in the experiment and how might it affect your experiment?

4. A 0.100 kg mass vibrates on the end of a spring with a period of vibration of 1.50 s and an amplitude of vibration of 0.08 m. (Friction is negligible.)

(a) Determine the frequency of motion of the mass-spring system.

(b) What is the spring constant of the spring?

(c) Determine the maximum velocity of the system and indicate the position where this occurs.

(d) What is the maximum acceleration of the system? Indicate where this occurs.

Answers

MULTIPLE-CHOICE QUESTIONS

1. **B** The period of motion of a spring mass system is given

   by $T = 2\pi\sqrt{\dfrac{m}{k}}$. Increasing the mass of the body attached to the

   spring by a factor of 2 will increase the period of vibration by a
   factor of the $\sqrt{2}$. It will not increase the amplitude of vibration of
   the system.
   (*College Physics* 9th ed. pages 446–447/10th ed. pages 454–455)
   (L.O. 3.B.3.1)

2. **C** The surface is frictionless and the conservation of energy

   applies to the system and $\Delta U_s = \Delta K$. $\dfrac{1}{2}kx^2 = \Delta K$ Substituting into

   the equation gives

   $$\dfrac{1}{2}\left(25.0 \ ^{N}\!/_{m}\right)(0.40 \ \text{m})^2 = 2.0 \ \text{J}$$

   (*College Physics* 9th ed. pages 441–113/10th ed. pages 449–452)
   (L.O. 5.B.4.2)

3. **D** The frequency of a simple pendulum is determined from the

   length of the pendulum and not its mass. $f = \dfrac{1}{2\pi}\sqrt{\dfrac{g}{I}}$ A shorter

   pendulum will have a shorter period and a higher frequency.
   (*College Physics* 9th ed. pages 451–454/10th ed. pages 460–462)
   (L.O. 3.B.3.1)

4. **A** The acceleration of the mass is determined from $\Sigma F = ma$. The
   force acting on the mass due to the elastic restoring force is
   $\left|\vec{F}_s\right| = k\left|\vec{x}\right|$. Since the displacement is $-0.150 \ \text{m}$, the acceleration
   will point toward equilibrium and is positive. Its value is
   determined from $k\left|\vec{x}\right| = ma$. The acceleration is

   $\left(20.0 \ ^{N}\!/_{m}\right)(0.15 \ \text{m}) = 0.250 \ \text{kg(a)}$. The acceleration is $12.0 \ ^{m}\!/_{s^2}$.
   (*College Physics* 9th ed. pages 437–438/10th ed. pages 445–446)
   (L.O. 3.B.3.4)

5. **A** The internal energy of a spring is given by $\dfrac{1}{2}kx^2$. The position

   indicating the greatest amplitude will have the greatest internal
   energy. This is point A, followed by D, then B. The energy at point
   C is all kinetic energy since the body is passing through
   equilibrium.
   (*College Physics* 9th ed. pages 441–445/10th ed. pages 449–453)
   (L.O. 5.B.3.1)

6. **C** The period of a simple pendulum in independent of its mass.
   Changing its altitude will change the intensity of the gravitational
   acceleration and therefore change its period. The intensity of the

field is determined from $g = \dfrac{GM_E}{r_E^2}$. Moving the pendulum to a

distance above the surface of the Earth gives $r_{altitude} = 2r_{Earth}$. A ratio

of $\dfrac{g_{surface}}{g_{altitude}} = \dfrac{(2r_E)^2}{r_E^2}$ is used to find the strength of the field. Solving

gives $g_{Earth} = 4g_{altitude}$. The value for the acceleration due to gravity
at the new location is ¼ as large. Thus the new period is twice as
large $T_2 = 2T_1$.
(*College Physics* 9th ed. pages 441–445/10th ed. pages 460–462)
(L.O. 5.B.3.1)

7. **C** The work done on the spring in elongating it goes into the
spring as elastic potential energy and is the area under the curve.

$W = \dfrac{1}{2}bh$ gives $\dfrac{1}{2}(10.0\ \text{N})(0.20\ \text{m}) = 1.0\ \text{J}$. This occurs at $x = \pm A$.

At the equilibrium position, the energy of the system is $1.0\ \text{J}$ and is
kinetic energy.
(*College Physics* 9th ed. pages 441–443/10th ed. pages 449–452)
(L.O. 5.B.3.1)

8. **B** The period of vibration for a mass-spring system is given by

$T = 2\pi\sqrt{\dfrac{m}{k}}$.

The spring constant k is determined from $\left|\vec{F}_s\right| = k\left|\vec{x}\right|$.

$$k = \dfrac{(0.200\ \text{kg})\left(9.80\,{}^{m}\!/_{s^2}\right)}{0.100\ \text{m}} = 19.6\ {}^{N}\!/_{m}\ .$$

Then the period of vibration becomes

$$T = 2\pi\sqrt{\dfrac{0.400\ \text{kg}}{19.6\ {}^{N}\!/_{m}}} = 0.897\ \text{s}\ .$$

(*College Physics* 9th ed. pages 446–447/10th ed. pages 454–455)
(L.O. 3.B.3.3)

9. **C** The slope of length L as a function of T^2 will give them
information that they can use to determine the experimental value

for g. $g_{exp} = 4\pi^2\dfrac{L}{T^2}$

(*College Physics* 9th ed. pages 451–454/10th ed. pages 460–462)
(L.O. 3.B.3.3)

10. **A** The force acting on the spring is $\left|\vec{F}_s\right| = k\left|\vec{x}\right|$. This force causes

the mass on the spring to undergo a variable acceleration given by
$\Sigma F = ma$. The mass will undergo simple harmonic motion SHM
under this force. The acceleration will vary in magnitude and
always point toward the equilibrium position.
(*College Physics* 9th ed. pages 437–438/10th ed. pages 445–446)
(L.O. 3.B.3.4)

11. **D** The spring oscillates between the extremes of the amplitude of vibration. As it does, the internal energy of the spring changes from $\frac{1}{2}kA^2$ to zero to $\frac{1}{2}kA^2$.
(*College Physics* 9th ed. pages 441–445/10th ed. pages 449–452)
(L.O. 3.B.4.1)

12. **A** The elastic potential energy of the spring is determined from $\frac{1}{2}kx^2$. The spring with the greatest elongation or compression from equilibrium has the greatest internal energy. The ranking is D > C > A > B.
(*College Physics* 9th ed. pages 441–445/10th ed. pages 443–446)
(L.O. 5.B.4.1)

13. **B** From the graph, the period of oscillation of the 2.0 kg mass is 4.0 s. Using $T = 2\pi\sqrt{\dfrac{m}{k}}$ and substituting, $4.0\text{ s} = 2\pi\sqrt{\dfrac{2.0\text{ kg}}{k}}$ and solving, $k = \dfrac{\pi^2}{2}$.
(*College Physics* 9th ed. pages 441–445/10th ed. pages 449–452)
(L.O. 3.B.3.3)

14. **B** The necessary equations are $T = 2\pi\sqrt{\dfrac{L}{g}}$ and $T = 2\pi\sqrt{\dfrac{m}{k}}$. The simple pendulum is independent of the mass of the bob and increasing the mass of the bob by a factor of 2 will not change the period of vibration. Increasing the mass on the spring by a factor of 2 will increase the period by a factor of $\sqrt{2}$.
(*College Physics* 9th ed. pages 446–447, 451–454/10th ed. pages 445–446, 460–462)
(L.O. 3.B.3.1)

15. **C** Increasing the spring constant will increase the maximum velocity of the mass as it moves through the equilibrium position, not the amplitude of vibration. The energy in the system is constant since the mass moves on a flat frictionless surface. Thus $\frac{1}{2}k_i x^2 = \frac{1}{2}mv_i^2$. Increasing k_i to $4k_i$ gives $4k_i = v_{new}^2$ and will increase the maximum velocity by a factor of 2. The velocity of the mass as it passes through the equilibrium is now $2v_i$.

Also $v_{max} = \vec{\omega}A$ and $\omega = \sqrt{\dfrac{k}{m}}$ therefore v_{max} will increase by a factor of 2.
(*College Physics* 9th ed. pages 441–443/10th ed. pages 449–452)
(L.O. 5.B.4.2)

FREE-RESPONSE PROBLEMS

1. (a) The amplitude of motion can be read directly from the graph of displacement versus time. The peak positions give the amplitude. From the graph this is

$$|A| = \pm0.30 \text{ m}$$

(b) The period of motion can also be read directly from the graph. One complete cycle is completed in **4.0 s**.

(c) The spring constant can be determined from $T = 2\pi\sqrt{\dfrac{m}{k}}$.

Substitutions gives $4.0 \text{ s} = 2\pi\sqrt{\dfrac{0.60 \text{ kg}}{k}}$. Squaring and solving

will give $(4.0 \text{ s})^2 = 4\pi^2\left(\dfrac{0.60 \text{ kg}}{k}\right)$

$$k = 1.5 \text{ N}\!/\!\text{m}$$

(d) The velocity as a function of time is shown below.

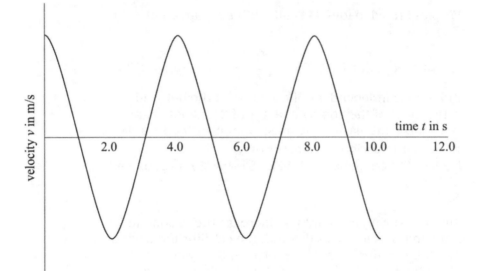

(e) The acceleration as a function of time is shown below.

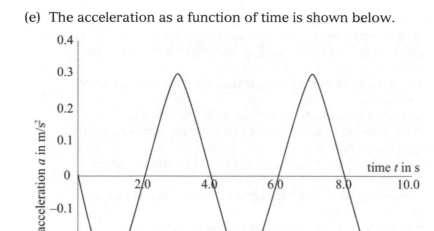

(*College Physics* 9th ed. pages 446–447, 449–451/10th ed. pages 457–458, 458–459)
(L.O. 3.B.3.1, 3.B.3.3)

2. (a) Correct line checked is ___√___ Produce no change in the amplitude.
   The amplitude of vibration is independent of the mass on the spring.
   (b) Correct line checked is ___√___ Increase the period.
   The period of vibration is proportional to the square root of the mass. Therefore doubling the mass will change the period of vibration by $T_2 = \sqrt{2}(T_i)$.
   The new period is then **5.66 s**.
   (c) The position as a function of time for the new mass on the spring is shown below.

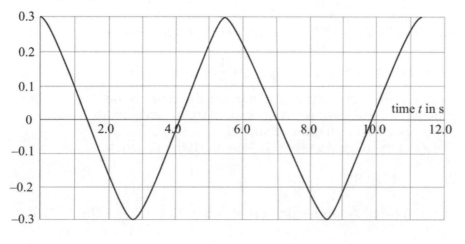

(*College Physics* 9th ed. pages 446–447, 449–451/10th ed. pages 457–458, 458–459)
(L.O. 3.B.3.1, 3.B.3.3)

3. (a) Hang a spring on a vertical support and attach a mass hanger to one end of the spring.
   Place a mass on the end of the spring, and record the mass in the data chart.
   Indicate the number of complete vibrations that you will record for the oscillations.
   Pull the mass downward a few centimeters and release.
   Determine the time for the number of complete vibrations you chose for your experiment.
   Record this time and then calculate the time for one complete vibration.
   Repeat the reading for at least three trials and average the time for one complete vibration.
   Increase the mass on the spring and repeat the above procedure for at least 6 mass readings.

   (b) Data that will be recorded will be the mass on the spring, the time for one complete vibration, and the period squared. The period is related to the spring constant by $T = 2\pi\sqrt{\dfrac{m}{k}}$. The spring constant may be determined from substitution into the equation.

   (c) A more consistent value for the spring constant can be obtained by using the data from the slope of the mass as a function of period squared graph and multiplying the slope by $4\pi^2$.

   (d) Assuming the spring is massless will cause an error in the experiment. When the spring-mass system vibrates, 1/3 of the mass of the spring is actually vibrating during the oscillation. (The derivation for this requires calculus and so is not part of the scope of the course, but you can look it up on the internet or in a calculus-based physics text.) The spring constant will have a smaller experimental value if its mass is ignored. Using a spring-mass system such as an experimental Hooke's law apparatus requires that you use the mass of the pan attached to the spring as well as the mass placed on the pan.

   The equation $T = 2\pi\sqrt{\dfrac{m_{effective}}{k}}$ is the correct form making the

   effective mass equal to $m_{pan} + m_{supported} + \dfrac{1}{3}m_{spring}$.

   Counting too few vibrations might increase the error in the experiment if miscounted. A larger error exists when 9 or 10 vibrations are completed rather than 30.
   (*College Physics* 9th ed. pages 446–447, 449–451/10th ed. pages 454–455, 458–459)
   (L.O. 3.B.3.1, 3.B.3.2, 3.B.3.3)

4. (a) Period and frequency are reciprocals of each other. $f = \dfrac{1}{T}$. The frequency is
   $$f = \frac{1}{1.50\ s}; f = \frac{1}{1.50\ s} = \textbf{0.667 Hz}$$

(b) The spring constant k is determined from $T = 2\pi\sqrt{\dfrac{m}{k}}$.

$$1.50 \ s = 2\pi\sqrt{\dfrac{0.100 \text{ kg}}{k}}$$

and $k = \mathbf{1.75} \ \mathbf{N/m}$.

(c) Since friction is negligible, the maximum internal energy of the spring $U_s = \dfrac{1}{2}kA^2$ will be equal to the maximum kinetic energy as the mass moves through the equilibrium position.

$\dfrac{1}{2}kA^2 = \dfrac{1}{2}mv_{max}^2$. Substitution gives

$$\left(1.75 \ \dfrac{\text{N}}{\text{m}}\right)(0.080 \text{ m})^2 = (0.100 \text{ kg})v_{max}^2$$

$$v_{max} = \mathbf{0.335} \ \mathbf{m/s}$$

(d) The maximum acceleration occurs at the end points and is calculated from $|\vec{a}| = \dfrac{k}{m}x$.

The acceleration is $\left(\dfrac{1.75 \ \text{N/m}}{0.100 \text{ kg}}\right)(0.080 \text{ m}) = \mathbf{1.40} \ \mathbf{m/s^2}$

(*College Physics* 9th ed. pages 437–438, 446–447, 449–451/10th ed. pages 445–446, 454–455, 458–459)
(L.O. 3.B.3.1, 3.B.3.3, 5.B.3.2, 5.B.4.1, 5.B.4.2)

10

FLUIDS

FLUIDS IN GENERAL

(*College Physics* 9th ed. pages 874–877/10th ed. pages 870–872)

Matter exists in three phases: the solid phase, the liquid phase, and the gaseous phase. The particles in a solid have strong attractions for one another and give the solid a shape and a volume. The particles of a liquid are moving in such a way to reduce the attractions between them, allowing them to flow. Liquids have the volume and shape of their container. The molecules of a gas are a thousand times farther apart with little or no attractions on each other. Gases have no shape or volume. The individual molecules move freely until they fill their container.

Because of the fact that liquids and gases flow, we call them *fluids*.

The study of fluids at rest is called *hydrostatics*. The study of fluids in motion is called *hydrodynamics*.

DENSITY

(*College Physics* 9th ed. pages 874–877/10th ed. pages 870–872)

The mass density or *density*, ρ, of a substance is defined as its mass per unit volume, or

$$\rho = \frac{m}{V}$$

The SI density unit is the kilogram per cubic meter, kg/m^3. Copper, for example, has a density $\rho = 8890 \ kg/m^3$. Another common way of expressing density is in grams per cubic centimeter, g/cm^3. Because $1000 \text{ g} = 1 \text{ kg}$ and $1 \text{ m}^3 = 1 \times 10^6 \text{ cm}^3$ we can write the density of copper as $8.89 \text{ } g/cm^3$. Density is a scalar quantity.

SPECIFIC GRAVITY

(*College Physics* 9th ed. pages 874–877/10th ed. pages 870–872)

Another quantity commonly used to describe densities is specific gravity, SG, which is described as the ratio of the density of a material to that of water, $\rho_w = 1000 \text{ } kg/m^3$. Specific gravity, like density, is a scalar quantity.

$$SG = \frac{\rho_{material}}{\rho_w}$$

SAMPLE PROBLEM 1

Find the SG of

(a) lead: $\rho_{Pb} = 11{,}300 \text{ } kg/m^3$

(b) ice: $\rho_{ice} = 917 \text{ } kg/m^3$

(c) What is the density of ethyl alcohol whose SG is 0.81?

SOLUTION TO PROBLEM 1

(a) $SG = \dfrac{\rho_{Pb}}{\rho_w} = \dfrac{11{,}300 \text{ } kg/m^3}{1000 \text{ } kg/m^3} = \mathbf{11.3}$. Notice that there are no units associated with specific gravity. The answer is a pure number and means that lead is 11.3 times more dense than an equal volume of water.

(b) $SG = \dfrac{\rho_{ice}}{\rho_w} = \dfrac{917 \text{ } kg/m^3}{1000 \text{ } kg/m^3} = \mathbf{0.917}$. Ice is 0.917 times as dense as an equal volume of water.

(c) To find a density from SG we rearrange terms and get $\rho_{alcohol} = SG \times \rho_w = 0.81 \times 1000 \text{ } kg/m^3 = \mathbf{810} \text{ } \mathbf{kg/m^3}$.

To find SG from density we divide by $1000 \text{ } kg/m^3$ and to find a density from SG we multiply by $1000 \text{ } kg/m^3$.

PRESSURE

(*College Physics* 9th ed. pages 874–877/10th ed. pages 870–872)

When a force acts perpendicular to a surface, the *pressure, p,* exerted is the ratio of the magnitude of the normal force, *F*, to the area, *A*, of the surface, or

$$p = \frac{F}{A}$$

The SI unit of pressure is the *pascal,* Pa. The pascal is defined as a newton per square meter, $1 \text{ Pa} = 1 \text{ N}/\text{m}^2$. Pressure is a scalar, it has only magnitude. A more appropriate measure is the kilopascal, kPa and $1 \text{ kPa} = 1000 \text{ Pa} = 1000 \text{ N}/\text{m}^2$.

Pressure is a useful quantity where fluids—liquids and gases—are concerned because of the following fluid properties:

At any given depth the force exerted in a fluid is the same in all directions.

The forces that fluids exert on the walls of its container, and those the walls exert on the fluid, always act perpendicular to the walls.

An external pressure exerted on a fluid is transmitted uniformly and undiminished throughout the fluid.

That does not mean that the pressures in a fluid are the same everywhere, because the weight of the fluid itself exerts pressure that increases with increasing depth. The pressure at a depth *h* in a fluid having a density ρ due to the weight of the fluid above is

$$p = \rho g h$$

And the total pressure at that fluid depth is found by

$$p = p_{external} + \rho g h$$

A fluid in an open container has the atmosphere exerting an external pressure on it.

SAMPLE PROBLEM 2

A 1.4 m-long metal cylinder has a cross section of 35 cm^2 and a mass of 90 kg. It is stood upright on a concrete floor. What pressure does the cylinder exert on the floor?

SOLUTION TO PROBLEM 2

Pressure is defined as force per unit area. The force the cylinder exerts is its weight, *mg*. The area, *A*, must be in SI units. To convert cm^2 to m^2 we multiply by 10^{-4}.

$$p = \frac{F}{A} = \frac{w}{A} = \frac{mg}{A} = \frac{(90 \text{ kg})\left(9.8 \text{ m}/\text{s}^2\right)}{\left(35 \times 10^{-4} \text{ m}^2\right)} = \textbf{252 kPa}$$

SAMPLE PROBLEM 3

Fresh water has a density of 1000 kg/m^3.

(a) What hydrostatic pressure exists at a depth of 3.0 m in a fresh water lake?

(b) What hydrostatic pressure exists at a depth of 30.0 m in a fresh water lake?

(c) At what depth will the hydrostatic pressure be 75.5 kPa?

SOLUTION TO PROBLEM 3

Hydrostatic pressure refers to the pressure of the water only.

(a) $p = \rho g h = \left(1000 \ kg/m^3\right)\left(9.8 \ m/s^2\right)(3.0 \ m) = \textbf{29.4 kPa}$

(b) $p = \rho g h = \left(1000 \ kg/m^3\right)\left(9.8 \ m/s^2\right)(30 \ m) = \textbf{294 kPa}$

(c) $h = \dfrac{p}{\rho g} = \dfrac{75.5 \times 10^3 \ N/m^2}{\left(1000 \ kg/m^3\right)\left(9.8 \ m/s^2\right)} = \textbf{7.7 m}$

GAUGE PRESSURE

(*College Physics* 9th ed. pages 874–877/10th ed. pages 870–872)

Pressure gauges measure the difference in pressure between an unknown pressure and atmospheric pressure, p_{atm}. What they measure is called *gauge pressure*, p_{gauge}, and the true pressure is called the *absolute pressure*.

Absolute pressure = gauge pressure + atmospheric pressure

$p = p_{gauge} + p_{atm}$

Atmospheric pressure at sea level is 101.3 kPa. By definition 1 standard atmosphere at sea level and 0°C is

$$1 \text{ atm} = 101.3 \text{ kPa} = 1.013 \times 10^5 \ \frac{N}{m^2} = 76 \text{ cm of Hg} = 0.76 \text{ m of Hg}$$

The atmosphere will support a column of mercury, Hg, in a barometer. We can use cm of Hg and m of Hg as pressure units. There are others but these support our needs.

A common device for measuring gauge pressure is the open-tube manometer. The manometer is a U-shaped tube containing a dense liquid such as mercury. The element mercury has a density $\rho = 13,600 \ kg/m^3$. When both ends of the tube are open the liquid seeks its own level because 1 atmosphere of pressure is exerted. When one end of the manometer is attached to a pressurized tank of a gas, the mercury rises in the open end until the pressures are equalized. The difference between the two levels of the mercury in the manometer is a measure of the gauge pressure.

SAMPLE PROBLEM 4

A pressurized tank containing carbon dioxide is attached to a mercury manometer. The difference in the mercury levels is 36 cm. Calculate the absolute pressure of the carbon dioxide inside the tank.

SOLUTION TO PROBLEM 4

The gauge reads a difference of 0.36 m. This is the gauge pressure. Atmospheric pressure is 1.00 atmosphere or 0.76 m of Hg. Absolute pressure is equal to the gauge pressure plus the atmospheric pressure.

Absolute pressure = 0.36 m + 0.76 m = 1.12 m of Hg

The pressure in the tank is equivalent to the pressure at the bottom of a column 1.12 m in height.

$$p = \rho g h = \left(13{,}600\ \frac{kg}{m^3}\right)\left(9.8\ \frac{m}{s^2}\right)(1.12\,m) = 149\ \textbf{kPa}$$

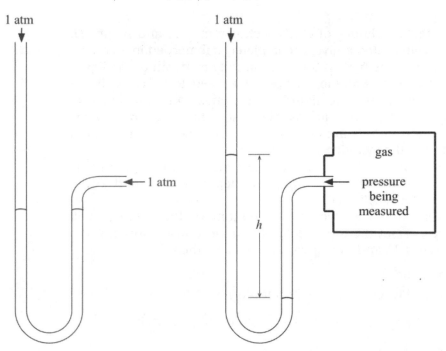

ARCHIMEDES' PRINCIPLE

(*College Physics* 9th ed. pages 874–877/10th ed. pages 870–872)

An object immersed in a fluid is acted upon by an upward force that rises because pressures in a fluid increase with depth. The upward force on the bottom of the object is greater than the force on its top. The difference between these two forces, called the *buoyant force*, is equal to the weight of the fluid displaced by the immersed object.

This is a statement of Archimedes' Principle: The buoyant force on a submerged object is equal to the weight of the fluid the object displaces. Archimedes (287–212 B.C.E.) was the ancient Greek mathematician who first studied fluid behavior.

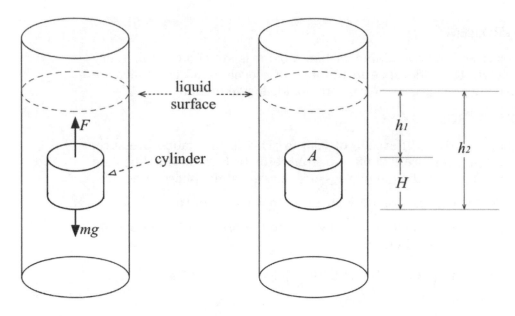

Consider a metal cylinder of cross sectional area A and height H. The cylinder, as illustrated above, is completely submerged in a liquid.

As we have seen, the hydrostatic pressure at any depth of the liquid is $p = \rho g h$. Since the container is open, we need to work with the absolute pressure within the liquid so we must add the external pressure exerted by the atmosphere so that $p_1 = p_{atm} + \rho g h_1$ (downward) where p_{atm} is atmospheric pressure and h_1 is the liquid depth at the top of the cylinder.

The upward pressure p_2 on the bottom of the cylinder is $p_2 = p_{atm} + \rho g h_2$ (upward), where h_2 is the depth of the liquid at the bottom of the metallic cylinder.

Since $h_2 > h_1$, the pressure on the bottom of the cylinder will exceed the pressure at the top, resulting in a net upward force. If the downward force is F_1 and the upward force is F_2, then

$$F_1 = p_1 A \text{ and } F_2 = p_2 A$$

The net upward force is the buoyant force F_B is

$$F_B = F_2 - F_1 = A(p_2 - p_1) = A(p_{atm} + \rho g h_1 - p_{atm} - \rho g h_2)$$

$$F_B = A\rho g(h_1 - h_2) = A\rho g H$$

where $H = h_1 - h_2$ and the volume of the cylinder is $V = AH$. Then

$$F_B = V\rho g = mg$$

buoyant force = weight of displaced fluid

If the buoyant force is less than the weight of the object itself, the object sinks.

If the buoyant force equals the weight of the object, the object floats in equilibrium at any depth in the fluid.

If the buoyant force is more than the weight of the object, the object floats with part of its volume above the surface of the fluid.

SAMPLE PROBLEM 5

A block of aluminum, $SG_{Al} = 2.700$, has a mass of 25 g.

(a) Find the volume of the block.

(b) Determine the tension, T, in the cord that suspends the block when it is totally submerged in water.

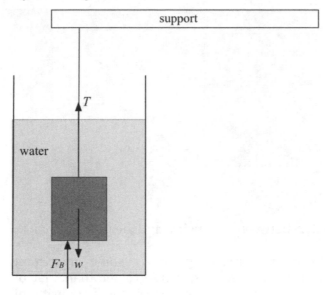

SOLUTION TO PROBLEM 5

(a) From $\rho = \dfrac{m}{V}$ we write

$$V = \frac{m}{\rho_{Al}} = \frac{0.025 \text{ kg}}{2700 \text{ }^{kg}\!/_{m^3}} = \mathbf{9.26 \times 10^{-6} \text{ m}^3}$$

(b) The block displaces 9.26×10^{-6} m^3 of water when submerged. The buoyant force, F_B, acting on the block is:

$F_B =$ weight of displaced water $= V\rho_w g$

$$F_B = \left(9.26 \times 10^{-6} \text{ m}^3\right)\left(1000 \text{ }^{kg}\!/_{m^3}\right)\left(9.8 \text{ }^{m}\!/_{s^2}\right) = 0.091 \text{ N}$$

The tension in the support cord plus the buoyant force must equal the weight of the block if it is to be in equilibrium.

$$T = w - F_B = mg - F_B = \left(0.025 \text{ kg}\right)\left(9.8 \text{ }^{m}\!/_{s^2}\right) - 0.091 \text{ N} = \mathbf{0.154 \text{ N}}$$

SAMPLE PROBLEM 6

A wooden block is placed on the bottom of a beaker when water is poured in. The contact between the bottom of the block and the bottom of the beaker is so good that no water gets between them. Is there a buoyant force acting on the block?

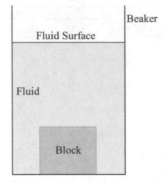

SOLUTION TO PROBLEM 6

No. There must be water between the block and beaker bottom to exert an upward force.

The specific gravity of a material gives us some important information. If a material has a specific gravity greater than that of water, the material will sink in the water. Steel has a density of 7860 kg/m^3. The SG of steel is 7.860 and water is 1.000. Steel, when placed in water, will sink to the bottom of the container. When something sinks in a liquid it always sinks to the bottom.

When a material has an SG less than that of water, the material will float in the water. Ice has a SG of 0.917 and water 1.000. Ice floats in water. Not only does it float, but the SG tells us what percentage of the ice is beneath the surface of the water, 91.7%.

SAMPLE PROBLEM 7

The liquid element mercury has a density of 13,600 kg/m^3. Will steel float in mercury? The mass density of steel is $\rho_{steel} = 7860$ kg/m^3.

SOLUTION TO PROBLEM 7

Yes, since $SG_{steel} < SG_{Hg}$.

FLUID FLOW

(*College Physics* 9th ed. pages 874–877/10th ed. pages 870–872)

In our study of the dynamics of fluids, as a first approximation we will assume that all fluids in motion exhibit *streamline flow*. Streamline flow is the motion of a fluid in which all particles of the fluid follow the same path past a given point as that followed by previous particles.

The *rate of flow*, R, is defined as the volume of fluid that passes a certain cross-sectional area per unit time. It is also called the *rate of discharge*.

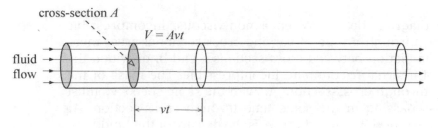

cross-section A

$V = Avt$

fluid flow

vt

Consider a fluid flowing through the pipe diagramed above with an average speed v. Over a time interval, t, each particle in the fluid travels a distance vt. The volume, V, flowing through a cross-section is $V = Avt$. Then the rate of flow, R, (the volume per unit time) is found by

$$R = \frac{Avt}{t} = Av$$

The SI unit of R is expressed in m^3/s.

Variations in the pipe cross-section will result in change in speed causing Av to remain a constant, and since R is constant,

$$R = A_1 v_1 = A_2 v_2$$

We call this relationship the equation of continuity. A liquid flows faster through a narrow pipe section and slower through a wider cross-section.

SAMPLE PROBLEM 8

Home heating oil flows through a pipe 10 cm in diameter with a velocity of 3 m/s. What is the flow rate?

SOLUTION TO PROBLEM 8

The area of the pipe is $A = \pi r^2 = \frac{1}{4}\pi D^2$. The flow rate is

$$R = Av = \left(\frac{1}{4}\pi D^2\right)v = \frac{\pi(0.10 \text{ m})^2 \left(3 \text{ m}/\text{s}\right)}{4} = 0.024 \text{ m}^3/\text{s}$$

SAMPLE PROBLEM 9

The velocity of benzene in a pipe having a radius of 4 cm is 0.44 m/s. Find the velocity of the liquid in a 1 cm radius pipe that connects with it. Both pipes have the benzene flowing full.

SOLUTION TO PROBLEM 9

$R = A_1 v_1 = A_2 v_2 = \text{constant}$. Radii are given and area is $A = \pi r^2$. $A_1 v_1 = A_2 v_2$ and $\pi r_1^2 v_1 = \pi r_2^2 v_2$. Solving for v_2 gives

$$v_2 = \frac{r_1^2 v_1}{r_2^2} = \frac{(0.04 \text{ m})^2 \left(0.44 \text{ m}/\text{s}\right)}{(0.01 \text{ m})^2} = 7.04 \text{ m}/\text{s}$$

BERNOULLI'S THEOREM

(*College Physics* 9th ed. pages 874–877/10th ed. pages 870–872)

Consider the diagram below. When a non-viscous, incompressible fluid is flowing through a pipe of varying cross-sectional area, there can be no accumulation between cross-sections a and b, provided the liquid is free of internal friction and incompressible. The mass of the liquid passing through cross-section A_1 with the same speed v_1 must equal the mass passing in the same time through cross-section A_2 with speed v_2, $A_1 v_1 \rho t = A_2 v_2 \rho t$ where ρ is the density of the fluid.

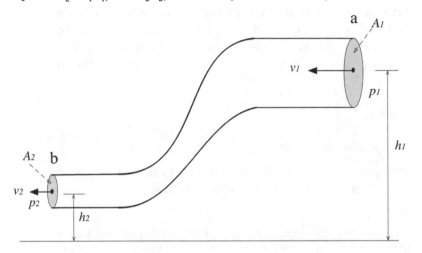

Two important things are immediately apparent from the equation. Since $A_1 v_1 = A_2 v_2$, it follows that the speed of flow in a pipe is greater where there is a constriction. The speed at b is greater than at a. The liquid experiences an acceleration between cross-sections a and b. The pressure is least where the speed is greatest.

Energy must be conserved as the incompressible liquid flows between a and b. In any time interval, t, the volume, V, flowing through cross-section a is the same as through cross-section b. Since the pressure is different at the two ends, work is done on the liquid by an amount $W = p_1 V - p_2 V$ since

$$W = Fx = (pA)(vt) = pV$$

The work done is equal to the change in energy, both gravitational potential and kinetic.

$$W = p_1 V - p_2 V = \Delta U + \Delta K = (mgh_2 - mgh_1) + \left(\frac{1}{2} mv_2^2 - \frac{1}{2} mv_1^2\right)$$

Since $V = \dfrac{m}{\rho}$

$$p_1 \frac{m}{\rho} - p_2 \frac{m}{\rho} = (mgh_2 - mgh_1) + \left(\frac{1}{2} mv_2^2 - \frac{1}{2} mv_1^2\right)$$

Simplifying

$$\frac{p_1}{\rho g} + h_1 + \frac{v_1^2}{2g} = \frac{p_2}{\rho g} + h_2 + \frac{v_2^2}{2g}$$

Each term in this form of Bernoulli's equation has the dimensions of a length. In the pressure-depth relationship, the depth, h, of a fluid is commonly called the *elevation head*. In an analogy then, each term is called a head: $p/\rho g$ is the *pressure head*; $v^2/2g$ the *velocity head*. Daniel Bernoulli (1700–1782) was the first to relate pressure, density, fluid velocity, and fluid depth to describe the behavior of fluid flow.

Multiplying the above equation by ρg gives another form of the Bernoulli equation

$$p_1 + h_1 \rho g + \frac{v_1^2 \rho}{2} = p_2 + h_2 \rho g + \frac{v_2^2 \rho}{2}$$

Bernoulli's Theorem: At any two points along a streamline in an ideal fluid in steady flow, the sum of the pressure, the potential energy per unit volume, and the kinetic energy per unit volume is a constant.

TORRICELLI'S THEOREM

(*College Physics* 9th ed. pages 874–877/10th ed. pages 870–872)

Suppose that a tank contains a liquid and is open to the atmosphere at its top. If an *orifice*, an opening, exists in the tank at a distance h below the surface of the liquid, then the velocity of the outflow from the orifice is $v = \sqrt{2gh}$, provided that the liquid obeys Bernoulli's equation and the surface of the liquid is motionless. As the liquid escapes it gains kinetic energy at the expense of the potential energy of the remaining liquid. Evangelista Torricelli (1608–1647) was one of the first scientists of his day to make a study of fluid behavior and fluid pressures. He first studied liquids escaping from an opening in a container in 1644.

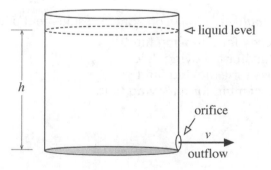

SAMPLE PROBLEM 10

A cylindrical water tank has an orifice of 4 cm^2. The opening is on the wall at the bottom, 3 m below the surface of the water as diagramed above. Assume there is no wasted energy as the water exits the orifice, what is the rate of discharge?

SOLUTION TO PROBLEM 10

Rate of discharge $= R = Av$. The speed of the water as it exits is $v = \sqrt{2gh}$. Then

$$R = A\sqrt{2gh} = \left(4 \times 10^{-4} \text{m}^2\right)\sqrt{2\left(9.8 \text{ }\frac{\text{m}}{\text{s}^2}\right)(3 \text{ m})} = \mathbf{3.07 \times 10^{-3} \text{ }\frac{m^3}{s}}$$

FLUIDS: STUDENT OBJECTIVES FOR THE AP EXAM

- You should be able to define density and specific gravity and to relate them.
- You should be able to explain what supports a column of mercury in a barometer.
- You should be able to define absolute pressure, gauge pressure, and atmospheric pressure.
- You should be able to explain why pressure in a fluid depends only on depth beneath the surface and not on the shape of the container.
- You should be able to explain whether the pressure at a given depth will increase, decrease or remain the same if the liquid becomes compressible.
- You should be able to express Archimedes' principle and to design an experiment to determine the volume of an irregular solid.
- You should be able to explain why it is necessary to use absolute pressure when using Bernoulli's equation.

MULTIPLE-CHOICE QUESTIONS

1. Bernoulli's equation $p + \rho gh + \frac{1}{2}\rho v^2 = $ a constant is a statement of the
    (A) conservation of energy for a moving fluid
    (B) equation of continuity for a moving fluid
    (C) conservation of mass for a moving fluid
    (D) conservation of momentum for a moving fluid

2. Water flows through a horizontal pipe from a region where the diameter of the pipe is 5.0 cm into a region where the diameter of the pipe is 3.0 cm. The velocity v_2 in terms of v_1 is

(A) $v_2 = \dfrac{5}{3} v_1$

(B) $v_2 = \sqrt{\dfrac{5}{3}}\, v_1$

(C) $v_2 = \dfrac{9}{25} v_1$

(D) $v_2 = \dfrac{25}{9} v_1$

3. A horizontal pipe, diagramed below, carries water, $\rho = 1000\ \mathrm{kg}/\mathrm{m}^3$, from a region of cross-sectional area of 12.0 cm² and pressure of 2.15 × 10⁵ Pa where the velocity of the water is 5.00 m/s into a region where the cross-sectional area is 6.00 cm². What is the pressure in this region?

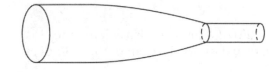

(A) 1.78×10^5 Pa
(B) 2.13×10^5 Pa
(C) 2.28×10^5 Pa
(D) 2.52×10^5 Pa

4. An ideal fluid moves through a horizontal pipe from a region of cross-sectional area A_1 through a constriction into a region of cross-section area A_2 as shown below.

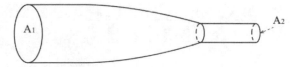

(A) Friction acts parallel to the flow of the fluid supplying the pressure differential in the two regions.
(B) Friction acts anti-parallel to the flow slowing the fluid when it enters A_2.
(C) Friction depends on the area of the pipe and is therefore different in the two sections.
(D) Since the fluid is ideal, there is no friction between the layers of the fluid.

5. A wooden block is placed into a beaker of water as shown below. It is observed that 40% of its volume is above the water level.

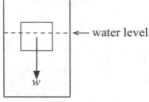

Which of the following vector arrows best illustrates the correct magnitude and direction for the buoyant force acting on the block?

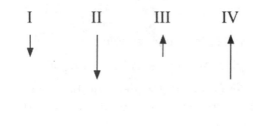

(A) I
(B) II
(C) III
(D) IV

6. Four cylinders contain a fluid of a given density. Rank the containers for pressure exerted on the bottom of the cylinders from greatest to least.

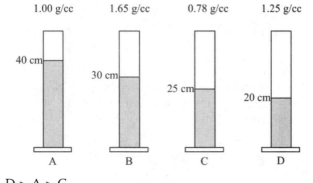

(A) B > D > A > C
(B) A > B > C > D
(C) B > A > C > D
(D) B > A > D > C

7. A pipe carries water to the third floor in a building. Which bar chart best describes the conservation of energy using Bernoulli's equation?

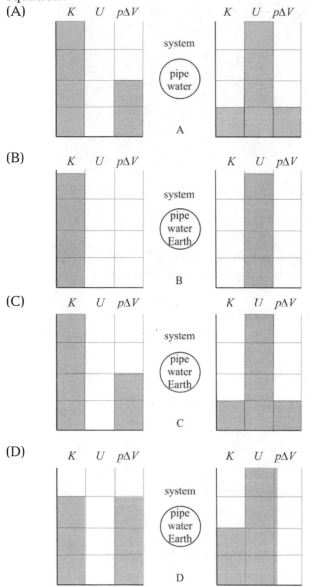

Use the following diagram to answer multiple-choice questions 8 and 9.

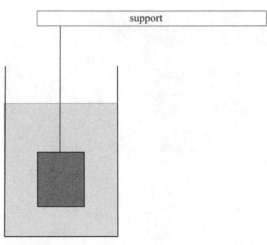

8. A 3.31 N aluminum block, whose volume is 1.25×10^{-4} m^3, is suspended from a cord as shown in the diagram above and submerged in water.

   The buoyant force acting on the block is
   (A) 2.34 N directed downward
   (B) 2.34 N directed upward
   (C) 0.968 N directed downward
   (D) 0.968 N directed upward

9. The tension in the string holding the aluminum block is
   (A) 0.968 N
   (B) 2.34 N
   (C) 3.31 N
   (D) 4.28 N

10. Bernoulli's equation can be simply stated as

   $$p + \frac{1}{2}\rho v^2 + \rho gh = \text{constant.}$$

   The units for each term in the equation are units of
   (A) energy
   (B) force
   (C) momentum
   (D) pressure

11. A fluid, because it has mass and density, must obey the same conservation laws that apply to solids. The work done on a fluid must equal the total changes in gravitational potential energy of the fluid-Earth system and kinetic energy of the moving fluid. This work is the

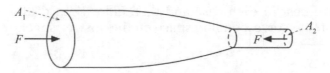

(A) sum of the work of the input force and the work of the resistive output force
(B) sum of the work of the input force and the negative work done by the resistive output force
(C) work done by the input force
(D) work done by the resistive output force

12. Three differently-shaped inner connected glass tubes contain a liquid. Compare the pressure at the bottom of each tube.

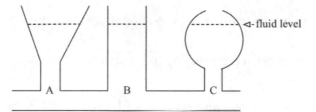

(A) B has the greatest pressure since it contains the most liquid.
(B) A has the greatest pressure since it has the smallest cross-sectional area.
(C) C has the greatest pressure since it is spherical.
(D) All three have the same pressure at the bottom of the tubes.

Questions 13 to 15

Directions: For each of the questions or incomplete statements below, <u>two</u> of the suggested answers will be correct. For each of these questions, you must select <u>both</u> correct answers to earn credit. No partial credit will be earned if only one correct answer is selected. Select the two that are best in each case and then enter both of the appropriate answers in the corresponding space on the answer sheet.

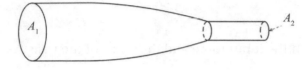

13. A horizontal pipe diagrammed above contains water moving from A_1 to A_2 without backing up and requires the
    (A) speed v_2 in the constricted area A_2 to be greater than its speed in A_1
    (B) speed v_2 in the constricted area A_2 to be smaller than its speed in A_1
    (C) pressure p_2 in the constricted area A_2 to be larger than the pressure in A_1
    (D) pressure p_2 in the constricted area A_2 to be smaller than the pressure in A_1

14. An open tank with three equally spaced holes with the same diameter as shown in the diagram discharges water through the holes, which strikes the floor some distance from the base of the tank.
    (A) The velocity of the emerging water is greatest when it issues from the bottom hole.
    (B) The range is greatest as it emerges from the hole that is in the center of the tank.
    (C) The top and bottom holes have the greatest range.
    (D) The rate of flow is greatest for the hole that is in the center of the tank.

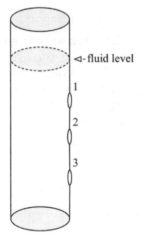

◁-fluid level

15. You are watering your garden with a hose and need to reach a section, but do not have sufficient length of hose to move to that region. You can water this section by
    (A) increasing the size of the opening of the hose to obtain a larger volume of water
    (B) increasing the rate of flow by opening the tap connected to the hose to produce a greater flow rate of water
    (C) reducing the size of the opening to get a greater speed, therefore increasing the range of the water stream
    (D) elevating the hose so that gravitational potential energy will give more energy to the water issuing from the hose

FREE-RESPONSE PROBLEMS

1. (a) Design an experiment to verify a prediction about the density
    of an object placed in fluid in enough detail that another
    student can duplicate your experiment and obtain the same
    results.
    (b) What measurements will you take and how will you use them
    to determine the density of the object?
    (c) Another student has obtained the following set of data of an
    object placed in a fluid. The student used a cylinder that has a
    cross-sectional area of 4.91×10^{-5} m^2 in his/her experiment.

Scale reading	Depth of cylinder submerged
N	10^{-2} m
3.80	0
3.45	1.0
3.00	2.0
2.65	3.0
2.30	4.0
1.90	5.0
1.50	6.0

   i.   Plot the above data on the graph provided below.

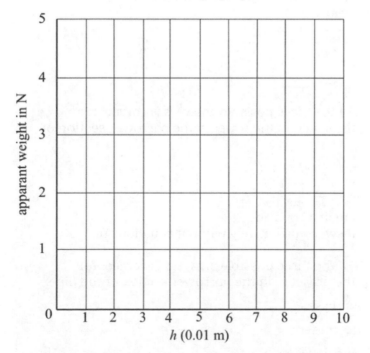

   ii. What is the slope of the best fit curve?
   iii. Using the slope of the line how can you determine the
        density of the cylinder used in this experiment?

2. A water tank, open at the top, is filled with water to a depth *d*. A small hole opens at the base of the tank at height *h* above the ground and a stream of water emerges.

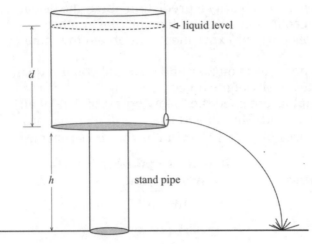

(a) Explain, without calculations or measurements, how you can determine the range of the water stream after leaving the opening in the tank.

(b) If you know the diameter of the hole in the tank, explain, without calculations or measurements, how you can determine the rate of flow of the water from the hole.

3. Water flows through a horizontal pipe from a region where the pipe diameter is 6.0 cm into a region where the diameter is 3.0 cm. See the diagram below.

(a) Check which of the three possible answers is correct for determining the speed of the water in the narrower section of the pipe.

_____ increases

_____ decreases

_____ remains constant

Justify your answer qualitatively without equations or calculations.

(b) Check which of the three possible answers is correct for determining the pressure in the narrower section of the pipe.

_____ increases

_____ decreases

_____ remains constant

Justify your answer qualitatively without equations or calculations.

(c) Check which of the three possible answers is correct for determining the volume rate of flow going from the larger pipe section to the smaller pipe section.

_____ increases

_____ decreases

_____ remains constant
Justify your answer.

4. When an object whose volume is $3.00 \times 10^{-4} \, \text{m}^3$ is hung from a spring scale in air, the scale reads 25.50 N. The object is then lowered into a fluid until it is completely submerged and the scale reading is now 21.50 N.
(a) Determine the density of the fluid.
(b) Determine the density of the object.
(c) If the body is later submerged in a container holding water, compared to the initial values the spring scale reading will

_____ increase

_____ decrease

_____ remain constant

Justify your answer without calculations.

Answers

MULTIPLE-CHOICE QUESTIONS

1. **A** The statement $p + \rho g h + \frac{1}{2} \rho v^2 = \text{constant}$ is a statement of conservation of energy as applied to an ideal fluid.
(*College Physics* 9th ed. pages 302–305/10th ed. pages 307–310)
(L.O. 5.B.10.4)

2. **D** The equation of continuity is $A_1 v_1 = A_2 v_2$. Entering the constriction, the flow rate must be the same. Since the area decreases, the speed must increase.

Substituting into the equation: $\pi \dfrac{D_1^2}{4} v_1 = \pi \dfrac{D_2^2}{4} v_2$ gives

$\pi \dfrac{(5.0 \text{ cm})^2}{4} v_1 = \pi \dfrac{(3.0 \text{ cm})^2}{4} v_2$ and $v_2 = \dfrac{25}{9} v_1$.

(*College Physics* 9th ed. pages 299–301/10th ed. pages 305–307)
(L.O. 5.F.1.1)

3. **A** Bernoulli's equation applies to the problem

$$p_1 + \frac{1}{2}\rho v_1^2 + \rho g h_1 = p_2 + \frac{1}{2}\rho v_2^2 + \rho g h_2 .$$

The pipe is horizontal so the terms containing $\rho g h$ will not be included.

The equation of continuity $A_1 v_1 = A_2 v_2$ must be used to determine the velocity in the constriction.

$(12.0 \text{ cm}^2)(5.00 \text{ m}/\text{s}) = (6.00 \text{ cm}^2)(v_2)$. The velocity $v_2 = 10.0 \text{ m}/\text{s}$.

Solving for the pressure p_2 using Bernoulli's equation gives

$$2.15 \times 10^5 \text{ Pa} + \frac{1}{2}\left(1000.0 \text{ kg}/\text{m}^3\right)\left(5.00 \text{ m}/\text{s}\right)^2$$

$$= p_2 + \frac{1}{2}\left(1000.0 \text{ kg}/\text{m}^3\right)\left(10.0 \text{ m}/\text{s}\right)^2$$

and

$$P_2 = 1.78 \times 10^5 \text{ Pa}$$

(*College Physics* 9th ed. pages 299–305/10th ed. pages 305–310)
(L.O. 5.B.10.3)

4. **D** The fluid flow is streamlined and non-viscous; thus there is no friction between the layers.
(*College Physics* 9th ed. pages 299–301/10th ed. pages 305–307)
(L.O. 3.C.4.2, 5.B.10.3)

5. **D** The buoyant force arises from pressure differences between the upper and lower surfaces of the object which can also be shown to be the weight of the displaced fluid. Since the block floats $F_B = w$ its direction is upward.
(*College Physics* 9th ed. pages 293–295/10th ed. pages 299–301)
(L.O. 3.C.4.2)

6. **D** Pressure is the measure of $\dfrac{F}{A}$ exerted on the bottom of the container. The gauge pressure $\rho g h + p_{atm} = p_{abs}$.

The gauge pressure of cylinder A is

$$\left(1000.0 \text{ kg}/\text{m}^3\right)(0.400 \text{ m})\left(9.80 \text{ m}/\text{s}^2\right) = 3920 \text{ Pa} .$$

Substitution into the equation will give the pressures for the other cylinders as

Cylinder B = 4850 Pa; cylinder C = 1910 Pa and cylinder D = 2450 Pa.

The correct ranking is B > A > D > C.
(*College Physics* 9th ed. pages 288–290/10th ed. pages 293–295)
(L.O. 5.C.4.2)

7. **C** The system involved must include all the items involved in the problem. The system includes the water, the pipe, and the Earth. Bernoulli's equation is a statement of conservation of energy

$p + \frac{1}{2}\rho v^2 + \rho gh = \text{constant}$. The bar chart must show that there is work done on the ends of the pipe as well as the correct changes in kinetic energy and gravitational potential energy. Pressure is $p = \frac{F}{A}$ and from that $F = pA$. Work is defined as $W = F\Delta x$. Volume is $V = A\Delta x$. The work is then $W = pA\Delta x = p\Delta V$.
(*College Physics* 9th ed. pages 302–305/10th ed. pages 307–310)
(L.O. 5.C.4.2)

8. **D** The buoyant force on the aluminum block is equal to the weight of the water displaced.
$$F_B = \rho_{water} V_{water} g$$

$$F_B = \left(1000.0 \ \frac{kg}{m^3}\right)(1.25 \times 10^{-4} \ m^3)\left(9.80 \ \frac{m}{s^2}\right).$$

The buoyant force is 0.968 N and is directed upward.
(*College Physics* 9th ed. pages 293–299/10th ed. pages 299–304)
(L.O. 3.C.4.2)

9. **B** The tension in the string is determined from the first condition for equilibrium $\Sigma F_y = 0$ equation.

$T + F_B - W = 0$. The tension is 2.34 N.
(*College Physics* 9th ed. pages 99, 296/10th ed. pages 102, 302)
(L.O. 3.A.2.1, 3.A.3.1, 3.C.4.2)

10. **D** The units in Bernoulli's equation are pressure units. Pressure p is measured in Pa which is $\frac{N}{m^2}$.

The term $\frac{1}{2}\rho v^2$ unitwise is $\left(\frac{kg}{m^3}\right)\left(\frac{m}{s}\right)^2$ which is $\frac{N}{m^2}$ or Pa.

ρgh is also in Pa units $Pa = \left(\frac{kg}{m^3}\right)\left(\frac{m}{s^2}\right)(m)$

(*College Physics* 9th ed. pages 302–303/10th ed. pages 307–309)
(L.O. 5.B.10.1, 5.B.1.2)

11. **B** Bernoulli's equation is a statement of conservation of energy. The net work done on the moving fluid is $W = (p_1 - p_2)V$. The input force and the flow of liquid are in the same direction and therefore work is positive. The output force is opposite to the flow of liquid and therefore negative. The work goes in to changing the kinetic energy of the moving fluid and gravitational potential energy of the fluid-Earth system.
(*College Physics* 9th ed. pages 302–303/10th ed. pages 307–308)
(L.O. 5.B.10.4)

12. **D** The weight of the liquid in the tubes exerts a downward force, determined by the amount of fluid in the tube. Pressure is determined by depth only. Since the fluid level in the tubes is the same, the fluid pressure from ρgh is the same.
(*College Physics* 9th ed. pages 288–290/10th ed. pages 293–295)
(L.O. 5.C.4.1)

13. **A and D** The equation of continuity requires $A_1v_1 = A_2v_2$. If the area is reduced, the speed must increase. Bernoulli's equation tells us that where the fluid speed is increased the pressure is decreased.
(*College Physics* 9th ed. pages 299–303/10th ed. pages 304–305)
(L.O. 5.B.10.2)

14. **A and B** Bernoulli's equation is

$p_1 + \frac{1}{2}\rho v_1^2 + \rho gh_1 = p_2 + \frac{1}{2}\rho v_2^2 + \rho gh_2$. Because the tank is

open, $p_1 = p_2$. The water level drops slowly so the velocity at the top is zero, and each hole is the reference point for measuring the change in the gravitation potential energy of the water-Earth system. Thus the equation simplifies to $v = \sqrt{2gh}$. The bottom hole has the greatest change in h. The range, $(x = vt)$ is determined by

the speed and the time $t = \sqrt{\frac{2h}{g}}$, it takes the water to fall to the

ground from each hole. The bottom hole has the least time to drop and will not have as large a range as the water from the middle hole. In fact, water from the top and bottom hole will have the same range.
(*College Physics* 9th ed. pages 63–65, 302–303/10th ed. pages 65–67, 307–309)
(L.O. 5.B.10.2)

15. **B and C** Reducing the size of the opening, from the equation of continuity, $A_1v_1 = A_2v_2$ will increase the speed of the water issuing from the opening. The horizontal distance is therefore increased.
$v_xt = x$
(*College Physics* 9th ed. pages 299–300/10th ed. pages 304–305)
(L.O. 5.F.1.1)

FREE-RESPONSE PROBLEMS

1. (a) A body that has a density less than water will float and one that has a density greater than water will sink when placed in the water.

   Measure the dimensions of several different blocks of regular solids–blocks of a given substance.

   Determine the volume of the solids and record the substance and its volume.

   Solution for materials whose density is less than that of water will float.

   Place each object in beaker of water and carefully measure the height of the object that is submerged.

   Calculate the submerged volume.

   Repeat for other objects to verify the assumption.

<u>Solution for materials whose density is greater than that of water will sink.</u>

Determine the true weight of the body by placing it on a spring scale; record this value.

Lower the object into the water until it is submerged and read the apparent weight of the object and record.

(b) Solution for materials whose density is less than that of water will float.

Measure the height of the object that is below the surface of the water and record.

Calculate the submerged volume.

The object floats; thus the buoyant force is equal to the weight of the object: $F_B = W$.

The buoyant force is equal to the weight of the water that is displaced and we can write $F_B = \rho_{water} V_{displaced} g = \rho_{obj} V_{obj} g$; this

yields the ratio $\dfrac{\rho_{obj}}{\rho_{water}} = \dfrac{V_{displaced}}{V_{obj}}$ that can be used to solve for the

density.

<u>Solution for materials whose density is greater than that of water will sink.</u>

Using the spring scale, suspend the object and measure the weight of the object in air and record this value.

Lower the object hanging from the spring scale until it is submerged in the water and read the apparent weight from the spring scale and record.

The apparent weight is the difference between the weight and the buoyant force.

$$W_{apparent} = W_{air} - \rho = W_{air} - \rho_{water} Vg = W_{air} - F_B = \left(\rho_{obj} - \rho_{water} \right) Vg$$

(c) i.   Graph of the data shown below.

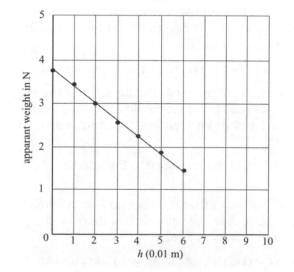

ii. The slope of the line is $\dfrac{(1.51 \text{ N} - 3.02 \text{ N})}{(0.06 \text{ m} - 0.02 \text{ m})} = -37.75 \text{ N}/_\text{m}$. The

negative slope shows that the apparent weight decreases as the object is lowered into the water.

iii. The density of the body is the mass per unit volume, and

$$\rho = \dfrac{\text{slope of the line}}{gA}$$

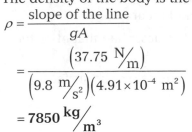

$$= \dfrac{\left(37.75 \text{ N}/_\text{m}\right)}{\left(9.8 \text{ m}/_{\text{s}^2}\right)\left(4.91 \times 10^{-4} \text{ m}^2\right)}$$

$$= 7850 \text{ kg}/_{\text{m}^3}$$

(*College Physics* 9th ed. pages 293–297/10th ed. pages 299–304)
(L.O. 1.E.1.1, 1.E.1.21)

2. (a) Bernoulli's equation can be used to determine the speed of the water as it leaves the hole. Since the tank is open to the air, the pressure at the top of the tank and at the exit hole is the same. The water level drops slowly, therefore the speed is zero. The exit point is the reference point relative to the top of the tank used to determine the change in the gravitational potential energy of the water–Earth system.

   The velocity can be calculated from the square root of twice the product of the gravitational acceleration, *g*, times *d*, the height from the top of the container to the opening.

   When the water exits the hole its velocity is horizontal with no vertical component.

   The time it takes the water to reach the ground is the square root of twice the drop from the tank to the ground divided by the acceleration due to gravity. The time of fall is the same time for the water to reach its range. Range is horizontal velocity multiplied by the time.

   (b) The rate of flow of the water is the velocity of the water times the cross-sectional area of the hole.
   (*College Physics* 9th ed. pages 299–305/10th ed. pages 304–310)
   (L.O. 1.E.1.1, 5.B.10.1, 5.B.10.3, 5.B.10.4, 5.F.1.1)

3. (a) The correct box checked is the speed of the water increases.

   The equation of continuity shows that the product of the area and the velocity is a constant. The water flows from a larger area with some speed and when it enters the smaller area, the speed must increase.

   (b) The correct box checked is the pressure in the smaller section decreases.

   Bernoulli's equation indicates that the pressure in the smaller section will decrease because the velocity has increased. Where velocity is high, pressure is low.

   (c) The correct box checked is the rate of flow in the smaller section is the same as in the larger section of the pipe. Mass is

conserved and the flow rate is steady. The mass that flows through the larger section in a time interval Δt must equal the mass that flows in the smaller section in the same time interval Δt. The rate of flow is the product of the area and the velocity.
(*College Physics* 9th ed. pages 299–304/10th ed. pages 304–310)
(L.O. 5.B.10.1, 5.B.10.2, 5.B.10.3, 5.B.10.4, 5.F.1.1)

4. (a) The buoyant force acting on the body is found from
$F_B = w_{air} - w_{apparent}$. Solving for the buoyant force

$F_B = 25.50 \text{ N} - 21.50 \text{ N} = 4.00 \text{ N}$

The buoyant force is equal to the weight of the fluid displaced by the object, $F_B = \rho g V$.

Solving for the mass density

$$\rho = \frac{F_B}{gV} = \frac{4.00 \text{ N}}{\left(9.8 \text{ }^m\!/_{s^2}\right)\left(3.00 \times 10^{-4} \text{ m}^3\right)} = 1360 \text{ }^{kg}\!/_{m^3}$$

(b) The density of the body can be found from $\dfrac{\rho_{obj}}{\rho_{fluid}} = \dfrac{w_{air}}{F_B}$. Solving for the mass density of the object

$$\rho_{obj} = \frac{w_{air}\rho_{fluid}}{F_B} = \frac{(25.50 \text{ N})\left(1360 \text{ }^{kg}\!/_{m^3}\right)}{(4.00 \text{ N})} = 8670 \text{ }^{kg}\!/_{m^3}$$

The density of the object can also be calculated from $\rho_{obj} = \dfrac{m}{V}$ and

$$\rho_{obj} = \frac{m}{V} = \frac{\,^w\!/_g\,}{V} = \frac{w}{gV} = \frac{(25.50 \text{ N})}{\left(9.8 \text{ }^m\!/_{s^2}\right)\left(3.00 \times 10^{-4} \text{ m}^3\right)} = 8670 \text{ }^{kg}\!/_{m^3}$$

(c) The correct answer is that the scale will have a higher reading. Water is less dense than the initial fluid, therefore the weight of the displaced water is less and the buoyant force will be smaller. The apparent weight will be larger.
(*College Physics* 9th ed. pages 293–297/10th ed. pages 299–303)
(L.O. 3.C.4.2)

11

THERMAL PHYSICS

THE ZEROTH LAW OF THERMODYNAMICS

(*College Physics* 9th ed. pages 332–333/10th ed. pages 337–338)

If objects having different temperatures are placed in an isolated enclosure, all objects eventually will come to the same temperature.

TEMPERATURE SCALES

(*College Physics* 9th ed. pages 333–337/10th ed. pages 338–342)

Temperature is, qualitatively speaking, a property that governs the direction of heat flow. It is a measure of the relative degree of hotness or coldness. Heat will flow from regions of high temperature to regions of low temperature. Heat and temperature are not to be confused; the measurement of heat and the measurement of temperature are entirely different procedures.

The Fahrenheit temperature scale is commonly used in the United States. Under standard conditions, the boiling temperature of water is 212° F and the freezing point is 32°F. The difference between these two temperatures is 180 F°. The rest of the world and the scientific community use the Celsius temperature scale, with the boiling temperature of water at 100°C and the freezing point at 0°C. Between these two temperatures we have a difference of 100 C°. The ratios of 100 and 180 reduce to the fractions $\frac{5}{9}$ and $\frac{9}{5}$.

To convert from Fahrenheit to Celsius we use $T_C = \frac{5}{9}(T_F - 32)$. To convert from Celsius to Fahrenheit we use $T_F = \frac{9}{5}T_C + 32$.

AP Tip

When stating a specific temperature we express the temperature in degrees Fahrenheit, °F or degrees Celsius, °C. When stating difference between temperature readings we express it as Fahrenheit degrees, F°, or Celsius degrees, C°. A temperature of a material and a temperature difference are two distinct things.

Temperature is directly related to the average kinetic energy of the particles of an object. Materials are made of atoms or molecules or ions or some combination. In general, we will refer to atoms, molecules, and ions as particles.

As the temperature of a material decreases, the average kinetic energy of the particles decreases. There is a minimum energy that the particles must have; a decrease below this energy is not possible.

This minimum possible energy defines the minimum possible temperature: absolute zero, –273.15°C. This is a statement of the *third law of thermodynamics, the lowest possible temperature in the universe is absolute zero*. The Kelvin temperature scale is an absolute scale that is based on this fact. To convert from the Celsius to the Kelvin scale we use $K = C + 273.15$.

AP Tip

The degree symbol is not used when we express Kelvin temperatures. The temperature is expressed in kelvins, K.

THERMAL EXPANSION OF SOLIDS AND LIQUIDS

(*College Physics* 9th ed. pages 337–342/10th ed. pages 343–347)

In general, when a material is heated, whether solid, liquid, or gas, it expands as the particles of the material gain kinetic energy. The linear coefficient of thermal expansion α is defined as the change in length per unit length of a material per 1° rise in temperature. Once the coefficient is known, the linear expansion for any length material can be calculated for any change in temperature. The change in length of a material is calculated by

$$\Delta L = L_0 \alpha \Delta T$$

Area and volume calculations are made by using $\Delta A = A_0 \gamma \Delta T$ and $\Delta V = V_0 \beta \Delta T$ where γ is defined as the area coefficient of thermal expansion and β is defined as the volume coefficient of thermal expansion.

SAMPLE PROBLEM 1

A long, thin metal rod has a length of 0.60 m when its temperature is 25.0°C. The rod has a coefficient of linear expansion of 19.8×10^{-6} $\frac{1}{°C}$. At what temperature will the rod have a length of 0.60015 m?

SOLUTION TO PROBLEM 1

First, find the change in length

$$\Delta L = 0.60015 \text{ m} - 0.60 \text{ m} = 1.50 \times 10^{-4} \text{ m}$$

The change in temperature is given by

$$\Delta T = \frac{\Delta L}{L_0 \alpha} = \frac{1.50 \times 10^{-4} \text{ m}}{(0.60 \text{ m})\left(19.8 \times 10^{-6} \frac{1}{°C}\right)} = 12.6°C$$

With the change in temperature known we can determine its final temperature by

$$\Delta T = T - T_0 = T - 25.0°C = 12.6°C$$

$$T = \textbf{37.6°C}$$

KINETIC THEORY OF GASES

(*College Physics* 9th ed. pages 343–353/10th ed. pages 349–358)

The average kinetic energy, $\bar{K}$, of a gas has been shown to be directly proportional to the absolute or kelvin temperature of the gas. We call this the kinetic energy interpretation of temperature

$$\bar{K} = \left(\frac{1}{2}mv^2\right)_{average} = \frac{3}{2}k_B T$$

where k is the Boltzmann constant and is $k_B = 1.38 \times 10^{-23}$ J/K.

The term $\left(v^2\right)_{average}$ or $\left(v^2\right)_{ave}$ is called the mean square speed of the molecules of a gas. When we take the square root of this term we obtain the root-mean-square speed of gas molecules (loosely defined as the average particle speed).

$$v_{rms} = \sqrt{\frac{3k_B T}{m}}$$

SAMPLE PROBLEM 2

Calculate the rms, root-mean-square, speed of oxygen molecules at 100°C.

SOLUTION TO PROBLEM 2

To calculate the rms speed, we need to find the mass of an oxygen molecule, O_2. So

$$m = \frac{M}{N_0} = \frac{32 \times 10^{-3} \text{ kg}/\text{mol}}{6.02 \times 10^{23} \text{ mol}^{-1}} = 5.32 \times 10^{-26} \text{ kg}$$

$$\frac{1}{2}mv_{rms}^2 = \frac{3}{2}k_B T$$

and

$$v_{rms} = \sqrt{\frac{3k_B T}{m}} = \sqrt{\frac{3\left(1.38 \times 10^{-23} \text{ J}/\text{K}\right)(100 + 273)\text{K}}{5.32 \times 10^{-26} \text{ kg}}} = \textbf{540 m/s}$$

SAMPLE PROBLEM 3

A free electron moves in an isolated environment with an average kinetic energy of 1.60×10^{-20} J. In Celsius degrees, what is the temperature of the environment?

SOLUTION TO PROBLEM 3

The average kinetic energy of the electron is $\bar{K} = \frac{3}{2}k_B T$. Solving for the absolute temperature, we have

$$T = \frac{2\bar{K}}{3k_B} = \frac{2\left(1.60 \times 10^{-20} \text{ J}\right)}{3\left(1.38 \times 10^{-23} \text{ J}/\text{K}\right)} = 772.95 \text{ K}$$

The Celsius temperature is $C = T - 273.15 = (772.95 - 273.15)°C$, or $T_C = \textbf{500 °C}$.

AP Tip

Answers should have a reasonable number of significant figures. Do your rounding off at the end of the calculations.

THE GAS LAWS

(College Physics 9th ed. pages 343–348/10th ed. pages 349–354)

Early experiments on confined gases revealed several basic but important relationships concerning the state variables pressure P, volume V, absolute temperature T, and the number of moles n.

Boyle's law: $P_1V_1 = P_2V_2$

Charles' law: $\dfrac{V_1}{T_1} = \dfrac{V_2}{T_2}$

General gas law: $\dfrac{P_1V_1}{T_1} = \dfrac{P_2V_2}{T_2}$

Combining these equations gives us the ideal gas law, $PV = nRT$.

In all cases the volume, V, of the gas is expressed in m^3, pressure, P, in Pa, is absolute and not gauge pressure, the absolute temperature, T, in kelvins, n is the number of moles of gas, and R is the ideal gas constant 8.31 J/mol K.

SAMPLE PROBLEM 4

A 0.01 m^3 sample of oxygen exists under a pressure of 1.52 MPa when its temperature is 25°C. Determine the mass density of the gas. Treat the gas as being ideal.

SOLUTION TO PROBLEM 4

First, write the ideal gas equation: $PV = nRT$. We define mass density as $\rho = m/V$. The mass of the oxygen, O_2, present in the sample can be found from $n = m/M$, where m is the mass of O_2 and M is the molecular weight of the O_2. One mol of O_2 is 32×10^{-3} kg.

The ideal gas law can now be written as

$$PV = \frac{m}{M}RT \text{ and } PM = \frac{m}{V}RT$$

Because $\rho = m/V$, we can write the mass density variation of the ideal gas law $PM = \rho RT$.

Now we can find the mass density

$$\rho = \frac{PM}{RT} = \frac{\left(1.52 \times 10^6 \text{ Pa}\right)\left(32 \times 10^{-3} \text{ kg}\big/\text{mol}\right)}{\left(8.31 \text{ J}\big/\text{mol K}\right)\left(25 + 273.15 \text{ K}\right)} = 19.6 \text{ kg}\big/\text{m}^3$$

FIRST LAW OF THERMODYNAMICS AND WORK

(*College Physics* 9th ed. pages 395–410/10th ed. pages 402–417)

Thermodynamics is a branch of both physics and engineering that deals basically with the conversion of thermal energy into useful work.

The first law of thermodynamics is a statement of the law of conservation of energy. When thermal energy (heat), Q, is transferred to a system, the internal energy, U, of the system increases and/or the system does work. This law can be expressed as

$$\Delta U = \Delta Q + \Delta W$$

Note that ΔQ is positive when heat is added to a system and ΔW is positive when work is done on the system. When heat is extracted from a system and work is done by the system, both ΔQ and ΔW must be taken as negative.

U	*Q*	*W*
When ΔU is positive (+) the temperature increases.	When Q is positive (+) heat enters the system.	When W is positive (+) work is done on the system.
When ΔU is negative (−) the temperature decreases.	When Q is negative (−) heat leaves the system.	When W is negative (−) work is done by the system.

SAMPLE PROBLEM 5

Consider the following three systems. What is the change in the internal energy in each system?

(a) System 1 absorbs 2.21 kJ as heat and at the same instant does 600 J of work.

(b) System 2 absorbs 1170 J as heat and at the same time 500 J of work is done on it.

(c) A total of 6285 J is removed from system 3 as the volume of the system is held constant.

SOLUTION TO PROBLEM 5

(a) Write the first law of thermodynamics

$$\Delta U = \Delta Q + \Delta W$$

$$\Delta U = 2.21 \times 10^3 \text{ J} + (-600 \text{ J}) = \textbf{1.61 kJ}$$

(b) Solving for the change in internal energy

$$\Delta U = \Delta Q + \Delta W$$

$$\Delta U = 1170 \text{ J} + 500 \text{ J} = \textbf{1.67 kJ}$$

(c) The work done at constant volume is $\Delta W = P\Delta V = 0$. So,

$$\Delta U = 6285 \text{ J} - 0 \text{ and } \Delta U = \textbf{-6.29 kJ}.$$

THERMODYNAMIC PROCESSES

(*College Physics* 9th ed. pages 404–410/10th ed. pages 411–417)

During an *isothermal* process, the temperature of the system remains constant, $\Delta T = 0$. There is no change in the internal energy of the gas and $W = -Q$.

The system does an amount of work exactly equal to the quantity of thermal energy transferred to it.

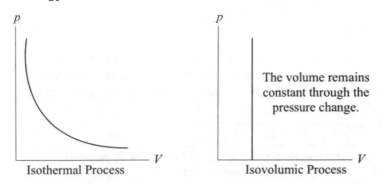

Isothermal Process   Isovolumic Process

During an *isovolumic*, which is also called *isochoric*, process, $\Delta V = 0$. Because the volume of the system does not change, no work can be done by or on the system, and $W = 0$. All thermal energy entering the system goes into changing the internal energy of that system. So, $\Delta U = Q$.

During an *isobaric* process, the pressure of the system remains constant, and $\Delta P = 0$. When heat is transferred to an isobaric system, the system changes volume to maintain constant pressure. Since this process is not isothermal, the temperature changes, which causes a change in the internal energy of the gas confined.

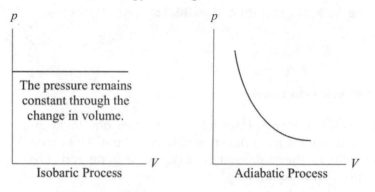

Isobaric Process   Adiabatic Process

During an *adiabatic* process, no heat is transferred into or out of the system, and $Q = 0$. The work done on or by such a system changes the internal energy. Therefore, $\Delta U = W$.

SAMPLE PROBLEM 6

A 1.00 kmol sample of helium is taken through the cyclic process as shown. Path BC is isothermal. The pressure at point A is 1.20×10^5 Pa, the volume at point A is 40.0 m³ and the pressure at point B is 2.40×10^5 Pa. What are the temperatures at points A and B and what is the volume of the gas at point C?

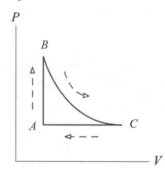

SOLUTION TO PROBLEM 6

Applying the ideal gas law $PV = nRT$ and solving for the temperature, T_A, we write

$$T_A = \frac{P_A V_A}{nR}$$

$$T_A = \frac{\left(1.20 \times 10^5 \text{ Pa}\right)\left(40.0 \text{ m}^3\right)}{\left(1.00 \text{ kmol}\right)\left(8.314 \times 10^3 \text{ } \frac{\text{J}}{\text{kmol K}}\right)} = \textbf{577 K}$$

Because the process AB is isochoric, $T_B = \left(\frac{p_B}{p_A}\right)T_A$. Notice that $p_B = 2p_A$ making $T_B = 2T_A$ and $T_B = \mathbf{1150\ K}$.

For the volume of the gas at point C, we use $V_C = \left(\frac{T_C}{T_A}\right)V_A$. The process C is isothermal, so $T_C = T_B = 2T_A$. The process CA is isobaric and $\frac{V_C}{T_C} = \frac{V_A}{T_A}$. So $V_C = 2V_A$ and then $V_C = \mathbf{80.0\ m^3}$.

HEAT TRANSFER

(*College Physics* 9th ed. pages 375–386/10th ed. pages 380–393)

Heat transfer involves a transfer of internal energy from one location to another due to the temperature difference between them. The three principal ways in which thermal energy can be transferred are conduction, convection, and radiation.

Conduction is heat flow through a material substance by means of molecular collisions transferring kinetic energy from one particle to another. The rate at which heat is conducted from the higher temperature face to the lower temperature face is determined from

$$H = \frac{\Delta Q}{\Delta t} = \frac{kA\Delta T}{L}$$

$H = \frac{\Delta Q}{\Delta t}$ is the time rate of heat flow.

L is the length of the conductor, A is the cross-sectional area of the conductor, k is the thermal conductivity of the substance measured in W/m·K, and ΔT is the temperature difference in C°.

SAMPLE PROBLEM 7

A metal plate 4.0 cm thick has a cross-sectional area of 0.50 m². The inner face of the plate is at a temperature of 100°C and the outer plate is at 120°C. For the metal, $k = 75.0\ \frac{W}{m \cdot K}$. What quantity of heat leaks through the plate each second?

SOLUTION TO PROBLEM 7

The quantity of heat flowing from the outer plate to the inner in a given time period is

$$H = \frac{\Delta Q}{\Delta t} = \frac{kA\Delta T}{L}$$

Substituting

$$H = \frac{\Delta Q}{\Delta t} = \frac{\left(75.0\ \frac{W}{m \cdot K}\right)\left(0.5\ m^2\right)\left(120°C - 100°C\right)}{0.04\ m} = \mathbf{19\ \frac{kJ}{s}}$$

Convection is the heat transfer by the movement of a substance that is either a liquid or a gas.

Radiation is heat transfer by electromagnetic radiation. Bodies hotter than their environment radiate infrared radiation that cooler bodies absorb. The surface molecules absorb this energy and gain kinetic energy as a result. In theory, blackbody radiators are ideal radiators. The power, P, a blackbody radiator can emit is a function of the fourth power of the absolute temperature of the radiator. The Stefan-Boltzmann law is

$$P = \varepsilon A \sigma T^4$$

The constant ε is the emissivity of the radiator and is dimensionless, A is the surface area, and the Stefan-Boltzmann constant is $\sigma = 5.67 \times 10^{-8} \; \text{W}/\text{m}^2 \cdot \text{K}^4$.

SAMPLE PROBLEM 8

A spherical body has a diameter of 0.01 m and is maintained at a temperature of 500°C. Treating the sphere as a blackbody, at what rate is energy being radiated from the sphere?

SOLUTION TO PROBLEM 8

First, find the surface area of the sphere.

$$A = 4\pi r^2 = 4\pi \left(0.01 \; \text{m}^2\right) \text{ and } A = 1.26 \times 10^{-3} \text{m}^2$$

For a blackbody radiator we write the Stefan-Boltzmann Law $P = \varepsilon A \sigma T^4$.

The Stefan-Boltzmann constant $\sigma = 5.67 \times 10^{-8} \; \text{W}/\text{m}^2 \cdot \text{K}^4$ and the emissivity of a blackbody is unity, $\varepsilon = 1$.

$$P = (1)\left(1.26 \times 10^{-3} \; \text{m}^2\right)\left(5.67 \times 10^{-8} \; \text{W}/\text{m}^2 \cdot \text{K}^4\right)(500 + 273 \; \text{K})^4$$
$$= 25.4 \; \text{W}$$

HEAT ENGINES

(*College Physics* 9th ed. pages 410–418/10th ed. pages 417–426)

A heat engine is a device of sorts that converts thermal energy into useful work, A heat engine extracts heat, Q_{hot}, from a hot source, a reservoir, at absolute temperature T_{hot} and converts a quantity of this energy into useful work. The remaining heat, Q_{cold}, is dumped into a heat sink, cold reservoir, at temperature T_{cold}.

The fundamental basis of the functioning of all heat engines is the Second Law of Thermodynamics: The efficiency, e, of heat engines producing mechanical energy is considerably less that 100%. The theoretical efficiency of a heat engine is defined as

$$e = \frac{Q_{hot} - Q_{cold}}{Q_{hot}}$$

In 1824, Carnot described a cycle for a heat engine that can have the highest possible efficiency. No other heat engine can get more work out of an input of heat than the Carnot engine. He showed that the efficiency of such a cycle is

$$e = \frac{T_{hot} - T_{cold}}{T_{hot}}$$

SAMPLE PROBLEM 9

A heat engine extracts heat from a source at 327°C, does some external work, and dumps the remaining energy into a heat sink at 127°C. If 600 kJ of heat is taken from the heat source, how much work does the engine do? How much heat is dumped into the heat sink?

SOLUTION TO PROBLEM 9

The efficiency of the heat engine is $e = \dfrac{Q_{hot} - Q_{cold}}{Q_{hot}} = \dfrac{T_{hot} - T_{cold}}{T_{hot}}$.

$$\frac{600\ J - Q_{cold}}{600\ J} = \frac{(327 + 273\ K) - (127 + 273\ K)}{(327 + 273\ K)}$$

$$Q_{cold} = \mathbf{400\ J}$$

$$W = \Delta Q = 600\ J - 400\ J = \mathbf{200\ J}$$

THE SECOND LAW OF THERMODYNAMICS AND ENTROPY

(*College Physics* 9th ed. pages 415–423/10th ed. pages 426–431)

No physical system is ideal. When a machine is manufactured and operated, heat is always lost due to friction. Friction creates heat that can be accounted for by the law of conservation of energy. Recall that heat flows from hotter bodies to cooler ones. Thus, if there is a heat reservoir at a high temperature, the system will draw energy from the reservoir. Only a certain amount of energy is required to do work, and so the remainder, if any, is released as exhaust at a lower temperature.

The first law of thermodynamics is a statement of the conservation of energy. It is a very useful statement of how the universe is observed to behave, but in itself it does not give a complete description of how things behave.

Real processes are irreversible. They go in one direction only. The entropy of an isolated system, S, either remains the same or increases.

AP Tip

$\Delta S = 0$ for a reversible cycle and $\Delta S > 0$ for an irreversible cycle.

The second law of thermodynamics is a statement about which processes can occur in nature and which cannot. The second law can be stated in several ways, and all of them are equivalent.

Heat flows spontaneously from a hot body to a cold body and never flows spontaneously from a cold body to a hot one.

Like internal energy, pressure and temperature, entropy, S, is a thermodynamic quantity and it is a function of the state of the system. The change in entropy, ΔS, during a reversible exchange of heat, Q, at Kelvin temperature, T, is

$$\Delta S = \frac{Q}{T}$$

ΔS is always positive for any natural process. The SI unit of entropy is the J/K.

Addition of heat to a system increases its entropy. From a molecular point of view, additional heat increases molecular disorder. Entropy is a measure the disorder of a system.

The second law can be stated as: *A natural process always moves from a state of relative order to a state of disorder. Natural processes tend to move toward a state of greater disorder.* As the disorder of the universe increases in natural processes, the energy available to do work decreases.

The most probable state of a gas is one in which the molecules are disordered. Since entropy is related to the molecular disorder, when a system increases entropy its molecular disorder increases and the system passes from a less probable state to a more probable state. Similarly, when entropy decreases, the molecular disorder decreases and the system passes from a more probable state to a less probable state. Entropy is a measure of probability of obtaining a state. Since entropy increases in any natural processes, only those processes which are highly probable occur in nature. The second law of thermodynamics in terms of probability means that probability is extremely low for natural processes that decrease entropy.

THERMAL PHYSICS: STUDENT OBJECTIVES FOR THE AP EXAM

- ▪ You should understand that the exchange of energy between two objects because of their temperature difference is called heat.
- ▪ You should understand that heat added to or removed from a substance causes the material to change in dimensions and you should be able to solve problems involving these dimensional changes.
- ▪ You should know that heat can be transferred by conduction, convection, and radiation and you should be able to solve for the rate at which energy transfer occurs.
- ▪ You should understand that P, V, T, and n amount of gas in a container are related to one another by an equation of state and you should be able to solve a problem involving any of these parameters.
- ▪ You should know and be able to apply the kinetic theory of gases, in particular the root-mean-square (rms) speed of a molecule.
- ▪ You should know the equation for the work done in a thermodynamic process and should be able to apply it to work done on/by a gas.

■ You should understand that work done on a gas is positive and that work done by a gas is negative.

■ You should know that work is the area beneath the curve in a *PV* diagram.

■ You should understand and apply the first law of thermodynamics to the various processes.

■ You should be able to solve and draw *PV* diagrams to evaluate work done, heat transferred, and changes in the internal energy.

■ You should understand the second law of thermodynamics.

■ You should be able to solve multiple-choice questions/problems with a calculator.

MULTIPLE-CHOICE QUESTIONS

1. Four identical containers hold 1 mol of each of the following gases, H_2, He, O_2, and CO_2, at 373 K.

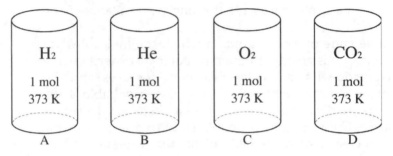

Rank the containers from highest root-mean-squared speed, v_{rms}, to lowest.
(A) D > C > A > B
(B) A = B = C = D
(C) A > B > C > D
(D) D > C > B > A

2. Every time a molecule of a gas strikes the walls of a container there is a change in momentum for the molecule. This occurs because the
(A) walls of the container exert a force on the molecule
(B) action-reaction forces exist between the molecule and the walls of the container
(C) pressure exerted on the molecule is equal to the pressure exerted on the wall by the molecule
(D) temperature of the gas has increased, increasing the velocity, and thus increasing the momentum

3. The change in the momentum for a molecule of an ideal gas in the rigid container after it has struck the left wall is

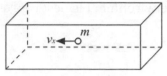

(A) $m\Delta v_x$

(B) $+2mv_x$

(C) $-2mv_x$

(D) $-m\Delta v_x$

4. The work done by the system in the diagram shown below as the gas is taken along the path ABCA is

(A) -880 J

(B) $+320$ J

(C) $+880$ J

(D) -1200 J

5. The change in the internal energy, in the graph of problem 4, of the gas as it moves along the path ABCA is

(A) 0 J

(B) 320 J

(C) 880 J

(D) 1200 J

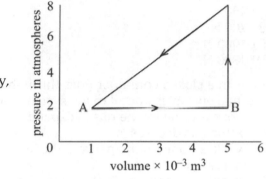

6. A gas is taken through the process ABCDA as shown in the diagram below.

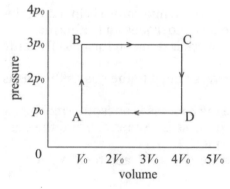

Rank the temperature of the gas at the positions from highest to lowest.

(A) $A > B > C > D$

(B) $C > B = D > A$

(C) $B > A > D > C$

(D) $C > D > B > A$

7. Heat from a reservoir is added to a gas in a container with a moveable piston in a reversible isothermal process. The change in entropy of the system and the environment is best represented by which of the following?

	ΔS gas	ΔS reservoir	ΔS net
(A)	+	−	0
(B)	−	+	0
(C)	+	+	+
(D)		−	−

8. A movable piston, with an area of 4.00×10^{-3} m^2, takes a gas from 1.50 atmospheres of pressure and a volume of 3.00×10^{-3} m^3 to a volume of 1.00×10^{-3} m^3 during an isothermal compression. What is the magnitude of the force exerted on the piston by the molecules in the gas when the volume has reached 1.00×10^{-3} m^3?
   (A) 460 N
   (B) 780 N
   (C) 1000 N
   (D) 1820 N

9. A gas in a closed container goes through an isochoric process. Thermal energy is added to the system and as a result
   (A) work is done by the gas in expanding and the internal energy of the gas decreases
   (B) work is done on the gas and the internal energy of the gas increases
   (C) there is an increase in the internal energy of the system since the work done on the system in the isochoric process is zero
   (D) there is a decrease in the internal energy of the system since the work done on the system in the isochoric process is zero

10. One mole of an ideal gas at room temperature is in a container with a movable piston. The gas undergoes an isothermal compression when 800 J of work is done on the gas. The entropy of the gas
   (A) increases because energy is added to the gas as the gas is compressed
   (B) remains constant since the process is an isothermal process
   (C) decreases because the process is isothermal, and the gas occupied a smaller volume
   (D) remains constant since the $Q = -\Delta W$ and then $\Delta U = 0$

11. Students are given data from an experiment to support the graph shown below of the volume of constant mass of an ideal gas confined in a container as a function of the absolute temperature of the gas in kelvins.

V (×10^{-3} m^3)	T (K)
12.50	500.0
11.25	450.0
10.00	400.0
9.00	360.0
8.00	320.0
6.00	240.0

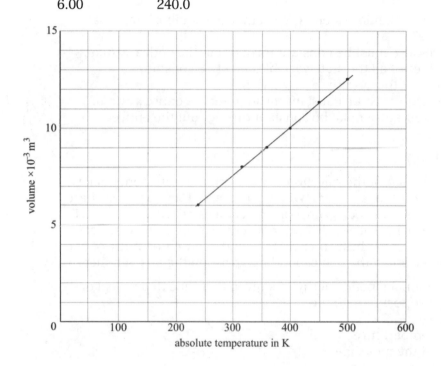

Analysis of the graph indicates
(A) the graph cannot be extrapolated beyond the data points since there is not enough information given in the data
(B) when the volume of the gas is zero, extrapolation of the graph will produce a negative value for the temperature
(C) when the volume of the gas approaches zero, the temperature cannot be lower than 240 K because the pressure cannot be reduced to zero in the container
(D) extrapolation of the graph indicates that when the volume of the ideal gas is zero, that the temperature of the ideal gas will also be zero

12. What must happen for two bodies to have the same temperature?
    (A) They must be in physical contact if energy is to transit from one body to another.
    (B) They must have the same phase, otherwise they have different heat contents and are therefore not in thermal equilibrium.
    (C) They must be in thermal contact and have the same mass to cause the interactions on the microscopic level to produce an equilibrium temperature.
    (D) They must be in thermal equilibrium because interactions at the microscopic level have transferred energy and momentum from the body that had the higher temperature to the body with the lower temperature until they reached the same temperature.

13. For a thermodynamic system to be in thermal equilibrium, what must be true?
    (A) The pressure must be constant throughout the entire system.
    (B) The values of all the state variables must be constant throughout the system.
    (C) The volume must be constant throughout the entire system.
    (D) The temperature must be constant throughout the entire system.

Questions 14 to 15

Directions: For each of the questions or incomplete statements below, <u>two</u> of the suggested answers will be correct. For each of these questions, you must select <u>both</u> correct choices to earn credit. No partial credit will be earned if only one correct answer is selected. Select the two that are best in each case and then enter both of the appropriate answers in the corresponding space on the answer sheet.

14. The translational kinetic energy of a given molecule of an ideal gas is directly proportional to the
    (A) pressure
    (B) kelvin temperature
    (C) speed of the molecule
    (D) momentum of the molecule

15. Several students performed an experiment using a syringe form of a Boyle's law apparatus and obtained the following data.

Absolute Pressure	Volume
(10^5 Pa)	(10^{-3} m^3)
1.11	10.0
1.20	9.2
1.30	8.5
1.40	7.9
1.50	6.2
1.80	5.6

Which of the graphs shown below is the correct graph that will permit them to determine the work done in the compression?

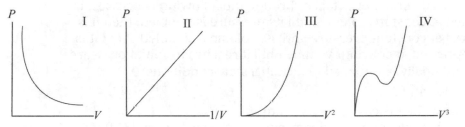

FREE-RESPONSE PROBLEMS

1. (a) Your physics teacher gives you the apparatus shown below and asks you to design an experiment to determine the relationship between the pressure exerted on the syringe and the volume of the gas trapped inside the syringe in enough detail that another student could duplicate your results.

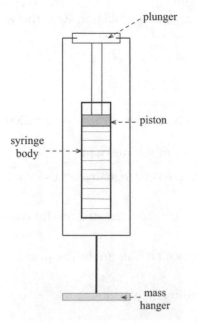

(b) i. Explain, using the correct scientific terms, what measurements you would take and how you would use these measurements. You do not need to do any calculations, but provide complete instructions so that another student could use them to determine the relationship between pressure and volume.

ii. What calculations would you make to evaluate your data from the measurements you made in part i?

(c) i. If you plotted a graph in your experiment to determine the number of moles of the trapped gas, what would you plot?

ii. How would you use the graph to determine the relationship between pressure and volume?

(d) Does Boyle's law hold for all pressures and all temperatures? Justify your answer.

2. One mole of He at a pressure p_0, volume V_0 and temperature T_0 in a closed container is taken through the following processes. It is heated at constant volume until its pressure is doubled; then it is heated at constant pressure until its volume is doubled. Next it is compressed at constant volume until it reaches its initial pressure p_0 and finally is returned to its initial state conditions of p_0, V_0, and T_0.

(a) Draw the process on a pV diagram.

i. Indicate on your diagram where thermal energy Q flows into the system.

ii. indicate on your diagram where thermal energy Q flows out of the system.

(b) Calculate the net work done in the process in terms of p_0 and V_0.

(c) What is the net energy Q added to the system? Justify your answer without calculations.

3. An ideal gas is confined in a rigid container at some temperature above 0 K. A gas molecule approaches the left-hand wall of the container as shown making an elastic collision with the wall.

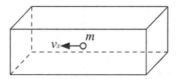

In order to change its momentum a force must be applied over a short period of time.

(a) Increasing the temperature of the gas will

_____ increase the pressure on the walls of the container

_____ decrease the pressure on the walls of the container

_____ produce no change in the pressure on the walls of the container

Justify your answer without calculations.

(b) If the same gas placed in a container with a moveable piston goes through an isothermal expansion as the gas does work on the piston, the entropy of the molecules will

_____ increase

_____ decrease

_____ remain constant

Justify your answer without calculations.

(c) Two very large reservoirs are shown in the diagram below.

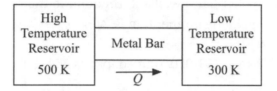

The reservoirs are very large so that their temperature remains fairly constant while the metal bar is in contact with them transferring thermal energy. The flow of thermal energy through the bar is from the hot reservoir to the cold reservoir. The net entropy of the system

_____ increases

_____ decreases

_____ remains constant

Justify your answer without calculations.

4. A closed steel cylinder contains 4.0 g of He at a gauge pressure of 9.1×10^5 Pa and a temperature of 67°C.
   (a) Determine the root-mean-square speed, v_{rms}, for the gas.
   (b) Calculate the volume of the cylinder.
   (c) Some time later, the cylinder is checked, and the temperature of the gas has dropped to 27°C and the gauge pressure is measured at 5.2×10^5 Pa. How many grams of He have leaked from the container?
   (d) Sketch the process on a pV diagram.

Answers

MULTIPLE-CHOICE QUESTIONS

1. **C** The root-mean-square speed (rms speed) is given by $v = \sqrt{\dfrac{3RT}{M}}$.

   The speed of the gases in the containers at the same temperature is therefore proportional to their molar mass. The order is from the lightest to the heaviest molecule H_2, He, O_2, CO_2. This is the correct ranking in terms of mass and therefore the correct order for _rms_ speed.
   (_College Physics_ 9th ed. pages 351–353/10th ed. pages 357–368)
   (L.O. 7.A.2.1, 7.A.2.2)

2. **B** Every time a molecule makes a collision with a wall of the container, action-reaction forces arise between the wall and the molecule. The walls are considered to be rigid and the molecules may be considered to be hard small spheres so that the collisions are elastic and the momentum change results in a change of direction—from into the wall to rebounding from the wall in the opposite direction.
(*College Physics* 9th ed. pages 348–352/10th ed. pages 354–358)
(L.O. 7.A.1.1)

3. **B** The molecules are moving to the left in the container with $p_i = -mv_x$. They strike the left-hand wall and rebound to the right with $p_f = mv_x$. The change in the momentum is $\Delta p = p_f - p_i$, $\Delta p = mv_x - (-mv_x) = 2mv_x$.
(*College Physics* 9th ed. pages 348–350/10th ed. pages 354–356)
(L.O. 5.A. 2.1)

4. **D** The work done is the area under the curve, $W = \frac{1}{2}bh$. The work done is

$$\frac{1}{2}\left(5.0\times10^{-3} \text{ m}^3 - 1.0\times10^{-3} \text{ m}^3\right)(8.0 \text{ atm} - 2.0 \text{ atm})\left(1.013\times10^{5} \text{ Pa}\middle/\text{atm}\right).$$
$$= 1200 \text{ J}$$

Since the work is done by the system, the work is negative, $W - 1200 \text{ J}$.
(*College Physics* 9th ed. pages 395–397/10th ed. pages 402–405)
(L.O. 5.B.5.5, 5.B.5.6)

5. **A** The process ABCA is a cyclic process; the system is returned to its original state conditions of p, T, and V. There is no change in the temperature and therefore the change in the internal energy ΔU is zero.
(*College Physics* 9th ed. pages 395–397, 398–400, 407–408/10th ed. pages 402–405, 406–408, 414–415)
(L.O. 5.B.7.1)

6. **D** The gas is confined in a container where p, V, and T can change. The internal energy (absolute temperature) can be determined using $\frac{pV}{T} = \text{constant}$. At A, the state conditions are $\frac{p_0 V_0}{T_0}$. At B,

$\frac{p_0 V_0}{T_0} = \frac{3p_0 V_0}{T_B}$ thus the temperature at B is $3T_0$. At C,

$\frac{3p_0 V_0}{3T_0} = \frac{3p_0 4V_0}{T_C}$. The temperature at C is $12T_0$. Finally at D,

$\frac{3p_0 4V_0}{12T_0} = \frac{p_0 4V_0}{12T_0}$, the temperature is $4T_0$. The correct ranking is C > D > B > A.
(*College Physics* 9th ed. pages 343–348/10th ed. pages 349–354)
(L.O. 5.B.7.3)

7. **A** The entropy of the gas increases as the entropy of the reservoir decreases, since the reservoir transfers thermal energy into the gas. Since the process is isothermal, both the gas and the reservoir are at the same temperature; the internal energy is the same and the net change in entropy ΔS_{net} is 0.
    (*College Physics* 9th ed. pages 418–423/10th ed. pages 426–431)
    (L.O. 5.B.4.1, 7.B.2.1)

8. **D** Since it is an isothermal compression, the temperature does not change and $p_1 V_1 = p_2 V_2$ Substitution into the equation to

    determine $p_2 = \dfrac{1.50 \text{ atm}(1.013 \times 10^5 \text{ }^{Pa}\!/_{atm})(3.00 \times 10^{-3} \text{ m}^3)}{1.00 \times 10^{-3} \text{ m}^3}$ gives a

    pressure of $p_2 = 4.56 \times 10^5 \text{ }^N\!/_{m^2}$.

    Then since $p = \dfrac{F}{A}$ force is

    $F = (4.56 \times 10^5 \text{ }^N\!/_{m^2})(4.00 \times 10^{-3} \text{ m}^2) = 1820 \text{ N}$.

    (*College Physics* 9th ed. pages 343–348/10th ed. pages 349–354)
    (L.O. 7.A.1.2)

9. **C** First law of thermodynamics applies. Since it is an isochoric process, no change in the volume occurs and thus no work is done. Thus $Q = \Delta U$. Thermal energy is added to the system; therefore the internal energy of the system must increase.
    (*College Physics* 9th ed. pages 398–400, 406/10th ed. pages 406–407, 413)
    (L.O. 5.B.4.1)

10. **C** The first law of thermodynamics applies. Since this is an isothermal compression in which the temperature of the system remains constant, when 800 J of work is done on the gas in the container, 800 J of thermal energy, Q, must leave the system. The second law of thermodynamics applies since Q is negative and the gas occupies a smaller volume with less disorder. Thus the entropy decreases.
    (*College Physics* 9th ed. pages 398–400, 407, 415–416, 418–419/10th ed. pages 406–407, 414, 423–424, 426–427)
    (L.O. 7.B.2.1)

11. **D** The equation of state, $pV = nRT$, for the ideal gas in the

    container gives a relationship of $\dfrac{p_1 V_1}{T_1} = \dfrac{p_2 V_2}{T_2}$. Extrapolation of the

    data points will indicate that when the ideal gas reaches a volume of zero, the molecules in the gas would have no energy of external vibration (still would have internal energy) and thus the temperature of the gas would be zero K. Since the translational kinetic energy is zero, there would be no collisions with the walls of the container and the pressure would also be zero.
    (*College Physics* 9th ed. page 343–348/10th ed. pages 349–354)
    (L.O. 7.A.3.1)

12. **D** If there is no exchange of energy between the bodies, they must be in thermal equilibrium and are therefore at the same temperature. Thermal energy will flow from the object that has the higher temperature to the body with the lower temperature by molecular interaction, until both objects are in thermal equilibrium. Since thermal energy is transferred by conduction, convection, and radiation, objects may be in thermal contact, but not in thermal equilibrium. They do not have to be in the same phase.
(*College Physics* 9th ed. pages 375–383/10th ed. pages 380–388)
(L.O. 4.C.3.1, 5.B.6.1)

13. **B** The internal energy of any isolated system must remain constant so $\Delta U = 0$.

If the system goes through a cyclic process, the change in the internal energy will be zero and p, V, T, and n must return to their initial values.
(*College Physics* 9th ed. pages 398–399/10th ed. pages 406–407)
(L.O. 5.A.2.1)

14. **A** and **B** The average translational kinetic energy of a molecule is directly proportional to the both the pressure of a gas in a container and the kelvin temperature of the gas. Not all molecules in the container are moving in the same direction with the same speed or momentum.
(*College Physics* 9th ed. pages 348–353/10th ed. pages 354–358)
(L.O. 7.A.2.1, 7.A.2.2)

15. **A** and **B** The work done is the area under a pressure vs. volume curve. Both graphs will give the work done; in A, work is estimated since the graph is hyperbolic. In B, the graph has been linearized making it easier to determine the work done.
(*College Physics* 9th ed. pages 396–397/10th ed. pages 404–405)
(L.O. 5.B.7.2)

FREE-RESPONSE PROBLEMS

1. (a) Measure the diameter of the plunger in the syringe using a Vernier caliper. Record the diameter of the plunger in m and the cross sectional area in m².

   Record both the atmospheric pressure and the temperature in the room.

   Trap air in the syringe and record the initial volume of air in m³.

   Place a mass on the syringe. After the plunger has stopped moving, record the new volume of air in the syringe and the mass. (Do not touch the syringe; the temperature must remain constant. Do not perform the experiment too rapidly; the system must adjust; if it does not, the temperature will not be constant.)

   Continue adding masses until you have 6 to 8 readings.

(b) i. Measurements taken in the experiment:
- Diameter of the syringe in m
- Masses placed on the syringe in kg
- Volume of gas trapped in the syringe
- Temperature and the atmospheric pressure in the room

   ii. The calculations needed to evaluate the data will be determined from the measurements taken in the experiment.
- The cross-sectional area of the plunger will be calculated in m².
- The gauge pressure is the weight on the syringe divided by the cross-sectional area.
- The absolute pressure will be calculated and recorded.
- The absolute pressure is the gauge pressure plus the atmospheric pressure.
- The volume of each reading in ml will be converted into m³.

(c) i. A plot of pressure versus volume is hyperbolic and would not give the relationship to evaluate a constant. The graph must be linear. Plotting the pressure as a function of the reciprocal of volume is linear.

   ii. The general gas law is $pV = nRT$. The slope of the line is $pV = k$, therefore the slope of the line is the constant $k = nRT$. Since $R = 8.31 \dfrac{J}{mol \cdot K}$ and the readings of the syringe at room temperature have been taken over sufficient time for the temperature in the syringe to adjust, the number of moles of air trapped in the syringe can be determined.

The area under the curve is the work done in the experiment.

(d) No. At room temperature and low pressure the air in the syringe will act as an ideal gas. When pressure is high, the density of the gas increases and the collisions are more violent and no longer elastic.

(*College Physics* 9th ed. pages 292, 345, 395–397, 407/10th ed. pages 297, 350, 402–405, 414–415)

(L.O. 5.B.5.6, 5.B.7.2, 5.B.7.3)

2. (a) The correct graph drawn for the information is shown below.

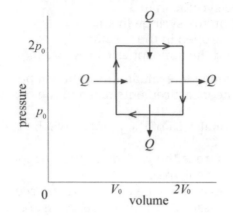

(b) The work done on the gas in the process is the area bounded by the cycle. The work is equal to the base times the height. The work is $p_0 V_0$.

(c) The process is a cyclic process in which the gas returns to its original state conditions of p_0, V_0, and T_0. Therefore since the gas returns to its original temperature, the change in the internal energy is zero. The net energy Q removed from the system is equal to the net work W which is the area bounded by the cycle, $p_0 V_0$.

(*College Physics* 9th ed. pages 395–403, 406/10th ed. pages 402–408, 413)

(L.O. 5.B.4.1, 5.B.7.1, 5.B.7.2, 5.B.7.3)

3. (a) The correct line checked is

    ____√ ___ increases

If the temperature of the gas in the container increases, the kinetic energy and the velocity will also increase. By conservation of momentum the force must also increase. Increasing the force that each gas molecule exerts on the walls of the container will increase the pressure.

(b) The correct line checked is

    ____√ ___ increases

An isothermal expansion of the gas requires that thermal energy must be added to the container in order to maintain a constant temperature for the gas which now occupies a larger volume. The system is in a higher disordered state since the volume has increased.

(c) The correct line checked is

    ____√ ___ increases

The entropy of the large hot reservoir decreases and the entropy of the large cold reservoir increases. Because the hot reservoir loses heat its change in entropy is negative and is smaller than the increase in the entropy of the cold reservoir.

Since $\Delta S = \dfrac{Q}{T}$ the entropy of the metal bar does not change since the same amount of thermal energy enters the bar as leaves the bar. The process is an irreversible process. The net entropy change in the system will increase. In all irreversible processes, the entropy will increase. This is a general statement of the second law of thermodynamics.

(*College Physics* 9th ed. pages 348–353, 418–423/10th ed. pages 354–358, 426–431)

(L.O. 7.A.1.1, 7.A.2.1, 7.B.1.1, 7.B.2.1)

4. (a) The root-mean-square speed for the gas is found by using

$$V_{rms} = \sqrt{\frac{3RT}{M}}$$

$$V_{rms} = \sqrt{\frac{3(8.31 \text{ J/mol} \cdot \text{K})(67 + 273 \text{ K})}{4 \times 10^{-3} \text{ kg/mol}}} = \textbf{1456 m/s}$$

   (b) Next, we find the absolute pressure of the gas

$$pV = nRT$$

$$p_{abs} = p_{gauge} + p_{atm}$$

$$p_{abs} = 9.1 \times 10^5 \text{ Pa} + 1.01 \times 10^5 \text{ Pa} = 10.11 \times 10^5 \text{ Pa}$$

$$pV = \frac{m}{M} RT$$

Now we solve for the volume

$$V = \frac{mRT}{Mp}$$

$$V = \frac{\left(4 \times 10^{-3} \text{ kg}\right)(8.31 \text{ J/mol K})(340 \text{ K})}{\left(4 \times 10^{-3} \text{ kg/mol}\right)\left(10.11 \times 10^5 \text{ Pa}\right)} = \textbf{2.79} \times \textbf{10}^{\textbf{-3}} \textbf{ m}^{\textbf{3}}$$

   (c) The gauge pressure changes changing the absolute pressure. So,

$$p_{abs} = 5.2 \times 10^5 \text{ Pa} + 1.01 \times 10^5 \text{ Pa} = 6.21 \times 10^5 \text{ Pa}$$

$$pV = nRT$$

Solving for the number of moles gives $n = pV/RT$. So,

$$n = \frac{\left(6.21 \times 10^5 \text{ Pa}\right)\left(2.79 \times 10^{-3} \text{ m}^3\right)}{(8.31 \text{ J/mol K})(300 \text{ K})} = 0.69 \text{ mol}$$

The number of moles of helium lost is
$\Delta n = 1.0 \text{ mol} - 0.69 \text{ mol} = 0.31 \text{ mol}$, and the mass is
$m = \Delta n\, M = (0.31 \text{ mol})(4.0 \text{ g/mol}) = \textbf{1.24 g}$.

(d) A sketch is as shown.

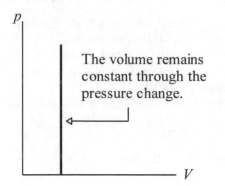

(*College Physics* 9th ed. pages 343–353, 406/10th ed. pages 349–358, 413)
(L.O. 5.B.7.2, 7.A.2.1)

ELECTROSTATICS

ELECTRICAL CHARGE

(*College Physics* 9th ed. pages 513–515/10th ed. pages 523–525)

The basic components of all matter are the electron, the proton, and the neutron. The electron carries a negative charge, and the proton carries a positive charge. The neutron is electrically neutral. Charge is quantized which means that every electron in nature carries the same charge as all other electrons and every proton has the same charge as every other proton.

The SI unit of charge is the coulomb, C. The charge of the electron is -1.60×10^{-19} C, and the charge of the proton is $+1.60 \times 10^{-19}$ C.

SAMPLE PROBLEM 1

A metal sphere is given a charge of 1.0 C. How many electrons were removed from the sphere?

SOLUTION TO PROBLEM 1

The elemental charge is $e = 1.60 \times 10^{-19}$ C.

$$1.0 \text{ C} \times \frac{1e}{1.60 \times 10^{-19} \text{ C}}$$

Coulomb and coulomb divide out giving us

$$1 \text{ C} = 6.25 \times 10^{18} e$$

We call the magnitude of this charge the elemental charge, e. The electron carries the charge $-e$ and the proton, $+e$. These elemental charge are also denoted as e^- and e^+.

The masses of the elementary particles are

$$m_e = 9.109 \times 10^{-31} \, kg$$

$$m_p = 1.673 \times 10^{-31} \, kg$$

$$m_n = 1.675 \times 10^{-31} \, kg$$

The law of conservation of electrical charge states that the total charge existing in the universe is constant. In a system, the total charge before and after changes remains the same.

In atoms, the proton population of the nucleus equals the electron population that surrounds the nucleus. Atoms that have lost or gained electrons are called ions. An atom that has lost an electron(s), a positive ion, is called a cation.

$$A \rightarrow e^- + A^+$$

An atom that gains an electron(s), a negative ion, is called an anion.

$$A + e^- \rightarrow A^-$$

The usual units of an electrical charge range from several micro coulombs, μC, to several nano coulombs, nC, with values as follows

$$1 \, \mu C = 1 \times 10^{-6} C$$

$$1 \, nC = 1 \times 10^{-9} C$$

Charges larger than several hundred micro coulombs are difficult to produce and maintain. Very large charges are quite dangerous.

CONDUCTORS AND INSULATORS

(*College Physics* 9th ed. pages 515–516/10th ed. pages 525–526)

All metal atoms have a common property: they easily lose their valence electrons. Metals may be thought of as positive ions embedded in a sea of free electrons. The electrons belong to the entire metal and are mobile; they are free to move. We call metals conductors of electricity.

Non-metals have structures that are either atomic or molecular. There are no free electrons. These materials tend to prevent the flow of electricity. We call them insulators.

ELECTROSTATIC ATTRACTION, ELECTROSTATIC REPULSION, AND ELECTROSTATIC FORCE

(*College Physics* 9th ed. pages 517–522/10th ed. pages 870–872)

Electrostatic means electricity at rest, and the words attraction and repulsion refer to the forces charged bodies exert upon one another at a distance. Like charges repel one another and unlike charges attract.

AP Tip

Attractions and repulsions are forces. Forces are vectors and have both magnitude and direction.

Surrounding every positive charge is an electric field. We assign the positive charge to be a source of the electric field. Surrounding a negative charge is an electrical field that we assign to be a field sink; the field flows into the sink, the negative charge.

In electrostatic repulsion, like fields interact is such a way as to repel. Two positive charges repel one another and two negative charges repel one another.

In electrostatic attraction, unlike fields interact as to produce electrostatic attraction.

COULOMB'S LAW

(*College Physics* 9th ed. pages 517–522/10th ed. pages 527–532)

The magnitude of the electrostatic force F between charges q_1 and q_2 that are separated by distance R is given by Coulomb's Law

$$F = \frac{1}{4\pi\varepsilon_o} \frac{q_1 q_2}{R^2}$$

where ε_o is a constant called the permittivity of free space and its value is

$$\varepsilon_o = 8.85 \times 10^{-12} \frac{C^2}{N \cdot m^2}$$

The constant ε_o is usually written in terms of a new constant k called the Coulomb constant. And we define it as $k = \dfrac{1}{4\pi\varepsilon_o}$. In SI units, we will express the constant as: $k = 9 \times 10^9 \ N \cdot m^2/C^2$. Coulomb's Law now takes the form

$$F = k \frac{q_1 q_2}{R^2}$$

SAMPLE PROBLEM 2

Two fixed point charges, $q_1 = +3 \ \mu C$ and $q_2 = -8 \ \mu C$, exert an electrostatic force of attraction of 540 N on one another.

(a) What is their separation?

(b) How many excess electrons are on point charge q_2?

SOLUTION TO PROBLEM 2

Opposite charges attract, making the force between them electrostatic attraction.
Write Coulomb's Law and then solve for R.

(a) We can write Coulomb's law and then solve for R:

$$F = k\frac{q_1 q_2}{R^2}$$

$$R = \sqrt{\frac{kq_1 q_2}{F}} = \sqrt{\frac{\left(9 \times 10^9 \ \text{N} \cdot \text{m}^2/\text{C}^2\right)\left(3 \times 10^{-6} \ \text{C}\right)\left(8 \times 10^{-6} \ \text{C}\right)}{540 \ \text{N}}} = \textbf{0.02 m}$$

(b) Next we determine the number of excess electrons

$$8 \times 10^{-6} \ \text{C} \times \frac{6.24 \times 10^{18} e}{1 \ \text{C}} = \textbf{5} \times \textbf{10}^{\textbf{13}} \ e$$

SUPERPOSITION

(*College Physics* 9th ed. pages 519–522/10th ed. pages 530–532)

When a number of charges in a system act on a particular charge, each exerts an electrostatic force on that charge as well as on each other. These electrical forces are all calculated separately, one at a time, and are then added as vectors. This is called the superposition principle.

SAMPLE PROBLEM 3

Two fixed point charges, $q_1 = +4 \ \text{nC}$ and $q_2 = +6 \ \text{nC}$, are 10 cm apart. What is the force acting on a test charge, $q_0 = +1 \ \text{nC}$, place midway between q_1 and q_2?

SOLUTION TO PROBLEM 3

Point charge q_1 exerts a force of electrostatic repulsion, F_{10}, to the right on the test charge q_0, and charge q_2 exerts electrostatic force, F_{20}, to the left of test charge q_0 as shown.

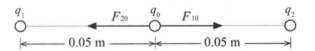

Use Coulomb's Law to determine F_{10}

$$F_{10} = k\frac{q_1 q_0}{R^2}$$

$$= \frac{\left(9 \times 10^9 \ \text{N} \cdot \text{m}^2/\text{C}^2\right)\left(4 \times 10^{-9} \ \text{C}\right)\left(1 \times 10^{-9} \ \text{C}\right)}{\left(0.05 \ \text{m}\right)^2}$$

$$= 1.44 \times 10^{-5} \ \text{N at } 0°$$

We do the same for F_{20}

$$F_{20} = k\frac{q_1 q_o}{R^2}$$

$$= \frac{\left(9 \times 10^9 \ \text{N} \cdot \text{m}^2/\text{C}^2\right)\left(6 \times 10^{-9} \ \text{C}\right)\left(1 \times 10^{-9} \ \text{C}\right)}{\left(0.05 \ \text{m}\right)^2}$$

$$= 2.16 \times 10^{-5} \text{N at } 180°$$

We can apply the superposition principle to find that these two forces are antiparallel, and their resultant is found by

$$F = F_{10} - F_{20} = 1.44 \times 10^{-5} \ \text{N} - 2.16 \times 10^{-5} \ \text{N} = -7.2 \times 10^{-6} \ \text{N}$$

The negative sign implies that the resultant force acts at 180°. The resultant force acting on q_0 is therefore **7.2×10^{-6} N at 180°**.

SAMPLE PROBLEM 4

Point charges $q_1 = -2 \ \text{nC}$ and $q_2 = -5 \ \text{nC}$ are 50.0 cm apart as shown. Where between the charges should a test charge q_0 be placed so that the resultant force acting on it is zero?

SOLUTION TO PROBLEM 4

The force F_{10} acting on point charge q_0 by q_1 is found from Coulomb's law. The test charge will be placed a distance x from q_1 and we write

$$F_{10} = k\frac{q_1 q_0}{x^2}$$

The force F_{20} acting on point charge q_0 by q_2 is also found from Coulomb's law, and q_0 will be placed a distance 0.50–x from q_2. Thus

$$F_{20} = k\frac{q_2 q_0}{\left(0.5 - x\right)^2}$$

If $F_{10} = F_{20}$, then

$$k\frac{q_1 q_0}{x^2} = k\frac{q_2 q_0}{\left(0.5 - x\right)^2}$$

The terms k and q_0 are common to both sides of the equation and divide out. After cross-multiplying, we have

$$q_1\left(0.5 - x\right)^2 = q_2 x^2$$

Dividing both sides by q_1 and expanding gives

$$0.25 - x + x^2 = \frac{q_2}{q_1} x^2$$

$$0.25 - x + x^2 = \frac{\left(5 \times 10^{-9}\right)}{\left(2 \times 10^{-9}\right)} x^2$$

$$0.25 - x + x^2 = 2.5x^2$$

Transposing and simplifying yields $1.5x^2 + x - 0.25 = 0$. Notice that this is a quadratic equation of the form $ax^2 + bx + c = 0$ with solutions

$$x = \frac{-b \pm \sqrt{b^2 - 4ac}}{2a} = \frac{-1 \pm \sqrt{1^2 - 4(1.5)(-0.25)}}{2(1.5)}$$

$$x = 0.194 \text{ m and } -0.860 \text{ m}$$

We wanted the position of q_0 between the two point charges; q_0 should be placed 0.194 m to the right of q_0. Notice that we did not need to know the value of q_0.

ALTERNATE SOLUTION TO PROBLEM 4

An alternate solution uses $F_{10} = F_{20}$ and

$$k\frac{q_1 q_0}{x^2} = k\frac{q_2 q_0}{(0.5 - x)^2}$$

Here, k and q_0 are common to both sides, so they divide out leaving

$$\frac{q_1}{x^2} = \frac{q_2}{(0.5 - x)^2}$$

Substituting in for the charge on both sides of the equation gives

$$\frac{2 \text{ nC}}{x^2} = \frac{5 \text{ nC}}{(0.5 - x)^2}$$

The nC units are common to both sides and divide out. So

$$\frac{2}{x^2} = \frac{5}{(0.5 - x)^2}$$

Taking the square root of both sides yields $\sqrt{2}/x = \sqrt{5}/(0.5 - x)$. Cross multiplying gives $1.414(0.5 - x) = 2.2311$, or $x = \mathbf{0.194 \text{ m}}$.

THE ELECTRIC FIELD

(*College Physics* 9th ed. pages 522–526/10th ed. pages 532–536)

Fields are modifications of space. Masses generate a gravitational field, or g-field. You cannot see or feel or smell the g-field of the Earth, but it is there. We can test to see if a g-field is present by taking a test body of mass m_0 and dropping it. The g-field of the mass interacts with the g-field of the Earth and it falls vertically downward under gravitational force. The gravitational force is the weight of the body, $F = w = mg$.

The electric field, E, is a vector with magnitude and direction. Surrounding all electrical charge are E-fields of intensity E. To test for an E-field, we place a positive test charge q_0 in the field and measure the electrostatic force F acting on it. If q_0 is repelled, the charge creating the field is positive, and if q_0 is attracted, the charge creating the field is negative. We define the E-field as

$$E = \frac{F}{q_0}$$

The magnitude of the E-field at a point in space set up by a point charge can be calculated by using a modification of Coulomb's law where R represents the distance from the charge setting up the field and the point in question

$$E = k\frac{q}{R^2}$$

The SI unit of the electric field is the newton per coulomb, N/C.

LINES OF FORCE

(*College Physics* 9th ed. pages 526–528/10th ed. pages 536–538)

To aid in visualizing the electric field, the concept of lines of force is frequently used. A line at every point indicates, by its direction, the direction a unit charge would take if placed there, directly away from a positive charge and directly toward a negative charge.

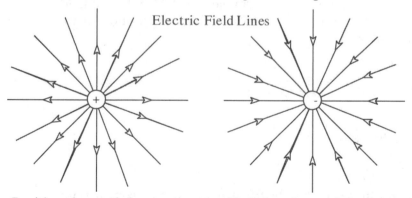

Electric Field Lines

Positive charges behave as a source of an electrical field.

Negative charges behave as a sink for an electrical field.

The direction of a line of force at any point in an electrical field is the same as the direction of the resultant E-field vector at that point. There are three rules to be followed when sketching electric field lines:

1. Lines of force never cross one another.

2. Lines of force in a grouping of point charges begin on a positive charge and end on a negative charge.

3. The number of lines leaving a positive charge or ending on a negative charge is proportional to the magnitude of the charges.

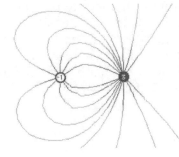

The lines of force associated with point charges +3q and –q illustrating electrostatic attraction.

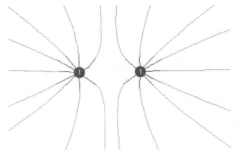

The line of force associated with point charges +q and +q illustrating electrostatic repulsion.

SAMPLE PROBLEM 5

A charge $q = +2$ nC is placed in a uniform electrical field. In the field, q experiences a force $F = 4 \times 10^{-4}$ N. What is the magnitude of the electrical field intensity?

SOLUTION TO PROBLEM 5

Using the definition of the E-field we write

$$E = \frac{F}{q} = \frac{4 \times 10^{-4} \text{ N}}{2 \times 10^{-9} \text{ C}} = 2 \times 10^{5} \text{ N}\!\big/\!_{C}$$

SAMPLE PROBLEM 6

Determine the magnitude of the electrical field 2.0 cm from a point charge $q = +10$ nC.

SOLUTION TO PROBLEM 6

This time, we use the modification of Coulomb's law and substitute

$$E = k \frac{q}{R^2} = \frac{\left(9 \times 10^{9} \text{ N} \cdot \text{m}^2/\text{C}^2\right)\left(10 \times 10^{-9} \text{ C}\right)}{\left(0.02 \text{ m}\right)^2} = 2.25 \times 10^{5} \text{ N}\!\big/\!_{C}$$

SAMPLE PROBLEM 7

Two fixed point charges, $q_1 = +8 \ \mu C$ and $q_2 = -2 \ \mu C$, are 10 cm apart as shown. What is the electrical field intensity at the midpoint of the line connecting q_1 and q_2?

SOLUTION TO PROBLEM 7

First, determine the electric field contributions due to each point charge.

$$E_1 = k\frac{q_1}{R^2} = \frac{\left(9 \times 10^9 \ N \cdot m^2 \big/ C^2\right)\left(8 \times 10^{-6} \ C\right)}{(0.05 \ m)^2} = 29 \times 10^6 \ \frac{N}{C} \text{ to the right}$$

$$E_2 = k\frac{q_2}{R^2} = \frac{\left(9 \times 10^9 \ N \cdot m^2 \big/ C^2\right)\left(2 \times 10^{-6} \ C\right)}{(0.05 \ m)^2} = 7.2 \times 10^6 \ \frac{N}{C} \text{ to the right}$$

Note: The directions of E_1 and E_2 are established by the charges on q_1 and q_2 and therefore the negative sign for q_2 need not be included in the calculation of E_2.

Applying the superposition principle gives

$$E = E_1 + E_2 = 29 \times 10^6 \ N\big/C + 7.2 \times 10^6 \ N\big/C = \mathbf{3.6 \times 10^7} \ N\big/C \textbf{ to the right}$$

Field strengths, or field intensities, are important for a major reason: they allow us to find force. From $E = F / q$ it is easy to see that

$$F = Eq$$

SAMPLE PROBLEM 8

Two charged, parallel metal plates have a gap of 4.0 mm and the E-field between the plates is 6000 N/C directed downward. An electron is released from rest from the negative plate.

(a) What force does the electron experience?

(b) Calculate the acceleration the electron experiences in the E-field.

SOLUTION TO PROBLEM 8

(a) Since the plates cannot be considered as point charges in this problem, we cannot use the modification of Coulomb's law. We use the above equation instead and substitute:

$$F = Eq = Ee = \left(6000 \ N\big/C\right)\left(1.60 \times 10^{-19} \ C\right) = \mathbf{9.6 \times 10^{-16} \ N}$$

Because the field is directed downward, the upper plate is positive and the force acting on the electron is upward. The force acting on the electron is therefore $\mathbf{9.6 \times 10^{-16} \ N}$ **at** $\mathbf{90°}$.

(b) The acceleration is found from Newton's second law:

$$F = ma \text{ and } a = \frac{F}{m} = \frac{9.6 \times 10^{-16} \text{ N}}{9.11 \times 10^{-31} \text{ kg}} = 1.1 \times 10^{15} \text{ m}\big/_{s^2} \text{ upward}$$

ELECTRIC POTENTIAL

(*College Physics* 9th ed. pages 548–558/10th ed. pages 558–568)

Electrical force is a conservative force, and as a result there is an electrical potential energy, U, associated with the electric force, F. The change in electrical potential energy between two points, ΔU, is the work, W, done moving a charged particle between these two point in an electric field. In equation form, the work done is $\Delta U = W = Fd = Eq_0 d$.

We define the change in electric potential, ΔV, as

$$\Delta V = \frac{\Delta U}{q_o} = \frac{W}{q_o}$$

The SI unit of electric potential is the volt, V, and is defined as a joule per coulomb $(1 \text{ V} = 1 \text{ J}/C)$.

The electric potential due to a point charge can also be calculated by

$$V = k\frac{q}{R}$$

Voltage, or electric potential, is a scalar quantity.

> ## AP Tip
>
> In lifting a mass in a gravitational field a distance, h, a force must be applied. The minimum force required is the weight, mg, of the mass. The force does work on the Earth-mass system. The work done is $W = mgh$.

SAMPLE PROBLEM 9

How much work is done moving a small body with a charge of +25 μC from point A to point B through a potential difference of 40.0 V?

SOLUTION TO PROBLEM 9

Solving $\Delta V = W/q_0$ for work done gives

$$W = \Delta V q_0 = (40.0 \text{ V})(25 \times 10^{-6} \text{ C}) = 0.001 \text{ J}.$$

SAMPLE PROBLEM 10

Find the electrical potential 2.0 cm from a point charge $q = -12 \mu$C.

SOLUTION TO PROBLEM 10

The electric potential is

$$V = k\frac{q}{R} = \frac{\left(9 \times 10^9 \ \text{N} \cdot \text{m}^2 \middle/ \text{C}^2\right)\left(-12 \times 10^{-6} \ \text{C}\right)}{(0.02 \ \text{m})} = \textbf{-5.4} \times \textbf{10}^6 \ \textbf{V}$$

Note: Since V is not a vector quantity and cannot be represented by a directional vector, the negative sign must be included in the calculation of V.

SAMPLE PROBLEM 11

A point charge of $q_1 = +2.0 \ \mu\text{C}$ is placed at the origin of a frame of reference, and a second point charge of $q_2 = -8.4 \ \mu\text{C}$ is placed at the position $x = 80.0$ cm as shown. Calculate the potential midway between these point charges.

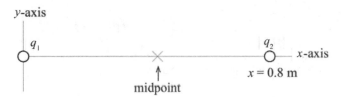

SOLUTION TO PROBLEM 11

The total electric potential of an arrangement of two or more charges by superposition is

$$V = k\sum\left(\frac{q_i}{r_i}\right) = \left(9 \times 10^9 \ \text{N} \cdot \text{m}^2 \middle/ \text{C}^2\right)\left[\left(\frac{2.0 \times 10^{-6} \ \text{C}}{0.4 \ \text{m}}\right) + \left(\frac{-8.4 \times 10^{-6} \ \text{C}}{0.4 \ \text{m}}\right)\right]$$

Simplifying the algebra, we have

$$V = \frac{\left(9 \times 10^9 \ \text{N} \cdot \text{m}^2 \middle/ \text{C}^2\right)}{0.4 \ \text{m}}\left[(2.0) + (-8.4)\right] \times 10^{-6} \ \frac{\text{C}}{\text{m}} = \textbf{-1.44} \times \textbf{10}^5 \ \textbf{V}$$

Since V is a scalar quantity, the potentials were added algebraically.

SAMPLE PROBLEM 12

In air, a metal sphere of radius $R = 10.0$ cm is given an electrical charge of $q = +100$ nC.

(a) What is the electrical potential at the surface of the sphere?

(b) What is the electrical potential at a point 20.0 cm from the surface of the sphere?

(c) Determine the maximum electrical field intensity for the sphere.

SOLUTION TO PROBLEM 12

(a) The electric potential at the surface of the sphere is

$$V = k\frac{q}{R} = \frac{\left(9 \times 10^9 \text{ N} \cdot \text{m}^2 / \text{C}^2\right)\left(100 \times 10^{-9} \text{ C}\right)}{(0.10 \text{ m})} = 9 \times 10^9 \text{ V}$$

(b) The electric potential at a point 20.0 cm from the surface of the sphere is

$$V = k\frac{q}{R} = \frac{\left(9 \times 10^9 \text{ N} \cdot \text{m}^2 / \text{C}^2\right)\left(100 \times 10^{-9} \text{ C}\right)}{(0.10 \text{ m} + 0.20 \text{ m})} = 3 \times 10^3 \text{ V}$$

(c) The maximum electrical field intensity exists on the surface of the sphere. So

$$E = k\frac{q}{R^2} = \frac{\left(9 \times 10^9 \text{ N} \cdot \text{m}^2 / \text{C}^2\right)\left(100 \times 10^{-9} \text{C}\right)}{(0.10 \text{ m})^2} = 9 \times 10^4 \text{ N} / \text{C}$$

Notice that a relationship exists between E and V.

$$V = \frac{kq}{R} \text{ and } E = \frac{kq}{R^2}$$

$$VR = kq = ER^2$$

Therefore

$$V = ER$$

So, reworking part (c), we then have

$$E = \frac{V}{R} = \frac{9 \times 10^3 \text{ V}}{0.1 \text{ m}} = 9 \times 10^4 \text{ V} / \text{m}$$

All electrical fields have two properties at every point in space:

1. The electrical field, E, which allows us to calculate the force acting on any charged particle placed at that point.

2. Electrical potential, V, which allows us to find the work done transporting a point charge to that position from a great distance away.

EQUIPOTENTIAL SURFACES

(*College Physics* 9th ed. pages 559–560/10th ed. pages 570–571)

A collection of points that all have the same electrical potential constitutes what is called an equipotential surface. The equipotential surfaces of a spherical surface are concentric spheres perpendicular to the electric field lines as shown. For a region in space where an electric field exists, the equipotential surfaces are always perpendicular to the electrical field lines.

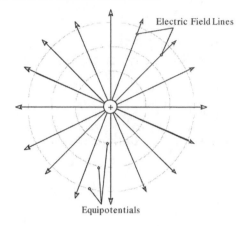

The work done to move a charge, q, between two points on an equipotential surface is $W = q\Delta V = 0$ regardless of the path taken because every point on the surface is at the same electric potential.

The surface of a conductor is itself an equipotential surface.

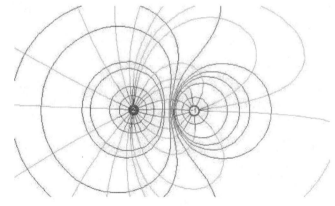

The lines of force and the equipotential lines associated with a point charges $+2q$ and $-q$ in electrostatic attraction.

DIELECTRIC STRENGTH

(*College Physics* 9th ed. pages 573–577/10th ed. pages 584–587)

There is a limit to the maximum electrostatic field that air will support. This limit is called the dielectric strength, and for air it is 3×10^6 V/m. When this value is exceeded, the air molecules in the field ionize, causing the charge creating the field to be reduced. The maximum electrical potential in a medium such as air is related to the maximum electrical field the air will support by

$$V_{max} = E_{max}R$$

SAMPLE PROBLEM 13

Consider Example 11 again. In air, a metal sphere of radius $R = 10.0$ cm is given an electrical charge of $q = +100$ nC. What is the electrical potential at the surface of the sphere?

SOLUTION TO PROBLEM 13

For a charged metallic sphere, the charge exists on the surface. The maximum electrical potential that can exist on the surface of the sphere is

$$V_{max} = E_{max}R = \left(3 \times 10^6 \frac{V}{m}\right)(0.10 \text{ m}) = 3 \times 10^5 \text{ V}$$

The electrical potential at the surface of Example 11 is less than this value.

ELECTRICAL POTENTIAL ENERGY

(*College Physics* 9th ed. pages 555–558/10th ed. pages 565–568)

The total energy of a charge in an electrical field is conserved. The electrical potential energy, U, of two point charges separated by distance R is

$$U = k\frac{q_1 q_2}{R}$$

SAMPLE PROBLEM 14

Two point charges, $q_A = +12 \ \mu C$ and $q_B = -22 \ \mu C$, are brought from infinity to a distance of 0.40 m of one another. How much work was done to assemble this system?

SOLUTION TO PROBLEM 14

First, find the electrical potential energy.

$$U = k\frac{q_A q_B}{R}$$

$$= \frac{\left(9 \times 10^9 \text{ N} \cdot \text{m}^2 / \text{C}^2\right)\left(+12 \times 10^{-6} \text{ C}\right)\left(-22 \times 10^{-6} \text{ C}\right)}{(0.40 \text{ m})}$$

$$= -5.9 \text{ J}$$

Because the particles attract, their fields do -5.9 J work in assembling the system. To separate the particles to infinity, some outside agent would have to do $+5.9$ J of work.

Note: Since U is not a vector quantity and cannot be represented by a directional vector, the negative sign must be included in the calculation of U.

SAMPLE PROBLEM 15

Four point charges, $q_1 = 2.5\ \mu C$, $q_2 = -1.5\ \mu C$, $q_3 = 7.5\ \mu C$ and $q_4 = -5.5\ \mu C$ are arranged in a square measuring $x = 0.35$ m on a side.

(a) How much work was done by outside forces to arrange the charges in the square?

(b) What is the electric potential V at the center of the square?

(c) An electron initially at rest starts from a great distance away and moves toward the center of the square. What classical velocity will the electron have when it reaches the center?

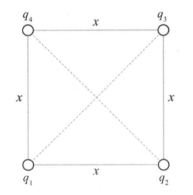

SOLUTION TO PROBLEM 15

(a) The point charges are assembled one charge at a time. To place q_1 requires zero work, $W_1 = 0$, since there are no other charges present. Positioning q_2 requires outside work W_2 that equals the electrical potential energy of q_1 and q_2. So,

$$W_2 = U = k\frac{q_1 q_2}{x} = \frac{k}{x}(q_1 q_2)$$

$$W_2 = \frac{\left(9\times10^9\ N\cdot m^2\big/C^2\right)}{0.35\ m}\left(2.5\times10^{-6}\ C\right)\left(-1.5\times10^{-6}\ C\right)$$

$$W_2 = \frac{\left(9\times10^9\ N\cdot m^2\big/C^2\right)}{0.35\ m}\left[(2.5)(-1.5)\right]\times10^{-6}\ C = -0.096\ J$$

To place the third point charge, additional work is due to the two point charges already in place. A diagonal of the square forms a right triangle with sides x and hypotenuse $x\sqrt{2}$. Each diagonal has a length $x\sqrt{2}$. So

$$W_3 = kq_3\left(\frac{q_1}{x_{13}} + \frac{q_2}{x_{23}}\right)$$

$$W_3 = kq_3 \left(\frac{q_1}{x\sqrt{2}} + \frac{q_2}{x} \right)$$

$$W_3 = \left(9\times10^9 \text{ N}\cdot\text{m}^2\middle/\text{C}^2\right)\left(7.5\times10^{-6} \text{ C}\right)\left[\left(\frac{2.5\times10^{-6} \text{ C}}{\sqrt{2}(0.35 \text{ m})}\right) + \left(\frac{-1.5\times10^{-6} \text{ C}}{0.35 \text{ m}}\right)\right]$$

Simplifying gives

$$W_3 = \left(9\times10^9 \text{ N}\cdot\text{m}^2\middle/\text{C}^2\right)\left(7.5\times10^{-6} \text{ C}\right)\left[\left(\frac{2.5}{0.49}\right) + \left(\frac{-1.5}{0.35}\right)\right]\times10^{-6} \frac{\text{C}}{\text{m}} = \mathbf{0.055 \text{ J}}$$

Positioning point charge q_4 requires work of W_4.

$$W_4 = kq_4 \left(\frac{q_1}{x_{14}} + \frac{q_2}{x_{24}} + \frac{q_3}{x_{34}} \right)$$

$$W_4 = kq_4 \left(\frac{q_1}{x} + \frac{q_2}{x\sqrt{2}} + \frac{q_3}{x} \right)$$

$$W_4 = \left(9\times10^9 \text{ N}\cdot\text{m}^2\middle/\text{C}^2\right)\left(-5.5\times10^{-6} \text{ C}\right)\left[\left(\frac{2.5\times10^{-6} \text{ C}}{0.35 \text{ m}}\right) + \left(\frac{-1.5\times10^{-6} \text{ C}}{(\sqrt{2})(0.35 \text{ m})}\right) + \frac{(7.5\times10^{-6} \text{ C})}{0.35 \text{ m}}\right]$$

Simplifying yields

$$W_4 = \left(9\times10^9 \text{ N}\cdot\text{m}^2\middle/\text{C}^2\right)\left(-5.5\times10^{-6} \text{ C}\right)\left[\left(\frac{2.5}{0.35}\right) + \left(\frac{-1.5}{0.49}\right) + \frac{(7.5)}{0.35}\right]\times10^{-6} \frac{\text{C}}{\text{m}} = \mathbf{-1.26 \text{ J}}$$

Therefore, the total work is $\Sigma W = W_1 + W_2 + W_3 + W_4$.

$$\Sigma W = 0 + (-0.096 \text{ J}) + 0.055 \text{ J} + (-1.26 \text{ J}) = \mathbf{-1.30 \text{ J}}$$

(b) With all of the point charges in place, the potential at the center is

$$V = V_1 + V_2 + V_3 + V_4 = k\left[\frac{q_1 + q_2 + q_3 + q_4}{(0.5x)\left(\sqrt{2}\right)}\right]$$

$$V = \left(9\times10^9 \text{ N}\cdot\text{m}^2\middle/\text{C}^2\right)\left[\frac{2.5 - 1.5 + 7.5 - 5.5}{(0.175)\left(\sqrt{2}\right)}\right]\times10^{-6} \frac{\text{C}}{\text{m}}$$

$$= \mathbf{1.09\times10^5 \text{ V}}$$

(c) The electron must lose electrical potential energy $\Delta U = Ve$.

$$\Delta U = \left(1.09\times10^5 \text{ V}\right)\left(-1.60\times10^{-19} \text{ C}\right) = \mathbf{-1.75\times10^{-14} \text{ J}}$$

This electrical potential energy becomes kinetic energy at the center of the square and $K = 1.75\times10^{-14} \text{ J}$. Therefore $K = \frac{1}{2}mv^2$ and

$$v = \sqrt{\frac{2K}{m}} = \sqrt{\frac{2\left(1.74\times10^{-14} \text{ V}\right)}{9.11\times10^{-31} \text{ kg}}} = \mathbf{1.96\times10^8 \frac{\text{m}}{\text{s}}}$$

THE PARALLEL-PLATE CAPACITOR

(College Physics 9th ed. pages 563–565/10th ed. pages 573–576)

One of the most useful electrical devices in many aspects of electricity is the parallel-plate capacitor. The plates are metal and are separated by a plate gap, *d*. Connecting the capacitor to a battery charges the plates. Think of a battery as an electron pump. It removes electrons from what becomes the positive plate and places an equal number of electrons on what becomes the negative plate (charging a capacitor is done by electrostatic repulsion). It takes a brief period of time to charge the capacitor, and then the battery can be removed. The magnitude of the charges on the plates are equal, $\left|q_{plate\ 1}\right| = \left|q_{plate\ 2}\right|$. The amount of charge on each plate is proportional to the potential difference, *V*, across the plates

$$C = \frac{q}{V}$$

We call the constant of proportionality, *C*, the capacitance of the capacitor.

The SI unit of capacitance is the farad, F, and is defined as $1\ F = 1\ C/V$. The farad is a very large unit. The usual capacitance of a capacitor is on the order of several microfarads, μF, to several picofarads pF. In short

$$1\ \mu F = 1 \times 10^{-6}\ F$$

$$1\ nF = 1 \times 10^{-9}\ F$$

$$1\ pF = 1 \times 10^{-12}\ F$$

The upper plate in the diagram shown below has been charged positive. The field always points from positive charge to negative. Ignoring the edges of the plates, the electrical field between the plates is uniform.

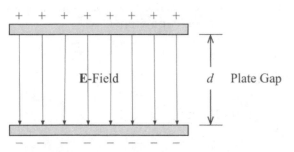

For a parallel-plate capacitor, the relationship between the electrical field, *E*, between the plates, the potential difference across the plates and the plate gap is

$$V = Ed$$

SAMPLE PROBLEM 16

A parallel plate capacitor has a potential difference of 100 V across its plates and a plate gap of 2.0 mm. What electric field, E, exists between the plates?

SOLUTION TO PROBLEM 16

$$E = \frac{V}{d} = \frac{100 \text{ V}}{2 \times 10^{-3} \text{m}} = 5 \times 10^4 \text{ V/m}$$

The student should prove that prove that $1 \text{ N/C} = 1 \text{ V/m}$.

The equipotential surfaces between the plates of a parallel capacitor are planes that are perpendicular to the field lines.

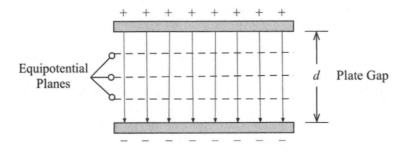

The capacitance of a parallel-plate capacitor can be calculated by using

$$C = \varepsilon_o \frac{A}{d}$$

where ε_o is the permittivity constant of free space and A is the area of one of the plates. It gives us information on how well an E-field is set up in space. In SI units, $\varepsilon_o = 8.85 \times 10^{-12} \text{ C}^2/\text{N} \cdot \text{m}^2$.

SAMPLE PROBLEM 17

A set of capacitor plates each measures 10.0 cm by 12.0 cm, and they have a plate gap of 3.0 mm. Calculate the capacitance.

SOLUTION TO PROBLEM 17

The area of one of the plates is

$$120 \text{ cm}^2 \times \frac{1 \text{ m}^2}{1 \times 10^4 \text{cm}^2} = 120 \times 10^{-4} \text{m}^2$$

Therefore

$$C = \varepsilon_o \frac{A}{d} = \frac{\left(8.85 \times 10^{-12} \text{ C}^2/\text{N} \cdot \text{m}^2\right)\left(120 \times 10^{-4} \text{m}^2\right)}{3 \times 10^{-3} \text{m}} = 35 \text{ pF}$$

DIELECTRICS

(*College Physics* 9th ed. pages 573–578/10th ed. pages 584–587)

When an insulating material called a dielectric is inserted between the plates of a capacitor, the capacitance increases. The dielectric is represented by a dimensionless quantity called the dielectric constant, κ. With a dielectric inserted between the plates, the capacitance becomes

$$C = \kappa \varepsilon_o \frac{A}{d}$$

SAMPLE PROBLEM 18

A parallel-plate capacitor of plate gap $d = 2.0$ mm has a capacitance $C_0 = 3.0 \ \mu F$. A battery is used to charge the plates with a potential difference $V_0 = 600$ V. After the charging process, the battery is removed.

(a) What is the potential difference across the capacitor when a 2.0 mm thick slab of a dielectric of $\kappa = 7.5$ is sandwiched between the plates?

(b) What is the new capacitance?

(c) What is the permittivity of the dielectric?

SOLUTION TO PROBLEM 18

Proportionally, the dielectric constant is $\kappa = V_0/V$ and

(a) $V = V_0/\kappa = 600 \text{ V}/7.5 = \textbf{80 V}$

(b) $C = \kappa C_0 = 7.5(3.0 \times 10^{-6} \text{ F}) = \textbf{22.5 } \boldsymbol{\mu}\textbf{F}$

(c) $\varepsilon = \kappa \varepsilon_0 = 7.5(8.85 \times 10^{-12} \text{ C}^2/\text{N} \cdot \text{m}^2) = \textbf{6.64} \times \textbf{10}^{-11} \textbf{ C}^2/\textbf{N} \cdot \textbf{m}^2$

ELECTRICAL ENERGY STORED IN A CAPACITOR

(*College Physics* 9th ed. pages 571–573/10th ed. pages 582–584)

Parallel-plate capacitors not only produce uniform electrical fields between their plates and store charge on the plates; they also store electrical energy. The energy stored in the field between the plates may be calculated by

$$U = \frac{1}{2} C V^2$$

or $\quad U = \frac{1}{2} q V$

or $\quad U = \frac{1}{2} \frac{q^2}{C}$

SAMPLE PROBLEM 19

A parallel-plate capacitor with a plate gap of 0.6 mm has a capacitance of 6.0 μF. A battery charges the plates with a potential difference of 500 V and is then disconnected.

(a) Calculate the energy stored in the capacitor.

(b) What charge exists on the plates?

SOLUTION TO PROBLEM 19

(a) Because the capacitance and potential difference are given, we will use $U = \dfrac{1}{2}CV^2$ to find the energy stored. Therefore

$$U = \frac{1}{2}CV^2 = \frac{1}{2}\left(6.0 \times 10^{-6}\,\text{F}\right)\left(500\,\text{V}\right)^2 = \textbf{0.75 J}$$

(b) The charge is then

$$q = CV = \left(6.0 \times 10^{-6}\text{F}\right)\left(500\,\text{V}\right) = \textbf{3} \times \textbf{10}^{-3}\ \textbf{C}$$

COMBINATIONS OF CAPACITORS

(*College Physics* 9th ed. pages 565–571/10th ed. pages 576–582)

Electrical circuits frequently contain two or more capacitors grouped together to serve a particular function. In considering the effect of such groupings, it is convenient to use a circuit diagram. In such diagrams, electrical components are represented by symbols. The symbol for a battery is a set of unequal parallel lines. The high-potential terminal (+ terminal) of a battery is represented by the longer line. The capacitor is diagramed as a set of equal-length parallel lines. Wires are shown as lines that connect components. Electrical circuit diagrams are also called electrical schematics.

When capacitors are arranged in parallel, their combined capacitance is the arithmetic sum of the individual capacitors.

$$C_{eq} = C_1 + C_2 + C_3 + \ldots$$

SAMPLE PROBLEM 20

Three capacitors, $C_1 = 0.5\mu$F, $C_2 = 0.3\ \mu$F and $C_3 = 0.2\ \mu$F are arranged in parallel. Calculate the equivalent capacitance.

SOLUTION TO PROBLEM 20

We start with a circuit diagram and then substitute values.

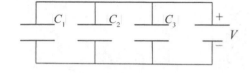

$$C_{eq} = C_1 + C_2 + C_3 = (0.5 + 0.3 + 0.2)\,\mu F = \mathbf{1.0}\ \mu\mathbf{F}$$

When capacitors are arranged in series, the reciprocal of the combined capacitance is the sum of the reciprocals of the capacitors.

$$\frac{1}{C_{eq}} = \frac{1}{C_1} + \frac{1}{C_2} + \frac{1}{C_3} + \ldots$$

SAMPLE PROBLEM 21

Three capacitors, $C_1 = 0.5\mu F$, $C_2 = 0.3\ \mu F$ and $C_3 = 0.2\ \mu F$, are arranged in series. Calculate the equivalent capacitance, C_{eq}.

SOLUTION TO PROBLEM 21

Again we start with a circuit diagram and substitute

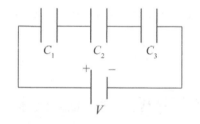

$$\frac{1}{C_{eq}} = \frac{1}{C_1} + \frac{1}{C_2} + \frac{1}{C_3} = \frac{1}{0.5\ \mu F} + \frac{1}{0.3\ \mu F} + \frac{1}{0.2\ \mu F}$$

$$C_{eq} = \mathbf{0.097}\ \mu\mathbf{F}$$

SAMPLE PROBLEM 22

(a) Calculate the total capacitance of the circuit shown below.

(b) Find the charge on each capacitor in the circuit.

(c) Calculate the voltage drop across capacitor C_2.

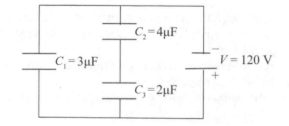

SOLUTION TO PROBLEM 22

(a) Capacitors C_2 and C_3 are in series with one another and their equivalent capacitance is

$$\frac{1}{C_{eq}} = \frac{1}{C_1} + \frac{1}{C_2} = \frac{1}{4\ \mu\mathrm{F}} + \frac{1}{2\ \mu\mathrm{F}}$$

$$C_{eq} = \mathbf{1.33}\ \boldsymbol{\mu}\mathbf{F}$$

The circuit is now reduced as shown below.

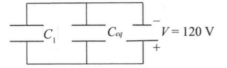

The two remaining capacitances are arranged in parallel and $C = C_1 + C_{eq} = 3\ \mu\mathrm{F} + 1.33\ \mu\mathrm{F} = \mathbf{4.33}\ \boldsymbol{\mu}\mathbf{F}$.

(b) The total charge in the capacitors is $q = CV = (4.33\ \mu\mathrm{F})(120\ \mathrm{V}) = $ **520 μC**. The charge, q_1, on C_1 is $q_1 = C_1 V = (3\ \mu\mathrm{F})(120\ \mathrm{V}) = $ **360 μC** and the remaining charge is $q - q_1 = 520\ \mu\mathrm{C} - 360\ \mu\mathrm{C} = 160\ \mu\mathrm{C}$. The 160 μC must be deposited on capacitors C_2 and C_3. So, $q_2 = q_3 = \mathbf{160}\ \boldsymbol{\mu}\mathbf{C}$.

(c) The voltage drop is $V = q_2 / C_2 = \mathbf{40\ V}$.

ELECTROSTATICS: STUDENT OBJECTIVES FOR THE AP EXAM

- ▣ You should know that there are two fundamental charges.
- ▣ You should understand Coulomb's law for the fundamental electrostatic force between point charges and that the electrical fields produced by these charges are vector quantities with magnitude and direction.
- ▣ You should know how to use the equations, identify the charges, and sketch the directions for the forces and field in solving problems that involve these quantities.
- ▣ You should know that potential difference and electrical potential, closely related concepts, are scalar quantities.
- ▣ You should know how to use the equations, identify the charges, and solve problems involving potential difference and electrical potential.
- ▣ You should know that the equations of potential difference and electrical potential can be used to solve conservation of energy and work–energy theorem problems.
- ▣ You should know the relationship between electric field lines and equipotential lines and be able to sketch them.
- ▣ You should know that the electron volt, eV, is a unit of work and energy.

■ You should be able to work with a capacitor, a device that stores energy.
■ You should be able to solve multiple-choice questions/problems with a calculator.

MULTIPLE-CHOICE QUESTIONS

1. Two uncharged objects, a glass rod and a silk cloth, are rubbed together.

   The glass rod acquires a positive charge, while the silk cloth
   (A) remains uncharged
   (B) becomes negatively charged
   (C) is also positively charged
   (D) has a negative charge of twice the magnitude of the positive charge transferred to the glass rod

2. A positively charged glass rod is brought near a neutral isolated conducting sphere.

   Which of the following illustrations is the correct representation of the charge distribution on the sphere?

   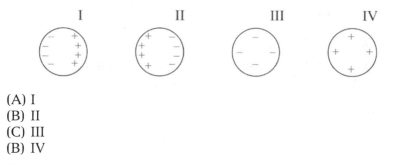

   (A) I
   (B) II
   (C) III
   (B) IV

3. Electrical charge that is transferred in the process of conduction when a charging wand touches an isolated body can produce charges on the body equal to
   (A) $\pm\dfrac{1}{2}e$
   (B) $\pm\dfrac{2}{3}e$
   (C) $\pm\dfrac{3}{2}e$
   (D) $\pm e$

4. A metal sphere A carries a charge of –3Q and an identical sphere, B, has a charge of +Q. The magnitude of the force, F, that A exerts on B compared to the force that B exerts on A is

(A) $\frac{1}{3}F$

(B) F

(C) $3F$

(D) $9F$

5. A charge of +Q is located in the center of a neutral ring that has an inner radius of r_1 and an outer radius of r_2 as shown below.

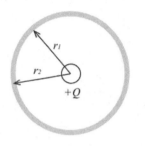

The charge induced on the

(A) inner surface of the ring is $-Q$

(B) inner surface of the ring is $-\frac{1}{2}Q$

(C) outer surface of the ring is $+\frac{1}{2}Q$

(D) outer surface of the ring is $-Q$

6. A positively charged glass rod is brought near a neutral isolated conducting sphere as shown in the diagram below.

The positively charged glass rod is removed. The isolated conducting sphere will have

(A) a net positive charge

(B) a net negative charge

(C) charge separated, negative on one side of the sphere and positive on the other side

(D) zero net charge

7. An electron is placed in a uniform E-field between two charged parallel plates as shown in the diagram below.

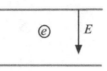

What is the magnitude and the direction of the force on the electron given that the strength of the field is 2000 N/C?

(A) 3.2×10^{-16} N downward

(B) 3.2×10^{-16} N upward

(C) 1.8×10^{-27} N downward

(D) 1.8×10^{-27} N upward

8. The magnitude and the direction of the acceleration of the electron in problem 7 is correctly given in which of the following choices?

(A) 1.9×10^{11} m/s^2 toward the upper plate

(B) 1.9×10^{11} m/s^2 toward the lower plate

(C) 3.5×10^{14} m/s^2 toward the upper plate

(D) 3.5×10^{14} m/s^2 toward the lower plate

9. Isolines representing the electrical potential in a region are shown in the diagram below.

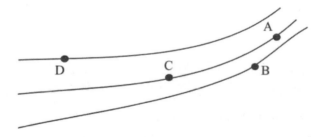

Rank the magnitude of the strength of the electric field from largest to smallest.

(A) D > C > B > A

(B) D = C = B = A

(C) D > B > C > A

(D) A > B > C > D

10. Three point charges, $+q_1$, $+q_2$, and $-q_3$ are equally spaced along the straight line shown below.

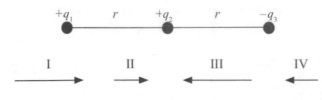

Which of the above vectors best represents the net force acting on the point charge $+q_2$?

(A) I
(B) II
(C) III
(D) IV

11. Two isolated identical spheres kept at rest at a separation of 0.10 m from center to center have charges as shown in the diagram below.

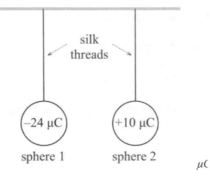

A copper wire is used to connect the two spheres and is then removed. The charge on each sphere after the copper wire was removed is

(A) -14 μC on sphere 1 and 0 on sphere 2
(B) -7 μC on sphere 1 and $+7$ μC on sphere 2
(C) -7 μC on sphere 1 and -7 μC on sphere 2
(D) zero on each since the excess charge remains in the wire when it is removed

12. During a physics laboratory experiment, an electron is placed in the electric field between the parallel plates shown in the diagram below.

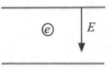

When the electron is released from rest, it will experience an acceleration due to the field that is

(A) less than the acceleration due to gravity and in the same direction as the gravitational acceleration

(B) less than the acceleration due to gravity and in the opposite direction as the gravitational acceleration

(C) much greater than the acceleration due to gravity and in the same direction as the gravitational acceleration

(D) much greater than the acceleration due to gravity and in the opposite direction as the gravitational acceleration

Questions 13 to 15

Directions: For each of the questions or incomplete statements below, <u>two</u> of the suggested answers will be correct. For each of these questions, you must select <u>both</u> correct choices to earn credit. No partial credit will be earned if only one correct answer is selected. Select the two that are best in each case and then enter both of the appropriate answers in the corresponding space on the answer sheet.

13. Which of the following statements is true concerning the work done on an electron by the electric field when the electron is moved at constant speed between two points?

(A) The electron moved in the direction of the electrical field; therefore there was no change in its kinetic energy and thus no work done.

(B) The electron moved in the direction opposite the electrical field; therefore there was no change in its kinetic energy and thus no work done.

(C) The electron moved perpendicular to the electrical field; therefore there was no change in its kinetic energy and thus no work done.

(D) The electron moved along an equipotential line connecting the two points.

14. A charging wand is brought near four conducting spheres as shown in the illustration below. Which illustration indicates the correct charge on the sphere?

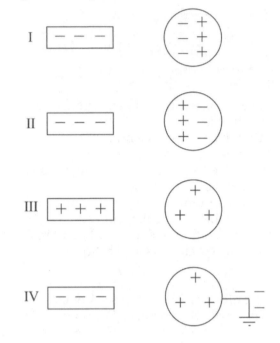

(A) I
(B) II
(C) III
(D) IV

15. In comparing the gravitational force to the Coulomb force, we find that
    (A) the gravitational force acts at a distance while the Coulomb force is a contact force
    (B) they are inverse square laws
    (C) they are both forces of attraction
    (D) the Coulomb force acting between an electron and a proton is stronger than the gravitational force acting between the two

FREE-RESPONSE PROBLEMS

1. A tiny sphere of mass 8×10^{-13} kg and charge $q = -4.8 \times 10^{-18}$ C is placed between the plates of a parallel-plate capacitor with plate gap $d = 20.0$ mm. The sphere remains suspended in the electric field of the capacitor as shown.

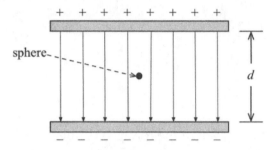

   (a) On the diagram, show the forces acting on the sphere.
   (b) How many electrons are in excess on the sphere?
   (c) What is the strength of the electric field?
   (d) Determine the potential difference across the plates.
   (e) The charge is removed from the field. Both upper and lower plates are symmetrical, and each measures 25.0 cm by 25.0 cm. Find the capacitance of the capacitor.
   (f) What charge exists on the lower plate of the capacitor?

2. Four identical charges $q = +6.0$ μC are arranged in a square that measures $R = 0.04$ m on a side as shown. L is the distance from the center of the square to each of the charges.

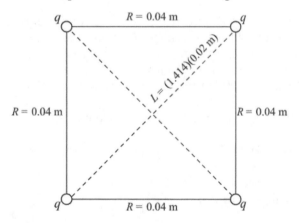

   (a) Find the electric field at the center of the square.
   (b) Determine the electric potential at the center of the square.

3. Two small identical Styrofoam spheres of mass m connected by silk threads of length L to a common point receive equal charges q from a charging wand. After charging, the angle each silk thread makes with the vertical is 10° as illustrated in the diagram below.

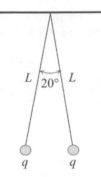

(a) i.   Make a free-body diagram of the forces on either Styrofoam sphere.
    ii.   If you drew a free-body diagram of the forces acting on the second sphere, how would they compare?
   iii.   Does your free-body diagram depend on whether q is + or –? Explain your answer using the correct scientific terms.

(b) Using your free-body diagram, explain how you would write a mathematical representation for the forces exerted on the sphere.

(c) Explain how you would use the mathematical representation to determine the magnitude of the charge.

(d) Explain how you would determine the separation, r, of the spheres.

4. In an experiment, students noted that three small isolated identical spheres A, B, and C exhibited forces of attraction and repulsion between various combinations of the three spheres when pairs of the spheres were brought to positions that were 0.05 m apart.
    A repelled B with a force of 1.00 N when they were placed 0.05 m apart.
    A attracted C with a force of 0.50 N when they were placed 0.05 m apart.
    B attracted C with a force of 0.25 N when they were placed 0.05 m apart.
    If the charge on A is +2Q, what are the charges on B and C?
    Explain each step of your reasoning.

Answers

MULTIPLE-CHOICE QUESTIONS

1. **B** Charge is conserved. If the glass rod acquired a positive charge in the process of rubbing the two materials together, the silk cloth acquires the same magnitude of negative charge.
    (*College Physics* 9th ed. pages 514–515/10th ed. pages 524–525)
    (L.O. 1.B.1.1)

2. **A** The sphere is polarized due to the charging wand. The only charge that can move in a sphere is the negative charge. The electrons will move to the side of the sphere closest to the positive charging wand. The side opposite the wand will have a positive charge.
    (*College Physics* 9th ed. pages 515–516/10th ed. pages 525–526)
    (L.O. 1.B.1.2, 1.B.2.2)

3. **D** The charge on an object is a whole number multiple of e.
    (*College Physics* 9th ed. pages 515–516/10th ed. pages 525–526)
    (L.O. 1.B.3.1)

4. **B** Coulomb's law relates the magnitude of the force acting between two point charges, $F = k_e \dfrac{q_1 q_2}{r^2}$. The forces are action-reaction pair forces. $F_{AB} = -F_{BA}$. The force is attractive since the charges are $-3Q$ and $+Q$.
    (*College Physics* 9th ed. pages 517–519/10th ed. pages 527–530)
    (L.O. 3.C.2.1)

5. **A** Charge is conserved. Since a charge of $+Q$ is located in the center of the conducting ring, the charge on the inner surface is $-Q$ and the charge on the outer surface is $+Q$.
    (*College Physics* 9th ed. pages 517–519/10th ed. pages 527–530)
    (L.O. 5.A.2.1)

6. **D** The realignment of charge is called polarization. When the positive charging wand in problem 2 is removed, the negative charge will realign and the sphere will still have zero net charge.
    (*College Physics* 9th ed. pages 515–516/10th ed. pages 525–526)
    (L.O. 1.B.2.3)

7. **B** The direction of the field is the direction that a positive charge would move when placed in the field. The electron will experience a upward force. The magnitude of the force is given by $F = Eq = (2000 \ \text{N/C})(1.6 \times 10^{-19} \ \text{C}) = 3.2 \times 10^{-16} \ \text{N}$.
    (*College Physics* 9th ed. pages 522–523/10th ed. pages 532–533)
    (L.O. 2.C.1.1, 2.C.1.2)

8. **C** The direction of the field is the direction of the force on a positive charge will move when placed in the field. The electron will move to the upper plate, against the field. The magnitude of the acceleration is given by

$$a = \frac{Eq}{m} = \frac{(2000 \; ^N\!/_C)(1.6 \times 10^{-19} \; C)}{9.11 \times 10^{-31} \; kg} = 3.5 \times 10^{14} \; ^m\!/_{s^2}$$

(*College Physics* 9th ed. pages 522–523/10th ed. pages 532–534)
(L.O. 3.A.1.1, 3.A.3.1)

9. **D** The points where the isolines are closer together indicate a stronger electric field in the region.
(*College Physics* 9th ed. pages 555–560/10th ed. pages 565–570)
(L.O. 2.E.3.1)

10. **A** The forces between the charges, $q_1 q_2$ and $q_2 q_3$, have the same magnitude since the charges are of the same magnitude and the separation between $q_1 q_2$ and $q_2 q_3$ is the same. The force between $q_1 q_2$ is repulsive and the force between $q_2 q_3$ is attractive making vector I the proper choice.
(*College Physics* 9th ed. pages 522–523/10th ed. pages 532–534)
(L.O. 3.A.3.4)

11. **C** Charge is conserved within an isolated system. When the wire connects the two spheres, negative charge will move from sphere 1 to sphere 2, cancelling the positive charge. The remaining charge will redistribute due to repulsive forces between the charges. Since the spheres are identical, the charge on each will be the same.
(*College Physics* 9th ed. pages 514–515, 517–519/10th ed. pages 524–525, 527–530)
(L.O. 5.C.2.1)

12. **D** The electrical field exerts a force on the electron that is much greater than the force exerted on it by the gravitational field. (Refer to the answer given for the numerical calculation in problem 10 for the value of its acceleration.) The direction of the field determines if the acceleration is in the same direction as the gravitational field or opposite to the gravitational field. In the diagram, the field points downward and the electron will experience a force due to the electric field upward, against the field.
(*College Physics* 9th ed. pages 522–523/10th ed. pages 532–533)
(L.O. 3.G.2.1)

13. **C and D** No work is done by a given force on a body when the angle between the force and the displacement is 90°. No work is done by the electric field in moving a charge along an equipotential in an electric field.
(*College Physics* 9th ed. pages 522–523/10th ed. pages 532–534)
(L.O. 3.A.1.1)

14. **B and D** In a metal conductor or insulator, the only charge that can move is the negative charge. The spheres are isolated and are not in contact in examples I to III, thus charge cannot leave or move onto the spheres. In II, the sphere is polarized due to repulsion of the negative charge to the negatively charged wand.

The side closest to the negative wand will be the positive side. The sphere in IV is connected to ground so that charge can move to ground, leaving it positively charged.
(*College Physics* 9th ed. pages 515–516/10th ed. pages 525–526)
(L.O. 4.E.3.1, 4.E.3.2)

15. **B** and **D** The two forces $F = k_e \dfrac{q_1 q}{r^2}$ and $F = G \dfrac{m_1 m_2}{r^2}$ are field forces that are inverse square laws. Gravitational forces are always forces of attraction where the Coulomb force can be either attractive (opposite charges) or repulsive (like charges). Electrical forces between a proton and an electron are much stronger than gravitational forces between the two.
(*College Physics* 9th ed. pages 517–519/10th ed. pages 527–530)
(L.O. 3.C.2.2)

FREE-RESPONSE PROBLEMS

1. (a)

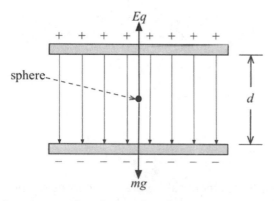

(b) Using the conversion factor for the charge on the electrons gives

$$4.8 \times 10^{-18} \ \text{C} \times \frac{1 \ e}{1.60 \times 10^{-19} \ \text{C}} = 30 \ e$$

(c) In static equilibrium, the upward electrostatic force acting on the negative sphere equals the weight of the sphere. So, $qE = mg$, and

$$E = \frac{mg}{q} = \frac{\left(8 \times 10^{-13} \ \text{kg}\right)\left(9.8 \ \text{m/s}\right)}{4.8 \times 10^{-18} \ \text{C}} = \mathbf{1.63 \times 10^6 \ V/m}$$

(d) The potential difference can be found by
$$V = Ed = \left(1.63 \times 10^6 \ \text{V/m}\right)\left(20 \times 10^{-3} \ \text{m}\right) = \mathbf{33 \ kV}.$$

(e) The capacitance is

$$C = \varepsilon_0 \frac{A}{d} = \frac{\left(8.85 \times 10^{-12} \ \text{F}/\text{m}\right)(0.25 \ \text{m})^2}{\left(20 \times 10^{-3} \ \text{m}\right)} = \mathbf{0.28 \ pF}$$

(f) The charge on the lower plate is

$$q = CV = (0.28 \times 10^{-12} \text{ F})(1.63 \times 10^6 \text{ V}) = \mathbf{4.56 \times 10^{-5} \text{ C}}$$

(*College Physics* 9th ed. pages 522–526/10th ed. pages 532–533)
(L.O. 2.C.1.1, 2.C.1.2)

2. (a) The distance, L, from the center of the square to each point charge is half the length of the diagonal of the square. So

$$L = \sqrt{2}\,\frac{R}{2} = (1.414)\left(\frac{0.04 \text{ m}}{2}\right) = 0.028 \text{ m}$$

The charges q are identical and so are the distances L. Logically, the magnitude of the electrical field vectors, E, for each charge will all be equal. The directions will differ and will be directed along the diagonals. Therefore, **by symmetry, the net E-field will be zero.**

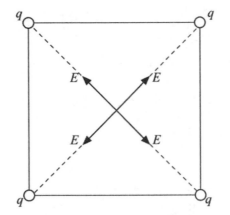

To calculate the resultant electrical field at the center of the square, first determine the x component of the resultant **E**-vector:

$$E_x = E(\cos 45°) + E(\cos 135°) + E(\cos 225°) + E(\cos 315°)$$

$$E_x = E(0.707) + E(-0.707) + E(-0.707) + E(0.707) = 0$$

Next, find the y component of **E**:

$$E_y = E(\sin 45°) + E(\sin 135°) + E(\sin 225°) + E(\sin 315°)$$

$$E_y = E(0.707) + E(0.707) + E(-0.707) + E(-0.707) = 0$$

Both the x component and the y component of the resultant **E** are zero, which means that the resultant electrical field intensity at the center of the square is itself zero and **E = 0.**

(b) Even though the field intensity at the center of the square is zero when identical charges are at each vertex, it does not necessarily mean that the electric potential is likewise zero. The electrical potential due to i number of charges at a given point is found by $V = k \Sigma (q_i/r_i)$. Here, $i = 4$ charges, and the electric potential is calculated by

$$V = \frac{k}{L}\left(q_1 + q_2 + q_3 + q_4\right)$$

$$V = \left(\frac{9 \times 10^9 \, \text{N} \cdot \text{m}^2/\text{C}^2}{0.028 \, \text{m}}\right)(6.0 + 6.0 + 6.0 + 6.0) \times 10^{-6} \, \text{C}$$

$$= \textbf{7.71} \times \textbf{10}^{\textbf{6}} \textbf{ V}$$

There is electric potential at the center of the square.
(*College Physics* 9th ed. pages 555–558/10th ed. pages 565–568)
(L.O. 3.A.4.3)

3. (a) i. The free-body diagram for the sphere on the right in the system is

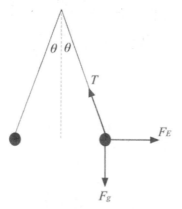

ii. The electrostatic forces between the charged Styrofoam spheres are action-reaction pairs. They are equal in magnitude and opposite in direction. $F_{12} = -F_{21}$. The free-body diagrams would be mirror images.
iii. Since the charges are equal in magnitude and repulsive it makes no difference if they are positive or negative.

(b) The forces acting on the Styrofoam are F_g, F_E and the tension T in the silk thread.

These forces form a right triangle and the $\tan \theta = \dfrac{F_E}{F_g}$.

(c) The sum of both the force x-components and the y-components are written as $\Sigma F_x = 0$ and $\Sigma F_y = 0$. The x-component becomes $\dfrac{kq^2}{r^2} = T \sin \theta$ and the y-component is $\dfrac{mg}{\cos \theta} = T$. Combine both equations by eliminating T, gives $k_e \dfrac{q^2}{r^2} = (mg) \tan \theta$.

(d) Since the silk threads have length L, the relationship between the length of the threads and the sin 10° will give the distance each sphere moves from equilibrium position. The distance of separation of the two spheres r, is equal to $2L\sin 10°$.

(*College Physics* 9th ed. pages 514–519/10th ed. pages 524–529)

(L.O. 3.A.4.3, 3.C.2.3)

4. A repels B and attracts C.

B attracts C.

Since A is positive, then B is positive, and C is negative.

Set up ratios for the forces. Note that $\dfrac{k_e}{r^2}$ is constant and will not be used in the ratios.

$$\left|\frac{F_{AB}}{F_{AC}}\right| = \frac{Q_A Q_B}{Q_A Q_C}$$

Substituting the forces will give $\dfrac{1.00\text{ N}}{0.50\text{ N}} = \dfrac{Q_B}{Q_C}$ giving $2Q_C = Q_B$.

A second ratio will give Q_B in terms of Q_A.

$$\left|\frac{F_{AB}}{F_{BC}}\right| = \frac{Q_A Q_B}{Q_B \dfrac{Q_B}{2}}$$

Again substitution of the forces gives $\dfrac{1.00\text{ N}}{0.25\text{ N}} = \dfrac{Q_A}{0.5Q_B}$

Yielding $2\,Q_B = Q_A$.

Since $A = +2Q$, $B = +Q$ and $C = -\dfrac{1}{2}Q$.

(*College Physics* 9th ed. pages 517–519/10th ed. pages 527–530)

(L.O. 3.C.2.1)

DC Circuits

Electric Current

(*College Physics* 9th ed. pages 590–596/10th ed. pages 600–606)

Certain materials, metals in particular, are better conductors of electricity than others. When a conductive path is provided between two points originally at different potentials, charge will move. Current is defined as the flow of charge q, and the intensity of the current, I, is defined as the time rate of flow of charge, or

$$I = \frac{q}{t}$$

The SI unit of current is the ampere, A. We define the ampere as $1\ A = 1\ C/s$.

The direction of current is a matter of convention. Since the concept of positive charge is basic to electrical terminology, the direction of conventional current is from positive (+) to negative (–). On the other hand, current in metallic conductors is a matter of electron flow, which is from negative (–) to positive (+).

AP Tip

The direction of conventional current is always the same as the direction that positive charges would move, even if the actual current consists of a flow of electrons.

When current through a conductor is always in the same direction, it is called direct current or DC.

AP Tip

Current means running or flowing and it is not proper to say that a "current flows." Current used in conjunction with the word *flows* is a redundancy.

SAMPLE PROBLEM 1

A charge of 22.0 C flows through a cross section of wire every minute.

(a) What is the current?

(b) How many electrons go through the cross section each minute?

SOLUTION TO PROBLEM 1

(a) $I = \dfrac{q}{t} = \dfrac{22\ \text{C}}{60\ \text{s}} = 0.37\ \text{A}$

(b) $22.0\ \text{C} \times \dfrac{1\ e}{1.60 \times 10^{-19}\text{C}} = 1.38 \times 10^{20}\ e$

EMF

(*College Physics* 9th ed. pages 616–617/10th ed. pages 626–627)

Although electromotive force, (emf), $\mathcal{E}$, and potential difference, ΔV, are both measured in volts, there is a real distinction between them. The emf is defined as the work per unit charge done by a battery or a generator on the charges in moving them around the circuit. Potential difference between two points is defined as the work per unit charge done by the electrical forces in moving the charge from one point to the other. It is convenient to think of a source of emf as a kind of pump that acts on charge to bring it to a higher potential energy.

The SI unit of emf is the volt and it is defined as: $1\ V = 1\ \text{J/C}$. A seat of emf will perform 1 J of work on each 1-C charge that passes through it.

The most familiar source or seat of emf is the battery. A battery should be thought of as a *charge pump* that sends conventional current into a closed circuit. The seat of emf gives the current electrical energy and the resistors in the circuit use up that energy.

RESISTANCE

(*College Physics* 9th ed. pages 596–600/10th ed. pages 606–611)

Resistance, R, is a physical characteristic of matter. Every material offers some resistance to electrical current. Good conductors like the metals copper, silver, and aluminum offer very little resistance to current. Nonconductive materials like rubber, plastic, and glass offer very high resistance to current.

The SI unit of resistance is the ohm (Ω) and is defined as $1\ \Omega = 1$ volt/ampere $= 1$ V/A.

OHM'S LAW

(*College Physics* 9th ed. pages 596–601/10th ed. pages 606–611)

Ohm's law is the fundamental law in electricity that makes it possible to determine the potential difference, V, across the ends of a resistor when the current, I, through it and its resistance, R, are known. Ohm's law for a resistor is

$$V = IR$$

> ## AP Tip
>
> Circuit diagrams will greatly help in understanding a problem. Draw diagrams when working and solving problems.

SAMPLE PROBLEM 2

A battery is directly connected to a small light bulb. The battery maintains a potential difference of 6.0 V across the bulb. If the current in the circuit is 0.5 A, what is the resistance of the light bulb?

SOLUTION TO PROBLEM 2

First make a circuit diagram. The light bulb is a resistor and we show it in the circuit diagram as such.

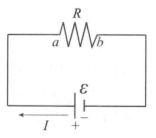

The voltage drop across R is $V_{ab} = 6.0\ V$. So, $R = V / I = 6.0\ V/0.5\ A = 12\ \Omega$.

Although the resistance calculated in sample problem 2 is assumed to be the resistance of the light bulb, it really includes the resistance of the connecting wires and the resistance of the battery. In practice, we use wires of very low resistance, so this factor can be neglected in most calculations. Internal resistance in many sources of emf can be quite low and as a result can be neglected in some of our problem work.

We call the drop in voltage across the resistor an IR drop.

POWER

(*College Physics* 9th ed. pages 601–603/10th ed. pages 611–614)

Electrical power is the rate at which energy is produced or used. Sources of emf do work on charge and give it energy. The power output of an emf source, measured in watts, is given by

$$P_0 = I\mathcal{E}$$

Resistors use electric energy, and the rate at which heat is dissipated in a circuit is called the power loss. The power loss in a resistor is given by

$$P = IV = I^2R = \frac{V^2}{R}$$

The power output of the seat of emf equals the power loss in the external circuit.

SAMPLE PROBLEM 3

A resistor uses 12.5 A when connected across 120 V.

(a) What is the resistance of this electrical component?

(b) Determine the power loss through the resistor.

SOLUTION TO PROBLEM 3

(a) $R = V / I = 120 \text{ V}/12.5 \text{ A} = 9.6 \text{ }\Omega$

(b) $P = IV = (12.5 \text{ A})(120 \text{ V}) = 1.5 \text{ kW}$

SAMPLE PROBLEM 4

A 420-W resistor with a resistance of 60 Ω is used in a circuit.

(a) Determine the potential difference across the ends of the resistor.

(b) What current passes through the resistor?

SOLUTION TO PROBLEM 4

Notice that the rules for the use of significant figures are not followed when using resistance in calculations since they are not calibrated to have significant figure values. Instead, they may have a tolerance of as much as ±20% so that the value of a 60-Ω resistor could range from between 48 Ω to 72 Ω. Be reasonable with your answers and do not exceed two decimal places in your problem work. Do any rounding off at the end of your calculations.

(a) $P = V^2 / R$ and $V = \sqrt{PR} = \sqrt{(420 \text{ W})(60 \text{ }\Omega)} = 159 \text{ V}$

(b) $I = V / R = 159 \text{ V}/60 \text{ }\Omega = 2.65 \text{ A}$

SAMPLE PROBLEM 5

A battery has an emf, $\mathcal{E} = 24.0 \text{ V}$. When connected in a circuit it delivers a current of 3.4 A. The battery has an internal resistance of $1.5 \text{ }\Omega$.

(a) What is the terminal voltage?

(b) There is an external resistor in the circuit. What is the potential difference across this resistor?

(c) What is the power loss in this external resistor?

SOLUTION TO PROBLEM 5

(a) $V_T = \mathcal{E} - Ir = 24.0 \text{ V} - (3.4 \text{ A})(1.5 \text{ }\Omega) = 18.9 \text{ V}$

(b) The external resistor must use whatever battery voltage the battery puts into the external circuit. The external resistor has a potential difference of 18.9 V.

(c) $P = IV = (3.4 \text{ A})(18.9 \text{ V}) = 64.3 \text{ W}$

RESISTIVITY

(*College Physics* 9th ed. pages 597–599/10th ed. pages 607–609)

Several factors determine the resistance of any section of wire: (1) the length, L; (2) the cross-sectional area, A; and (3) the resistivity, ρ, a property of the material of which the wire is composed. The resistivity indirectly gives a measure of how well a current will be conducted through a piece of wire. Resistivity is related to resistance by the relationship

$$R = \rho \frac{L}{A}$$

SAMPLE PROBLEM 6

A 120-m long sector of circular wire has a diameter of 1.2 mm. The wire has a resistivity $\rho = 3.6 \times 10^{-8} \text{ }\Omega \cdot \text{m}$.

(a) What is the resistance of this length of wire?

(b) What is the potential difference across the ends of the wire when a current of 2.4 A is sent through it?

SOLUTION TO PROBLEM 6

The radius of the wire is $r = 0.6 \times 10^{-3} \text{ m}$.

(a) Then

$$R = \rho \frac{L}{A} = \frac{(3.6 \times 10^{-8} \Omega \cdot \text{m})(120 \text{ m})}{\pi (0.6 \times 10^{-3} \text{ m})^2} = 3.8 \text{ }\Omega$$

(b) $V = IR = (2.4 \text{ A})(3.8 \text{ }\Omega) = 9.2 \text{ V}$

RESISTORS IN SERIES

(*College Physics* 9th ed. pages 617–620/10th ed. pages 628–630)

When two or more resistances are connected in series in an electrical circuit, the current through all parts of the series combination is the same.

The sum of the voltage drops across the resistors in series is the sum of the voltage drop across each resistor. The equivalent resistance, R_{eq}, of the resistors in series is the sum of their resistances.

$$R_s = R_1 + R_2 + R_3 + \ldots$$

AP Tip

The current through resistors in series is the same in each resistor and the potential difference across them is additive.

SAMPLE PROBLEM 7

The three resistors, $R_1 = 12\ \Omega$, $R_2 = 6\ \Omega$ and $R_3 = 8\ \Omega$, are arranged in series.

(a) Find the equivalent resistance of the combination.

(b) The resistors are connected to a seat of emf. The current through the resistors is 2.4 A. What is the *IR*-drop across junctions *a* and *b*?

SOLUTION TO PROBLEM 7

(a) First, make a diagram.

$$12\ \Omega \qquad 6\ \Omega \qquad 8\ \Omega$$
$$a \longrightarrow\!\!\!\bigwedge\!\!\!\bigwedge\!\!\!\bigwedge\!\!\!\longrightarrow b$$

For a set of resistors combined in a series, the equivalent resistance is the sum of the resistors as shown, and $R_s = R_{ab} = R_1 + R_2 + R_3 =$ $12\ \Omega + 6\ \Omega + 8\ \Omega = 26\ \Omega$. The three resistors behave like a single 26-Ω resistor.

$$26\ \Omega$$
$$a \longrightarrow\!\!\!\bigwedge\!\!\!\longrightarrow b$$

(b) The *IR*-drop between junctions *a* and *b* is $V_{ab} = IR_s =$ $(2.4\ \text{A})(26\ \Omega) = 62.4\ \text{V}.$

RESISTORS IN PARALLEL

(College Physics 9th ed. pages 620–622/10th ed. pages 631–634)

When resistors are arranged in a parallel combination, the current splits. The sum of the currents in each branch is equal to the current that enters the combination. The voltage drop across the combination is equal to the voltage drop across each resistor in parallel.

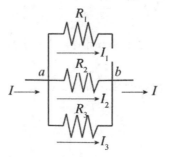

The reciprocal of the equivalent resistance, R_{eq}, of the resistors in parallel is the sum of the reciprocals of the individual resistances.

$$\frac{1}{R_{eq}} = \frac{1}{R_1} + \frac{1}{R_2} + \frac{1}{R_3} + \ldots$$

SAMPLE PROBLEM 8

The three resistors, $R_1 = 12\ \Omega$, $R_2 = 6\ \Omega$ and $R_3 = 8\ \Omega$, are arranged in parallel.

(a) Calculate their equivalent resistance.

(b) Junctions a and b are connected across an emf. If a current of 2.4 A enters junction a, what is the IR drop across junctions a and b?

(c) What is the current through each resistor in the parallel bank?

SOLUTION TO PROBLEM 8

(a) First, make a diagram of the resistor arrangement.

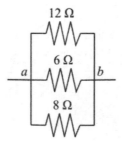

For a set of resistor combined in parallel, the reciprocal equivalent resistance is the sum of the reciprocals of the resistors.

$$\frac{1}{R_{eq}} = \frac{1}{R_{ab}} = \frac{1}{R_1} + \frac{1}{R_2} + \frac{1}{R_3} = \frac{1}{12\ \Omega} + \frac{1}{6\ \Omega} + \frac{1}{8\ \Omega} = 0.375\ \frac{1}{\Omega}$$

© 2015 Cengage Learning. All Rights Reserved. May not be copied, scanned, or duplicated, in whole or in part, except for use as permitted in a license distributed with a certain product or service or otherwise on a password-protected website for classroom use.

Then

$$R_{eq} = R_{ab} = \frac{1}{0.375} \,\Omega = 2.67\,\Omega$$

The three resistors in parallel function as a single 2.67 Ω resistor as shown.

$$a \overset{2.67\,\Omega}{-\!\!\!\bigwedge\!\!\!\bigvee\!\!\!-} b$$

(b) Current $I = 2.4$ A enters the resistor at point a. The IR drop is
$$V_{ab} = IR_s = (2.4\text{ A})(2.67\,\Omega) = 6.4\text{ V}$$

(c) Each resistor in parallel undergoes the same voltage or IR drop, and that is 6.4 V. So, the current in R_1 is

$$I_1 = \frac{V_{ab}}{R_1} = \frac{6.4\text{ V}}{12\,\Omega} = 0.53\text{ A}$$

The current in R_2 is

$$I_2 = \frac{V_{ab}}{R_2} = \frac{6.4\text{ V}}{6\,\Omega} = 1.07\text{ A}$$

The current in R_3 is

$$I_3 = \frac{V_{ab}}{R_3} = \frac{6.4\text{ V}}{8\,\Omega} = 0.80\text{ A}$$

The sum of the currents going through the resistors in a parallel bank must equal the current entering the bank. As a check add the currents of the resistors in parallel

$$I = I_1 + I_2 + I_3 = 0.53\text{ A} + 1.07\text{ A} + 0.80\text{ A} = 2.4\text{ A}$$

They do check.

AP Tip

The largest resistor in parallel carries the smallest current and the smallest resistor in parallel carries the largest current. Current tends to take the path of least resistance.

COMBINATION CIRCUITS

(*College Physics* 9th ed. pages 623–625/10th ed. pages 634–636)

In most electrical circuits, resistors are wired partly in series and partly in parallel. In such circuits, the rules for determining the equivalent resistance are applied to each part of the circuit for circuit analysis.

SAMPLE PROBLEM 9

The electrical circuit diagram below contains a seat of emf with zero internal resistance, three resistors, an ammeter, and a voltmeter. Ammeters are electrical instruments designed to measure electric current. An ammeter has low resistance and is connected in series so that all of the current passes through it. Voltmeters are designed to measure the potential difference across a resistor. Voltmeters have a high resistance and are connected in parallel across a resistor.

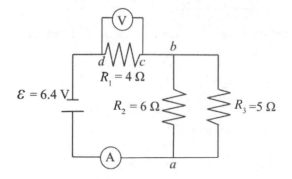

Perform the following analysis on the circuit.

(a) Find the total resistance of the circuit.

(b) What current will the ammeter A read?

(c) Determine the current in each resistor.

(d) What will the voltmeter V across resistor R_3 read?

(e) Calculate the power output of the battery.

(f) Find the power drop in each resistor.

SOLUTION TO PROBLEM 9

Current I is issued from the positive terminal of the battery. At junction a, the current splits and current I_1 passes through R_2 and I_2 passes through R_3. I_1 and I_2 merge at junction b. The full current passes through the ammeter. See the figure below.

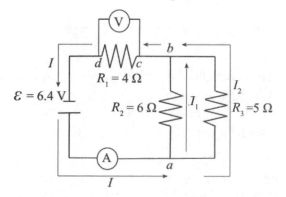

(a) Resistors R_1 and R_2 are in parallel and their equivalent resistance is

$$\frac{1}{R_{12}} = \frac{1}{R_1} + \frac{1}{R_2}$$

Using another approach, we can find that the equivalent resistance is also the reciprocal of the sum of the reciprocals, or

$$R_{12} = \frac{1}{1/R_1 + 1/R_2} = \frac{1}{1/6\,\Omega + 1/5\,\Omega} = \frac{1}{11/30\,\Omega} = \frac{30\,\Omega}{11} = 2.73\,\Omega$$

Resistor R_3 is in series with the 2.73 Ω and the equivalent resistance, R_{eq}, of the circuit is

$$R_{eq} = R_3 + 2.73\,\Omega = 4\,\Omega + 2.73\,\Omega = 6.73\,\Omega$$

(b) The current issued by the battery, which is the current read by the ammeter, is found by using Ohm's law

$$I = \frac{\mathcal{E}}{R_{eq}} = \frac{6.4\text{ V}}{6.73\,\Omega} = 0.95\text{ A}$$

(c) At junction a, the current splits and current I_1 goes through R_1 and current I_2 goes through R_2. All resistors suffer the same IR drop in parallel. The equivalent resistance, R_{12}, of R_1 and R_2 was found in (a) to be $R_{12} = 2.73\,\Omega$. By Ohm's law

$$V_{12} = IR_{12} = (0.95\text{ A})(2.73\Omega) = 2.59\text{ V}$$

$$I_1 = \frac{V_{12}}{R_1} = \frac{2.59\text{ V}}{6\Omega} = 0.43\text{ A}$$

$$I_2 = \frac{V_{12}}{R_2} = \frac{2.59\text{ V}}{5\,\Omega} = 0.52\text{ A}$$

(d) What will the voltmeter V across resistor R_3 read? The voltmeter will read the IR drop across R_3. The full current passes through R_3 and by Ohm's law $V_3 = IR_3 = (0.95\text{ A})(4\,\Omega) = 3.80\text{ V}$.

(e) The battery power output is the product of the current issued to the circuit and the emf: $P_{output} = I\mathcal{E} = (0.95\text{ A})(6.4\text{ V}) = 6.08\text{ W}$.

(f) Resistors R_1 and R_2 are in parallel, and the power dissipated in each can be found by taking the product of the current squared and the resistance. So, for resistor 1: $P_1 = I_1^2 R_1 = (0.43\text{ A})^2 (6\,\Omega) = 1.11\text{ W}$ and for resistor 2: $P_2 = I_2^2 R_2 = (0.52\text{ A})^2 (5\,\Omega) = 1.35\text{ W}$. Resistor R_3 is in series, and the power output can be calculated by taking the product of the IR drop and the current through the resistor. So, $P_3 = IV_3 = (0.95\text{ A})(3.80\text{ V}) = 3.61\text{ W}$.

KIRCHHOFF'S RULES

(*College Physics* 9th ed. pages 625–629/10th ed. pages 636–640)

In a complex electrical circuit consisting of a number of loops and seats of *emf*, Ohm's law becomes difficult for circuit analysis. Gustav Kirchhoff, in the nineteenth century, developed a more straightforward procedure for analysis of such circuits. The procedure involves the use of two rules that we call *Kirchhoff's rules*.

1. The junction rule: the sum of the currents entering a junction must equal the currents that exit that junction.

$$\Sigma I_{entering} = \Sigma I_{leaving}$$

This rule is actually a statement of the law of conservation of electrical charge. A junction refers to any point in a circuit where three or more wires come together. If 10 coulombs enters a junction each second, then 10 coulombs must leave that junction each second.

Note: When working with a circuit, the junction rule is only used once.

2. The loop rule: the sum of the *IR*-drops around a loop must equal the sum of all the *emf's* around that loop.

$$\Sigma \mathcal{E} = \Sigma IR$$

This rule is a statement of the law of conservation of energy.

When applying Kirchhoff's rules to a circuit, use the general rule of thumb, pick a junction and label it "*a*." Trace around the loop counterclockwise (CCW) seeking all of the *emf's* in that loop and add them in the following way:

A. If the negative (–) terminal of a seat of *emf* is encountered first as you trace, the *emf* is considered to positive (+).

B. If the positive terminal (+) of the seat of *emf* is encountered first, the *emf* is considered to be negative (–).

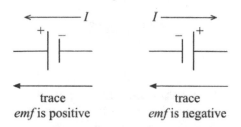

| trace | trace |
| *emf* is positive | *emf* is negative |

C. An *IR*-drop is considered positive (+) when the assumed current is in the same direction of the trace.

D. An *IR*-drop is considered negative (–) when the assumed current is against the direction of the trace.

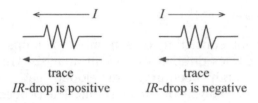

trace
IR-drop is positive

trace
IR-drop is negative

SAMPLE PROBLEM 10

Consider the following electrical circuit. To two decimal places, determine currents I_1, I_2 and I_3 using Kirchhoff's rules. The battery issues conventional current I_1. The current passes through the 4.0 Ω resistor to junction *a*. At *a*, the current splits into currents I_2 and I_3. At junction *b*, the currents recombine back into I_1 that goes to the negative terminal of the battery. Whatever leaves the battery must return to the battery. We will start at junction *a* and trace around the circuit. Always keep in mind that we trace around the circuit counterclockwise, CCW. Be consistent at all times.

Trace starts at junction *a*
and ends at junction *b*.

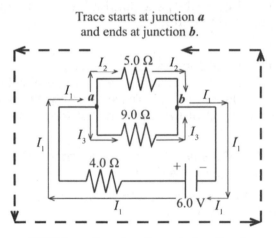

CCW trace from junction *a* to junction *b*.

SOLUTION TO PROBLEM 10

We trace CCW at junction *a* and note that the current runs contrary to the trace, making the signs of the currents negative. Since the current splits at junction *a*, we will apply the junction rule, and write $-I_1 = -I_2 - I_3$. Transposing the I_1 term gives us $I_1 - I_2 - I_3 = 0$. The junction rule is only used once.

We will remove the upper resistor and our circuit becomes

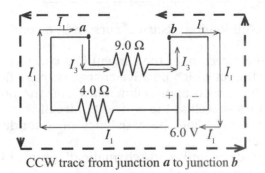

CCW trace from junction *a* to junction *b*

Keep in mind that we trace CCW. With our first trace we are looking for a seat of emf. Tracing from junction **a** CCW we encounter the positive terminal of the battery making the *emf* negative, –6.0 V. Make a second trace looking for *IR*-drops across resistors. Going opposite to the trace the 4.0 Ω resistor has a negative *IR*-drop of $-4.0I_1$ and through the 9.0 Ω resistor the *IR*-drop is $-9.0I_3$. Since $\Sigma \mathcal{E} = \Sigma IR$ then we write $-6.0 = -4.0I_1 - 9.0I_3$.

Next, we take the loop containing the only 5.0 Ω resistor and the 9.0 Ω resistor.

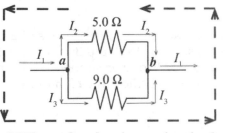

CCW trace from junction *a* to junction *b*

Trace from junction **a** CCW around the loop looking for a battery, but there is none. The emf in the loop is zero. As we trace CCW from **a**, we are going with the current, making the *IR*-drop across the 9.0 Ω resistor $9.0I_3$. Continuing around the loop we encounter the 5.0 Ω resistor and note that we are tracing against the current making this *IR*-drop $-5.0I_2$. Equating the emf to the *IR*-drops yields $0 = -5.0I_2 + 9.0I_3$.

The equations from the junction rule and the loop rule has given us

$$I_1 - I_2 - I_3 = 0$$

$$-6.0 = -4.0I_1 - 9.0I_3$$

$$0 = -5.0I_2 + 9.0I_3$$

Placing the above set of simultaneous equations into better form gives

$$I_1 - I_2 - I_3 = 0$$

$$-4.0I_1 - 9.0I_3 = -6$$

$$-5.0I_2 + 9.0I_3 = 0$$

Solving the equations simultaneously yields, $I_1 = 0.83$ A, $I_2 = 0.55$ A and $I_3 = 0.30$ A.

DC CIRCUITS: STUDENT OBJECTIVES FOR THE AP EXAM

- You should know the definition for electrical current in a conductor and be able to apply it.
- You should know that the direction of the current in a conductor is, by convention, the direction in which positive charge carriers flow.
- You should know and be able to apply Ohm's law and the power equations to all conductors as well as the entire DC circuit.
- You should know how to calculate the resistance of a conductor from its physical parameters.
- You should know how to draw and read schematic diagrams of the components in a direct-current circuit.
- You should know how to solve for equivalent resistance in series circuits, parallel circuits, and combination circuits.
- You should know how to solve for current, voltage, and power for an entire circuit and for each component of the circuit.
- You should know how to solve for terminal voltage in a DC circuit.
- You should be able to apply Kirchhoff's rules to more complex circuits.

MULTIPLE-CHOICE QUESTIONS

1. A simple circuit, shown in the diagram below, consists of a 20 Ω resistor in series with two resistors of 15 Ω and 30 Ω in parallel. The resistors are connected to a 12 V power supply. The current through the resistors is correctly identified in which of the following?

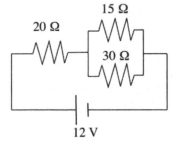

(A) $I_{15\,\Omega} = I_{20\,\Omega} = I_{30\,\Omega}$

(B) $I_{20\,\Omega} + I_{15\,\Omega} = I_{30\,\Omega}$

(C) $I_{20\,\Omega} = I_{15\,\Omega} + I_{30\,\Omega}$

(D) $I_{20\,\Omega} + I_{30\,\Omega} = I_{15\,\Omega}$

2. In reference to the above circuit in Problem 1, a voltmeter is placed across each of the resistors in turn and the electrical potential difference for each is indicated below. Which of the following gives the correct readings for the electrical potential difference across each of the resistors?

	20 Ω	15 Ω	30 Ω
(A)	6 V	6 V	6 V
(B)	8 V	8 V	4 V
(C)	8 V	4 V	8 V
(D)	8 V	4 V	4 V

3. A student wants to determine the resistivity of a conductor experimentally. The student needs to collect data in order to do this. The data taken should be the
   (A) potential difference across the ends of the conductor and the current flowing through it
   (B) type of material, the length of the conductor, and its cross-sectional area
   (C) potential difference across ends of the conductor and its length
   (D) potential difference across the ends of the conductor, the current flowing through it, and the length and cross section of the conductor

4. A circuit contains three resistors in different arrangements as shown in the schematic diagrams below. Rank the current flowing through the 10 Ω resistor in the various arrangements from highest to lowest.

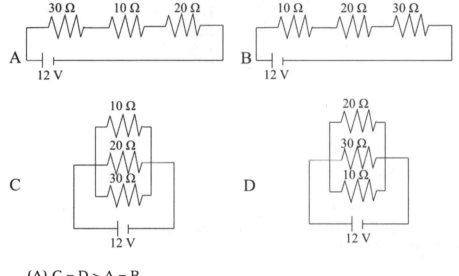

   (A) C = D > A = B
   (B) A = B > C = D
   (C) A > B > D > C
   (D) D > C > A > B

5. In the circuit shown below, what is the current in the 15 Ω resistor?

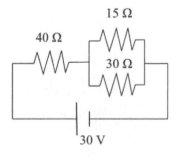

   (A) 0.6 A
   (B) 0.4 A
   (C) 0.3 A
   (D) 0.2 A

6. A wire whose resistivity is ρ has dimensions of length L and a radius of r, producing a resistance of R_0. The wire is replaced in the circuit with another wire whose resistivity ρ is the same, but it has a length of $2.0\ L$ and a radius $0.5\ r$. The new resistance is
   (A) $0.5R_0$
   (B) $2R_0$
   (C) $4\ R_0$
   (D) $8R_0$

7. In the diagram shown below, for the situation for when both switches are closed, rank the brightness of the bulbs from brightest to dimmest.

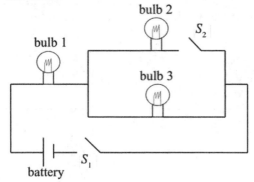

   (A) Bulb 1 > Bulb 2 = Bulb 3
   (B) Bulb 1 = Bulb 2 = Bulb 3
   (C) Bulb 1 > Bulb 2 > Bulb 3
   (D) Bulb 3 > Bulb 2 > Bulb 1

8. In the circuit shown below, what is the correct relationship for the currents flowing in the resistors?

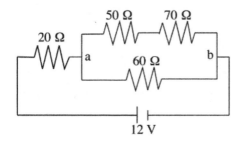

   (A) $I_{20\ \Omega} = I_{50\ \Omega} + I_{60\ \Omega} + I_{70\ \Omega}$
   (B) $I_{20\ \Omega} = I_{50\ \Omega} > I_{60\ \Omega} > I_{70\ \Omega}$
   (C) $I_{20\ \Omega} = I_{60\ \Omega} + (I_{50\ \Omega} = I_{70\ \Omega})$
   (D) $I_{20\ \Omega} = (I_{50\ \Omega} = I_{60\ \Omega}) + I_{70\ \Omega}$

9. An ammeter in the circuit shown below reads 0.10 A when connected in series with a 30.0 Ω resistor. What is the current in the 20.0 Ω resistor?

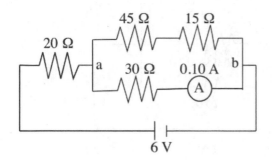

(A) 0.05 A
(B) 0.10 A
(C) 0.15 A
(D) 0.2 A

10. A group of physics students doing an experiment to determine if Kirchhoff's loop rule applies to a simple circuit sets up a circuit containing a 12.0 V battery with an internal resistance of 0.5 Ω that is connected to a 56.0 Ω resistor as shown below. A voltmeter placed across the ends of the resistor as shown below will indicate a potential difference equal to

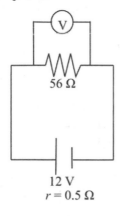

(A) the emf of the battery
(B) a potential difference greater than the emf of the battery
(C) a potential difference less than the emf of the battery
(D) zero because no current will flow from the battery because of the internal resistance

11. The circuit shown below has reached steady state values.

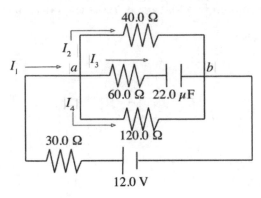

The correct values for the current into and out of the junction labeled a is indicated for values of

I_1	I_2	I_3	I_4
(A) .20 A	.15 A	0	.05 A
(B) .40 A	.15 A	.10 A	.15 A
(C) .20 A	.15 A	0.5 A	0
(D) .40 A	.10 A	0.5 A	0.5 A

12. Four capacitors shown in the schematic diagram below are connected to an 18.0V battery. When the capacitors have reached steady state, the charge on each in µC is given in which of the following choices?

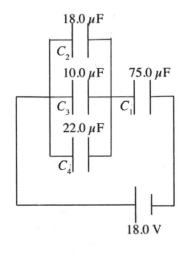

	Q_{C1}	Q_{C2}	Q_{C3}	Q_{C4}
(A)	540	180	180	180
(B)	540	194	108	238
(C)	1350	540	180	650
(D)	2250	750	550	950

13. The circuit shown below has reached steady state. Which of the following choices gives the correct potential difference in volts, across the elements in the circuit?

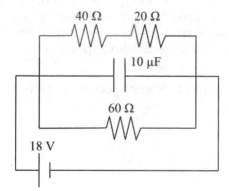

	$V_{40.0\,\Omega}$	$V_{20.0\,\Omega}$	$V_{60.0\,\Omega}$	$V_{10.0\,\mu F}$
(A)	18.0	18.0	18.0	18.0
(B)	12.0	6.0	18.0	18.0
(C)	12.0	6.0	18.0	0
(D)	9.0	9.0	18.0	0

14. Several students conduct an experiment using a variable power supply, a voltmeter, an ammeter, a set of connecting wires, and a resistor to test Ohm's law. Their data produces the following graph. The graph indicates that

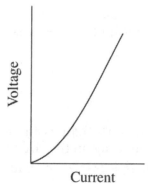

(A) the variable power supply had an internal resistance that they could not measure
(B) Ohm's law was valid for the experiment
(C) the resistance was non-ohmic since the graph did not indicate a linear relationship
(D) the resistance was independent of both potential difference and current

Question 15

Directions: For the incomplete statement below, <u>two</u> of the suggested answers will be correct. You must select <u>both</u> correct choices to earn credit. No partial credit will be earned if only one correct answer is selected. Select the two that are best in each case and then enter both of the appropriate answers in the corresponding space on the answer sheet.

15. A circuit has three identical light bulbs connected as shown in the schematic diagram below.

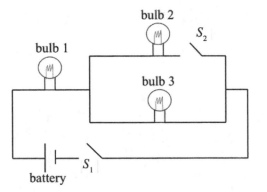

The two switches are initially closed in the circuit. When switch S_2 is opened,
(A) all three light bulbs go out
(B) only light bulb two goes out
(C) the brightness of light bulbs one and three increase
(D) the brightness of light bulbs one and two decrease

FREE-RESPONSE PROBLEMS

1. Consider the circuit diagram shown. The battery in the circuit has an emf of 12.0 V. The resistors connected in the circuit are $R_1 = 12.0\ \Omega$, $R_2 = 4.0\ \Omega$, $R_3 = 8.0\ \Omega$, and $R_4 = 22.0\ \Omega$. The battery has an internal resistance $r = 0.50\ \Omega$.

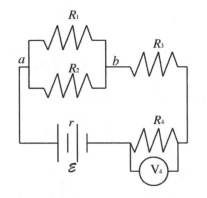

(a) Determine the current, I, issued by the battery.
(b) Calculate the terminal voltage of the battery.

(c) Find the current through R_1 and R_2.
(d) What is the total power output of the battery?
(e) What will meter V_4 read?

2. The circuit diagram shown has a battery with an emf, $\mathcal{E}$. The ammeter in the circuit reads 2.4 A. Resistors $R_1 = R_2 = R_3 = 18\Omega$, $R_4 = 8.0\Omega$, and $R_5 = 4.0\Omega$. The internal resistance of the battery is negligible.
   (a) Calculate the emf of the battery.
   (b) What is the electrical potential difference between junctions a and d?
   (c) Determine the power loss between junctions c and d.

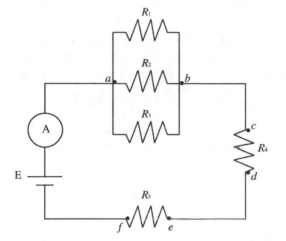

3. (a) Design an experiment to demonstrate that Kirchhoff's loop rule and junction rule are valid in a circuit using a battery, 3 resistors of the same known resistance, connecting wires and meters in enough detail that another student could duplicate your experiment and obtain the same results.
   (b) Draw a schematic of your circuit, properly labeling the elements and placing the meters in their correct positions.
   (c) What measurements are you going to make and how are you going to use them in evaluating Kirchhoff's loop rule and junction rule for your circuit?
   (d) What are two possible sources of error in your experiment and how might they affect the results you obtained?

4. You are given an aging 9.0 V battery, a known resistor, several segments of copper wire, an ammeter and a voltmeter.
   (a) Explain how you can determine the internal resistance of the battery.
   (b) Draw the circuit diagram of how you plan to use the equipment and indicate what readings you will take to find the internal resistance.
   (c) Write the mathematical solution that will permit you to solve for the internal resistance.

Answers

MULTIPLE-CHOICE QUESTIONS

1. **C** Charge is conserved in a circuit. The current $I = \dfrac{Q}{t}$, flowing through the 20 Ω resistor enters the junction a where it divides flowing into the two parallel branches $I_{20\,\Omega} = I_{15\,\Omega} + I_{30\,\Omega}$ and recombines.
   (*College Physics* 9th ed. pages 625–627/10th ed. pages 636–637)
   (L.O. 1.B.1.2)

2. **D** There can be only one potential difference between the same two points regardless of the number of paths. The parallel resistors will have the same voltmeter reading. The resistance in the parallel branch is found from $\dfrac{1}{15\ \Omega} + \dfrac{1}{30\ \Omega} = \dfrac{1}{R_{eq}}$. The 10 Ω equivalent resistance is in series with the 20 Ω resistor giving a total resistance of 30 Ω for the circuit, and thus the current in the circuit is $\dfrac{12\ \text{V}}{30\ \Omega} = 0.4\ \text{A}$. The voltmeter will read $V_{20\,\Omega} = (20\ \Omega)(0.4\ \text{A}) = 8\ \text{V}$ and therefore across the parallel resistors will read 4 V since Kirchhoff's loop applies.
   (*College Physics* 9th ed. pages 620–622/10th ed. pages 631–634)
   (L.O. 5.B.9.3)

3. **D** The resistance of a conductor is given by $R = \rho\dfrac{L}{A}$. Data needs to be taken concerning the length and the cross-sectional area. The resistance of the conductor can be calculated using a voltmeter to determine the potential difference across its ends and an ammeter that will record the current through it and using $R = \dfrac{V}{I}$.
   Substituting this resistance into the first equation will give the resistivity of the conductor.
   (*College Physics* 9th ed. pages 596–597/10th ed. pages 606–608)
   (L.O. 1.E.2.1)

4. **A** In the schematics C and D, the resistors are in parallel connected to the 12 V battery, and the 10 Ω resistor will have the most current regardless of its position in the parallel network. In the series arrangement, the 10 Ω resistor has the same current regardless of its position in the series path. The parallel arrangement has a net resistance less than 10 Ω and therefore the greatest current from the source. Thus the correct ranking is C = D > A = B.
   (*College Physics* 9th ed. pages 620–622/10th ed. pages 631–634)
   (L.O. 5.C.3.1)

5. **B** The resistance for the parallel combination is found from

   $\dfrac{1}{15\ \Omega}+\dfrac{1}{30\ \Omega}=\dfrac{1}{R_{eq}}$. The equivalent resistance of 10 Ω is in series

   with a 40 Ω resistor producing a total of 50 Ω. The total current in

   the arrangement is $I=\dfrac{V}{R}=\dfrac{30\ V}{50\ \Omega}=0.6\ A$. The potential difference

   across the 10 Ω equivalent is $V_{eq}=(10\ \Omega)(0.6\ A)=6\ V$. The current

   in the 15 Ω resistor is thus $\dfrac{6\ V}{15\ \Omega}=0.4\ A.$

   (*College Physics* 9th ed. pages 620–622/10th ed. pages 631–634)
   (L.O. 5.C.3.3)

6. **D** The original resistance is $R_0=\rho\dfrac{L}{A}=\rho\dfrac{L}{\pi r^2}$. Replacing the wire

   with a new wire with the given dimensions produces a resistance

   that is $R=\rho\dfrac{2L}{\pi(0.5r)^2}=\rho\dfrac{8L}{\pi r^2}$ thus $R=8R_0$.

   (*College Physics* 9th ed. pages 596–597/10th ed. pages 606–608)
   (L.O. 4.E.4.1)

7. **A** When both switches are closed, the entire current flows
   through the first lamp. It also has the largest potential difference
   across its ends. The potential on the parallel branch is less, and the
   current will divide between the two light bulbs, the one with the
   lowest resistance getting a higher current. In this case, inspection
   will tell you that the smaller resistance gets $\frac{2}{3}I_T$ and the other

   bulb gets $\frac{1}{3}I_T$. Since the brightness of a bulb is related to power,

   the bulb with the most current is the brightest.
   (*College Physics* 9th ed. pages 617–624/10th ed. pages 628–636)
   (L.O. 4.E.5.2)

8. **C** Kirchhoff's junction rule applies. The 20 Ω resistor is in series
   with a parallel arrangement that has two resistors in series in the
   upper branch; these two resistors have the same current. The
   current flow into and out of junction a is thus
   $I_{20\ \Omega}=I_{60\ \Omega}+(I_{50\ \Omega}=I_{70\ \Omega})$. Current must be conserved in a circuit.
   (*College Physics* 9th ed. pages 625–627/10th ed. pages 636–638)
   (L.O. 5.C.3.4)

9. **C** Kirchhoff's junction rule applies. The 30.0 Ω resistance has a
   current of 0.10 A as indicated from the ammeter. The potential
   difference across the ends of the resistor is 3.0 V. Since it is in
   parallel with an upper branch consisting of a 45.0 Ω resistor and a
   15.0 Ω resistor giving an equivalency of 60 Ω, this combination
   must have the same potential difference, 3.0 V, as does the lower
   branch. A current of 0.05 A exists in the upper branch. The total
   current flowing into the parallel arrangement is 0.15 A and thus
   the current in the 20.0 Ω resistor is 0.15 A.
   (*College Physics* 9th ed. pages 625–627/10th ed. pages 636–638)
   (L.O. 5.C.3.5)

10. **C** The total resistance in the circuit is $R + r$. This reduces the current in the circuit. Because the internal resistance in the battery dissipates some of the energy as internal energy (heat), the battery will deliver less energy to the circuit. The voltmeter will show a reading less than the emf of the source.
(*College Physics* 9th ed. pages 616–617/10th ed. pages 626–628)
(L.O. 5.B.9.7)

11. **A** Kirchhoff's junction rule applies. Steady state across the capacitor has also been reached. There is no longer a current I_3 flowing in the 60.0 Ω resistor. The total resistance consists of
$\dfrac{1}{40.0\ \Omega} + \dfrac{1}{120.0\ \Omega} = \dfrac{1}{R_{eq}}$. The equivalent resistance for the parallel arrangement, 30.0 Ω is in series with the 30.0 Ω resistor. The total resistance in the circuit is 60.0 Ω, which is connected to a 12.0 V battery. The current through the battery and into the junction a is
$I = \dfrac{12.0\ V}{60.0\ \Omega} = 0.20\ A$.

The potential difference across the 30.0 Ω resistor in series with the parallel arrangement is 6.0 V from $V = IR$. The potential difference across the parallel arrangement is 6.0 V, given from $V = IR$ I_2 = 0.15 A in the 40.0 Ω resistor. Current in the 120.0 Ω resistor is then 0.05 A. Current $I_3 = 0$.
(*College Physics* 9th ed. pages 617–627, 629/10th ed. pages 628–638, 640)
(L.O. 5.C.3.6)

12. **B** The three capacitors in parallel have a capacitance equivalent of 18.0 μF + 10.0 μF+ 22.0 μF = 50.0 μF. The total capacitance is found
from $\dfrac{1}{50.0\ \mu F} + \dfrac{1}{75.0\ \mu F} = \dfrac{1}{C_{eq}}$. The total capacitance for the circuit is 30.0 μF. The total charge on the plates of the capacitors is determined from $CV = Q$. On capacitor C_1 the charge is 540.0 μF. This charge will divide as it enters the parallel junction. The potential difference is needed to determine the charge on each capacitor in the parallel arrangement. The potential difference on C_1 is found from $V = \dfrac{Q}{C}$ substitution into the equation

$V = \dfrac{540.0\ \mu F}{75.0\ \mu C} = 7.20\ V$. The potential difference on the parallel arrangement is 18.0 V – 7.2 V = 10.8 V. Finally, solving for the charges gives Q_{C2} = 194 μF, Q_{C3} = 108 μF and Q_{C4} = 238 μF.
(*College Physics* 9th ed. pages 565–570/10th ed. pages 577–581)
(L.O. 5.C.3.7)

13. **B** Kirchhoff's loop rule applies. The potential difference across each the branches in the circuit is 18.0 V. The voltage on the 60.0 Ω resistor and the 10.0 μF capacitor are both 18.0 V since the circuit has reached steady state and no charge flows to the capacitor. The current through the upper branch is needed to determine the potential difference across the two resistors in this branch. The

equivalent resistance is 60.0 Ω in the upper branch in parallel with 60.0 Ω in the lower branch. $\dfrac{1}{60.0\ \Omega} + \dfrac{1}{60.0\ \Omega} = \dfrac{1}{R_{eq}}$. The current from the battery is $I = \dfrac{18.0\ V}{30.0\ \Omega} = 0.60\ A$. The top and bottom branches have equal resistances so there is 0.30 A entering the upper branch. Then $V_{40.0\ \Omega} = (0.30\ A)(40.0\ \Omega) = 12.0\ V$ and

$V_{20.0\ \Omega} = 18.0\ V - 12.0\ V = 6.0\ V$

(*College Physics* 9th ed. pages 617–627, 629/10th ed. pages 628–638, 640)
(L.O. 5.C.3.7)

14. **C** A linear relationship will indicate that the resistor obeys Ohm's law. An internal resistance in the power supply would still give a linear relationship $V = I(R + r)$. The graph indicates a non-ohmic resistance.
(*College Physics* 9th ed. pages 596–597, 616–617/10th ed. pages 606–608, 626–627)
(L.O. 5.B.9.7)

15. **B** and **D** When both switches are closed, the circuit consists of two bulbs in parallel connected in series to another bulb. When switch 2 is opened, bulb two goes out and the brightness of the two remaining bulbs decreases because the equivalent resistance in the circuit increased and thus the current in the circuit decreased.
(*College Physics* 9th ed. pages 617–624/10th ed. pages 628–636)
(L.O. 4.E.5.1)

FREE-RESPONSE PROBLEMS

1. (a) Ohm's law for a circuit is written as $\mathcal{E} = I\Sigma R$. Before we find the current issued by the battery, we need the total resistance of the entire circuit. Resistors R_1 and R_2 are in parallel with respect to each other, and their combined resistance, R_{ab}, is

$$R_{ab} = \dfrac{1}{1/R_1 + 1/R_2}$$
$$= \dfrac{1}{1/12\ \Omega + 1/4\ \Omega}$$
$$= \dfrac{1}{1/12\ \Omega + 3/12\ \Omega}$$
$$= \dfrac{1}{4/12\ \Omega}$$
$$= \dfrac{12}{4}\ \Omega = 3\ \Omega$$

where R_{ab}, R_3, R_4, and the internal resistance r of the battery are all in series and the total or equivalent resistance, ΣR, of the entire circuit is then

$\Sigma R = R_{ab} + R_3 + R_4 + r = 3\ \Omega + 8\ \Omega + 22\ \Omega + 0.50\ \Omega = 33.5\ \Omega$. From Ohm's law

$$I = \frac{\mathcal{E}}{\Sigma R} = \frac{12.0\ \text{V}}{33.5\ \Omega} = 0.36\ \text{A}$$

(b) By definition, the terminal voltage is
$V_t = \mathcal{E} - Ir = 12.0\ \text{V} - (0.36\ \text{A})(0.5\ \Omega) = 11.82\ \text{V}$.

(c) Resistors R_1 and R_2 are in parallel, and their equivalent resistance, R_{ab}, is known from part (a). Each resistor in parallel suffers the same voltage drop V_{ab}, and that is given from Ohm's law: $V_{ab} = IR_{ab} = (0.36\ \text{A})(3\ \Omega) = 1.08\ \text{V}$. 0.36 A enters the parallel branch at junction a then splits into currents I_1 and I_2. The current I_1 through resistor R_1 is

$$I_1 = \frac{V_{ab}}{R_1} = \frac{1.08\ \text{V}}{12\ \Omega} = 0.09\ \text{A}$$

The current I_2 through resistor R_2 is

$$I_2 = \frac{V_{ab}}{R_2} = \frac{1.08\ \text{V}}{4\ \Omega} = 0.27\ \text{A}$$

(d) The power output of a battery with internal resistance can be found by
$P_{\text{out}} = IV_t = (0.36\ \text{A})(11.82\ \text{V}) = 4.26\ \text{W}$.

Alternate Solution to Part (d)
The power output of a seat of emf is
$P_{\text{out}} = I\mathcal{E} = (0.36\ \text{A})(12.0\ \text{V}) = 4.32\ \text{W}$. An internal resistance r dissipates some of the energy produced by the battery into heat, however. The internal resistance uses up some of the power output, and that amount is
$P = IV = I(Ir) = I^2r = (0.36\ \text{A})^2(0.50\ \Omega) = 0.065\ \text{W}$. The actual power output of the battery is then
$P_{\text{out}} = 4.32\ \text{W} - 0.065\ \text{W} = 4.26\ \text{W}$.

(e) Voltmeters are placed in parallel, so V_4 will read the drop in voltage across resistor R_4. By Ohm's law
$V_4 = IR_4 = (0.36\ \text{A})(22.0\ \Omega) = 7.92\ \text{V}$

(*College Physics* 9th ed. pages 617–625/10th ed. pages 628–636)
(L.O. 5.B.9.3, 5.B.9.6, 5.C.3.3, 5.C.3.5)

2. (a) First, determine the equivalent resistance, R_{eq}, of the entire circuit. Starting with the parallel bank,

$$R_{ab} = \frac{1}{1/R_1 + 1/R_2 + 1/R_3} = \frac{1}{1/18\ \Omega + 1/18\ \Omega + 1/18\ \Omega}$$

$$= \frac{1}{3/18\ \Omega} = \frac{18\ \Omega}{3} = 6\ \Omega$$

The remainder of the circuit is in series, and
$R_{\text{eq}} = R_{ab} + R_4 + R_5 = 6\ \Omega + 8\ \Omega + 4\ \Omega = 18\ \Omega$. So, from Ohm's law
$\mathcal{E} = IR_{\text{eq}} = (2.4\ \text{A})(18\ \Omega) = 43.2\ \text{V}$.

(b) The *IR* drop across *ab* is found by

$V_{ab} = IR_{ab} = (2.4 \text{ A})(6 \text{ }\Omega) = 14.4 \text{ V}$, and across *cd*, it is found by

$V_{cd} = IR_4 = (2.4 \text{ A})(8 \text{ }\Omega) = 19.2 \text{ V}$. Therefore, between junctions *a* and *d*, it is

$V_{ad} = V_{ab} + V_{cd} = 14.4 \text{ V} + 19.2 \text{ V} = 33.6 \text{ V}$.

(c) The power loss across $R_4 = R_{cd}$ is $P_{cd} = I^2 R_{cd} = (2.4 \text{ A})^2 (8 \text{ }\Omega) = 46.1 \text{ W}$

(*College Physics* 9th ed. pages 617–625/10th ed. pages 628–636)
(L.O. 5.B.9.3, 5.B.9.5, 5.B.9.6, 5.C.3.3, 5.C.3.5)

3. (a)

- Place the ammeter in series with the battery to measure the total current in the circuit. Record the reading.
- Move the ammeter to other positions in the circuit measuring the current in each resistor. Record the ammeter reading for each position of the meter.
- Place the voltmeter into the circuit so that it is in parallel with each element in the circuit and record the reading across each element.

(b) Connect the circuit according to the schematic diagrams shown below. With three resistors there are four possible arrangements of the elements in the circuits.

Figure A

Figure B

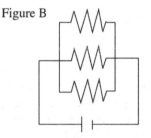

Figure C

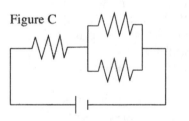

Figure D

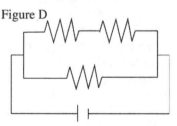

(c) Measurements are indicated for the four possible arrangements.

Figure A. Three resistors in series.

The voltmeter placed across each element, the battery and the resistors should indicate that $\mathcal{E} = V_1 + V_2 + V_3$.

The ammeter placed in the circuit for the current leaving the battery and entering each resistor in turn should indicate $I_{Battery} = I_{R_1} = I_{R_2} = I_{R_3}$.

Figure B. Three resistors in parallel.

The voltmeter placed across each element, the battery and the resistors should indicate that $\mathcal{E} = V_1 = V_2 = V_3$.

The ammeter placed in the circuit for the current leaving the battery and entering each resistor in turn.

Figure C. One resistor in series with a parallel combination of resistors.

The voltmeter placed across each element, the battery and the resistors should indicate that $\mathcal{E} = V_1 + (V_2 = V_3)$.

The ammeter placed in the circuit for the current leaving the battery and entering each resistor in turn should indicate $I_{Battery} = I_{R_1} = (I_{R_2} + I_{R_3})$.

Figure D. Two resistors in series connected in parallel with one additional resistor.

The ammeter will indicate that the resistors in the upper branch will each have the same current. The current from the battery into the junction will be

$$I_{total} = I_{top\ branch} + I_{bottom\ branch}.$$

The voltmeter will show that $\mathcal{E} = V_{bottom} + \Sigma V_{top\ branch}$.

(d) Possible Answers
- ▤ If the circuit operates for too long when readings are taken, the elements in the circuit could heat and the resistances in the circuit might increase. Thus the meters will give readings that are not consistent in the experiment.
- ▤ The meters themselves will affect the readings for the experiment. A voltmeter should have an extremely high resistance with no current flow through the meter, but it does. Likewise an ammeter should have no resistance, but it does and this will give readings that are slightly off.
- ▤ The connecting wires have resistance and will affect the readings.
- ▤ Common color code resistors used in most experiments have three bands to identify the resistors, such as red bands which indicates it as a 220 Ω. There is a fourth band which will give a tolerance of $\pm 20\%$, $\pm 10\%$, $\pm 5\%$. Thus the 220 Ω could have a range from 176 Ω to 264 Ω if its tolerance was $\pm 20\%$.

(*College Physics* 9th ed. pages 617–627, 629/10th ed. pages 628–636)

(L.O. 5.C.3.1, 5.C.3.2, 5.C.3.4)

4. (a) Voltmeter readings will indicate either the potential difference across the known resistor or the terminal potential difference across the battery. The ammeter will indicate the current in the circuit. These can be used to determine the internal resistance.
    (b) Two solutions are possible.

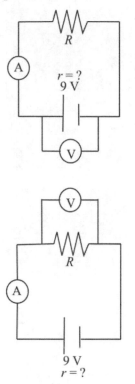

(c) Placing the voltmeter across the ends of the battery will give V_{AB}

$V_{ab} = IR$ then $\mathcal{E} - V_{AB} = Ir$.

Placing the voltmeter across the ends of the resistor will give $V_R = IR$

$\mathcal{E} = IR + Ir$.

(*College Physics* 9th ed. pages 616–617/10th ed. pages 626–627)
(L.O. 5.B.9.2, 5.B.9.6, 5.B.9.7)

14

THE MAGNETIC FIELD

MAGNETS AND MAGNETISM

(College Physics 9th ed. pages 648–652, 673–674/10th ed. pages 659–664, 685–686)

The forces magnets exert on one another are rather complicated. Sometimes they attract one another other and sometimes they repel. Most magnets have two ends, which are called the north-seeking pole, N-pole, and the south-seeking pole, S-pole, because the north end always points toward the north magnetic pole of the Earth when magnets are suspended and allowed to rotate freely. These poles behave somewhat like electric charges; that is, like poles repel and unlike poles attract.

But there is no other resemblance. Magnets cannot be broken into a single N-pole and into a single S-pole. No one has ever observed a magnetic monopole. Unlike electric charge, which is strictly conserved, magnets can be created and destroyed. If a permanent magnet is heated above a certain critical temperature, the Curie temperature, it loses all of its magnetic properties and behaves like an ordinary piece of iron. Placing a piece of iron into contact with a strong permanent magnet gives the piece of iron weak magnetic properties. Magnetism is a property that can be acquired or lost without regard to conservation laws.

Ferromagnetic substances such as iron, nickel, and cobalt have the following properties: (1) their atoms have electron orbits and electron spin (rotating charge) which are not canceled out; and (2) the forces between neighboring atoms is such that the atoms prefer to line up so that their current loops are all pointing in the same direction. A full explanation requires quantum mechanics that is beyond the scope of the course. Any sample of ferromagnetic material at room temperature is made up of microscopic *domains* (on the order of a few thousandths of a centimeter) where the atoms are completely lined up. In an unmagnetized sample, the domains are randomly oriented. In the process of magnetization the domains line up by movement of the domain boundaries, the domains favorably oriented with respect to the field growing at the expense of the others.

Magnetism is an interaction between moving electric charges. Electric charges create electrical fields, but only moving electric charges create magnetic fields. The magnetic field is in addition to the electric field. The charge has an electric field whether the charge is moving or not.

Magnets affect the space around them. Space is modified into a magnetic field that we can call a **B**-field. Magnetic fields have vector properties, they have an intensity, B, and a direction in space. Just as electric field lines are useful in describing electric fields, magnetic flux lines are useful for visualizing the magnetic field. Magnetic flux is defined as leaving the N-pole of a magnet and entering the S-pole. Unlike electric field lines, magnetic flux lines do not have origins and end points—they form continuous loops.

FORCE ON A MOVING CHARGE

(*College Physics* 9th ed. pages 652–655/10th ed. pages 663–667)

All moving charged particles generate a magnetic field. Electrons in atoms move in some fashion in atomic orbitals. Even the electron itself spins, giving it magnetic properties.

Consider a charged particle, q, moving through a magnetic field in a region in space where there is no electric field. The charge will experience a magnetic force, F_B. This force is dependent on several variables, including the charge q of the particle and its speed and its direction.

At any point in space in a magnetic field there is one particular direction in which the charge can move so that the force acting on it is zero, regardless of the speed. The relationship between the magnitude of charge q, its velocity v, the strength of the **B**-field and the magnetic force F_B acting on the charge is

$$F_B = qvB\sin\theta$$

Charge q is a scalar quantity, velocity v is a vector, the magnetic field B is a vector and the force F_B is also a vector. The angle θ is the angle between v and B. When $\theta = 0°$ or $180°$, $\sin 0° = 0$ making v and B parallel, the magnetic force on the charge is zero.

The SI unit of magnetic field, B, is the tesla, T, and it is defined as

$$1\,T = 1\,N/(C \cdot m/s) = 1\,N/A \cdot m$$

Note: The tesla is not a fundamental unit. It is related to the newton, the ampere, and the meter. The newton and the ampere are in turn related to the fundamental units of length, mass, time, and charge.

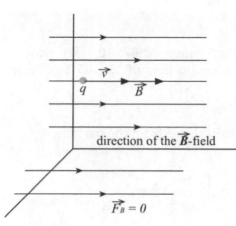

direction of the $\vec{B}$-field

$$\vec{F}_B = 0$$

Motion in any other direction will always produce a force. When $\theta = 90°$, $\sin 90° = 1$ making v and B perpendicular and the magnetic force is a maximum at

$$F_B = qvB$$

The direction of magnetic force on a positive charge that is moving perpendicular to the plane of the velocity vector v and the magnetic field vector B is found by the *right-hand charge rule*: *the right-hand is open and the thumb points in the direction of the magnetic force. The fingers point in the direction of the velocity and the palm of the hand points in the direction of the magnetic field.* For a negative charge the direction of the force vector is reversed.

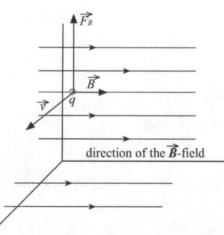

direction of the $\vec{B}$-field

AP Tip

Since the magnetic force $\vec{F}_B$ is perpendicular to the velocity vector $\vec{v}$, it a purely deflecting force. It changes the direction of $\vec{v}$ and not the speed. Because there cannot be a component of magnetic force along the motion, there is no tangential acceleration. *No work can be done on the moving charge q by the $\vec{B}$ -field and no change in energy can take place.*

SAMPLE PROBLEM 1

A proton of charge $q = +e$, mass 1.67×10^{-27} kg and speed $v = 2.9 \times 10^6$ m/s orbits in a magnetic field of $B = 1.5$ T directed into the page.

(a) What is the radius of the orbit?

(b) Find the force the magnetic field exerts on the particle.

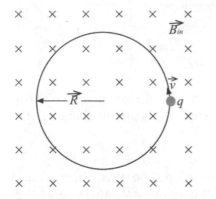

SOLUTION TO PROBLEM 1

(a) The magnetic force provides the centripetal force to the orbiting particle.

$$F_B = \frac{mv^2}{R} = qvB$$

Solving for R

$$R = \frac{mv}{qB} = \frac{\left(1.67 \times 10^{-27} \text{ kg}\right)\left(2.9 \times 10^6 \text{ m/s}\right)}{\left(1.5 \text{ T}\right)\left(1.60 \times 10^{-19} \text{ C}\right)} = \mathbf{0.02 \text{ m}}$$

(b) The magnetic force is

$$F_B = qvB = \left(1.60 \times 10^{-19} \text{ C}\right)\left(2.9 \times 10^6 \text{ m/s}\right)\left(1.5 \text{ T}\right) = \mathbf{7.0 \times 10^{-13} \text{ N}}$$

SAMPLE PROBLEM 2

A *velocity selector* is a device that is operated in vacuum and utilizes crossed E and B fields between a set of parallel-plate capacitors to select positively charged ions $+q$ of only one velocity. The ions are projected into the perpendicular fields at varying speeds. Particles with velocities sufficient to make the magnetic force equal and opposite to the electric force pass through the slit undeflected. Slower moving ions will be deflected out of the plane of the page while those with greater speed will be deflected into the page.

(a) Show that the speed of these particles is found from $v = \dfrac{E}{B}$.

(b) It is desired to have a beam of protons with a speed of 7.0×10^3 m/s. If $B = 0.25$ T, what should the strength of the electric field be?

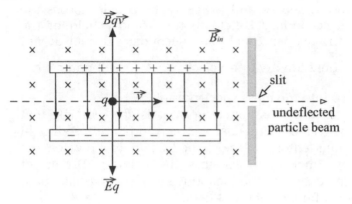

SOLUTION TO PROBLEM 2

(a) The upward force on $+q$ is qvB by the right-hand charge rule. The downward force is Eq. Equating the upward and downward forces

$$qvB = qE \text{ and } v = \frac{E}{B}$$

(b) $E = vB = \left(7.0 \times 10^3 \ \text{m/s}\right)(0.25 \text{ T}) = \mathbf{1.8 \times 10^3 \ N/C}$

In a vacuum, the path of a charged particle moving in a magnetic field depends on the mass, charge and velocity of the particle, and on the magnetic field intensity. If a beam of positively charged ions all having the same velocity and charge is projected perpendicularly into a uniform magnetic field, the ions will be bent into a circular path dependent upon their mass. Those with smaller mass will move in a path of smaller radius than those of more massive ions with the same charge. This is the principle of the *mass spectrograph*, a device used to separate ions of a given element into groups according to the mass of the ions. The diagram below represents the two major parts of a mass spectrograph.

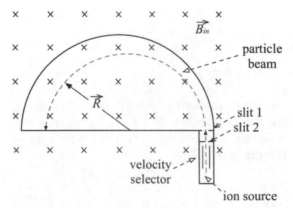

The first part is the ion source and velocity selector. The velocity selector is also referred to as a velocity filter. The ion source produces a beam of ions of varying velocities. The beam is directed into the velocity selector with crossed **E**- and **B**-fields. The **B**-field across the velocity selector is a secondary **B**-field to the primary field of the spectrograph. With the proper **E**-field and secondary **B**-field across the velocity selector, only ions with a velocity $v = \dfrac{E}{B_s}$ will enter slit 2 and then through slit 1 into the mass spectrograph.

The second part of the mass spectrograph is the portion that separates ions of equal velocity and charge according to differences in mass. The beam of ions enters a Dee-shaped chamber between the poles of an electromagnet that produces the primary **B**-field of intensity B. Within the chamber the ions move in a semicircular path of radius R under the influence of the **B**-field.

The magnetic field exerts centripetal force on each ion of mass m.

$$F_C = \frac{mv^2}{R} = qvB$$

and the mass of the ion is

$$m = \frac{BqR}{v}$$

SAMPLE PROBLEM 3

Ions of charge $q = +e$ are produced in the ion source of a mass spectrograph operated with a primary **B**-field of 0.40 T. The ion beam is directed into the velocity selector of sample problem 2 and then emerges with a velocity of 7.0×10^3 m/s. The ions enter the mass spectrograph where they travel a semicircular path of radius 7.2×10^{-3} m. Calculate the mass of one of these ions.

SOLUTION TO PROBLEM 3

The charge of an ion is $q = +e = +1.6010^{-19}$ C and the mass is found by

$$m = \frac{BqR}{v} = \frac{(0.40\ \text{T})(1.60 \times 10^{-19}\ \text{C})(7.2 \times 10^{-3}\ \text{m})}{7.0 \times 10^3\ \text{m}\big/\text{s}} = \mathbf{6.6 \times 10^{-26}\ kg}$$

FORCE IN A CURRENT-CARRYING WIRE

(College Physics 9th ed. pages 655–658/10th ed. pages 667–670)

The charge carriers in a wire under a potential difference are constrained to travel inside the conductor. When the charges are so constrained, the transverse force on them due to an external magnetic field is transmitted to the conductor.

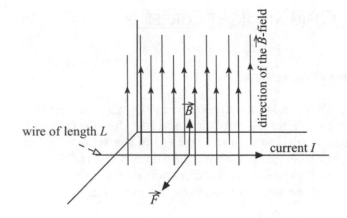

The magnetic force the wire experiences in the **B**-field is related to the current I, the length L of the segment of wire exposed to the field and the intensity B of the field as

$$F_B = ILB$$

In the event that L makes an angle θ with the field, the relationship becomes

$$F_B = ILB \sin \theta$$

SAMPLE PROBLEM 4

A wire connected across a potential difference carries a current $I = 2.4\ \text{A}$. The wire is inserted into a magnetic field of at a right angle to the field of $B = 0.5\ \text{T}$ that is directed into the page. If a length, $L = 0.5\ \text{m}$, is exposed to the field as illustrated below, what force acts on the wire?

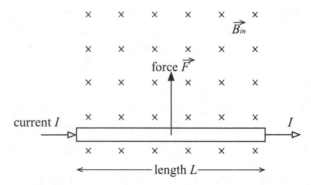

SOLUTION TO PROBLEM 4

By the right-hand charge rule, the **B**-field exerts an upward force on the wire segment. The magnitude of the force is

$$F_B = ILB = (2.4\ \text{A})(0.5\ \text{m})(0.5\ \text{T}) = \textbf{0.6 N upward}$$

Note: Once again the direction of F_B can also be defined as the result of the cross product of vector L and vector B.

MAGNETIC FIELD OF A LONG STRAIGHT CURRENT-CARRYING WIRE

(*College Physics* 9th ed. pages 664–667/10th ed. pages 676–679)

The magnetic lines of force near a current-carrying wire are in the form of concentric circles. The relationship between the direction of the magnetic field and the direction of the current in the wire is given by the *right-hand current rule:* *when a wire is grasped by the right hand in such a way that the thumb points in the direction of the current, the fingers encircle the wire in the same sense as the magnetic field.*

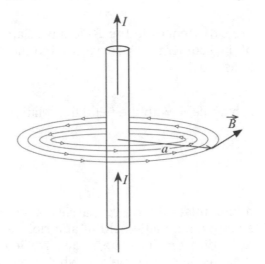

The magnitude of the **B**-field at a point near a long current-carrying wire is proportional to the current, I, carried in the wire and is inversely proportional to the perpendicular distance, a, from the center of the wire to the point in question. The expression is written as

$$B = k_B \frac{I}{a}$$

Here k_B is a constant of proportionality. In the SI the unit of the magnetic field strength, B, is the tesla, T. The tesla can be defined by taking the constant k_B to be exactly 2×10^{-7} T·m/A. This constant is usually written as $k_B = \frac{\mu_o}{2\pi}$ and μ_o is called the magnetic permeability of free space. Its value is $\mu_o = 4\pi \times 10^{-7}$ T·m/A.

$$B = k_B \frac{I}{a} \text{ now becomes}$$

$$B = \frac{\mu_o I}{2\pi a}$$

The gauss, G, is a common unit of the magnetic field strength. It is related to the tesla by $1\text{ T} = 10^4\text{ G}$ or $1\text{ G} = 10^{-4}\text{ T}$.

SAMPLE PROBLEM 5

A 2.00 m long, 1.20 mm diameter wire having a resistivity of $1.50 \times 10^{-6} \ \Omega \cdot m$ is connected to a 12.0 V battery. What is the magnitude of the **B**-field at a perpendicular distance of 1.0 cm from the center of the wire?

SOLUTION TO PROBLEM 5

First, we have to find the resistance of the wire and the current in the wire. Resistance is related to resistivity by

$$R = \rho \frac{L}{A} = \frac{\rho L}{\pi r^2} = \frac{\left(1.50 \times 10^{-6} \Omega \cdot m\right)\left(2.00 \ m\right)}{\pi \left(0.060 \times 10^{-3} m\right)^2} = 2.65 \ \Omega$$

The current is found by using Ohm's law $I = \dfrac{V}{R} = \dfrac{12.0 \ V}{2.65 \ \Omega} = 4.52 \ A$.

Now, the magnetic field strength 1.0 cm from the wire is

$$B = \frac{\mu_o I}{2\pi a} = \frac{\left(4\pi \times 10^{-7} \ T \cdot m/_A\right)\left(4.52 \ A\right)}{2\pi \left(0.01 \ m\right)} = 9.0 \times 10^{-5} \ T$$

SAMPLE PROBLEM 6

Two parallel wires of length 1.0 m are 8.0 cm apart and carry respective currents of $I_1 = 8.0 \ A$ and $I_2 = 6.0 \ A$. Note that the following diagrams are not to scale.

(a) Determine the magnetic force on wire 2 due to wire 1 when the currents are parallel.

(b) Calculate the magnetic force on wire 2 due to wire 1 when the currents are anti-parallel.

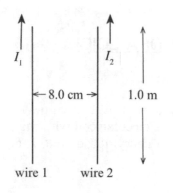

SOLUTION TO PROBLEM 6

(a) First, find the B-field at the position of wire 2 due to wire 1. The right-hand current rule indicates **B** at the position of wire 2 is directed into the page. The magnitude of **B** is then

$$B = \frac{\mu_o I}{2\pi r} = \frac{\left(4\pi \times 10^{-7} \ T \cdot m/A\right)\left(8.0 \ A\right)}{2\pi \left(0.08 \ m\right)} = 2.0 \times 10^{-5} \ T$$

The force on the 1.0 m length of wire 2 is then

$$F_B = ILB\sin\theta = (6.0\text{ A})(1.0\text{ m})(2.0\times10^{-5}\text{ T})(\sin90°)$$
$$= 1.2\times10^{-4}\text{ N to the left}$$

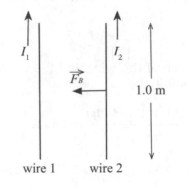

(b) The current in wire 2 is reversed but the force will have the same magnitude and now the opposite direction $F_B = 1.2\times10^{-4}$ **N to the right.**

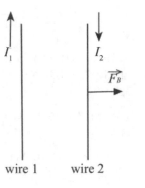

MAGNETIC FIELD AT THE CENTER OF A COIL

(*College Physics* 9th ed. pages 669–673/10th ed. pages 681–685)

The magnetic field produced by a current-carrying wire is greatly increased if the wire is wound into a circular coil with many turns. The magnetic field created by a flat coil carrying current I is complex as show below.

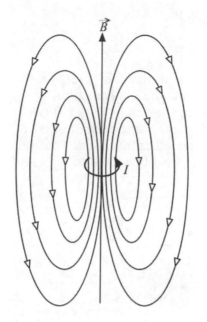

For a flat circular coil of n-turns and radius a, we can calculate the B-field at the very center of the coil, and it is

$$B = \frac{\mu_o nI}{2a}$$

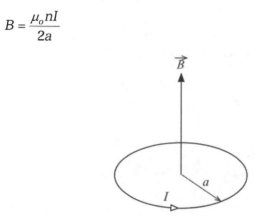

SAMPLE PROBLEM 7

A flat circular coil of 10 turns of wire has a radius, a, of 4.0 cm. Determine the **B**-field at the center of the coil when a current of 4.0 A is circulated through the coil.

SOLUTION TO PROBLEM 7

$$B = \frac{\mu_o nI}{2a} = \frac{\left(4\pi \times 10^{-7}\ \text{T} \cdot \text{m/A}\right)(10)(4.0\ \text{A})}{2(0.04\ \text{m})} = 6.3 \times 10^{-4}\ \text{T}$$

MAGNETIC FIELD OF A SOLENOID

(*College Physics* 9th ed. pages 670–672/10th ed. pages 882–884)

The solenoid is a helix, a long tube of many turns of wire N. The word solenoid itself stems from the Greek and it means tube.

The ideal parallel-plate capacitor has many uses but two of its major uses are that a uniform electric field can be established between the plates and electrical energy is stored in the field. The ideal solenoid will maintain a uniform magnetic field between its ends and will store magnetic energy in the field.

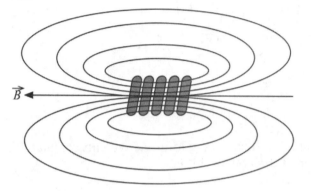

Solenoids are found in doorbells, speaker systems, TVs, computers, relays that control furnaces, and air conditioners. The MRI used in medical centers is a giant solenoid.

The magnetic field B established in a solenoid that is circulating current I through the N turns of wire is found by the equation

$$B = \frac{\mu_o NI}{L}$$

We can define the number of turns per unit length as $n = \dfrac{N}{L}$. Then we can write

$$B = \mu_o nI$$

SAMPLE PROBLEM 8

A 0.4 m long solenoid has 1600 turns. The magnetic field at the center of then solenoid is $B = 0.05\ T$. What current circulates through the wrappings of the solenoid?

SOLUTION TO PROBLEM 8

From the solenoid equation, $B = \dfrac{\mu_o NI}{L}$, we write the current as being

$$I = \frac{BL}{\mu_o N} = \frac{(0.05\ \text{T})(0.4\ \text{m})}{(4\pi \times 10^{-7}\,\text{T} \cdot \text{m/A})(1600)} = \textbf{10 A}$$

FARADAY'S LAW OF INDUCTION

(*College Physics* 9th ed. pages 688–701/10th ed. pages 699–712)

Michael Faraday discovered magnetic induction, the creation of an electric field by a changing magnetic field. Magnetic induction ranks with electromagnetism as one of the fundamental principles on which our modern technology is based. Electromagnetism provides the means by which electric energy can be converted into mechanical work; magnetic induction provides the means by which mechanical work can be converted into electric energy. All of our electric power comes from generators that operate on the principle of magnetic induction.

The magnetic flux ϕ_B through a loop of wire is defined as the product of the magnetic field that penetrates the loop and the area penetrated, or

$$\phi_B = BA$$

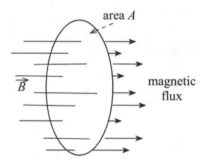

Faraday's law of magnetic induction states that when magnetic flux through a loop changes by an amount $\Delta\phi_B$ in a time period Δt, the emf induced in the loop during time period Δt is

$$\mathcal{E} = -\frac{\Delta\phi_M}{\Delta t}$$

When a conductor moves through a magnetic field and experiences a change in magnetic flux, the induced emf is called *motional emf*. For N loops we write Faraday's law as

$$\mathcal{E} = -N\frac{\Delta\phi_B}{\Delta t}$$

The SI unit of magnetic flux ϕ_B is the weber, *Wb*, and it is defined as: $1\,\text{Wb} = 1\,\text{T}\cdot\text{m}^2$.

SAMPLE PROBLEM 9

Imagine moving a conductor of length $L = 0.2\,\text{m}$ sliding along a stationary conducting loop with a velocity $v = 2.0\,\text{m/s}$. The loop, as is diagramed below, contains a resistor $R = 4.0\,\Omega$. The *B*-field has an intensity $B = 0.5\,\text{T}$ and is directed into the page. As the conductor slides to the right, the magnetic flux penetrating the loop increases as the area of the loop increases. An emf is induced in the loop as a result of this motion and a current is also induced in the circuit.

(a) Calculate the magnitude of the motional emf.

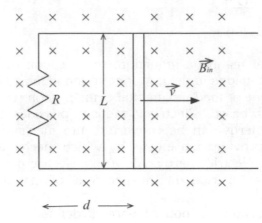

(b) What current is induced in the loop?

(c) What is the direction of this current?

SOLUTION TO PROBLEM 9

(a) The magnitude of the induced motional emf is

$$|\mathcal{E}| = \frac{\Delta\phi_B}{\Delta t} = \frac{\Delta(BA)}{\Delta t}$$

B is constant and

$$|\mathcal{E}| = \frac{\Delta(BA)}{\Delta t} = \frac{B\Delta A}{\Delta t} = \frac{B\Delta(Ld)}{\Delta t}$$

The length of the conductor L is constant and

$$|\mathcal{E}| = BL\frac{\Delta d}{\Delta t} = BLv = (0.5 \text{ T})(0.2 \text{ m})(2.0 \text{ m/s}) = \mathbf{0.2 \text{ V}}$$

(b) The current is found by using Ohm's law

$$I = \frac{\mathcal{E}}{R} = \frac{0.2 \text{ V}}{4.0 \text{ }\Omega} = \mathbf{5 \times 10^{-2} \text{ A}}$$

(c) The direction of the induced emf and the direction of any resulting induced current is determined by Lenz's law:

The direction of the induced emf is such as to oppose the change in magnetic flux that causes the induced emf.

The induced current is counterclockwise.

The words change and flux are very important. Consider the word change. Lenz's law says that when the flux is increasing, the induced emf tries to make it decrease; when flux is decreasing the induced emf tries to make it increase. Note that Lenz's law does not say the induced emf opposes the magnetic field, but rather it says it opposes the change in magnetic flux.

> ## AP Tip
>
> If the magnitude of the flux through a circuit is *increasing*, the induced *I*-field is in the *opposite* direction of the primary field. If the magnitude of the flux through a circuit is *decreasing*, the induced field is in the *same* direction as the primary field.

Lenz's law is required by the law of conservation of energy.

THE MAGNETIC FIELD: STUDENT OBJECTIVES FOR THE AP EXAM

- You should know and be able to apply the expression used for the magnitude of the magnetic field.
- You should know that force, velocity, and magnetic field intensity are all vector quantities that are mutually perpendicular to one another.
- You should be able to apply the right-hand rule for a positive charge to determine the direction of the unknown parameter when the other two are known.
- You should be able to state and apply the equation for the magnetic force on a moving conductor.
- You should be able to relate the magnetic force on a moving charge in a magnetic field that causes the particle to alter its direction of travel to the centripetal force and to evaluate the equations to solve for any unknown parameter either mathematically or by diagram.
- You should know and be able to apply the second right-hand rule to the direction of the magnetic field produced by a long straight wire carrying a current.
- You should be able to calculate the magnitude and direction of the *B*-field produced in a closed loop.
- You should know and be able to apply Faraday's and Lenz's laws for the magnitude and direction of the induced emf or current in closed loops.
- You should be able to draw or explain graphs involving changes in magnetic flux or induced emf as a function of time.
- You must be able to solve multiple-choice questions/problems with a calculator.

MULTIPLE-CHOICE QUESTIONS

1. A proton traveling at 5.0×10^5 $\mathrm{m/s}$ crosses the page to the right.
   The proton enters a **B**-field of 0.1 T that is directed toward the top
   of the page. The magnitude and the direction of the force acting on
   the proton is
   (A) 8.0×10^{-13} N into the page
   (B) 8.0×10^{-13} N out of the page
   (C) 3.2×10^{-13} N down the page
   (D) 3.2×10^{-13} N to the left on the page

2. Two wires carrying currents in opposite directions produce a
   magnetic field between the wires that is best illustrated by which
   of the following diagrams?

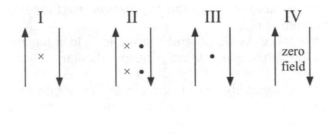

   (A) I
   (B) II
   (C) III
   (D) IV

3. A pair of bar magnets is used to show the direction of the
   magnetic field relating to the north and south poles of the
   magnets. Iron filings sprinkled around the magnets will indicate
   that the field produces
   (A) concentric circles of iron filings around the magnet
   (B) a repulsive field when placed in the region between a north
       and a south pole
   (C) an attraction field when placed in the region between a north
       and a south pole
   (D) no interaction with either magnet

4. Rank the domains in the ferromagnetic materials illustrated below that show the strength of the bar magnetic from the weakest magnetic field to the strongest magnetic field.

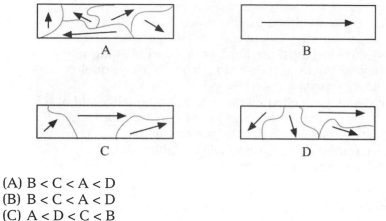

(A) B < C < A < D
(B) B < C < A < D
(C) A < D < C < B
(D) B < C < A = D

5. An electron moving with a constant velocity to the right along the positive x-direction enters a uniform magnetic field. The magnetic field is directed out of the page. The direction of the force acting on the electron as it moves through the field is shown by which of the force vectors shown below?

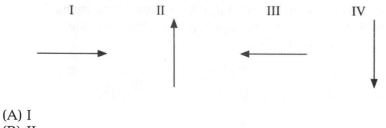

(A) I
(B) II
(C) III
(D) IV

6. A bar magnet suspended from its midpoint in a horizontal plane will align itself with the Earth's magnetic field with its north end pointing north.
   (A) The force that the Earth exerts on the bar magnet is greater that the force the bar magnet exerts on the Earth because the Earth's magnetic field is much larger.
   (B) The force the bar magnetic exerts on the Earth is larger because the bar magnet is suspended by a string and free to rotate.
   (C) The magnitude of the forces between the bar magnet and the Earth is the same since they are action-reaction pairs.
   (D) There is only a gravitational force acting between the magnet and the Earth.

7. Iron filings sprinkled around a bar magnet are good materials to use to indicate the strength and direction of the magnetic field associated with a magnetic pole or a pair of magnetic poles because
   (A) the domains in the iron filings can be affected by the field of a strong magnet so that they orient themselves with the field of the magnet(s) showing the field direction around the magnet(s)
   (B) they are weakly magnetic and do not interfere with magnetic field of the bar magnet(s)
   (C) since they are weakly repelled by the external magnetic field of the bar magnet(s) they do not crowd together along the magnet field lines associated with the bar magnet(s)
   (D) they are nonmagnetic materials and will not affect the magnetic field of the bar magnet(s)

8. A circular coil is placed on a horizontal surface. Initially a bar magnet is held above it with the N-pole pointing downward to the coil. When the magnet is moved toward the coil, it induces
   (A) a current in the coil that is counterclockwise as viewed from above
   (B) a current in the coil that is clockwise as viewed from above
   (C) no current in the coil since it is not connected to power supply
   (D) an alternating current in the coil

9. Two loops of wire as shown in the diagram have a common vertical axis. The current in the bottom loop is counterclockwise as shown and increasing. Which of the following best describes the induced current in the upper loop?

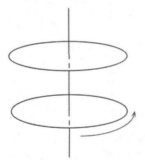

   (A) There is a clockwise current in the upper loop, but it will change due to the increasing current in the lower loop.
   (B) There is a counterclockwise current in the upper loop, but it will change due to the increasing current in the lower loop.
   (C) There is a constant clockwise current in the upper loop.
   (D) There is a constant counterclockwise current in the upper loop.

10. A proton, $+q$, moves to the right with a velocity of 1.0×10^4 m/s into the region between two parallel plates where both a uniform electric field of 1000 N/C and a magnetic field, $B = 0.1$ T, exist between the plates as shown in the diagram below.

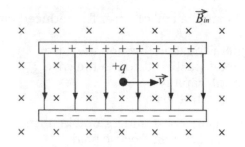

The electric and magnetic forces acting on the proton are
(A) in the same direction causing the proton to accelerate upward
(B) in opposite directions causing the proton to accelerate downward
(C) balanced and the proton will be stationary in the region between the plates
(D) balanced and the proton will move to the right horizontally with a constant velocity

11. A proton with a velocity, v, enters a region in which there is a magnetic field directed into the page. The proton follows the path shown below.

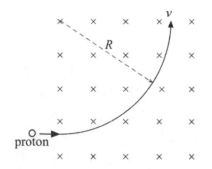

The magnetic field will
(A) produce an increase in the kinetic energy of the proton since the magnetic field does work on moving the charge
(B) decrease the kinetic energy of the proton since the magnetic field does not act parallel to the direction of motion of the moving charge
(C) increase the angular momentum of the proton since the field produces a torque on the proton
(D) only change the direction of motion of the proton since the velocity of the proton is perpendicular to the magnetic force

12. Magnetic field lines produced by a long straight wire carrying a current are
(A) in the same direction as the current in the wire
(B) in the opposite direction as the current in the wire
(C) are concentric circles around the wire
(D) are directed radially outward from the wire

13. A region of space surrounding a moving electron contains
    (A) an electric field, a gravitational field, and a magnetic field
    (B) an electric field and a gravitational field
    (C) an electric field and a magnetic field
    (D) a gravitational field and a magnetic field

14. A bar magnet is pushed through a coil of wire. The induced emf is greatest when the
    (A) north end of the magnet is pushed through the wire
    (B) south end of the magnet is pushed through the wire
    (C) magnet is pushed through rapidly
    (D) magnet is in equilibrium with the coil

15. The phenomenon of magnetism is best understood in terms of
    (A) the force exerted on a charge in an electric field
    (B) the magnetic field associated with moving charges
    (C) force fields between electron and protons
    (D) the existence of magnetic poles in materials

FREE-RESPONSE PROBLEMS

1. Each electron in a beam of electrons travels with the same velocity of 1.50×10^7 m/s. The beam is bent 90° through an arc length $s = 4.25$ mm by a uniform magnetic field perpendicular to the beam path.

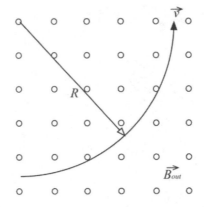

   (a) What is the magnetic field strength?
   (b) How much time is required for an electron to travel through the 90° arc?
   (c) What centripetal force does an electron experience in the magnetic field?
   (d) Through what potential difference were the electrons accelerated to acquire their velocity?
   (*College Physics* 9th ed. pages 652–654, 661–664/10th ed. pages 663–667, 673–676)
   (L.O. 2.D.1.1, 3.A.2.1, 3.C.3.1)

2. A square loop of wire 20.0 cm on a side enters a region in space where a magnetic field of 1.6 T is directed into the page and confined in a square of dimensions 70.0 cm by 70.0 cm. The loop of wire has a constant velocity $v = 10.0 \, \text{cm}/\text{s}$ perpendicular to the **B**-field as shown.

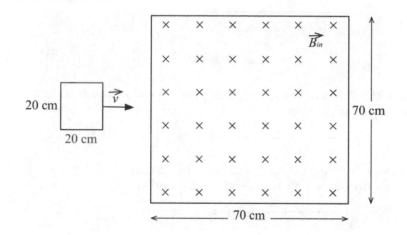

(a) i. What is the direction of the current in the loop as it enters the field?

ii. What is the direction of the current in the loop as it leaves the field?

iii. Justify your answers.

(b) i. How long does it take the loop to enter the magnetic field once the right-hand side contacts the field?

ii. How long does the loop, once the right-hand side first contacts the field, spend in crossing the field?

iii. How long does it take the loop to exit the field once the right-hand side reaches the edge of the field?

(c) What is the magnitude of the induced emf as it enters and leaves the **B**-field?

(d) Graph the emf as a function of time as the loop completely enters and completely emerges from the magnetic field.

(e) If the loop of wire has a resistance of 40.0 Ω, what is the magnitude of the induced current in the loop?

(f) Calculate the magnetic flux in the loop when it is completely immersed in the field.

(*College Physics* 9th ed. pages 688–701/10th ed. pages 699–712)
(L.O. 4.E.2.1)

3. A wire carrying a conventional current is placed in a magnetic field as illustrated below.

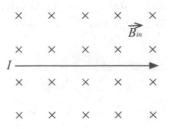

   (a) Indicate the direction of the force acting on the wire shown below. Justify your answer.

——————————————▶

   (b) If the magnetic field is reversed, indicate the direction of the force on the wire shown below. Justify your answer.

——————————————▶

   (c) If the current in the wire is reversed, indicate the direction of the force on the wire shown below. Justify your answer.

◀——————————————

   (d) i. If we double the current in the wire what happens to the force on the wire in (a)?
         _____ Increases
         _____ Decreases
         _____ Remains constant
      ii. Justify your answer.
   (*College Physics* 9th ed. pages 652–658/10th ed. pages 663–670)
   (L.O. 3.A.2.1, 3.C.3.1)

4. (a) A bar magnet is diagrammed below. Indicate the direction of the magnetic field surrounding the bar magnet. Draw vectors to scale to represent the direction and strength of the magnetic field produced by the bar magnet.

•

•

•   • | N   S | •   •

•

•

   (b) Compare the magnetic field of the bar magnet above to the
      electric field due to an electric dipole. List at least two ways
      that they are
      i. similar
      ii. different
(*College Physics* 9th ed. pages 648–651, 673–675/10th ed. pages
659–661, 685–687)
(L.O. 1.B.1.1, 1.B.3.1, 2.C.4.1, 2.D.1.1, 2.D.3.1)

Answers

MULTIPLE-CHOICE QUESTIONS

1. **B** The magnitude of the force is given by $F = qvB$. The force is
$\left(1.6 \times 10^{-19}\ \text{C}\right)\left(5.0 \times 10^{5}\ \frac{\text{m}}{\text{s}}\right)(0.1\ \text{T}) = 8.0 \times 10^{-15}\ \text{N}$. The direction of
the force is given by the *right-hand charge rule: the right-hand is
open and the thumb points in the direction of the magnetic force.
The fingers point in the direction of the velocity and the palm of the
hand points in the direction of the magnetic field.* The direction is
out of the page.
(*College Physics* 9th ed. pages 652–653/10th ed. pages 664–665)
(L.O. 2.D.1.1, 3.C.3.1)

2. **A** A current carrying wire produces a magnetic field that circles
the wire. Use your right hand to determine the direction by placing
your thumb in the direction of conventional (positive) current in
the wire. The curl of your fingers will give the direction of the field
associated with the current, × indicates into the paper, and o is
used to show a direction out of the paper. Superposition applies to
magnetic fields too. The wires carrying current in opposite
directions will attract each other in the same manner as N– and S–
poles of magnets.
(*College Physics* 9th ed. pages 667–669/10th ed. pages 664–665)
(L.O. 2.D.2.1)

3. **C** The iron filings become temporary magnets when placed in the
region around the bar magnets. The direction of the filings show
that an attractive field exists in the region between the north and
south poles of the magnet.
(*College Physics* 9th ed. pages 648–652/10th ed. pages 660–663)
(L.O. 2.D.3.1)

4. **C** Magnetic domains are regions in the bar magnet where
spinning electrons create current loops that are oriented in the
same direction. These domains can grow at the expense of other
regions in the presence of an external magnetic field. If the
domains are oriented in the same direction, they produce a strong
magnetic field. The most disorganized ferromagnetic material is
represented in A and the strongest in B. The correct order is A < D
< C < B.
(*College Physics* 9th ed. pages 673–674/10th ed. pages 685–686)
(L.O. 2.D.4.1)

5. **B** The direction of the force is given by the right-hand rule. The palm of your right hand will give the direction of the force on the charge. Since the charge is an electron, the direction of the force must be reversed.
   (*College Physics* 9th ed. pages 652–653/10th ed. pages 664–665)
   (L.O. 3.A.2.1, 3.C.3.1)

6. **C** The magnetic force between the bar magnetic and the Earth are equal in magnitude and opposite in direction. The Earth and the bar magnet produce forces that are action-reaction pairs.
   (*College Physics* 9th ed. pages 648–651/10th ed. pages 659–663)
   (L.O. 3.A.3.3)

7. **A** Ferromagnetic materials such as iron filings are good materials to use to indicate the presence of an external magnetic field. They have permanent magnetic moments that can be temporarily aligned with the magnetic field of the magnet(s) showing the magnetic field lines of the bar magnet(s).
   (*College Physics* 9th ed. pages 673–675/10th ed. pages 685–687)
   (L.O. 4.E.1.1)

8. **A** Both Faraday's and Lenz's laws apply. As the north end of magnet is moved toward the coil, the magnetic field and flux increases downward in the coil. The induced current in the coil is counterclockwise in the coil producing a **B**-field whose direction is upward to counter the increasing downward flux. Use the right-hand rule. If the fingers curl in the direction of the induced current the thumb will point in the direction of the magnetic field produced.
   (*College Physics* 9th ed. pages 691–695/10th ed. pages 702–706)
   (L.O. 4.E.2.1)

9. **A** An increasing counterclockwise current in the bottom loop will produce a **B**-field that is increasing. Use the right-hand rule. If the fingers curl in the direction of the current the thumb will point in the direction of the magnetic field. This behaves as if the North-pole of a bar magnet is being moved toward the upper loop. Accordingly, the induced current in the upper loop will circle clockwise producing a magnetic field that points downward to the lower loop. Because the current in the lower loop is increasing, the induced current in the upper loop will not be constant because the induced current depends on the rate change of flux.
   (*College Physics* 9th ed. pages 691–695/10th ed. pages 702–706)
   (L.O. 4.E.2.1)

10. **D** The vector sum of the forces acting on the proton are
    $\Sigma F = F_E + F_B$.

    $F_E = Eq$ acting downward and $F_B = qvB$ acting upward (right-hand rule).

    $$-1000\ ^N\!/_C(q) + q\left(1 \times 10^4\ ^m\!/_s\right)(0.1\ T) = \Sigma F$$

The net force is zero on the proton and it will continue to move to the right at constant velocity.
(*College Physics* 9th ed. pages 522–523, 652–655/10th ed. pages 532–534, 664–665)
(L.O. 2.C.1.1, 2.D.1.1, 3.A.2.1)

11. **D** Since the magnetic field produces a force that is perpendicular to both the velocity and itself, the field does no work on the proton. A force that is perpendicular to the velocity can only change the direction of the particle. The direction of the force is given by the right-hand rule.
(*College Physics* 9th ed. pages 652–653/10th ed. pages 664–665)
(L.O. 3.C.3.1)

12. **C** A current-carrying wire produces a magnetic field that circles the wire. Use your right hand to determine the direction by placing your thumb in the direction of conventional (positive) current in the wire. The curl of your fingers will give the direction of the field associated with the current, × indicates into the paper, and an o is used to show a direction out of the paper.
(*College Physics* 9th ed. pages 667–669/10th ed. pages 664–665)
(L.O. 2.D.2.1)

13. **A** The electron has mass and creates a gravitational field. Since it has a charge, it also creates an electric field. It will have a magnetic field associated with it only when it is moving.
(*College Physics* 9th ed. pages 522, 664–666/10th ed. pages 532, 674–678)
(L.O. 2.D.2.1)

14. **C** The induced emf given by Faraday's law relates the strength of the induced emf to the rate of change in the flux.
(*College Physics* 9th ed. pages 691–695/10th ed. pages 702–706)
(L.O. 4.E.2.1)

15. **A** We define the properties of a magnetic field at a point in space in terms of the magnetic force F_B exerted on a moving charge as
$F_B = qvB\sin\theta$.
(*College Physics* 9th ed. pages 652–653/10th ed. pages 664–665)
(L.O. 3.C.3.1)

FREE-RESPONSE PROBLEMS

1.

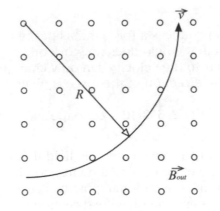

(a) To determine the strength of the magnetic field, we first need the radius of curvature, R, of the electron beam. Arc length s is related to radius by

$$s = \theta R \quad \text{and} \quad \theta = 90° = \frac{\pi}{2}$$

then

$$R = \frac{s}{\theta} = \frac{4.25 \times 10^{-3}\,\text{m}}{\pi/2\,\text{rad}} = 2.71 \times 10^{-3}\,\text{m}$$

$$B = \frac{mv}{eR} = \frac{\left(9.11 \times 10^{-31}\,\text{kg}\right)\left(1.50 \times 10^{7}\,\text{m/s}\right)}{\left(1.60 \times 10^{-19}\,\text{C}\right)\left(2.71 \times 10^{-3}\,\text{m}\right)} = \mathbf{3.15 \times 10^{-2}\ T}$$

(b) The time period is

$$t = \frac{s}{v} = \frac{4.25 \times 10^{-3}\,\text{m}}{1.50 \times 10^{7}\,\text{m/s}} = \mathbf{2.83 \times 10^{-10}\ s}$$

(c) The magnetic field provides the centripetal force

$$F_C = F_M = qvB = evB$$
$$= \left(1.60 \times 10^{-19}\,\text{C}\right)\left(1.50 \times 10^{7}\,\text{m/s}\right)\left(3.15 \times 10^{-2}\,\text{T}\right)$$
$$= \mathbf{7.56 \times 10^{-14}\ N}$$

(d) The potential difference is related to the kinetic energy by

$$Ve = \frac{1}{2}mv^2$$

Solving for V:

$$V = \frac{mv^2}{2e} = \frac{\left(9.11 \times 10^{-31}\,\text{kg}\right)\left(1.50 \times 10^{7}\,\text{m/s}\right)^2}{2\left(1.60 \times 10^{-19}\,\text{C}\right)} = \mathbf{640\ V}$$

(*College Physics* 9th ed. pages 652–654, 661–664/10th ed. pages 663–667, 673–676)
(L.O. 2.D.1.1, 3.A.2.1, 3.C.3.1)

2.

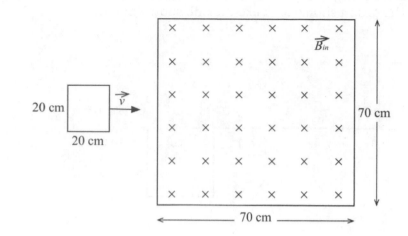

(a) i. Counterclockwise

ii. Clockwise

iii.

> Before the square loop enters the field, the flux through the loop is zero. As the loop enters the field, the flux increases until the left edge of the loop is just inside the field. The flux decreases to zero as the loop leaves the field.
>
> As the right side of the square loop enters the magnetic field, the magnetic flux directed into the page increases. According to Lenz's law, the induced current is counterclockwise because it must produce a magnetic field directed out of the page. The motional emf, BLv, arises from the magnetic force experienced by the charge carriers in the right side of the loop.
>
> Once the loop is entirely in the field, the change in the magnetic flux is zero. This happens because once the left side of the loop enters the field, the motional emf induced in it cancels the motional emf present in the right-hand side of the loop.
>
> As the right-hand side of the loop leaves the field, the flux inward begins to decrease, a clockwise current is induced, and the induced emf is $-BLv$. As soon as the left-hand side leaves the field, the emf decreases to zero.

(b)

i. $v = \dfrac{x}{t}$ and $t = \dfrac{x}{v} = \dfrac{0.2 \text{ m}}{0.10 \text{ m/s}} = \textbf{2.0 s}$

ii. $t_{total} = \dfrac{L}{v} = \dfrac{0.70 \text{ m}}{0.10 \text{ m/s}} = \textbf{7.0 s}$

iii. $t = \dfrac{x}{v} = \dfrac{0.2 \text{ m}}{0.10 \text{ m/s}} = \textbf{2.0 s}$

(c) $\mathcal{E} = BLv = (1.6 \text{ T})(0.2 \text{ m})(0.1 \text{ m/s}) = \textbf{3.2} \times \textbf{10}^{-2} \textbf{ V}$

(d) Two seconds are required for the loop to completely enter the magnetic field. During that time period, an emf of 0.032 V is induced. From 2.0 to 7.0 s, there is no change in flux and no motional emf. Another two seconds is required for the loop to exit the field. During this interval, an emf of –0.032 V is induced. The graph should look like the one shown below.

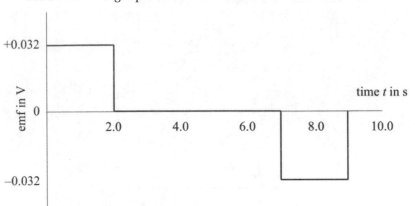

(e) Current is found by using Ohm's law

$$I = \frac{\mathcal{E}}{R} = \frac{3.2 \times 10^{-2}\,\text{V}}{40.0\,\Omega} = \mathbf{8.0 \times 10^{-4}\ A}$$

(f) The magnetic flux in the loop when it is completely immersed in the field is

$$\phi_B = BA = (1.6\ \text{T})(4 \times 10^{-2}\,\text{m}^2) = \mathbf{6.4 \times 10^{-2}\ Wb}$$

(*College Physics* 9th ed. pages 688–701/10th ed. pages 699–712)
(L.O. 4.E.2.1)

3. (a) The direction of the force on the wire is upward as shown on the diagram. The total force on the wire is given by the force on each charge times the number of charge carriers in the wire. $\Sigma F = (qv_{drift}B)(nAL)$ Since the current in the wire is $I = nqv_{drift}A$. The force on the wire is $F = BIL$.

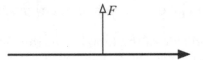

The right-hand rule applies to the wire in the same manner that applies to a charge moving in a magnetic field that is at right angles to the velocity.

(b) Reversing the magnetic field reverses the direction of the force on the wire as shown in the diagram below. The right-hand rule applies.

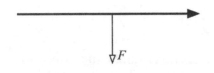

(c) Reversing the direction of the current produces a force on the wire as shown in the diagram below. Again, the right-hand rule applies.

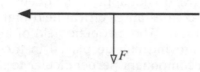

(d) i.   The correct block checked is increases.
    ii. Increasing the current increase the force on the wire as is indicated in part (a) of this question.
(*College Physics* 9th ed. pages 652–658/10th ed. pages 663–670)
(L.O. 3.A.2.1, 3.C.3.1)

4. (a) The diagram for the magnitude and direction of the field at the indicated points is shown.

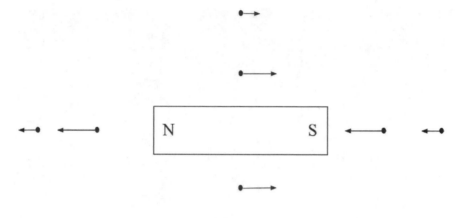

   (b) i.   Similarities between the magnetic field associated with the bar magnet and an electrical dipole include:
        ■ They are both inverse square laws; however, we usually do not solve for this when dealing with magnets.
        ■ The field direction is always out from the surface of a positive charge and into the negative charge. For a magnet, the field is defined as away from the N-pole of the magnet into the S-pole of the magnet.
        ■ Magnets exert attractive and repulsive forces on other magnets. Electric dipoles exert attractive and repulsive forces on other charges.
       ii. Differences between the magnetic field associated with the bar magnet and an electric dipole include:
        ■ An electric dipole can be separated into two point charges that are positive and negative. Breaking a magnet into two pieces results in two smaller magnets with N and S poles. Magnetic monopoles do not exist in nature.
        ■ Heating an electric dipole does nothing to the dipole, but heating a magnet reduces the magnetic properties since it puts random energy into the atoms of the

> magnetic material, reducing the alignment of the domains.

- ■ Conservation of charge applies to electrical dipoles but the conservation laws do not apply to magnets.
- ■ An electric dipole creates an electrical field that acts on any charge placed it in. The magnetic field of a magnet will only affect a moving charge placed in the field at some angle with a component perpendicular to the field. It will have no effect on a stationary charge or a charge moving parallel to the field.

(*College Physics* 9th ed. pages 648–651, 673–675/10th ed. pages 659–661, 685–687)
(L.O. 1.B.1.1, 1.B.3.1, 2.C.4.1, 2.D.1.1, 2.D.3.1)

15

Waves and Sound

Waves

(College Physics 9th ed. pages 455–456/10th ed. pages 464–465)

When a stone is dropped into a quiet pool of water, a disturbance is created where the stone enters the liquid. However the *disturbance* is not confined to the place of impact alone but spreads out so that it eventually reaches all parts of the pool. As the stone enters the water, it sets into motion the water molecules with which it comes into contact. These molecules set into motion neighboring molecules. They in turn produce similar motion in others, and so on, until the disturbance reaches water molecules at the edge of the pool. In this entire disturbance no molecules move far from their initial position. This is an example of a *mechanical* wave.

Only the disturbance moves through the water. This behavior is characteristic of all wave motions. The molecules move over short paths about their initial positions, and as a result a wave moves through the medium. *A mechanical wave is a disturbance that moves through a medium* in such a manner that at any point the displacement is a function of the time, while at any instant the displacement is a function of the position of the point. The medium as a whole does not progress in the direction of motion of the wave.

The motion of the wave through the medium is a result of the action of successive parts of the medium on each other. Such a wave can only travel in an *elastic medium*. If the molecules were entirely independent of each other, no waves could pass through.

There are several kinds of waves, their classification being made in accordance with the motion of the local part of the medium with respect to the direction of propagation. The most common types are *transverse* waves and *longitudinal* waves.

TRANSVERSE WAVES

(College Physics 9th ed. pages 456–463/10th ed. pages 465–472)

A sine wave is a repeating waveform that has amplitude, $\pm A$. The amplitude is the maximum displacement of the wave from equilibrium. The maximum positive displacement, $+A$, is called the crest of the wave. The negative displacement, $-A$, is the trough. The sine wave has a wavelength, λ. Wavelength is the distance between identical adjacent points on the wave. Distances are sometimes expressed in wavelengths.

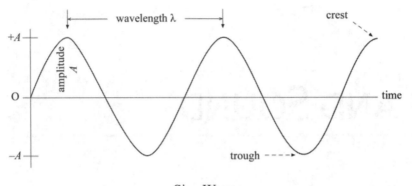

Sine Wave

In order for a mechanical wave to occur, it is necessary to have a *source* that produces a disturbance of some kind in an elastic medium through which the disturbance can be transmitted. An elastic medium behaves as if it were a succession of adjoining particles with each particle occupying an equilibrium position; if one of the particles is displaced, it is immediately subject to a restoring force as a result of interactions by neighboring particles, which in turn are subjected to reaction forces exerted by the original particle.

If one of the particles of the medium is given a sudden displacement by the source, this particle exerts forces on its immediate neighbors, which experience displacements; these immediately neighboring particles exert force on their neighbors, which also undergo displacements, and so on. In this way, the initial disturbance at the source causes a displacement wave to travel into the surrounding medium. Due to the inertia of the particles, the displacements of all particles do not take place at the same time; displacements far from the source occur later than the particles close to the source.

Consider a long, stretched string that is under tension, T, at the left. If the string is given a sudden upward displacement, a disturbance, the displaced portion of the string will exert forces tending to displace adjacent parts and at the same time will undergo forces tending to return the string to the undisturbed position. The result is a *pulse* that travels away from the disturbance.

The pulse, as shown below, travels with some velocity, v, to the right. The velocity is a function of the medium and the tension the string is under. Note that in I, II, III, and IV, it is the pulse that moves along the string.

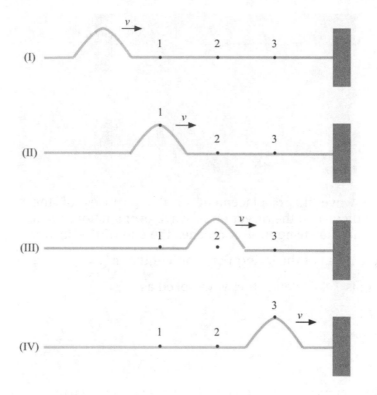

In VI and VII, the pulse collides with the barrier and is reversed in direction and the crest was inverted to become a trough. The wave travels with velocity –v to the left. The passage of a crest or a trough along a stretched string is an example of a *transverse* wave motion.

Note: When a wave reaches a rigid and fixed termination it will experience a phase inversion. At a loose termination the wave will rebound in phase.

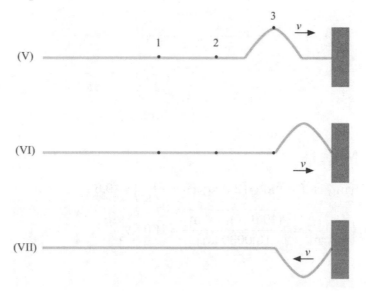

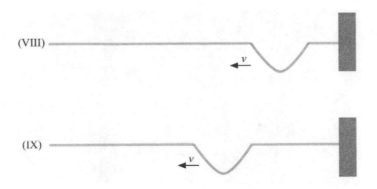

In a transverse wave the displacement of the particles of the medium are perpendicular to the direction of wave propagation. Each pulse will travel along the string until it reaches the end of the string.

Let μ represent the mass of the string per unit length, or $\mu = \dfrac{m}{L}$. The tension in the string is T. We define the wave speed as

$$v = \sqrt{\frac{T}{\mu}} = \sqrt{\frac{TL}{m}}$$

SAMPLE PROBLEM 1

A string 4.0 m in length has a mass of 3.0 g. The left end of the string is rigidly attached to a vertical wall. The other end hangs over a frictionless pulley with a 2.0 kg mass attached. What is the speed of a transverse wave in the string?

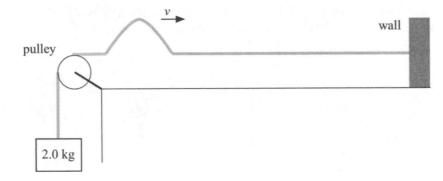

SOLUTION TO PROBLEM 1

The tension in the string is $T = mg = (2.0 \text{ kg})\left(9.8 \text{ m}/_{s^2}\right) = 19.6 \text{ N}$

The wave speed $v = \sqrt{\dfrac{TL}{m}} = \sqrt{\dfrac{(19.6 \text{ N})(4.0 \text{ m})}{(0.0030 \text{ kg})}} = 160 \text{ m}/_{s}$

LONGITUDINAL WAVES

(*College Physics* 9th ed. pages 456–459/10th ed. pages 465–468)

Another type of wave, which can occur in a helical coil, is shown below. Such a wave is called a *longitudinal wave*. In a longitudinal wave the displacements of the particles of the medium are parallel to the direction of propagation of the wave. Consider the stretched spring in diagram (a).

Suppose the left end of the spring is suddenly compressed by moving the end to the right. These coils exert forces on the adjacent coils, causing the compression to travel along the spring as a compression pulse. The speed of the wave is a function of the spring constant, k, and the mass per unit length, μ, of the spring. No part of the spring moves very far from its equilibrium position, but the longitudinal pulse continues to travel along the spring.

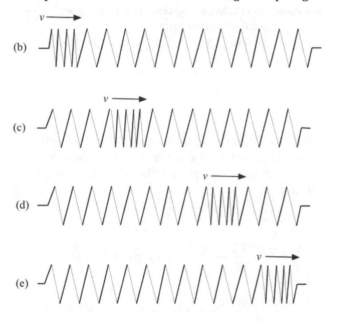

Note how the pulse travels along the spring to the right. The region where the coils are compressed is called a *condensation*. No part of the spring moves very far from its equilibrium position, but the pulse continues along the spring.

AP Tip

In a longitudinal wave the vibration of the individual particles is parallel to the direction of the wave propagation.

Had the coils on the left been forced apart, a *rarefaction* would have been formed. Upon removal of the force on the left, a longitudinal rarefaction pulse would have been propagated along the spring.

PROPERTIES OF WAVES

(*College Physics* 9th ed. pages 458–459/10th ed. pages 466–468)

Waves travel with a definite speed through a uniform medium. In wave motion, factors such as wave speed, wavelength, frequency, and amplitude must be considered. Some of these properties we have already discussed. Let us reiterate. The speed of a wave is the distance it advances per unit of time. The number of waves that pass a given point per unit time is called *frequency, f,* of the wave motion. The time it takes a single wave to pass a point is called the *period, T,* of the wave motion. The *wavelength, λ,* is the distance between two identical, adjacent points on the wave. The *amplitude, A,* of the wave is the maximum displacement from the equilibrium position.

When a wave passes from one medium into a second medium, the speed changes. In the process the frequency remains the same, but the wavelength changes in proportion to the wave speed; if v increases, λ also increases. This phenomenon is called *refraction*.

The relationship between wave speed, frequency, and wavelength are represented as

$$v = f\lambda$$

SAMPLE PROBLEM 2

A compression wave of frequency 250 Hz is set up in a steel rod and passes from the rod into the air. The speed of the wave in the steel rod is 4.88×10^3 m/s and 335.3 m/s in air. Determine the wavelength of the sound wave in both mediums.

SOLUTION TO PROBLEM 2

In steel the wavelength is $\lambda = \dfrac{v}{f} = \dfrac{4.88 \times 10^3 \text{ m/s}}{250 \text{ s}^{-1}} = \textbf{19.5 m}$

In air, the wavelength is $\lambda = \dfrac{v}{f} = \dfrac{335.3 \text{ m/s}}{250 \text{ s}^{-1}} = \textbf{1.3 m}$

SUPERPOSITION

(*College Physics* 9th ed. pages 461–463/10th ed. pages 470–472)

Suppose that two wave pulses, moments apart, are sent along a string that is under tension. The first wave, A, has been reflected and is on its way back and encounters the second oncoming wave, B. The two will interact. They are said to interfere. As they pass each other, their displacements will add and the displacement of the interfering waves is A + B. They simultaneously exist in the same medium, each wave traveling through the medium as though the other wave was not present. In the sense of propagation through the medium neither wave affects the other. However, at any point where two waves of the same kind reach simultaneously, the medium will have a displacement that is the *sum of the displacements of the individual waves*. If the two pulses are in phase, they will undergo *constructive interference*. When they are out of phase they suffer *destructive interference*.

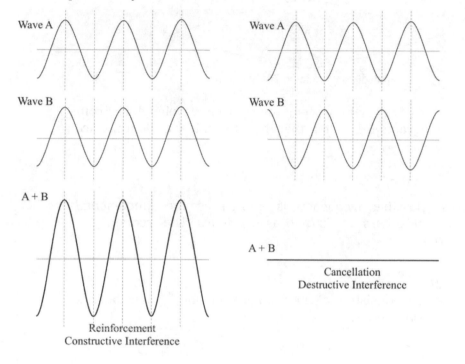

Wave A
Wave B
A + B
Reinforcement
Constructive Interference

Wave A
Wave B
A + B
Cancellation
Destructive Interference

STANDING WAVES

(*College Physics* 9th ed. pages 489–493/10th ed. pages 498–503)

Consider the waves set up by a vibrating string whose end points are fixed, as in the following diagrams. The fixed end points represent *boundary conditions* that restrict the possible wavelengths that produce standing waves. Two identical waves moving in opposite directions superimpose to produce a large amplitude *standing wave*. It is called a standing wave because it represents a pattern or oscillation with time in a fixed location. Points on a standing wave where there is no displacement are called *nodes*, N. Halfway between two consecutive nodes are points where displacement is a maximum. We call these points *antinodes*, A.

Standing waves can occur at more than one frequency. The frequencies at which standing waves are produced are called *resonance* or *natural frequencies*. The lowest frequency at which a standing wave is produced is called the *fundamental frequency*. It is also called the *first harmonic*. Other frequencies are called *overtones*.

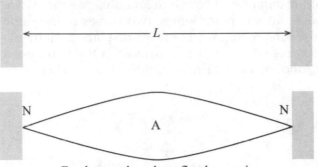

Fundamental mode or first harmonic.

Higher modes of oscillation occur for shorter wavelengths. From the following diagrams it is noted that the allowable wavelengths are given by

$$\lambda_n = \frac{2L}{n} \qquad n = 1, 2, 3, \cdots$$

The lowest possible frequency is known as the *fundamental frequency*, f_1. The others are known as *overtones*. The frequency is determined from

$$f_n = n\frac{v}{2L} \qquad n = 1, 2, 3, \cdots$$

The entire series consisting of the fundamental and its overtones is known as a *harmonic series*.

First overtone or second harmonic.

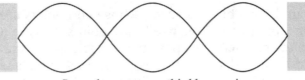

Second overtone or third harmonic.

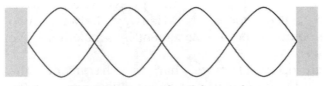

Third overtone or fourth harmonic.

SAMPLE PROBLEM 3

A 0.60 m long piece of steel piano wire has a mass of 10 g and is under a tension of 500 N. What is the frequency of its fundamental mode of vibration?

SOLUTION TO PROBLEM 3

The frequency of the fundamental standing wave is $f_n = n\dfrac{v}{2L}$. However we do not know the wave speed, v. Earlier we saw that the wave speed in a wire under tension is $v = \sqrt{\dfrac{TL}{m}}$. Combining equations gives

$$f_1 = \frac{n}{2L}\sqrt{\frac{TL}{m}} = \frac{1}{2(0.60\text{ m})}\sqrt{\frac{(500\text{ N})(0.60\text{ m})}{(0.010\text{ kg})}} = \textbf{144 Hz}$$

SOUND

(*College Physics* 9th ed. pages 473–478/10th ed. pages 481–485)

One of the most commonly observed types of mechanical waves is a sound wave. By means of a sound wave, tiny quantities of energy are carried to our ears and stimulate the nerves there to produce the sensation of sound. Usually the medium that transmits sound waves to our ears is the air that surrounds us. Air, as well as all gases, can transmit only longitudinal (compression) waves. As a sound travels it creates pressure and density variations in the air.

Although light and sound travel with a finite speed, the speed of light is so great in comparison that an instantaneous flash may be regarded as taking no time to travel many miles. When we see the light of a distant lightning flash we hear the sound of thunder later. The difference in time is due to the relatively low speed of sound.

As a general rule, sound travels faster in solids and liquids than it does in gases. Our air is a mixture of about 80% nitrogen and 20% oxygen. The speed of sound at sea-level, one atmosphere of pressure and 0°C is 341 m/s. The speed of sound increases as the temperature increases. The speed of sound can be approximated by

$$v = 331\,\text{m}/\text{s} + \left(0.6\,\frac{\text{m}/\text{s}}{\text{C}°}\right)t$$

where t is the temperature measured in °C.

When a sound wave strikes a large, smooth, rigid surface, it will be reflected. An observer may receive two impulses, the wave directly from the source and the reflected wave. Humans have a *persistence* of hearing of about 0.1 s. If the direct wave and the reflected wave arrive more than a tenth of a second apart, they are perceived as two distinct sounds, and the reflected wave is called an *echo*. If the difference between the arrival times is less than a tenth of a second, the sounds merge into a blurred *reverberation*.

Sound travels approximately 34 m in a tenth of a second. Since the reflected wave must travel to the reflecting surface and back to the observer, and if the observer is 17 or more meters away from the reflecting surface, the echo will not be heard. Rooms in ordinary homes pose no echo or reverberation problem because their dimensions are on the order of three to five meters. Auditoriums and theaters, however, must be designed to control echoes and reverberations. A sound once started in an auditorium or a large room will persist by repeated reflection from the walls until the sound intensity is reduced to the point where it can no longer be heard. The repeated reflection of sound that results is called reverberation.

Sonar (sound navigation and ranging) uses echoes in water to determine depth and distances to nearby ships. Sonar equipment has become so highly refined that it is ultra-sensitive to small objects on the sea bottom.

VIBRATING AIR COLUMNS

(*College Physics* 9th ed. pages 495–498/10th ed. pages 504–508)

Earlier in the chapter we described the possible modes of vibration for a string bound at both ends. Sound can also be produced by the longitudinal vibrations of a column of air in an open or closed pipe. As in a vibrating string, the possible modes of vibration are determined by the boundary conditions. When a compression wave is set up in a closed pipe, the displacement of the air molecules at the closed end must be zero.

AP Tip

The closed end of a pipe must be a displacement node.

Standing waves in air are longitudinal in character and they are difficult to represent with any drawing or diagram. For convenience only, it is customary to indicate the positions of nodes and antinodes as if they were transverse standing waves.

The various modes in which air columns may vibrate in open or closed pipes are shown in the following diagrams. With closed pipes, the lowest frequency is the fundamental, f_1, and the ones that follow are in odd multiples, $3f_1$, $5f_1$, $7f_1$, etc. No even-number harmonics can be sounded in a closed pipe. The wavelength of the standing wave will be $\lambda_n = \dfrac{4L}{n}$ and the frequency $f_n = \dfrac{nv}{4L}$.

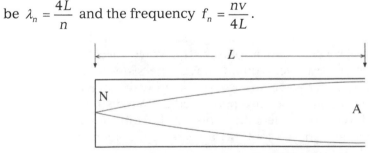

Fundamental mode or first harmonic.

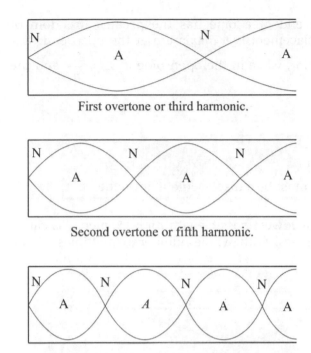

First overtone or third harmonic.

Second overtone or fifth harmonic.

Third overtone or seventh harmonic.

SAMPLE PROBLEM 4

Determine the frequencies of the fundamental and the first three overtones for a 14 cm long closed pipe on a day when the speed of sound is 342 m/s.

SOLUTION TO PROBLEM 4

First we need to find the fundamental and we do so by using $f_n = \dfrac{nv}{4L}$.

For the fundamental $n = 1$ and $f_n = \dfrac{nv}{4L} = \dfrac{1(342 \text{ m/s})}{4(0.14 \text{ m})} = \textbf{611 Hz}$.

The first, second and third overtones are the third, fifth and seventh harmonics.

First overtone $= nf_1 = 3(611 \text{ Hz}) = \textbf{1833 Hz}$

Second overtone $= nf_1 = 5(611 \text{ Hz}) = \textbf{3055 Hz}$

Third overtone $nf_1 = 7(611 \text{ Hz}) = \textbf{4277 Hz}$

AP Tip

Only the odd harmonics are allowed for a closed pipe.

The air at the open end of a pipe has the greatest freedom of motion, and so the displacement is a maximum at the open end. The wavelength of the standing wave in the open pipe is $\lambda_n = \dfrac{2L}{n}$ and the frequency is $f_n = \dfrac{nv}{2L}$.

AP Tip

The open end of a pipe must be a displacement antinode.

With an open pipe, the lowest possible vibration frequency is called the fundamental; the others, with whole-numbered multiples of the fundamental frequency, $2f_1$, $3f_1$, $4f_1$, etc., are possible harmonics.

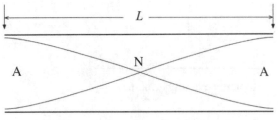

Fundamental mode or first harmonic.

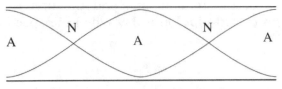

First overtone or second harmonic.

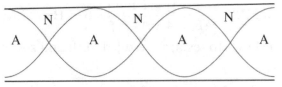

Second overtone or third harmonic.

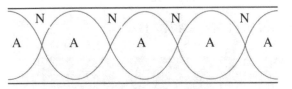

Third overtone or fourth harmonic.

Sample Problem 5

What is the speed of sound on a day when a 30 cm long open pipe has a frequency of 1200 Hz as its first overtone?

Solution to Problem 5

The first overtone in an open pipe is the second harmonic, so $n = 2$. For the second harmonic

$$f_n = \frac{nv}{2L} \text{ and solving for } v, \ v = Lf_2 = (0.30 \text{ m})(1200 \text{ Hz}) = \textbf{360 m/s}.$$

BEATS

(*College Physics* 9th ed. pages 499–500/10th ed. pages 508–509)

Consider two tuning forks whose frequencies differ only slightly in frequency. When they are struck simultaneously, they produce a sound that fluctuates in intensity, alternating between silence and a loud tone. The regular pulsations produced are called *beats*.

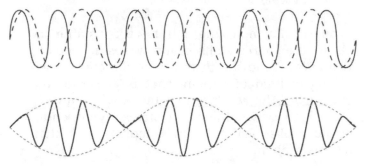

The superposition of the two sound waves produced by the vibrating tuning forks is the source of beats. The loud tones occur when the waves interfere constructively. The quiet tones are due to destructive interference. Observation shows that the number of beats, N, produced per second is given by the relationship $N = |f - f'|$. For example, tuning forks of frequencies 340 Hz and 343 Hz when struck simultaneously emit sound that pulsates 3 times per second.

THE DOPPLER EFFECT

(*College Physics* 9th ed. pages 482–486/10th ed. pages 491–494)

When a sound source is moving relative to an observer, the pitch of the sound heard by the observer will not be the same as when the source is at rest. As the source approached the observer, the listener will hear a higher pitch than the one produced when the source is at rest. As the sound source recedes, the pitch is observed to be lower.

This phenomenon is not restricted to the motion of the source. If the source is stationary, an observer moving toward the source will hear a similar rise in pitch. A moving observer leaving the sound source will hear a lower-pitched sound. The change in frequency due to relative motion between a source and observer is called the *Doppler effect.*

The Doppler effect refers to the apparent change in frequency of a source when there is relative motion of the source and the observer.

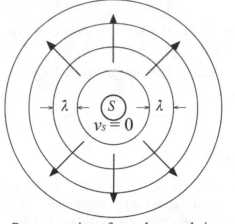

Representation of sound waves being
emitted from a stationary sound source *S*.

Consider the sound source moving to the right toward a stationary observer at location A. As the source emits sound waves, it tends to overtake the bunched up waves moving in the same direction. Each successive sound wave is emitted at a point that is closer to the observer than its predecessor. The result is that the wavelength, λ, keeps shrinking as the sound waves bunch. A smaller wavelength means a higher frequency. Observer A hears a higher pitch than observer B who hears a lower pitch.

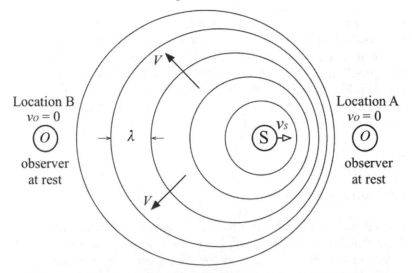

The waves show a Doppler shift. The waves in front of a moving
sound source are closer together than the waves behind the source.

V is the velocity of sound and f_s is the frequency of the sound source. The frequency the observer hears if f_o. The source moves with velocity v_s.

The velocity of sound in air is a function of the properties of air and is independent of the motion of the source. The frequency heard by a stationary observer from a moving sound source is given by

$$f_O = \frac{Vf_S}{V - v_S}$$

Where V is the velocity of sound, f_S is the frequency of the sound source, the frequency as heard by the observer is f_O and the speed of the sound source is v_S.

When the source is stationary, and the observer moves toward the source with speed v_O, the frequency heard by the observer is

$$f_O = \frac{f_S(V + v_O)}{V}$$

SAMPLE PROBLEM 6

A train whistle emits a sound with a frequency of 420 Hz. If the speed of sound is 336 m/s,

(a) what is the frequency of the sound heard by a stationary observer as the train moves toward that observer with a speed of 25 m/s?

(b) what frequency is heard as the train moves away from the observer at the same speed?

SOLUTION TO PROBLEM 6

(a) The train approaches the observer making its speed positive. The frequency is given by

$$f_O = \frac{Vf_S}{V - v_S} = \frac{\left(336 \ ^m\!/_s\right)\left(420 \ s^{-1}\right)}{\left(336 \ ^m\!/_s - 25 \ ^m\!/_s\right)} = \textbf{454 Hz}$$

(b) As the train recedes its velocity becomes negative making $v_S = -25 \ ^m\!/_s$, and the frequency heard is found by

$$f_O = \frac{Vf_S}{V - v_S} = \frac{\left(336 \ ^m\!/_s\right)\left(420 \ s^{-1}\right)}{\left[\left(340 \ ^m\!/_s\right) - \left(-25 \ ^m\!/_s\right)\right]} = \textbf{387 Hz}$$

If both the sound source and the observer are moving, the frequency heard by the observer becomes

$$f_O = f_S \frac{V + v_O}{V - v_S}$$

WAVES AND SOUND: STUDENT OBJECTIVES FOR THE AP EXAM

- ▣ You should be able to explain why the velocity of transverse waves differs from the velocity of longitudinal waves in a given medium.
- ▣ You should be able to explain why longitudinal waves can propagate in a gas but transverse waves cannot.
- ▣ You should be able to explain why waves of different frequencies may have different velocities in a given medium.
- ▣ You should be able to explain why increasing the tension in a string increases the velocity of the transverse waves.
- ▣ You should be able to discuss how interference could result from the overlapping of two waves with somewhat different amplitudes.
- ▣ You should be able to explain the phenomenon of beat frequency.
- ▣ You should be able to explain why a cold organ pipe plays flat.
- ▣ You should be able to determine frequencies in open and closed pipes.
- ▣ You should be able to explain the Doppler effect.

MULTIPLE-CHOICE QUESTIONS

1. Two transverse waves (1) and (2) travel with the same speed.

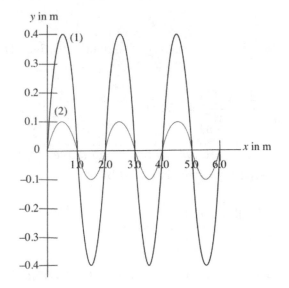

Which of the following choices is a correct statement?
(A) Both waves (1) and (2) have equal amplitudes; however, the wavelength of (1) is four times larger than the wavelength of (2).
(B) The waves have the same amplitude, but the wavelength of (1) is 0.4 m and the wavelength of (2) is 0.1 m.
(C) Both (1) and (2) have equal wavelength; however, the frequency of (1) is four times greater than the frequency of (2).
(D) Both (1) and (2) have equal wavelengths; however, the amplitude of wave (2) is one-fourth that of wave (1).

For questions 2 and 3, refer to the diagram below depicting the displacement of a vibrating string versus the position along the string at a particular instant. The wave on the string has a speed of 0.10 m/s.

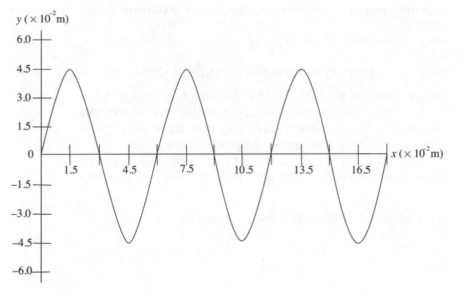

2. Using the diagram above, what is the correct wavelength of the wave?
    (A) 3×10^{-2} m
    (B) 6×10^{-2} m
    (C) 9×10^{-2} m
    (D) 12×10^{-2} m

3. What is the correct frequency of the wave indicated in the above diagram?
    (A) 0.06 Hz
    (B) 0.09 Hz
    (C) 1.11 Hz
    (D) 1.67 Hz

4. A transverse pulse is formed when a rope that is firmly attached at its ends between two barriers is pulled downward near one end and released. The pulse travels to the other end and the reflected pulse's amplitude is
    (A) inverted and none of the energy of the pulse is transferred to the barrier
    (B) inverted and some of the pulse's energy is transferred to the barrier
    (C) not inverted and none of the energy of the pulse is transferred to the barrier
    (D) is not inverted and some of the energy of the pulse is transferred to the barrier

5. Standing waves are produced in a string by the interference of two waves that have the same
   (A) frequency and amplitude moving in the same direction
   (B) amplitude moving in the same direction but with different frequencies
   (C) frequency and moving in opposite directions with different amplitudes
   (D) amplitude and frequency but moving in opposite directions

6. Several physics students performed an experiment to determine the speed of sound in the laboratory using a closed resonance tube that uses water to establish the length of the tube. By adjusting the water level in the resonance tube they had two consecutive resonance points that were 18.0 cm and 54.0 cm from the open end when they sounded a 460.0 Hz tuning fork over the air column in the tube.

   The velocity of sound they should have obtained for their experiment was
   (A) 318 m/s
   (B) 325 m/s
   (C) 331 m/s
   (D) 348 m/s

7. A pulse in a rope approaches a fixed boundary as shown in the illustration below.

   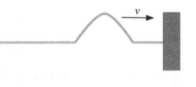

   Which of the four choices shows the correct motion for the reflected wave?

   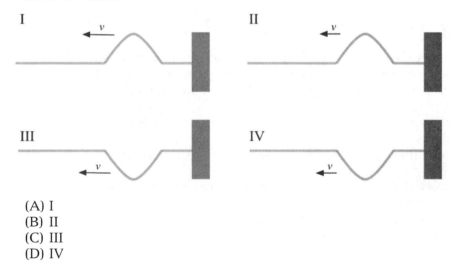

   (A) I
   (B) II
   (C) III
   (D) IV

8. Four waves are illustrated below. Rank the waves in order of energy from the greatest to the least.

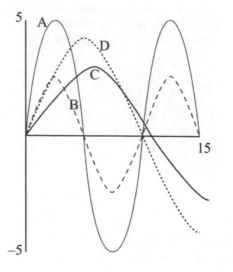

(A) B > C > D > A
(B) A > D > C > B
(C) D > C > A = B
(D) D > C > A > B

9. A 5.0 m cord is attached to a fixed support at one end and the other end is under tension from a weight handing over a pulley. A standing wave with 5 nodes is set up in the cord. If the velocity of the transverse wave is 15.0 m/s, what is the frequency of the wave?
(A) 3 Hz
(B) 6 Hz
(C) 9 Hz
(D) 12 Hz

10. If you increase the displacement amplitude for a given frequency of sound, the energy and the momentum of the wave carried by the cord will
(A) increase causing the wave to travel faster in the medium
(B) increase but the wave will slow as it moves through the medium
(C) only increase the speed of the wave in the medium but not change the energy or the momentum carried by the wave
(D) increase the momentum and energy carried by the wave which will continue to travel at the same speed in the medium

11. Sounds from a speaker radiate outward from the speaker in spherical waves. Two speakers producing sounds at the same frequency will produce spherical wave fronts that interfere with each other much like the interference pattern produced in water by two point sources oscillating with the same frequency.

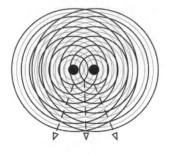

The nodal lines represent
(A) constructive interference of the waves
(B) destructive interference of the waves
(C) the amplitude of the wave
(D) the frequency of the wave

12. Students in a physics laboratory were experimenting with a resonance column over water and a tuning fork with a frequency of 520 Hz on a day when the speed of sound in the room is 343 m/s. By lowering the level of water in the tube, the fifth harmonic was heard. What was the length of the air column above the water?
(A) 16.5 cm
(B) 33.0 cm
(C) 66.0 cm
(D) 82.5 cm

13. You are stopped in your car at an intersection when a fire truck passes you, sounding its siren. The wave front produced by the moving fire truck passing you is illustrated in the diagram below.

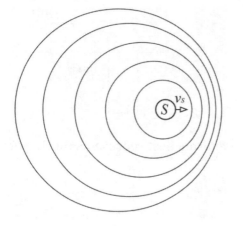

The frequency of the siren will
(A) decrease as the fire truck approaches and increase as it moves past you
(B) increase as the fire truck approaches and decrease as it moves past you
(C) will remain constant
(D) produce a resonance pattern as it passes you

14. Two sound wave forms are illustrated below.

The combined waveform produces beats.

How many beats per second will an observer hear?
(A) 3
(B) 5
(C) 8
(D) 12

15. Two rectangular waves A and B approach each other, as shown in the illustration shown below.

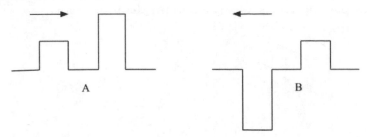

Which of the resulting waveforms best represents the interference of the two?

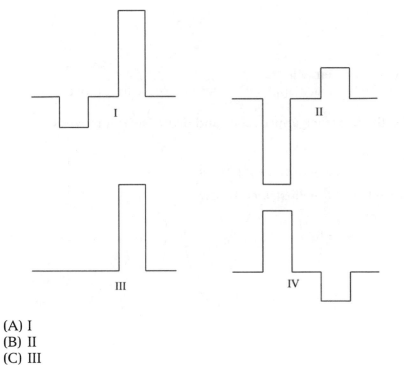

(A) I
(B) II
(C) III
(D) IV

FREE-RESPONSE PROBLEMS

1. Points on the transverse wave shown below are indicated.

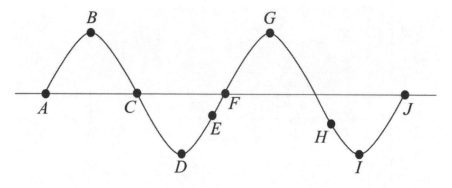

(a) Indicate the points that are
   i.   in phase. Explain your reasoning.
   ii. out of phase by $\lambda/4$. Explain your reasoning.
   iii. out of phase by $\lambda/2$. Explain your reasoning.

(b) Using the waveforms shown in Figure (1)

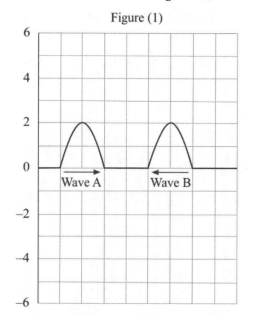

Figure (1)

i. Draw the superimposed waveforms as they pass through each other on the grid given below.

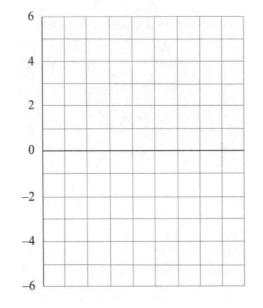

Using the waveforms shown in Figure (2)

Figure (2)

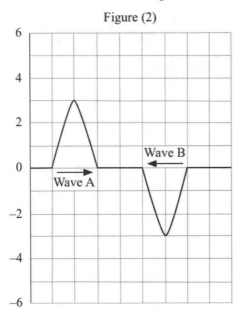

ii. Draw the superimposed waveforms as they pass through each other on the grid given below.

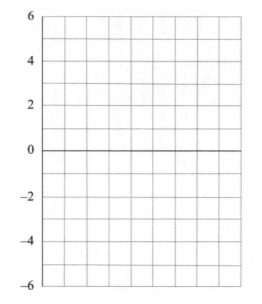

Using the waveforms show in Figure (3)

Figure (3)

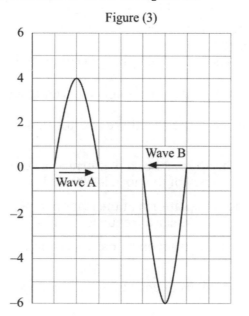

iii. Draw the superimposed waveforms as they pass through each other on the grid given below.

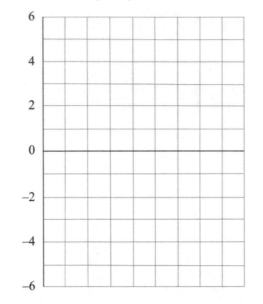

2. (a) On a day when the speed of sound is 343.0 $\frac{m}{s}$, what is the frequency of the fundamental in a pipe 2.50 m long when one end of the pipe is closed?
   (b) What are the frequencies of the first three overtones of this pipe?
   (c) If both ends of the pipe are opened, what is the frequency of the fundamental?
   (d) What are the frequencies of the first three overtones of the open pipe?

3. A train traveling at 50 km/hr approaches a platform at a station, sounding its horn. The frequency of the horn is 900 Hz.

   (a) As the train approaches the platform at the station, a person standing on the platform will hear a frequency that is

   _____ higher than the frequency that was produced by the train horn

   _____ lower than the frequency that was produced by the train horn

   _____ the same frequency as was produced by the train horn

   Justify your answer qualitatively without equations or calculations.

(b) As the train recedes from the platform of the station, a person standing on the platform will hear a frequency that is

_____ higher than the frequency that was produced by the train horn

_____ lower than the frequency that was produced by the train horn

_____ the same frequency as was produced by the train horn

Justify your answer qualitatively without equations or calculations.

(c) A passenger on the train will hear a frequency that is

_____ higher than the frequency that was produced by the train horn

_____ lower than the frequency that was produced by the train horn

_____ the same frequency as was produced by the train horn

(d) Sketch a wave front diagram that will illustrate how the apparent wavelength is related to the relative motion of the source and the stationary observer. Correctly label the wavelengths for approach and recession.

4. Design a laboratory experiment to determine the relationship between the wavelength, frequency, and velocity of a standing wave in a string. You have available a string, pulley and clamps, mass hanger, masses, meter stick, and an electrical string vibrator of constant frequency (120 Hz) as well as a platform balance.
    (a) Describe your experimental procedure in enough detail so that another student could perform your experiment and obtain results to determine the relationship between the wavelength and frequency. Include any measurement that you will take and how you will use these measurements.
    (b) Describe how you will use the measurements to determine the frequency of the electrical vibrator used to produce the standing wave in enough detail that another student could duplicate your method of determining the frequency.
    (c) What assumption did you make about the design of the experiment that might affect your results in determining the frequency? How might this assumption alter your results?
    (d) If you graphed your results, what would you graph? What would be the shape of the line?

Answers

MULTIPLE-CHOICE QUESTIONS

1. **D** Amplitude is the maximum displacement from the equilibrium position. From the scale, wave 1 has amplitude of about 0.4 m and wave 2 has amplitude of about 0.1 m. Their wavelengths are the same and since they travel with the same speed, their frequencies are the same.
(*College Physics* 9th ed. pages 458–459/10th ed. pages 466–467)
(L.O. 6.A.3.1)

2. **B** The wavelength is the distance between two points that have the same amplitude and are in phase with each other (moving in the same direction). From the graph this is 6×10^{-2} m .
(*College Physics* 9th ed. pages 458–459/10th ed. pages 466–467)
(L.O. 6.B.2.1)

3. **D** Frequency is determined using $v = \lambda f$. The frequency
is $f = \dfrac{0.10 \text{ m}/\text{s}}{0.06 \text{ m}} = 1.67$ Hz .
(*College Physics* 9th ed. pages 458–459/10th ed. pages 466–467)
(L.O. 6.B.1.1)

4. **B** When the incident pulse strikes a fixed barrier the wave is inverted (180°). Energy is always transferred to the medium of the barrier.
(*College Physics* 9th ed. pages 461–463/10th ed. pages 470–472)
(L.O. 6.B.1.1)

5. **D** Standing waves are produced by waves that have the same frequency and amplitude but move in opposite directions producing points where the displacement is always zero (nodes) and antinodes where the displacement is a maximum.
(*College Physics* 9th ed. pages 489–498/10th ed. pages 498–500)
(L.O. 6.D.3.4)

6. **C** The open end of the tube is an antinode and the closed end is a node. The fundamental wavelength is $\lambda = 4L$. If the first resonance is heard at 18.0 cm, the wavelength is 0.72 m.

The speed of sound is then $v = \lambda f = (0.72 \text{ m})(460.0 \text{ Hz}) = 331 \text{ m}/\text{s}$.

The second resonance pattern that occurred at $L = \dfrac{3}{4}\lambda$. The

wavelength is $\lambda = \dfrac{4}{3}(0.54 \text{ m}) = 0.72$ m and produced the same

velocity.
(*College Physics* 9th ed. pages 495–498/10th ed. pages 504–506)
(L.O. 6.D.3.1)

7. **C** Since the pulse strikes a fixed barrier it is reflected 180° out of phase. It returns with the same speed since speed is determined by

the medium in which the pulse travels. When a pulse transfers energy, its amplitude decreases.
(*College Physics* 9th ed. pages 461–463/10th ed. pages 470–472)
(L.O. 6.D.1.1)

8. **B** The energy carried by a wave is related to its amplitude. In the illustration the amplitude of wave A is ± 5 units on the vertical axis, followed by D, C, and then B.
(*College Physics* 9th ed. pages 458, 460/10th ed. pages 466, 468)
(L.O. 6.A.4.1)

9. **B** Since the cord is under tension and supports a standing wave that has 5 nodes, the wavelength is 2.5 m (the ends of the cords must be nodes). Since the velocity of the wave is 15.0 m/s the frequency is found from $v = \lambda f$ and $f = \dfrac{15.0 \text{ m/s}}{2.5 \text{ m}} = 6 \text{ Hz}$.
(*College Physics* 9th ed. pages 458, 489–493/10th ed. pages 467, 498–501)
(L.O. 6.D.4.2)

10. **D** Increasing the amplitude of vibration of a sound wave for a given frequency will increase the energy and the momentum of the particle that is displaced from the equilibrium. As the wave moves out from the disturbance, the energy is carried with it, but not the medium. The speed of the wave will not change since the speed is determined by the medium.
(*College Physics* 9th ed. pages 476–478/10th ed. pages 484–487)
(L.O. 6.A.2.1)

11. **B** The nodal lines indicate regions were no displacement from the equilibrium occurs.
(*College Physics* 9th ed. pages 481–482, 826/10th ed. pages 498–500, 837)
(L.O. 6.D.2.1)

12. **D** The tube is closed at one end; therefore only the odd harmonics are heard. The fundamental will be used to determine the length of the tube $520 \text{ Hz} = \dfrac{343 \text{ m/s}}{4L}$ and $L = 0.165 \text{ m}$ and then $\lambda = 4L = 0.66 \text{ m}$.

The fifth harmonic corresponds to the third resonance position.

The length of the air column for this resonance is $L = \dfrac{5}{4}\lambda$. This length is 0.825 m = 82.5 cm.
(*College Physics* 9th ed. pages 495–498/10th ed. pages 504–508)
(L.O. 6.D.4.2)

13. **B** The Doppler effect relates the apparent frequency to the actual frequency due to relative motion between the source and the observer. When the source moves toward a stationary observer, the wave fronts crowd together. As a result the stationary observer measures a smaller wavelength and thus a higher frequency. As the source moves away from the stationary

observer, the observer measures a longer wavelength and therefore a lower frequency.
(*College Physics* 9th ed. pages 482–485/10th ed. pages 491–495)
(L.O. 6.B.1.1)

14. **A** Two waveforms played at the same time will interfere with each other. Superposition tells us that variations in amplitudes will occur as the resulting wave oscillates in time. This variation produces "beats." The beat frequency is the difference in the frequencies of the waveforms. $f_{beats} = |f_2 - f_1|$

(*College Physics* 9th ed. pages 499–500/10th ed. pages 508–509)
(L.O. 6.D.5.1)

15. **A** Superposition principle applies to the combined waveform of A + B. Amplitudes must be added. When the leading edge of B combines with A, the amplitudes are + 1 for A and –2 for B as estimated from the diagram. The amplitude of the combination is –1. The trailing edge's addition is + 2 from A and + 1 from B for a total of +3.
(*College Physics* 9th ed. pages 461–462/10th ed. pages 470–472)
(L.O. 6.D.1.1, 6.D.2.1)

FREE-RESPONSE PROBLEMS

1. (a) i. The points on the transverse that are in phase are AFJ, BG, and DI.
   Points on the waveform that have the same amplitude or angular displacement and are moving with the same relative velocity are in phase.

   ii. Points that are out of phase by $\lambda/4$ or 90° are AB, BC, CD, DF, FG, and JI.
   These points are easy to locate since they have either amplitude $A = 0$ or $A = $ maximum displacement.

   iii. Points that are out of phase by $\lambda/2$ or 180° are AC, BD, CF, DG, GI.
   These points have the same amplitude but are moving in opposite directions as the wave passes through them.

(b) i. The two waves will superimpose with constructive interference. The combined amplitude when they are vertically aligned will be $y = +4$ units.

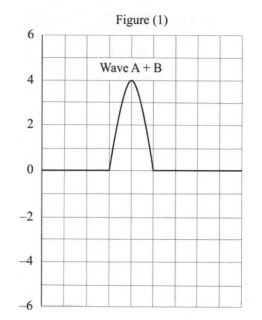

Figure (1)

ii. The two waves will superimpose with totally destructive interference. The combined amplitude when they are vertically aligned will be $y = 0$ units.

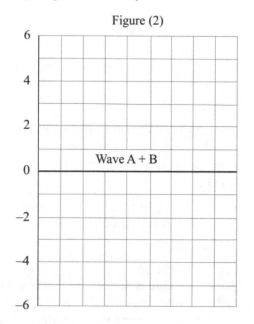

Figure (2)

iii. The two waves will superimpose for partial interference. The combined amplitude when they are vertically aligned will be $y = -2$ units .

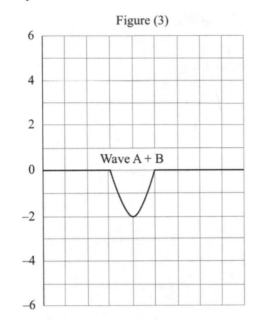

Figure (3)

(*College Physics* 9th ed. pages 461–463/10th ed. pages 470–472)
(L.O. 6.A.3.1, 6.B.2.1, 6.D.1.1, 6.D.2.1)

2. (a) If the pipe is closed at one end, the fundamental wave length is $\lambda = 4L$.
The wavelength is = $\lambda = 4(2.50 \text{ m}) = 10.0 \text{ m}$. Since $v = \lambda f$, the fundamental frequency is $f = \dfrac{343.0 \text{ m/s}}{10.0 \text{ m}} = \textbf{34 Hz}$. The frequency can be calculated in one step from $f_n = n\dfrac{v}{4L}$.

(b) If the pipe is closed at one end only the odd harmonics will be heard. The frequencies of the first three overtones are $f_3 = 3f_1$, $f_5 = 5f_1$ and $f_7 = 7f_1$. The frequencies are $f_3 = \textbf{102 Hz}$, $f_5 = \textbf{170 Hz}$ and $f_7 = \textbf{238 Hz}$.

(c) If the pipe is open at both ends, the fundamental wavelength is $\lambda = 2L$. The wavelength $\lambda = 2(2.50 \text{ m}) = 5.00 \text{ m}$ and the fundamental frequency is $f = \dfrac{343.0 \text{ m/s}}{5.00 \text{ m}} = \textbf{68.6 Hz}$.

(d) The pipe closed at both ends produces all the harmonics. The frequencies for the first three overtones are $f_2 = 2f_1$, $f_3 = 3f_1$, and $f_4 = 4f_1$. The frequencies are $f_2 = \textbf{137 Hz}$, $f_3 = \textbf{206 Hz}$ and $f_4 = 273.6 \text{ Hz} = \textbf{274 Hz}$.

(*College Physics* 9th ed. pages 495–498/10th ed. pages 504–506)
(L.O. 6.D.3.2, 6.D.4.2)

3. The Doppler effect relates the higher frequency heard by a stationary observer as a source approaches and the lower frequency heard when the source moves away from the observer. This relationship holds for a stationary source and a moving observer as well as both observer and source moving relative to each other.

   (a) ____√____ increase in frequency

   If both the source and observer are stationary, the observer hears the same frequency as the source because there is no change in the wavelength. As the source moves toward a stationary observer, the observer detects wave fronts that are closer together because the source is moving in the direction or prior fronts. The observer hears a higher frequency because the wave fronts crowd together producing a shorter wavelength than the sound from the source.

   (b) ____√____ decrease in frequency

   As the source moves away from a stationary observer, the observer detects longer wavelengths. The source is moving away from prior wave fronts increasing the distance between the fronts of the wave. The observer hears a lower frequency because the wave fronts have spread apart.

   (c) ____√____ no change in frequency

   The passenger in the train is moving with the same speed as the train. There is no relative motion between the two. Hence the passenger hears a 900 Hz frequency.

   (d) The diagram is shown below.

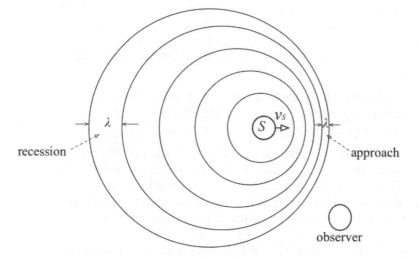

   (*College Physics* 9th ed. pages 482–486/10th ed. pages 491–494)
   (L.O. 6.B.5.1)

4. A standing wave set up in the string is dependent on the wave speed and the wavelength. Knowing these two values, the frequency of the waveform can be obtained by substitution into.

   $v = \lambda f$

   (a) 1. Measure the length of the entire string that will be used for the experiment.

      Determine the mass of the entire string and record both values.

2. Determine the linear mass density of the string. The linear mass density is its mass per unit length. Record the value.

3. Attach one end of the string to the string vibrator, and pass the other end over a pulley that you have clamped 1.00 m from the string vibrator. Attach a mass hanger to the string and add masses until you have the fundamental form of vibration for the standing wave in the string. Record the mass of the mass hanger and the masses on the hanger.

4. Measure the distance between the nodes. Since this is the fundamental, there are two nodes, one at each end of the string that is under tension. Record this value.

5. The fundamental wavelength is twice the length of the string between the nodes. Record this value.

6. Repeat for experiment by changing the tension on the string, setting up standing waves with 3, 4, and 5 nodes. This requires removing mass from the hanger.

(b) 1. The fundamental wavelength is twice the length of the string between the nodes.

2. The velocity of the wave is determined by taking the square root of the tension in the string divided by the linear mass density of the string. (The tension on the string is the weight of the mass hanger and the masses on the hanger.)

3. Determine the frequency by dividing the velocity of the wave in the string by the wavelength.

(c) If the distance for the fundamental was incorrectly measured, the wavelength is wrong. The string must be measured from the point where it is attached to the vibrator to the point where the string passes over the pulley (at its axle). If it is measured to the end of the pulley, the length is too long. Then, the wavelength is too large and the frequency will be smaller than it should be.

If the amplitude of vibration of the standing wave was not as large as possible, then the tension on the string was not accurate and the velocity of the wave is not accurate.

If the string stretched during the experiment, the linear mass density would decrease and the calculated velocity would increase. Thus the experimental frequency would decrease.

(d) A graph of wavelength as a function of the square root of the tension in the string should be plotted. The graph should be linear.

(*College Physics* 9th ed. pages 458–461, 489–493/10th ed. pages 469–470, 499–501)

(L.O. 6.D.1.2, 6.D.3.1 6.D.3.3, 6.D.4.2)

16

GEOMETRICAL OPTICS

REFLECTION OF LIGHT

(College Physics 9th ed. pages 762–765/10th ed. pages 774–776)

When light strikes the boundary between two media, such as air and glass, some of the incident light on the glass surface is reflected, and some of it will pass into the glass. The light entering the glass will be partially transmitted and partially absorbed. If the light enters the glass obliquely, the transmitted light undergoes a change in direction, called *refraction*.

Reflection is the ability of light to seemingly bounce off a surface. This phenomenon does not reveal the wave nature of light, and the notion of frequency or wavelength rarely enters into a description of reflection. If light is incident on a flat mirror, then the angle of incidence is measured with respect to a line perpendicular to the surface of the mirror called the *normal*. The light reflected at the surface obeys the *laws of reflection*:

1. The angle of incidence equals the angle of reflection.

2. The incident ray, the reflected ray, and the normal to the surface are all in the same plane.

Reflection helps explain the colors of opaque objects. Ordinary light contains many different colors all blended together to form white light. A red object looks red because of the selective reflection of red light due to the molecular make-up of the surface of the object. White objects reflect practically all the light incident on it. Black absorbs practically all the light falling on it. If light of a single wavelength can be isolated then it is said to be *monochromatic*.

Light in a medium exhibits the following behaviors:

1. The velocity of light in free space is the same for all colors.

2. The velocity of light in any medium is always less than its velocity in a vacuum.

3. The velocity of blue light in a given medium is less than the velocity of red light in that medium.

When a light ray is incident upon a reflective material, it is a simple demonstration to show that the angle of the incoming ray, called the *angle of incidence*, θ_i, equals the angle of the outgoing ray, the *angle of reflection*, θ_r. Known as the law of reflection, this occurs because, even though light travels in a straight path until it encounters a boundary, light exhibits particle-like properties, approximately analogous to the path of a linearly projected object. The convention for measuring the angles is to use a line that is perpendicular to the surface boundary that is called a *normal, N*. When reflection occurs, the incident and reflected rays remain in the same medium, in contrast to refraction, which will be discussed shortly.

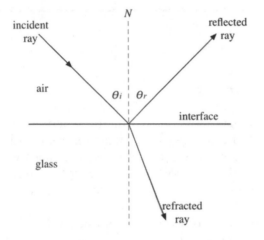

It is convenient to identify and distinguish between two kinds of reflection called *diffuse* and *specular*. In the case of diffuse reflection, light incident upon a surface is scattered in all directions, whereas in the case of specular reflection, as for light incident upon a polished, mirror-like surface, light is reflected symmetrically with an angle of incidence equal to the angle of reflection.

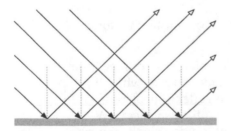

Specular reflection: parallel rays incident on a smooth surface remain parallel after being reflected.

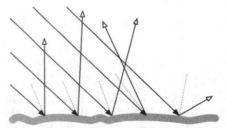

Diffuse reflection: parallel rays incident on a rough surface are no longer parallel after being reflected.

PLANE MIRRORS

(*College Physics* 9th ed. pages 790–793/10th ed. pages 801–804)

When you look at yourself in a plane mirror, your image appears to be directly in front of you and on the other side of the mirror. Everything about your image is the same as you except for a left-to-right reversal. No light originates from the other side of the plane mirror; it is for this reason your image is called *virtual*. A *virtual image* is one that seems to be formed by light coming from the image, but no rays of light actually pass through it, where a *real image* is formed by actual rays of light that pass through it. Real images can be projected on a screen. Since virtual images are not formed by real light rays, they cannot be projected on a screen.

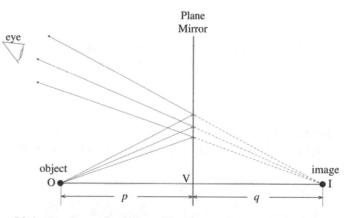

Light rays leave the object, O, and are reflected by the mirror. The eye, which assumes that they have traveled in a straight line, sees them as coming from the object.

SUMMARY OF THE PROPERTIES OF IMAGES IN PLANE MIRRORS

1. The images are upright and virtual.
2. The height of the image, h', is equal to the object height h.
3. The image distance, q, is equal to the object distance, p.
4. The images formed in a plane mirror are *perverted*, or reversed, right for left.

SPHERICAL MIRRORS

(College Physics 9th ed. pages 793–801/10th ed. pages 804–812)

Spherical mirrors are sections of a sphere. If the inside surface, the concave surface, is polished, the mirror is called a *concave mirror*. If the outside surface, the convex surface, is polished then the mirror is called a *convex mirror*. The *center of curvature*, C, is the center of the sphere of radius, R, of which the mirror is a section. The straight line connecting the center of curvature and the midpoint of the mirror is called the *mirror axis* or the *principal axis*. The diameter of a concave mirror, AB, is called the *aperture*. Most spherical mirrors used for optical purposes have apertures that are small compared with their radii of curvature.

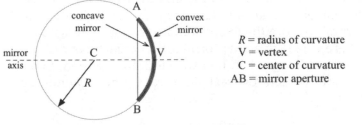

R = radius of curvature
V = vertex
C = center of curvature
AB = mirror aperture

Definition of Terms in Spherical Mirrors

The distance of the focal point, F, from the surface of the mirror is called the *focal length, f*. For a concave mirror, the focal length is positive and is

$$f = \frac{R}{2}$$

Images of objects formed by spherical mirrors can be located by either graphical or mathematical methods, both of which we will consider.

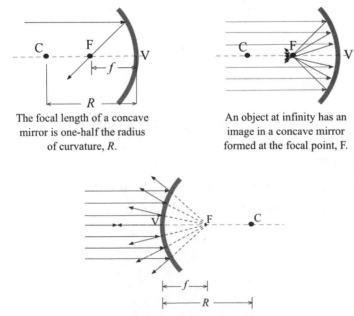

The focal length of a concave mirror is one-half the radius of curvature, *R*.

An object at infinity has an image in a concave mirror formed at the focal point, F.

The Focal Point of a Convex Mirror.

CONCAVE MIRRORS

(College Physics 9th ed. pages 793–801/10th ed. pages 804–812)

The concave mirror is an optical device that, like a glass lens, may by reflection form images on a screen.

It is necessary to adopt a set of conventions in order that algebraic signs may have physical significance. It is absolutely necessary to follow through consistently. Sign conventions cannot be changed in the middle of an analysis or a problem.

SUGGESTED SIGN CONVENTIONS FOR MIRRORS

(College Physics 9th ed. pages 795–800/10th ed. pages 806–812)

1. Always draw or sketch diagrams with light passing from left to right. Always place the object to the left of the spherical surface being studied.

2. Assume the object distance, p, to be positive when the object lies to the left of the vertex, V, of the mirror.

3. The image distance, q, is positive when the image lies to the left of the vertex and negative when it lies to the right of the vertex.

4. Consider the radius of curvature, R, to be positive when the image center lies to the left of the vertex.

5. Indicate the height of the object by h and consider it positive when it points downward. Let the image size be represented by h', which is also positive if it is upright and negative if it is inverted.

6. Note that the magnification $M = 1$ means the image has the same size as the object. Diminution, $M < 1$, does not mean negative magnification, but fractional magnification. Negative magnification merely means that the image is inverted with respect to the object.

RAY TRACING FOR SPHERICAL MIRRORS

(College Physics 9th ed. pages 795–800/10th ed. pages 806–809)

Ray tracing is a method for drawing and understanding the formation of images formed by spherical mirrors. Ray tracing consists of considering the reflections of a few rays diverging from some point on an object, O, that is not on the principal axis of the mirror. The point where the reflected rays intersect determines the location of the image. Starting at the head of the object, we work with three rays whose paths are easily traced.

- ■ *Ray 1:* A ray parallel to the principal axis of the mirror passes through the focal point of the concave mirror, or seems to come from the focal point of a convex mirror.
- ■ *Ray 2:* A ray that passes through the focal point of a concave mirror or proceeds toward the focal point of a convex mirror is reflected parallel to the principal axis of the mirror.

■ *Ray 3:* A ray that proceeds along the radius of the mirror is reflected back along its original path.

In any particular analysis or problem, only two of the rays are necessary to locate the image of the object. By choosing rays from an extreme point of the object, the remainder of the image can be filled in by symmetry. In the diagrams, virtual rays and virtual images are represented by dotted lines.

Consider the following cases where images are formed by converging mirrors.

Case 1 illustrates the image that is formed by an object, O, that is located beyond the center of curvature, C, of the mirror. The image is *real, inverted,* and *diminished* in size.

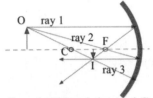

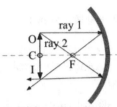

Case 1: Object is beyond C, the image is real, inverted, diminished in size, and is between F and C.

Case 2: Object is at C, the image is real, inverted, the same size, and is at C.

Case 2 shows that the object is located at the center of curvature. The concave mirror forms an image at the center of curvature that is *real, inverted,* and the *same size* as the object.

Case 3 positions the object between the center of curvature and the focal point. Ray tracing shows the image is located beyond the center of curvature. The image is *real, inverted,* and *larger* than the object.

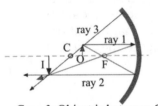

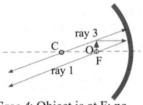

Case 3: Object is between C and F, the image is real, inverted, enlarged, and is beyond C.

Case 4: Object is at F; no image appears.

Case 4 places the object at the focal point, F. All reflected rays are parallel and never intersect. No image is formed or the image distance is infinite.

Case 5 locates the object inside the focal point, F. The image appears to be behind the mirror. The image is *virtual, enlarged,* and *upright.*

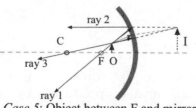

Case 5: Object between F and mirror surface, the image is virtual, upright, and is enlarged.

CONVEX MIRRORS

(*College Physics* 9th ed. pages 793–801/10th ed. pages 804–812)

For a convex mirror, the focal length is negative. The negative sign means that the focal point, F, lies behind the mirror.

$$f = -\frac{R}{2}$$

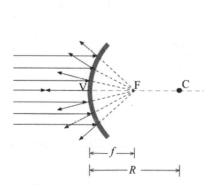

The Focal Point of a Convex Mirror.

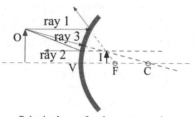

Principal rays for the convex mirror.

All images formed by convex mirrors have the same characteristics. Images are *virtual*, they are *upright*, and they are diminished in *size*.

AP Tip

No matter where a real object is located in front of a convex mirror, the image is virtual and cannot be formed on a screen.

THE MIRROR EQUATION

(*College Physics* 9th ed. pages 793–796/10th ed. pages 804–806)

Ray diagrams are most useful for developing a feel for the characteristics and formation of images produced by spherical mirrors. However, a set of analytical methods exist that will allow us to calculate the features of these images. The first of these is the *mirror equation*.

$$\frac{1}{p} + \frac{1}{q} = \frac{1}{f}$$

It is left to the student to derive this equation and to express it in its auxiliary forms

$$p = \frac{qf}{q-f} \qquad q = \frac{pf}{p-f} \qquad f = \frac{pq}{p+q}$$

Images formed by spherical mirrors may be equal in size, larger, or smaller compared to the object itself. We define *magnification, M*, as the ratio of the image size, *h′*, to the object size, *h*, or

$$\text{Magnification} = M = \frac{\text{image size}}{\text{object size}}$$

or

$$M = \frac{h'}{h}$$

Another useful relationship can be derived using object distance, *p* and image distance *q*.

$$M = \frac{-q}{p}$$

AP Tip

Inverted images will always have a negative magnification.
Upright images will always have a positive magnification.

SAMPLE PROBLEM 1

A flash drive standing on edge measures 6 cm in height and is positioned 60 cm from a concave mirror whose focal length is 20 cm. Calculate the position, nature, and size of the image.

SOLUTION TO PROBLEM 1

First, find the image distance, *q*

Write the mirror equation $\frac{1}{p} + \frac{1}{q} = \frac{1}{f}$ and solve for *q*.

$$q = \frac{pf}{p-f} = \frac{(60 \text{ cm})(20 \text{ cm})}{(60 \text{ cm-}20 \text{ cm})} = \frac{1200 \text{ cm}^2}{40 \text{ cm}} = \textbf{30 cm}$$

Since the image distance, q, is positive, the image is **real**.

To find the magnification write $M = -\dfrac{q}{p}$.

Solving for the image height, $h' = -\dfrac{qh}{p} = -\dfrac{(30\text{ cm})(6\text{ cm})}{60\text{ cm}} = $ **−3 cm**

The negative sign implies that the image is **inverted**. The magnification is **−0.5**.

SAMPLE PROBLEM 2

If a convex spherical mirror has a radius of curvature of 40 cm, where must an AA battery be positioned to form an image one-half the length of the battery?

SOLUTION TO PROBLEM 2

Find the focal length of the mirror: $f = \dfrac{R}{2} = \dfrac{-40\text{ cm}}{2} = $ **−20 cm**

The negative sign occurs because of the diverging mirror. Such a mirror always forms an upright image, reduced in size, and the magnification in this case is $+\dfrac{1}{2}$.

Then $M = -\dfrac{q}{p} = +\dfrac{1}{2}$ and $q = -\dfrac{p}{2}$.

From the mirror equation: $q = \dfrac{pf}{p-f}$. Combining equations:

$$\frac{pf}{p-f} = -\frac{p}{2}$$

Dividing by p gives: $\dfrac{f}{p-f} = -\dfrac{1}{2}$ and $2f = -p + f$

$$p = -f = -(-20\text{ cm}) = \textbf{20 cm}$$

When an object is held at a distance equal to the focal length from a convex mirror, the image size is one-half of the object size.

THE REFRACTION OF LIGHT

(*College Physics* 9th ed. pages 765–770/10th ed. pages 777–782)

The velocity of light in a vacuum is 3.0×10^8 m/s. However, when light passes through transparent materials, its velocity is reduced because of the electrical characteristics of the atoms and molecules and the chemical bonds connecting them. Recall that light is an electromagnetic wave. Since various media have different bonding properties, the velocity of light varies from one medium to another. The variation also depends to some extent on the wavelength of the light.

The ratio of the velocity of light, *c*, in a vacuum to its velocity, *v*, in a given medium is defined as the *index of refraction, n*, of that medium. Or

$$n = \frac{c}{v}$$

The index of refraction of plate glass is 1.52. This means that light travels 1.52 times as fast in vacuum as it does in plate glass.

> ## AP Tip
>
> The index of refraction of air is 1.0003, indicating that for our purposes we can consider the velocity of light in air to be the same as in a vacuum.

SAMPLE PROBLEM 3

What is the velocity of yellow light in water if the index of refraction of water for yellow light is 1.33?

SOLUTION TO PROBLEM 3

Write $n = \dfrac{c}{v}$ and solve for the velocity in water.

$$v = \frac{c}{n} = \frac{3.0 \times 10^8 \text{ m/s}}{1.33} = 2.25 \times 10^8 \text{ m/s}$$

In a given uniform medium, light travels in straight lines at a constant speed. When the medium changes, the speed of the light will also change and the light will travel in a straight line along a new path. The bending of a light ray as it passes obliquely from one medium to another medium is known as *refraction*. The principle of refraction is illustrated in the following figure for a light ray entering water from the air. The angle of incidence θ_i the ray makes with the normal, *N*, to the surface is called the *angle of incidence*. The angle θ_r between the refracted ray and the normal is referred to as the angle of refraction. In passing into the denser medium, the angle between the incident ray and the normal is decreased. The limiting value for the angle between a ray and a normal is 90°.

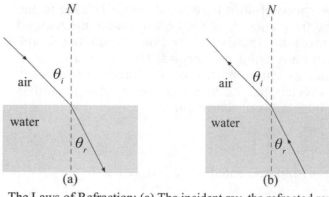

The Laws of Refraction: (a) The incident ray, the refracted ray and the normal to the surface all lie in the same plane. (b) The path of a ray refracted at the surface between two media is exactly reversible.

The relationship between the angles of incidence, refraction, and the velocities in the two media in question can be stated in the form of *Snell's law*, which states that the ratio of the sine of the angle of incidence to the sine of the angle of refraction is equal to the ratio of the velocities of light in the incident medium to that of the refracted medium, or

$$\frac{\sin\theta_1}{\sin\theta_2} = \frac{v_1}{v_2}$$

From above $v_1 = \dfrac{c}{n_1}$ and $v_2 = \dfrac{c}{n_2}$ then substituting gives

$$n_1 \sin\theta_1 = n_2 \sin\theta_2$$

AP Tip

Since the sine of an angle increases as the angle increases, an increase in the index of refraction results in a decrease in the angle and vice versa.

SAMPLE PROBLEM 4

A light ray passes from air into an organic liquid whose index of refraction is 1.39. Find the speed of light in the liquid and the angle of refraction if the light ray enters the liquid with an angle of incidence of 55°.

SOLUTION TO PROBLEM 4

$$v = \frac{c}{n} = \frac{3.0 \times 10^8 \text{ m/s}}{1.39} = 2.16 \times 10^8 \text{ m/s}$$

The angle of refraction is found from Snell'slaw: $n_1 \sin\theta_1 = n_2 \sin\theta_2$

$$\sin\theta_2 = \frac{n_1 \sin\theta_1}{n_2} = \frac{(1)(\sin 55°)}{1.39} \text{ and } \theta_2 = \sin^{-1}(0.5893) = \textbf{36.1°}$$

In a given medium, the speed of light is reduced and is related to the index of refraction. The frequency, *f*, of the light remains unchanged inside or outside the medium. This is true because frequency is the number of waves passing any point per second. The same number of waves leave the medium as enters each second. Thus the frequency cannot change. The wavelength, λ, however, does change and is related to the change in the index of refraction by

$$\frac{\lambda_1}{\lambda_2} = \frac{n_2}{n_1}$$

To summarize the relationship presented so far, we write

$$\frac{\sin \theta_1}{\sin \theta_2} = \frac{n_2}{n_1} = \frac{v_1}{v_2} = \frac{\lambda_1}{\lambda_2}$$

TOTAL INTERNAL REFLECTION

(*College Physics* 9th ed. pages 777–780/10th ed. pages 788–792)

The phenomenon of *total internal reflection* occurs when light encounters a boundary between such a medium as water with a higher index of refraction, n_w, and one such as air with a lower index of refraction, n_a. Consider a light ray traveling in water and meeting the boundary between the water and air, where n_w is greater than n_a. Refracted rays are bent away from the normal because n_w is greater than n_a. At some particular angle of incidence, θ_c, called the *critical angle*, the refracted light ray moves parallel to the boundary so that θ_a = 90°. For angles greater than θ_c, the light ray is entirely reflected at the boundary as is light ray 3. This ray is reflected as if it had struck a mirror. It and all rays like it obey the law of reflection.

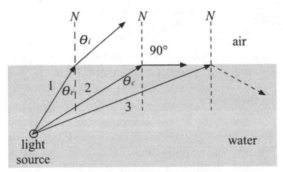

Critical angle of incidence.

At θ_c the angle of refraction is 90°, Snell's law gives: $n_w \sin \theta_c = n_a \sin 90° = n_a$. And in general when $n_1 > n_2$, the critical angle is

$$\sin \theta_c = \frac{n_2}{n_1}$$

> ## AP Tip
>
> Total internal reflection occurs only when light is incident on the boundary of a medium having a lower index of refraction than the medium in which it is traveling.

SAMPLE PROBLEM 5

Determine the critical angle for light passing from glass, $n_1 = 1.54$, to water, $n_2 = 1.33$.

SOLUTION TO PROBLEM 5

By definition and substituting $\sin \theta_c = \dfrac{n_2}{n_1} = \dfrac{1.33}{1.54} = 0.863$.

Solving for θ_c: $\theta_c = \sin^{-1}(0.863) = \mathbf{59.7°}$

APPARENT DEPTH

(*College Physics* 9th ed. page 778/10th ed. page 790)

The refraction of light causes objects that are submerged in a liquid of higher index of refraction to appear closer to the surface of the liquid than the object actually is. If q is the apparent depth of the liquid, p is the actual depth, n_1 is the index of refraction of the liquid, and n_2 is the index of refraction of air, then

$$\frac{\text{apparent depth } q}{\text{actual depth } p} = \frac{n_2}{n_1}$$

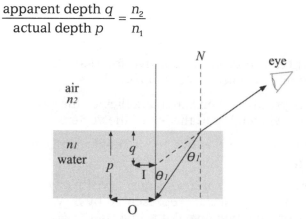

Relationship between actual and apparent depth.

SAMPLE PROBLEM 6

A brick rests at the bottom of a pool of water ($n_w = 1.33$) 3.0 m deep. What is the apparent depth of the pool?

Solution to Problem 6

For air, $n_a = 1.0$ is the index of refraction. The apparent depth is

$$q = \frac{pn_a}{n_w} = \frac{(3.0 \text{ m})(1.0)}{1.33} = \mathbf{2.3 \text{ m}}$$

Convex Lenses

(*College Physics* 9th ed. pages 874–877/10th ed. pages 870–872)

A *converging lens* is one that refracts and converges parallel light rays to a point focus beyond the lens.

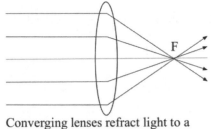

Converging lenses refract light to a
point focus beyond the lens.

Suggested Sign Conventions for Lenses

(*College Physics* 9th ed. pages 805–810/10th ed. pages 816–822)

1. Always make diagrams with light passing from left to right. Always place the object to the left of the surface being studied.

2. Object and image distances are taken as positive for real objects and images, negative for virtual objects and images.

3. The image distance, q, is positive when the image lies to the right of the vertex and negative when it lies to the left of the vertex.

4. Consider the focal length, f, to be positive for a convergent lens and negative for a divergent lens.

5. Indicate the height of the object by h and consider it positive when it points downward. Let the image size be represented by h', which is also positive if it is upright and negative if it is inverted.

6. Note that the magnification $M = 1$ means the image has the same size as the object. Diminution, $M < 1$, does not mean negative magnification, but fractional magnification. Negative magnification merely means that the image is inverted with respect to the object.

RAY TRACING FOR LENSES

(*College Physics* 9th ed. pages 807–810/10th ed. pages 818–822)

Converging lenses have two focal points. We define the first focal point, F_1, as the one that is located on the same side of the lens as the source of incident light. The second focal point, F_2, is located on the opposite side or the far side of the lens. There are three principal rays that we use to trace through a lens.

Ray Tracing: as with mirrors, we start at the head of the object, we work with three rays whose paths are easily traced.

■ *Ray 1:* A ray parallel to the principal axis of the lens passes through the second focal point, F_2, of the converging lens or seems to come from the first focal point, F_1, of a diverging lens.
■ *Ray 2:* A ray that passes through the first focal point, F_1, of a converging lens or proceeds toward the second focal point, F_2, of a diverging lens is refracted parallel to the principal axis of the lens.
■ *Ray 3:* A ray that proceeds through the geometric center of a lens will not be deviated.

Case 1: The object, O, is located beyond twice the focal point $2F_1$. The image, I, forms on the other side of the lens between F_2 and $2F_2$. It is *real*, *inverted*, and *diminished* in size.

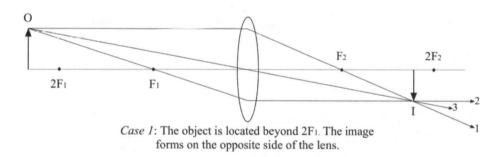

Case 1: The object is located beyond $2F_1$. The image forms on the opposite side of the lens.

Case 2: The object, O, is located at twice the focal point, $2F_1$. The image, I, forms on the other side of the lens and is *real*, *inverted*, and is the *same size* as O.

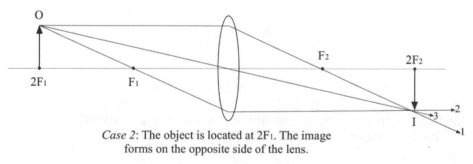

Case 2: The object is located at $2F_1$. The image forms on the opposite side of the lens.

Case 3: The object, O, is located between $2F_1$ and F_1. The image, I, forms beyond $2F_2$ on the other side of the lens and it is *real*, *inverted*, and *larger* than the object.

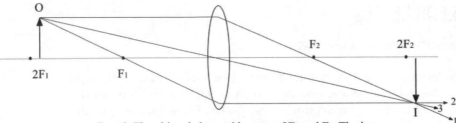

Case 3: The object is located between 2F₁ and F₁. The image
forms on the opposite side of the lens.

Case 4: The object, O, at the focal point, F₁. All reflected rays are
parallel and never intersect. No image is ever formed.

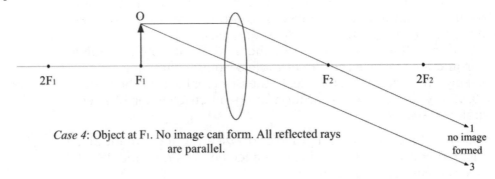

Case 4: Object at F₁. No image can form. All reflected rays
are parallel.

Case 5: The object, O, is inside the focal point, F₁. The image, I,
appears to be on the same side of the lens as O is *virtual, enlarged,* and
upright.

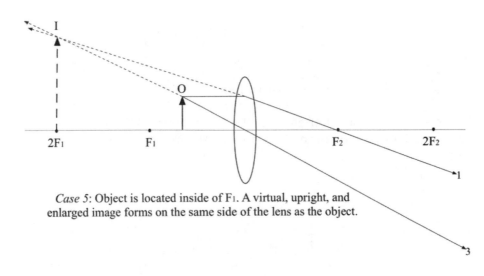

Case 5: Object is located inside of F₁. A virtual, upright, and
enlarged image forms on the same side of the lens as the object.

Images formed by *convex lenses* are similar to the images formed
by *concave mirrors*. Both converge light rays.

CONCAVE LENSES

(*College Physics* 9th ed. pages 805–810/10th ed. pages 816–822)

A *diverging lens* is one that refracts and diverges parallel light rays from a point located in front of the lens.

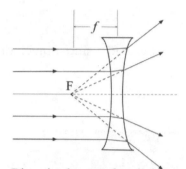

Diverging lenses refract light so that it appears to come from a point in front of the lens.

Images of real objects that are formed by diverging lenses are *always* virtual, upright, and diminished in size. Diverging lenses are frequently used to reduce the effects of converging lenses.

> ## AP Tip
>
> To avoid confusion, the student should identify both mirrors and lenses as either *converging* or *diverging*.

THE LENS EQUATION

(*College Physics* 9th ed. pages 805–810/10th ed. pages 816–822)

The nature of the images formed by lenses can be determined by the lens equation

$$\frac{1}{p} + \frac{1}{q} = \frac{1}{f}$$

where f = focal length of the lens
p = object distance
q = image distance

It is left to the student to derive the auxiliary forms of the lens equation

$$p = \frac{qf}{q-f} \qquad q = \frac{pf}{p-f} \qquad f = \frac{pq}{p+q}$$

The magnification, defined as images formed by lenses, may be equal in size, larger, or smaller compared to the object itself. We define, as we did with mirrors, *magnification, M,* as the ratio of the image size, *h′,* to the object size, *h,* or

$$\text{Magnification} = M = \frac{\text{image size}}{\text{object size}}$$

or

$$M = \frac{h'}{h}$$

Another useful relationship can be derived using object distance, *p* and image distance *q*.

$$M = \frac{-q}{p}$$

AP Tip

A positive magnification indicates that the image is upright whereas a negative magnification only occurs when the image is inverted.

SAMPLE PROBLEM 7

A thin converging lens has a focal length of 20 cm. An object that is 4 cm tall is placed 10 cm from the lens. What are the nature, size, and position of the image?

SOLUTION TO PROBLEM 7

The units are not changed into meters since they will divide out. The image distance is found using

$$q = \frac{pf}{p-f} = \frac{(10 \text{ cm})(20 \text{ cm})}{(10 \text{ cm}-20 \text{ cm})} = \textbf{-20 cm}$$

The negative sign means that the image is virtual.
   The magnification is

$$M = \frac{h'}{h} = -\frac{q}{p} \text{ and } h' = -\frac{qh}{p} = -\frac{(-20 \text{ cm})(4 \text{ cm})}{(10 \text{ cm})} = \textbf{+8 cm}$$

The positive sign means the image is upright.

SAMPLE PROBLEM 8

A diverging lens has a focal length of –16 cm. This lens is held 10 cm from an object. In cm, where is the image located? What is the magnification of this lens?

SOLUTION TO PROBLEM 8

Direct substitution into the lens equation gives

$$q = \frac{pf}{p-f} = \frac{(10 \text{ cm})(-16 \text{ cm})}{(10 \text{ cm}-(-16 \text{ cm}))} = \textbf{-6.15 cm}$$

The negative sign indicates that the image is virtual. Magnification is

$$M = -\frac{q}{p} = \frac{-(-6.15 \text{ cm})}{(10 \text{ cm})} = +0.62$$

Positive magnification means that the image is upright.

IMAGES PRODUCED BY TWO LENSES

(*College Physics* 9th ed. pages 811–814/10th ed. pages 822–825)

Systems of two or more lenses are generally used for magnification purposes, as in the microscope and the telescope. The magnification in these cases is, in general

$$M = M_1 \times M_2$$

The microscope is used to study small nearby objects where the refracting telescope is used to observe large distant objects. The optical system of both devices is basically the same. Each uses an eyepiece or an *ocular* to enlarge the image produced by an objective lens.

In the refracting telescope, the objective lens forms *real, inverted,* and *diminished images* of the distant object. The microscope eyepiece forms an *enlarged* and *virtual final image.*

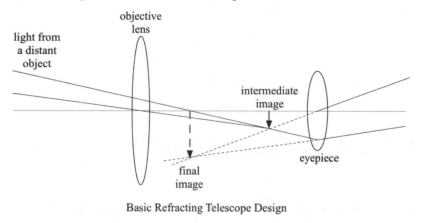

Basic Refracting Telescope Design

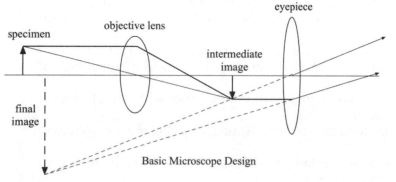

Basic Microscope Design

SAMPLE PROBLEM 9

The objective lens of a microscope has a focal length of 8 mm. The eyepiece has a focal length of 40 mm. When the two lenses are 200 mm apart the final image appears to be at a distance of 250 mm from the eyepiece.

(a) In mm, how far is the object from the objective lens?

(b) What is the magnification of the microscope?

SOLUTION TO PROBLEM 9

(a) The units will be left in mm. Label the objective lens as 1 and the eyepiece as 2. We will find the position of the intermediate image first.

$$p_2 = \frac{f_2 q_2}{q_2 - f_2} = \frac{(40 \text{ mm})(-250 \text{ mm})}{(-250 \text{ mm} - 40 \text{ mm})} = 34.5 \text{ mm}$$

The negative sign was used for the image distance q_2 because it was measured to a virtual image. Since p_2 is known, we can find the image distance q_1 for the first image.

$$q_1 = 200 \text{ mm} - 34.5 \text{ mm} = 165.5 \text{ mm}$$

The object distance p_1 is then:

$$p_1 = \frac{q_1 f_1}{q_1 - f_1} = \frac{(165.5 \text{ mm})(8 \text{ mm})}{(165.5 \text{ mm} - 8 \text{ mm})} = \textbf{8.41 mm}$$

(b) The magnification is the product of the individual magnifications

$$M = M_1 \times M_2 = \left(\frac{-q_1}{p_1}\right) \times \left(\frac{-q_2}{p_2}\right) = \frac{q_1 q_2}{p_1 p_2} = \frac{(165.5 \text{ mm})(-250 \text{ mm})}{(8.41 \text{ mm})(34.5 \text{ mm})} = \textbf{-143}$$

The negative magnification implies that the final image is inverted.

GEOMETRICAL OPTICS: STUDENT OBJECTIVES FOR THE AP EXAM

- You should be able to determine how the speed and wavelength of light change when light passes from one medium into another.
- You should be able to show on a diagram the directions of reflected and refracted rays.
- You should be able to use Snell's law to relate the directions of the incident ray and the refracted ray, and the indices of refraction of the media.
- You should be able to identify conditions under which total internal reflection will occur.
- You should understand image formation by plane or spherical mirrors.
- You should be able to relate the focal point of a spherical mirror to its center of curvature ($R = 2f$).
- You should be able to, given a diagram of a curved mirror with the focal point shown, locate by ray tracing the image of a real object and determine whether the image is real or virtual, upright or inverted, enlarged or reduced in size.

■ You should understand image formation by concave or convex lenses.

■ You should be able to determine whether the focal length of a lens is increased or decreased as a result of a change in curvature of its surface or in the index of refraction of the material of which the lens is made or the medium in which it is immersed.

■ You should be able to determine by ray tracing the location of the image of a real object located inside or outside the focal point of the lens, and state whether the resulting image is upright or inverted, real or virtual.

■ You should be able to use the thin lens equation to relate the object distance, image distance, and focal length for a lens and to determine the image size in terms of the object size (i.e., magnification).

■ You should be able to analyze simple situations in which the image formed by one lens serves as the object for another lens.

MULTIPLE-CHOICE QUESTIONS

1. A student uses a plane mirror to study image formation. Using pins and ray tracing the student is able to locate the images of the pins in the mirror for each position of the pin in front of the mirror. The student wants to make a graph of pin distance from the front of the mirror versus distance of the image of the pin to the mirror. Which of the following graphs best describe the relationship between object distance and image distance?

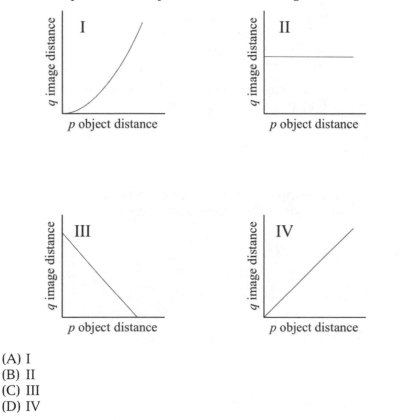

(A) I
(B) II
(C) III
(D) IV

2. When light is incident on a surface, all the electromagnetic radiation is
   (A) either reflected from the surface or transmitted
   (B) either reflected from the surface or absorbed
   (C) reflected, transmitted, and absorbed at a surface
   (D) either reflected from the surface or absorbed at the surface

3. Light incident on the interface between air $(n = 1)$ and water $(n = 1.33)$ along the normal to the interface
   (A) slows and is bent toward the normal
   (B) slows and is bent away from the normal
   (C) slows but is not bent since it travels along the normal
   (D) continues into the water at constant speed, but is bent toward the normal

4. Several students designed an experiment to determine the radius of curvature of an unknown mirror. They used an optical bench, a mirror, a film arrow, and a screen. Part of their data is shown below.

p (cm)	q (cm)	h_{obj} (cm)	h_{image} (cm)
15.0	30.0	1.00	1.99
20.0	20.0	1.00	1.00
25.0	16.7	1.00	0.67
40.0	13.3	1.00	0.33

   Using the data, the mirror is
   (A) concave with a radius of curvature of 10 cm
   (B) concave with a radius of curvature of 20 cm
   (C) convex with a radius of curvature of 10 cm
   (D) convex with a radius of curvature of 20 cm

5. A ray of light in air strikes the interface between air and water at some angle with the normal. In water, the ray has a
   (A) larger wavelength
   (B) larger frequency
   (C) smaller wavelength
   (D) smaller frequency

6. Students obtained the following data during an experiment using an optical bench, a convex lens, a film arrow, and a screen.

p (cm)	q (cm)
15.0	30.0
20.0	20.0
25.0	16.7
30.0	15.0
40.0	13.3
50.0	12.5

Which of the graphs shown below gives the correct relationship between p and q?

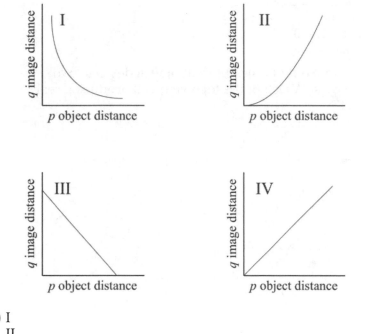

(A) I
(B) II
(C) III
(D) IV

7. A layer of water ($n = 1.33$) covers a block of glass with an index of refraction of $n = 1.52$. Total internal reflection at the interface between the two media
   (A) occurs whenever the ray of light goes from the glass to the water because the speed of light increases in the water
   (B) occurs whenever the ray of light goes from the water to the glass because the speed of light increases in the glass
   (C) may occur when the ray of light goes from the glass to the water because the speed of light increases in the water
   (D) may occur when the ray of light goes from the water to the glass because the speed of light increases in the glass

8. A real image twice as large as an object is produced when the object is placed 20.00 cm away from a converging lens. What is the focal length of the lens?
   (A) 13.3 cm
   (B) 15.5 cm
   (C) 25.0 cm
   (D) 40.0 cm

9. A 3.0 cm tall object is placed 25.0 cm from a diverging lens whose focal length is –10.0 cm. The image formed by this lens is
   (A) real and inverted with a magnification $|M| = 0.72$
   (B) virtual and inverted with a magnification of $|M| = 0.72$
   (C) real and upright with a magnification $|M| = 0.29$
   (D) virtual and upright with a magnification $|M| = 0.29$

10. Which of the following materials will produce a convex lens that has the longest focal length?
    (A) Crown glass with $n = 1.52$
    (B) Flint glass $n = 1.66$
    (C) Fused quartz $n = 1.458$
    (D) Zircon $n = 1.923$

11. An object is placed in front of four different optical devices: two lenses and two mirrors. Which of the following will produce a real image of the object?

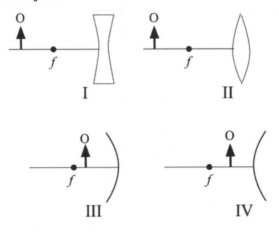

    (A) I
    (B) II
    (C) III
    (D) IV

12. A 580 nm beam of light traveling in air is incident on a cube of quartz ($n = 1.46$). In the quartz,
    (A) the speed of light is constant and the wavelength decreases because the frequency increases
    (B) the speed of light decreases and the wavelength also must decrease because the frequency remains constant
    (C) the speed of light decreases and the wavelength must increase because the frequency also decreases
    (D) there is no change in the wavelength since both the speed of light and the frequency of the beam decrease

13. Two physics students stand in front of a concave mirror with a radius of curvature of 4.00 m at an amusement park on physics day at the park. Their images are upright and appear to be 2.50 times taller than their actual height. How far are they standing from the mirror?
    (A) 1.20 m
    (B) 1.50 m
    (C) 2.20 m
    (D) 4.00 m

14. A ray of light originates in the lower medium water ($n = 1.33$) striking the boundary between the water and air. Which of the four possible rays gives a correct possible direction for the ray in the air?

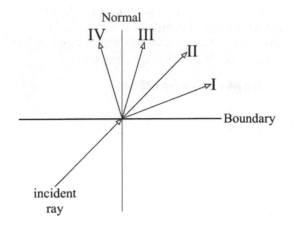

(A) I
(B) II
(C) III
(D) IV

Directions: For the question below, <u>two</u> of the suggested answers will be correct. You must select <u>both</u> correct choices to earn credit. No partial credit will be earned if only one correct answer is selected. Select the two that are best in each case and then enter both of the appropriate answers in the corresponding space on the answer sheet.

15. The diagram below shows the possible paths for a ray of light striking the interfaces between air, water, and glass. Which of the labeled rays is possible?

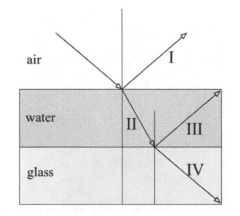

(A) I
(B) II
(C) III
(D) IV

FREE-RESPONSE PROBLEMS

1. A student designs an experiment to determine how the path of a ray of light from air incident on the upper surface of a liquid contained in a plastic box changes as it enters the liquid. The student uses a monochromatic laser $\lambda = 740$ nm and a protractor in the experiment. The student obtains the following data.

Angle of incidence θ_1	Angle of refraction θ_2
10°	7°
20°	13°
30°	20°
40°	26°
50°	31°
60°	35°

(a) Graphically determine the index of refraction in the glass by plotting on the same graph

   i. θ_1 / θ_2 as a function of θ_1

   ii. $\sin\theta_1 / \sin\theta_2$ as a function of θ_1

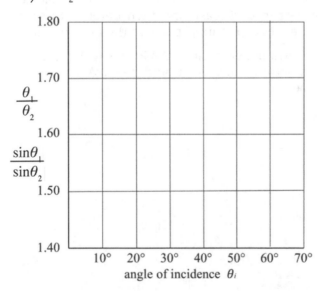

(b) Explain which relationship, (i) or (ii), if either, is more constant.

(c) Justify, without equations, why it is possible to neglect the refraction of the box containing the liquid.

(d) Clearly explain, without equations, how the angles of incidence and refraction of the beam of light at the entrance boundary are related to the angles of incidence and refraction of the beam of light at the exit boundary.

(e) How would you determine, without equations, what the wavelength of the beam of light was in the liquid?

2. (a) You are walking toward a full-length flat mirror at 1/40 m/s. Your image appears to be:

_____ approaching

_____ receding

_____ stationary

Explain your reasoning.

(b) What is the relative velocity between you and your image? Explain.

3. (a) A coin placed at the bottom of a glass paperweight, (n = 1.52), appears to be located at which position shown in the diagram when viewed by a person looking into the paperweight from the top (from air)?

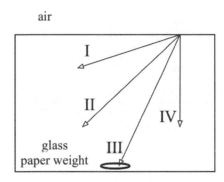

(b) Explain your answer using the correct scientific terms.

(c) If the coin is placed in flint glass (n = 1.61) the coin will appear to be

_____ higher in the flint glass paperweight

_____ lower in the flint glass paperweight

_____ no change in its position in the flint glass paperweight

Justify your answer.

4. Design an experiment to determine the focal length of a convex lens.

(a) Make a diagram of your laboratory setup, correctly labeling each piece of equipment in the diagram. Describe your experimental procedure in enough detail that another student could duplicate your experiment and obtain the same result.

(b) What measurements will you take in the experiment and how will you use them to determine the focal length of the convex lens?

(c) Show by ray diagram the formation of the image when the object is between the lens and the focal point.

(d) Another student performed a similar experiment and obtained the following graph. How can you use the graph to determine the focal length of the lens?

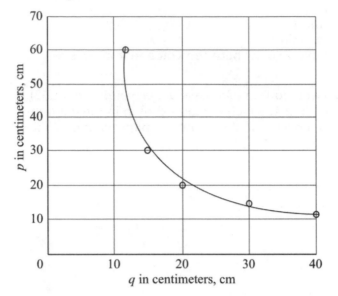

Answers

MULTIPLE-CHOICE QUESTIONS

1. **D** The image in a plane mirror is virtual, upright, and the same distance behind the mirror as the object is in front of it ($p = q$).

   The image also has the same height. The graph will show a linear relationship between the two. The graph is a straight diagonal line slanting upward to the right.
   (*College Physics* 9th ed. pages 790–793/10th ed. pages 801–804)
   (L.O. 6.E.2.1)

2. **C** When light from one medium strikes the surface of the second medium, some or all of the light may be turned back into the first medium—this is called reflection. If the surface is transparent or translucent, some of the light will be transmitted, undergoing a change in speed at the interface. Some of the light is absorbed by the surface as internal energy.
   (*College Physics* 9th ed. pages 762–764, 842–843/10th ed. pages 774–778, 855–856)
   (L.O. 6.E.1.1)

3. **C** A ray of light from air into water traveling along the normal between the two materials slows, but is not bent as it enters the water.
   (*College Physics* 9th ed. pages 765–769/10th ed. pages 774–778)
   (L.O. 6.E.3.1)

4. **B** The image distance is positive, therefore the mirror is concave. The image distance for a convex mirror is always negative.

    Substitution into the mirror equation $\frac{1}{f} = \frac{1}{p} + \frac{1}{q}$ from any of the data values listed will give a focal length of +10.0 cm. The focal length is related to the radius of curvature by $f = \frac{R}{2}$. The radius of curvature is 20.0 cm.

    (*College Physics* 9th ed. pages 793–795/10th ed. pages 804–809)
    (L.O. 6.E.4.1)

5. **C** The frequency of light inside the medium is the same as it is outside the medium because the number of waves entering and leaving the interface is the same. Since the index of refraction is greater in the water than in the air and the ray slows down, the wavelength must reduce as well.

    (*College Physics* 9th ed. pages 765–768/10th ed. pages 778–781)
    (L.O. 6.E.3.1)

6. **A** The equation for the relationship between f, p, and q is given by $\frac{1}{f} = \frac{1}{p} + \frac{1}{q}$. The lens remains the same in the experiment, thus

    $$\frac{1}{p_1} + \frac{1}{q_1} = \frac{1}{p_2} + \frac{1}{q_2} \qquad \frac{p_1 + q_1}{p_1 q_1} = \frac{p_2 + q_2}{p_2 q_2}.$$

    The product of pq is a constant. The graph is hyperbolic—graph A.

    (*College Physics* 9th ed. pages 805–807/10th ed. pages 816–818)
    (L.O. 6.E.5.2)

7. **C** Total internal reflection can occur only when light passes from a medium of greater optical density to one of lower optical density at an angle greater than the critical angle. When light travels from a medium where its speed is lower to one in which its speed is higher, total internal reflection will occur with light incident on the glass-water interface at the critical angle and the ray will be bent along the interface. At angles less than the critical angle, the light will leave the interface, bending away from the normal.

    (*College Physics* 9th ed. pages 777–780/10th ed. pages 778–792)
    (L.O. 6.E.3.3)

8. **A** The magnification of a thin lens produces an image that is twice as large as the object when the object is placed 20.0 cm from the convex lens, $|M| = \frac{|-q|}{|p|}$ gives $2p = q$. Substitution into $\frac{1}{f} = \frac{1}{p} + \frac{1}{q} = \frac{1}{20.0 \text{ cm}} + \frac{1}{40.0 \text{ cm}}$. The focal length of the convex lens is 13.3 cm.

    (*College Physics* 9th ed. pages 805–811/10th ed. pages 816–822)
    (L.O. 6.E.5.1)

9. **D** All images produced by an object placed in front of a diverging lens are upright and virtual with a magnification $|M| < 1$.

Substitution into $\dfrac{1}{f} = \dfrac{1}{p} + \dfrac{1}{q} = \dfrac{1}{-10.0 \text{ cm}} = \dfrac{1}{25.0 \text{ cm}} + \dfrac{1}{q}$ gives

$q = -7.14 \text{ cm}$. The magnification $|M| = \dfrac{|-q|}{|p|}$ produces a

magnification of 0.2857 which gives the correct answer 0.29.
(*College Physics* 9th ed. pages 805–811/10th ed. pages 816–822)
(L.O. 6.E.5.1)

10. **C** The longest focal length will be produced by the material that has the largest index of refraction when light from air enters the substance—bent the least because the speed of light is higher in the substance compared to the other materials listed. This is the material that has the smallest index of refraction. For the materials listed, fused quartz has the smallest index of refraction.
(*College Physics* 9th ed. pages 765–769, 805–807/10th ed. pages 777–782, 816–819)
(L.O. 6.E.3.1)

11. **B** Only concave mirrors or convex lenses can produce a real image of an object placed in front of it. The object is placed between the focal point and the concave mirror in figure III and produces a virtual image. The only diagram that can produce a real image of the object is diagram II.
(*College Physics* 9th ed. pages 793–798, 805–811/10th ed. pages 804–809, 816–822)
(L.O. 6.E.4.2, 6.E.5.1)

12. **B** The frequency of light inside the quartz is the same as it is outside the quartz because the number of waves entering and leaving the interface is the same. Since the index of refraction is greater than 1, the beam slows as it enters the interface; thus the wavelength of light must decrease.
(*College Physics* 9th ed. pages 767–770/10th ed. pages 778–781)
(L.O. 6.E.3.1)

13. **A** The radius of curvature is related to the focal length by $f = \dfrac{R}{2}$.

Thus the focal length of the mirror is 2.00 m. The magnification

$|M| = \dfrac{|-q|}{|p|} = 2.50$. The magnification gives q a value of $q = -2.50p$

since the image is upright and therefore behind the mirror.

Substitution into $\dfrac{1}{f} = \dfrac{1}{p} + \dfrac{1}{q}$ is $\dfrac{1}{2.00 \text{ m}} = \dfrac{1}{p} + \dfrac{1}{-2.5p}$ thus

$$\dfrac{1}{2.00 \text{ m}} = \dfrac{-2.5p + 1}{-2.5p^2}.$$

$$p = \dfrac{3.00 \text{ m}}{2.5} = 1.2 \text{ m}.$$

(*College Physics* 9th ed. pages 793–801/10th ed. pages 804–809)
(L.O. 6.E.4.2)

14. **A** The ray travels from water to air where the speed of the ray will increase. The ray will bend away from the normal as it crosses the boundary between water and air.
(*College Physics* 9th ed. pages 765–770/10th ed. pages 777–781)
(L.O. 6.E.4.2)

15. **A** and **B** The angle of incidence between the air and water interface shows a reflected angle $\theta_i = \theta_r$ so that that ray is possible.
The angle of refraction between the air and water interface shows the ray bending toward the normal. This ray is possible. The reflected ray at the interface between the water and the glass shows a ray parallel to the reflected ray at the upper surface. This is not a possible solution. The last ray shows light bending away from the normal as the ray travels from water to glass, where the index of refractions would indicate the ray slows down in glass and should bend toward the normal. Therefore this is not possible either.
(*College Physics* 9th ed. pages 762–770/10th ed. pages 774–781)
(L.O. 6.E.4.2)

FREE-RESPONSE PROBLEMS

1. (a)

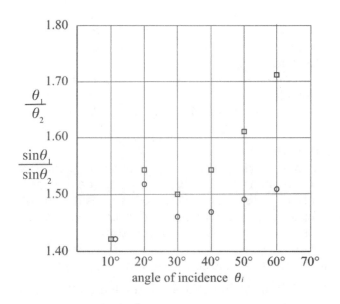

(b) The ratio of the $\sin\theta_1 / \sin\theta_2$ as a function of θ_1 is more constant than the ratio of θ_1 / θ_2.

The average value for $\sin\theta_1 / \sin\theta_2$ is 1.48. Snell's Law applies.

The index of refraction for air is one. Thus the index of refraction for the liquid is the ratio of $\sin\theta_1 / \sin\theta_2$.

(c) The ray refracts at the upper interface between air, plastic, and then refracts at the plastic, liquid interface. As the ray emerges from the liquid to plastic, the refraction is the opposite of the refraction at the upper boundary. This is also true for the refraction between the lower plastic boundary and the air since the speed in the medium (uniform density is the same; thus the speed changes are the same at these boundaries).

(d) The box has parallel sides; thus the ray emerges from the lower surface parallel to the ray striking the upper surface. The explanation may be done with a diagram showing the rays at the interfaces.

(e) The index of refraction is the ratio of the speed of light in air divided by the speed of light in the liquid. The frequency in air is the same as the frequency in the liquid since the number of waves crossing the boundary will not change. Knowing the product of the wavelength times the frequency is equal to the speed of light in the specific media, the wavelength in the liquid is equal to the wavelength in air divided by the index of refraction.

(*College Physics* 9th ed. pages 765–770/10th ed. pages 777–781)
(L.O. 6.E.3.1, 6.E.3.2, 6.E.3.3)

2. (a) You are walking toward a full length flat mirror at 1.40 m/s. Your image appears to be

    ____√____approaching

    The image seen in a flat mirror is virtual, erect, and as far behind the mirror as the object is in front of it. If you are approaching the mirror, your image is approaching you.

   (b) The image will be approaching the mirror at the same rate as you are approaching it.

    The relative velocity between you and your image will be twice as great as your velocity.

(*College Physics* 9th ed. pages 790–793/10th ed. pages 801–804)
(L.O. 6.E.2.1)

3. (a) The correct position identified is II.

   (b) The ray of light from the coin bends away from the interface as it leaves the glass and enters the air due to the change in speed at the interface between glass and air. The eye traces the ray of light from the coin back from the apparent source in a straight line. We perceive the coin to be located at position II.

   (c) Correct line checked is

    __√_____ higher in the flint glass paperweight.

    The index of refraction in the flint glass is higher than the index of refraction of the glass.

    The light passing from the flint glass into the air will be bent farther away from the normal because there is greater change in the speed. Tracing the apparent position of the coin in a straight line would make the image of the coin appear to be closer to the surface in the flint glass paperweight.

(*College Physics* 9th ed. pages 765–770/10th ed. pages 777–781)
(L.O. 6.E.2.1)

4. (a) Diagram of the experimental apparatus.

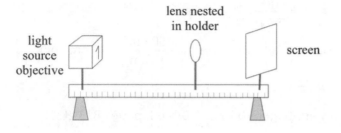

1. Set up the equipment as shown in the diagram above. Make sure that the pieces of equipment are centered in their respective holders.
2. Place the lens between the object (arrow) and the screen and move either the screen or the lens until a sharp real image is formed on the screen.
3. Measure the distance between the object and the lens (object distance p) and record this value in the data table. (Make sure that the distances are measured from the center of the holders.)
4. Measure the distance between the image on the screen and the lens (image distance q) and record this value in the data table. (Make sure that the distances are measured from the center of the holders.)
5. Repeat for other values.

(b) Using the values for the object distance p and the image distance q, and substituting into $\dfrac{1}{f} = \dfrac{1}{p} + \dfrac{1}{q}$ will give an experimental value for the focal length of the lens.

Averaging the values for the several trials will be considered the experimental focal length of the lens.

(c) Image formation for an object placed between the focal point and the lens

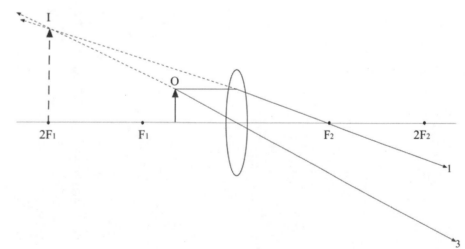

(d) Using data sets from the graph, the focal length can be determined from $f = \dfrac{qp}{q+p}$.

Looking at a few data sets, indicate $f = \dfrac{450 \text{ cm}^2}{45 \text{ cm}} = 10 \text{ cm}$, or

$f = \dfrac{720 \text{ cm}^2}{72 \text{ cm}} = 10 \text{ cm}$, etc.

(*College Physics* 9th ed. pages 805–811/10th ed. pages 816–822)
(L.O. 6.E.5.1, 6.E.5.2)

WAVE OPTICS

DISPERSION

(*College Physics* 9th ed. pages 771–775/10th ed. pages 784–786)

Measurements on the refraction of light as it passes from air into glass show that the degree of refraction is dependent upon wavelength. Light of all wavelengths is reduced in speed in glass, but violet light, which is refracted the greatest amount, travels more slowly than red light, which is refracted least. This effect is called *dispersion*. The diagram shows the result of directing a narrow beam of white light at one face of a glass prism.

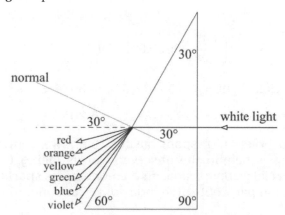

The initial beam is separated into beams of various colors, from which we conclude that white light is actually a mixture of light of various colors. The band of colors that emerges from the glass prism is known as a *spectrum*. When the ray of white light is broken into its components, each component color is deviated by a different angle, for example, δ_r for red light and δ_v for violet light. The *angular dispersion* ψ between the violet and red regions is the difference between the deviations: $\psi = \delta_v - \delta_r$.

SAMPLE PROBLEM 1

Consider the 30°-60°-90° glass prism in the diagram above. The glass has an index of refraction of $n_r = 1.62$ for a particular wavelength of red light and $n_v = 1.72$ for a particular wavelength of violet light. To 3 significant figures:

(a) What is the deviation angle, δ_r for red light and the deviation angle for this violet light δ_v?

(b) What is the angular dispersion, ψ?

SOLUTION TO PROBLEM 1

(a) The angle of incidence and the angle of refraction of the white light on the vertical side of the prism is 0° but on the slanted side of the prism the ray of white light has an angle of incidence of 30.0°. The angles of refraction are different for each color.

Using Snell's law to find the angle of refraction of the red light $n_1 \sin \theta_1 = n_2 \sin \theta_2$

Solving for θ_2

$$\theta_2 = \sin^{-1}\left(\frac{n_1}{n_2}\sin\theta_1\right) = \sin^{-1}\left[\left(\frac{1.62}{1.00}\right)\sin 30.0°\right] = 54.1°$$

The deviation angle for red light = $\delta_r - 30.0° = 54.1° - 30.0° =$ **24.1°**

Using Snell's law to find the angle of refraction of the violet light: $n_1 \sin \theta_1 = n_2 \sin \theta_2$

Solving for θ_2

$$\theta_2 = \sin^{-1}\left(\frac{n_1}{n_2}\sin\theta_1\right) = \sin^{-1}\left[\left(\frac{1.72}{1.00}\right)\sin 30.0°\right] = 59.3°$$

The deviation angle for violet light = $\delta_v - 30.0° = 59.3° - 30.0° =$ **29.3°**

(b) The angular dispersion: $\psi = \delta_v - \delta_r = 29.3° - 24.1° =$ **5.20°.**

Dispersion in water droplets is responsible for rainbows, which are seen when the sun is behind the observer who is facing the rain. Dispersion is especially conspicuous in diamonds. The sparkle of a cut diamond is due in part to its high index of refraction and in part to the way it is cut.

ELECTROMAGNETIC WAVES

(*College Physics* 9th ed. pages 746–749/10th ed. pages 757–760)

As we saw earlier, when a stone is thrown into water a disturbance is created by the energy added to the water by the stone. Water is a medium that reacts to the disturbance by creating water waves that carry the outside energy away from the point of the disturbance. We say that water waves radiate away from the point of the disturbance at some wave speed. Slam a book on a desktop and a disturbance is created in the surrounding air and the air, the medium, reacts by creating a sound wave that carries the energy away from the point of disturbance. Here we say that sound waves radiate away from the point of the disturbance at the speed of sound.

The electrons in the outer portions of atoms have both electrical and magnetic properties. Disturb the atom with heat or electrical energy and these outer electrons are displaced to higher electron positions in what is now an excited atom. The electrons create electromagnetic waves as they accelerate back to their ground states. The electromagnetic waves carry the added energy away from the atom at the speed of light. These electromagnetic waves are classified as *light*.

Note that water waves travel in the medium water. Sound waves travel in the medium air. Electromagnetic waves do not need a medium. Light travels in vacuum as well as in air, water, or glass.

Visible light is not the only type of electromagnetic wave. All electromagnetic waves share the basic properties of frequency f, wavelength λ and they all travel at the same speed in vacuum, the speed of light c. The speed of light is related to these properties by $c = f\lambda$.

Because of the small wavelengths of light radiation, it is convenient to define a smaller unit of measure. The SI unit is the *nanometer* (nm). One nanometer (1 nm) is defined as one-billionth of a meter, or: $1 \text{ nm} = 10^{-9} \text{ m}$.

The student should be aware that some textbook authors express the wavelength of light in terms of an older unit, the millimicron (mμ). The student should verify that $1 \text{ nm} = 1 \text{ m}\mu$. An even older unit of wavelength measure is still in use. It is the angstrom (Å). The angstrom was originally defined as $1 \text{ Å} = 1 \times 10^{-10} \text{ m}$ making $1 \text{ nm} = 10 \text{ Å}$.

The names given to various portions of the electromagnetic spectrum are simply for the convenience in describing the region of the spectrum where they are found. In many instances there is considerable overlap between classifications. There is no sharp dividing point between one type of electromagnetic radiation and the next. Every form of electromagnetic wave is produced by the same thing, accelerating electrical charges.

Electromagnetic Radiation	Sources	Wavelength Range
Radio waves	Radio waves are the result of accelerating electrons through a transmitting antenna by an oscillator. Radio waves are the basis of television and radio communications systems.	From more than 10^4 m to about 0.1 m.
Microwaves	Electronic devices produce microwaves. Radar systems generate microwaves and microwave ovens, which produce a wavelength of $\lambda = 12.2$ cm, are a common household device.	From approximately from 0.3 m to 10^{-4} m.
Infrared waves (IR)	Molecules and room-temperature objects produce infrared waves. Some IR is produced by outer electron transitions in excited atoms.	From 10^{-3} m to 700 nm.
Visible light	Visible light is the part of the electromagnetic spectrum the human eye detects. Light is produced by electron transitions in the outer electron shell of excited atoms and molecules. The sensitivity of the human eye is at a maximum of 550 nm at yellow green.	From 700 nm for red light to 400 nm for violet light.
Ultraviolet waves (UV)	Ultraviolet waves are produced by electron transitions in the outer shells of excited atoms. The surface of the Sun produces great quantities of UV.	From about 400 nm to 0.6 nm.
X-rays	The most common source of X-rays is the deceleration of high-energy electrons bombarding a heavy metal target in a vacuum tube. X-rays are also produced by the electron transitions that follow the removal of electrons from the inner electron shells of heavy metal atoms.	From approximately 10^{-8} m to 10^{-12} m.
Gamma rays	Gamma rays are the result of the rearrangement of neutrons and electrically charged protons in the nucleus after alpha or beta radioactive decay. Gamma rays are a component of high-energy cosmic radiation that enters the Earth's atmosphere from deep space. Matter-antimatter interactions also produce gamma rays.	From about 10^{-10} m to less than 10^{-14} m.

Sample Problem 2

(a) Calculate the frequency of yellow light, $\lambda = 600 \text{ nm}$.

(b) Find the wavelength of radio waves whose frequency is $f = 1.00 \text{ MHz}$.

Solution to Problem 2

(a) The frequency is found using

$$f = \frac{c}{\lambda} = \frac{3.00 \times 10^8 \text{ m/s}}{600 \times 10^{-9} \text{ m}} = 5.00 \times 10^{14} \text{ Hz}.$$

(b) Solving for wavelength $\lambda = \dfrac{c}{f} = \dfrac{3.00 \times 10^8 \text{ m/s}}{1.00 \times 10^6 \text{ s}^{-1}} = 300 \text{ m}$.

Conditions for Interference

(*College Physics* 9th ed. pages 824–825/10th ed. pages 835–836)

In our study of mechanical waves we saw that two waves could, by superposition, add together constructively or destructively. In constructive interference the amplitude of the resultant wave is the sum of the amplitudes of the interacting waves. In destructive interference, the resultant amplitude is less than the sum of the interacting waves or even zero. Light waves also interact constructively or destructively. The interference between light waves is an interaction of the electromagnetic fields of the individual waves.

Light waves having a constant phase relationship with one another are said to be *coherent*. Laser beams have this property. On the other hand, light streaming from the Sun or a light bulb consists of a great number of short segments of sine waves and the phase of one segment is not related to any other and such light is said to be *incoherent*. Two coherent waves of the same wavelength (*monochromatic light*) may interfere. This means they can undergo constructive interference or they may cancel one another out as in destructive interference.

There are two conditions that must be met in order to produce interference:

1. The light source must be coherent, meaning emits light of the same phase.

2. The light must be monochromatic, meaning identical wavelengths.

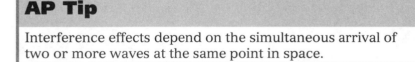

AP Tip

Interference effects depend on the simultaneous arrival of two or more waves at the same point in space.

YOUNG'S DOUBLE-SLIT EXPERIMENT

(*College Physics* 9th ed. pages 825–830/10th ed. pages 836–841)

In 1801 Thomas Young conducted a brilliant experiment that established the wave theory of light. He directed monochromatic light on a screen with a single narrow slit that behaved like a point source S. The light passes through the single slit and encounters a second screen with two narrow slits A and B. Each of the slits acts as a secondary source emitting coherent light.

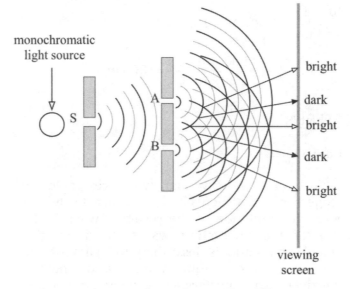

Two wave fronts emanate from these slits. Where crests coincide, the light is reinforced, and where a crest encounters a trough, the light cancels. The two sets of waves are directed on to a screen where one sees a pattern of bright and dark bands.

Consider point P on the viewing screen as shown on the diagram below. Note that the diagram is not to scale. The screen is positioned a perpendicular distance L from the screen containing slits A and B that are separated by a distance d.

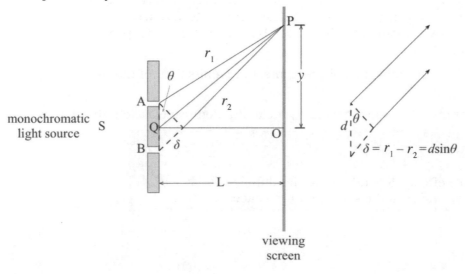

Both r_1 and r_2 are the distances rays travel from the slits to the screen. The rays emanating from A and B have the same frequency, the same amplitude, and start out in phase. The intensity of the light at point P is the result of light from both slits. Light from slit B travels further than a wave from slit A by an amount $d \sin\theta$. This distance is called the path difference δ, where

$$\delta = r_2 - r_1 = d \sin\theta$$

The above equation assumes that r_1 and r_2 travel in parallel lines because $L \gg d$.

The value of the path difference determines whether the two waves are in phase at point P. If the path difference is either zero or some integral multiple of the wavelength λ the waves will be in phase and constructive interference will take place.

The condition for constructive interference and bright fringes at point P is

$$d \sin\theta_{bright} = m\lambda \qquad \text{where } m = 0, \pm 1, \pm 2, \cdots$$

The number m is the *order number*. The central bright fringe at $\theta_{bright} = 0$ is the zeroth-order maximum. The maximum on each side of the zeroth-order maximum where $m = \pm 1$ is called the first-order maximum, and so forth.

When the path difference is an odd multiple of $\lambda/2$ then the two waves arriving at point P are 180° out of phase and causes destructive interference. The condition for destructive interference and dark fringes at point P is

$$d \sin\theta_{dark} = \left(m + \frac{1}{2}\right)\lambda \qquad \text{where } m = 0, \pm 1, \pm 2, \cdots$$

Constructive Interference

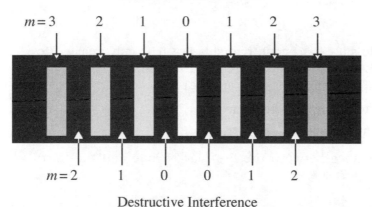

Destructive Interference

The spacing in the diagram is somewhat exaggerated. The spacing between the fringes is not uniform and increases as θ increases.

When $m = 0$, the path difference is $\lambda/2$, which is the first dark fringe on either side of the central maximum. When $m = 1$, the path difference is $3\lambda/2$, which is the condition for the second dark fringe and so forth.

In addition to the assumption of $L \gg d$, we also assume that $d \gg \lambda$. Under these conditions, θ is quite small, usually less than 4°. For such a small angle we can use the approximation $\sin\theta \cong \tan\theta$.

Then from the triangle OPQ: $y = L\tan\theta \approx L\sin\theta$. From this equation and $d\sin\theta_{bright} = m\lambda$ we find the positions of bright fringes measured from O by

$$y_{bright} = \frac{\lambda L}{d}m \qquad \text{where } m = 0, \ \pm 1, \ \pm 2, \ \cdots$$

And for dark fringe positions

$$y_{dark} = \frac{\lambda L}{d}\left(m + \frac{1}{2}\right) \qquad \text{where } m = 0, \ \pm 1, \ \pm 2, \ \cdots$$

Will there be an infinite number of fringes on a screen where constructive and destructive fringes occur? The $\sin\theta$ cannot exceed one. Thus, there is an upper limit to the values of m. The maximum value of m is the integer closest to the value but smaller than d/λ. There are a finite number of constructive and destructive interference fringes regardless the size of the screen.

AP Tip

Constructive interference occurs when the waves arrive in phase with one another.

AP Tip

Destructive interference occurs when the phase difference is a half-integral number of wavelengths.

SAMPLE PROBLEM 3

In a Young's double-slit experiment, two slits are 0.02 mm apart. The screen is located 1.80 m from the source and the third order bright fringe is located 12.50 cm from the central fringe.

(a) Determine the wavelength of the source.

(b) Where will the first dark fringe appear?

(c) What is the distance between the first dark fringe and the third order bright fringe?

SOLUTION TO PROBLEM 3

(a) Since θ is small we can use $\sin\theta \cong \tan\theta$ and can substitute y/L for θ. For a 3rd order bright fringe, $m = 3$. The wavelength is then found by using

$$\lambda = \frac{y_{bright}d}{mL} = \frac{(0.125 \text{ m})(2.00\times10^{-5} \text{ m})}{3(1.80 \text{ m})} = \mathbf{4.63\times10^{-7} \text{ m} = 463 \text{ nm}}$$

(b) For the first dark fringe $m = 0$. The position of the first dark fringe is found from

$$y_{dark} = \frac{\lambda L}{d}\left(m + \frac{1}{2}\right) = \frac{\left(4.63 \times 10^{-7}\ \text{m}\right)\left(1.80\ \text{m}\right)}{2\left(2.00 \times 10^{-5}\ \text{m}\right)} = \mathbf{2.08\ cm}$$

(c) The difference is simply $\Delta y = 12.6\ \text{cm} - 2.1\ \text{cm} = \mathbf{10.5\ cm}$

AP Tip

When calculating the maximum value of m we do not round off m_{max} to the nearest integer. Even if the calculation gives $m_{max} = 5.92$, we conclude that the maximum value of m possible is $m = 5$. It is rounded down to the nearest integer.

THIN FILMS

(*College Physics* 9th ed. pages 830–836/10th ed. pages 841–847)

Interference effects are commonly observed in thin films such as thin layers of oil on water and the thin surface of a soap bubble. The varied colors observed when incoherent white light is incident on such films result from the interference of light waves reflected from the two surfaces of the film.

Consider a thin film of thickness, t, as illustrated below. The light incident on the film is incident in a direction that is perpendicular to the surface of the film. The principle involved here would be the same for a different angle to the surface, but the calculations become more complicated and so we will deal with light being perpendicular to the surface of the film. The incident ray is partially reflected at the top of the film, surface A, as it travels from a material of index of refraction n_1 to the film that has an index of refraction of n_2. For clarity, the reflected ray, ray 1, is displaced slightly to the left.

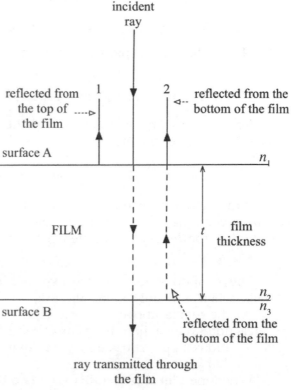

The remainder of the incident ray is transmitted through the film and reaches its bottom, surface B, where it encounters another medium with an index of refraction n_3 and is partially reflected and partially transmitted into the new material of index of refraction n_3.

The reflected ray, ray 2, then travels back to the top surface of the film where it is now transmitted into the material of original index n_1.

We have two rays that travel together away from the upper surface of the film; ray 1 that reflected from the top of the film and ray 2 that was reflected from the bottom of the film. These two rays can, in general, interfere with one another.

To determine whether the reflected rays interfere constructively or destructively, we note the following rules.

1. A light wave traveling from a medium of index of refraction n_1 toward a medium of index of refraction n_2 undergoes a 180° (π radian) phase change on reflection when $n_2 > n_1$. There is no phase change in the reflected light wave if $n_2 < n_1$.

2. The wavelength of light λ_n in a medium with index of refraction n is given by $\lambda_n = \lambda / n$ where λ is the wavelength of light in vacuum.

According to the first rule, ray 1, which is reflected from surface A, undergoes a phase change of 180° with respect to the incident ray. Ray 2, which is reflected from lower surface B, undergoes no phase change with respect to the incident ray. Ray 1 is 180° out of phase with ray 2, which is equivalent to a path difference of $\lambda_n / 2$. We must also consider the fact that ray 2 travels an extra distance of $2t$ before the two rays can recombine above surface A.

If $2t = \lambda_n / 2$, then rays 1 and 2 recombine in phase and constructive interference takes place. The condition for constructive interference in thin films is

$$2t = \left(m + \frac{1}{2} \right) \lambda_n \qquad \text{where } m = 0, 1, 2, \cdots$$

The above conditions take two factors into account:

1. The difference in path length for the two rays, which is the term $m\lambda_n$.

2. The 180° phase change upon reflection, which is the term $\lambda_n / 2$.

Since $\lambda_n = \lambda / n$ we can write the *condition for constructive interference* in thin films as

$$2nt = \left(m + \frac{1}{2} \right) \lambda \qquad \text{where } m = 0, 1, 2, \cdots$$

If the extra distance $2t$ traveled by ray 2 is a multiple of λ_n, the two waves combine out of phase and destructive interference results. The *condition for destructive interference* in thin films is

$$2nt = m\lambda \qquad \text{where } m = 0, 1, 2, \cdots$$

The equations for constructive and destructive interference are valid when and only when there is one phase reversal! This occurs when the media above and below the thin film both have indices of refraction greater than the index of refraction of the film or when both have indices of refraction less than the film ($n_1 > n_2 < n_3$ or $n_1 < n_2 > n_3$).

When the film is placed between two different media, one having a lower index of refraction than the film and one of higher index of refraction, the above equations are reversed ($n_1 < n_2 < n_3$ or $n_1 > n_2 > n_3$).

> ## AP Tip
>
> For thin film interference, an extra half-wavelength phase shift occurs when light reflects off an optically more dense medium, going from a material of lesser to a greater index of refraction.

SAMPLE PROBLEM 4

A student observes the interference of light with a soap bubble ($n = 1.33$) surrounded by air ($n = 1.00$).

(a) What is the minimum thickness for yellow light, $\lambda = 580$ nm, to be strongly reflected when the soap bubble is illuminated by white light and observed from directly above?

(b) What is the minimum thickness needed to remove the yellow light, $\lambda = 580$ nm from the reflection of white light from the soap bubble?

(c) In a third thin-film interference observation an organic material ($n = 1.36$) is placed on a layer of glass ($n = 1.50$). What wavelength of white light is strongly reinforced in the reflected light if the film has a thickness of 184.0 nm?

SOLUTION TO PROBLEM 4

(a) The light coming from air to the soap bubble encounters a medium of higher index of refraction and undergoes a 180° phase shift in the reflection from the upper surface. Reflection from the lower surface is in phase.

Minimum thickness means that $m = 0$. Since $n_{air} > n_{bubble} < n_{air}$, we write

$$2n_{film}t = \left(m + \frac{1}{2}\right)\lambda$$

Solving for the thickness of the film, t

$$t = \left(m + \frac{1}{2}\right)\frac{\lambda}{2n_{film}} = \left(0 + \frac{1}{2}\right)\frac{\lambda}{2n_{film}} = \frac{\lambda}{4n_{film}} = \frac{580 \text{ nm}}{4(1.33)} = \textbf{109 nm}$$

(b) The minimum thickness for destructive interference to occur requires a path length in the film of $\lambda/2$. The ray reflected from the lower surface of the film has traveled a total length of λ. The minimum thickness requires $m = 1$ and then $2n_{film}t = m\lambda$. Solving for t

$$t = \frac{m\lambda}{2n_{film}} = \frac{1(580 \text{ nm})}{2(1.33)} = \textbf{218 nm}$$

(c) The ray reflected from the upper surface undergoes a phase shift of 180°. The ray reflected from the lower surface also undergoes a phase shift of 180°, since $n_1 < n_2 < n_3$, and for constructive interference $m = 1$: $2n_{film}t = m\lambda$

Solving for λ,

$$\lambda = \frac{2n_{film}t}{m} = \frac{2(1.36)(184 \text{ nm})}{1} = \textbf{500 nm}$$

OPTICAL COATINGS

(*College Physics* 9th ed. page 833/10th ed. page 844)

Interference in a thin film is desirable to reduce unwanted reflections from the glass of a camera lens or the lenses of a pair of binoculars. Lenses are often coated with thin films of transparent, durable materials such as magnesium fluoride, MgF_2. Destructive interference in an optical coating minimizes unwanted reflections from glass.

SAMPLE PROBLEM 5

To produce a minimum reflection of wavelengths near the middle of the visible spectrum, 550 nm, how thick of a coating of MgF_2 ($n = 1.38$) should be vacuum-coated on a camera lens ($n = 1.55$)?

SOLUTION TO PROBLEM 5

Consider incident light to be normal to the surface of the film.

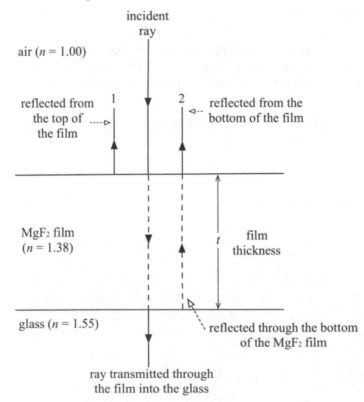

incident ray

air ($n = 1.00$)

reflected from the top of ----▷ the film   1   2   reflected from the bottom of the film

MgF_2 film ($n = 1.38$) t film thickness

glass ($n = 1.55$)   reflected through the bottom of the MgF_2 film

ray transmitted through the film into the glass

We wish to cause destructive interference between ray 1 and ray 2 so that maximum energy passes into the glass. A phase change occurs with each ray for both the upper and the lower surfaces of the MgF$_2$ film. Since $n_1 < n_2 < n_3$ and for destructive interference and setting $m = 0$ we can write: $2n_{film}t = \left(m + \dfrac{1}{2} \right)\lambda$

Solving for the film thickness

$$t = \left(m + \frac{1}{2} \right)\frac{\lambda}{2n_{film}} = \frac{\lambda}{4n_{film}} = \frac{550 \text{ nm}}{4(1.38)} = \textbf{99.6 nm}$$

DIFFRACTION

(College Physics 9th ed. pages 836–837/10th ed. pages 847–848)

Light travels in straight lines in a uniform medium but commonly changes directions where there is a change of medium or a change in the properties of a single medium. This, of course, is the cause of reflection and refraction. Careful observation shows that there is also a slight bending around opaque objects placed in a beam of light. The spreading of light into the region behind an obstacle is called *diffraction*. Diffraction occurs in accordance with Huygen's principle and is an interference phenomenon.

Any obstacle placed into a light beam coming from a point source will cause diffraction effects under proper conditions. A slit, a thin wire, and a razor edge are examples of such objects. A razor's edge illuminated by a beam of monochromatic light from a point source casts a shadow that is not geometrically sharp. A small amount of light bends around the edge into the geometric shadow, and a series of alternating light and dark bands are found to border the shadow.

If a hole on a screen is illuminated by monochromatic light, the image formed on a screen is not a single well-defined spot of light but rather a series of light and dark rings.

SINGLE-SLIT DIFFRACTION

(College Physics 9th ed. pages 837–839/10th ed. pages 848–850)

Consider a beam of monochromatic light illuminating a narrow slit of width *a*. In the illustrations below, sets of arrows were drawn to suggest that the wave front can be imagined to consist of many coherent secondary sources. Rays going straight ahead are all in phase and when they fall on a screen they will appear as a bright band.

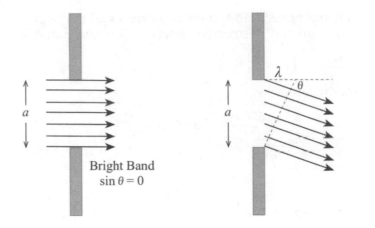

Bright Band
$\sin \theta = 0$

In the diagram on the right, consider the two rays 1 and 4. Note in the diagram that these as two light sources are distance $a/2$ apart. They give an interference pattern much like that due to double slits; that is, when $(a/2)\sin\theta = \lambda/2$, these two waves cancel. Consider another pair of rays just below 1 and 4. These, too, also cancel. Keep moving down the slit in this manner and you will see that each ray can be paired off with another ray that will cancel it.

Repeating the process by dividing the slit into four parts rather than two and using similar reasoning. The effective slit spacing is $a/4$, so $(a/4) = \sin\theta = \lambda/2$, or $a\sin\lambda = 2\lambda$. We can divide the slit into 6 zones and then 8 zones and so on. The general result is

$$\sin\theta_{dark} = \frac{m\lambda}{a} \qquad \text{where } m = 1,\ 2,\ 3\ \cdots \text{ single slit minima}$$

Do not confuse this with the condition for maxima in the double slit experiment, even though the equations appear similar.

SAMPLE PROBLEM 6

In a laboratory experiment, a student observes a diffraction pattern in which a single slit, of width a, is illuminated by monochromatic light of wavelength $\lambda = 540$ nm.

(a) If the first dark band is 5.2° from the central axis, what is the width of the slit?

(b) At what angle will the student locate the third dark band?

SOLUTION TO PROBLEM 6

(a) Solving for the width a

$$a = \frac{m\lambda}{\sin\theta_{dark}} = \frac{(1)(5.4\times10^{-7}\text{ m})}{\sin 5.2°} = 6\times10^{-6}\text{ m}$$

(b) To find the angle we use

$$\sin\theta_{dark} = \frac{m\lambda}{a} \text{ and}$$

$$\theta_{dark} = \sin^{-1}\left(\frac{m\lambda}{a}\right) = \sin^{-1}\left[\frac{3\left(5.4\times10^{-7}\text{ m}\right)}{6\times10^{-6}\text{ m}}\right] = \mathbf{15.7°}$$

THE DIFFRACTION GRATING

(College Physics 9th ed. pages 839–842/10th ed. pages 851–854)

The principles of interference and diffraction find importance in measuring wavelengths of light with the optical diffraction grating. A grating for use with transmitted light is a glass plate ruled with a large number of equally spaced opaque lines, usually several thousand lines per centimeter. A grating is specified in terms of its number of lines per centimeter. The spacing, d, between the rulings is the inverse of the line population per centimeter. If a grating is specified as having 2500 lines/cm or 2500 cm^{-1}, the spacing is $d = 1/N = 1/2500$ cm$^{-1} = 4.0\times10^{-4}$ cm $= 4.0\times10^{-6}$ m . A diffraction grating is basically a system with a large number of optical slits.

The interference pattern produced by a diffraction grating is a series of sharp, widely spaced bright fringes that are called *principal maxima*. Dark regions with a number of weak secondary maxima separate the principle maxima fringes. The angle at which a principal maximum appears is dependent on the wavelength of light that passes through the grating. The grating acts like a prism by sending various components of white light off in different directions. Unlike the prism, the diffraction grating spreads light over a wider range.

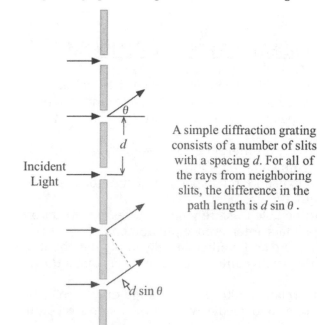

A simple diffraction grating consists of a number of slits with a spacing d. For all of the rays from neighboring slits, the difference in the path length is $d\sin\theta$.

To find the angles at which principal maxima are formed, consider a diffraction grating of large number of slits where each one is separated by a distance d, as illustrated in the above diagram. A beam of light of wavelength λ illuminates the left side of the grating and is diffracted to the right on to a screen on to a distant screen. At angle θ to the incident direction the path difference between adjacent slits is $d \sin\theta$ as shown above.

Constructive interference and a principal maximum produced by a diffraction grating occurs when the path difference is an integral number of wavelengths, λ

$$d \sin\theta = m\lambda \qquad \text{where } m = 0, \ \pm 1, \ \pm 2, \cdots$$

When a grating has more lines per centimeter, d is smaller, and the angle θ becomes greater spreading the incoming light over a wider range of angles.

SAMPLE PROBLEM 7

A diffraction grating, ruled with 200 lines per millimeter, is used to determine the wavelength of a monochromatic light source. If the third-order spectrum occurs at an angle of 19.0°, what is the wavelength of the source?

SOLUTION TO PROBLEM 7

First we need to determine the width of the lines.

$$d = \frac{1}{200 \text{ mm}^{-1}} = 5 \times 10^{-3} \text{ mm} = 5 \times 10^{-6} \text{ m}$$

To find the wavelength we use $d \sin\theta = m\lambda$ and

$$\lambda = \frac{d \sin\theta}{m} = \frac{\left(5 \times 10^{-6} \text{ m}\right)\left(\sin 19°\right)}{3} = \textbf{543 nm}$$

WAVE OPTICS: STUDENT OBJECTIVES FOR THE AP EXAM

■ You should know that all electromagnetic waves travel with the same speed, c, in a vacuum and be able to state and relate the relationship between speed, wavelength, and frequency of these waves.

■ You should know the difference between parts of the electromagnetic spectrum and their sources.

■ You should be able to explain why dispersion occurs for the visible part of the electromagnetic spectrum.

■ You should know and be able to state what is necessary for two or more light waves to produce interference phenomena.

■ You should be able to state and mathematically apply the equations for constructive and destructive interference in the *Young's double-slit experiment*.

■ You should be able to relate a 180° phase change due to reflection at the boundary between two media when $n_2 > n_1$, and recognize that there is no phase change at the boundary between the two media when $n_2 < n_1$.

- You should also recognize that the interference between the waves reflected from the upper and lower surface of a thin film also depends on the path length 2t in the film before the waves combine at the upper surface.
- You should be able to solve for thin-film interference, both constructive and destructive, when one and two phase changes occur at the boundaries between the media.
- You should be able to apply the equations for constructive and destructive interference in a diffraction pattern.
- You should be able to solve multiple-choice questions/problems with a calculator.

MULTIPLE-CHOICE QUESTIONS

A double-slit interference pattern, as illustrated in the diagram below, is to be used to answer questions 1 and 2.

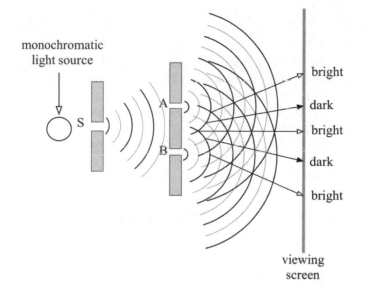

1. The slits A and B in the above diagram can be moved relative to each other. Based on this, which of the following is true?
   (A) Decreasing the slit separation increases the width of the fringes.
   (B) Decreasing the slit separation decreases the width of the fringes.
   (C) Increasing the slit separation increases the width of the fringes.
   (D) Changing the slit separation does not alter the width of the fringes.

2. In the double-slit interference pattern shown above, when the path difference between two waves is
   (A) even multiples of $\lambda/2$, destructive interference occurs, producing a dark fringe
   (B) odd multiples of $\lambda/2$, destructive interference occurs, producing a dark fringe
   (C) even multiples of λ, destructive interference occurs, producing a bright fringe
   (D) odd multiples of λ, destructive interference occurs, producing a bright fringe

3. In a double-slit interference pattern, using different wavelengths of light to produce fringes, rank the wavelength of light illuminating the slits that will produce fringe patterns on the screen whose spacing is closer together to further apart.
   (A) red, orange, green, blue
   (B) green, blue, orange, red
   (C) blue, red, green, orange
   (D) blue, green, orange, red

4. In a single-slit experiment, increasing the width of the slit results in
   (A) widening the diffraction pattern moving the secondary bands farther from a wider central band
   (B) narrowing the diffraction pattern moving the secondary bands closer a narrower central band
   (C) no change in the central band while moving wider secondary bands farther away from the central band
   (D) increasing the width of the central band while decreasing the width of the secondary bands

5. White light falling on a prism as shown in the diagram below

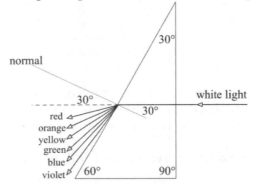

refracts the light and produces a series of colors known as a visible spectrum. This is due to the fact that the index of refraction, n, which relates the speed of light in air to the speed of light in the prism,
   (A) is independent on the wavelength of the light in the prism
   (B) is dependent on the angle of incidence
   (C) is dependent on the wavelength of the light in the prism with shorter wavelengths refracted the least
   (D) is dependent on the wavelength of the light in the prism with shorter wavelengths refracted the most

6. Rank the frequency of the light in the prism from highest to lowest.
   (A) violet > blue > green > red
   (B) violet = blue = green = red
   (C) red > green > blue > violet
   (D) red > green > blue = violet

7. A 765 nm beam of light passes through several narrow slits, producing the diffraction patterns shown below. Rank the pattern from the widest slit to the narrowest.

   (A) A > B > C > D
   (B) C > B > A > D
   (C) A > D > B > C
   (D) D > A > B > C

8. Colors are observed in soap bubbles suspended in air. These are caused by interference between the light reflected from the upper surface and the lower surface of the soap bubble and the thickness of the soap bubble. (Assume near normal angles for the surfaces of the film and uniform thickness of the film.) Which of the following statements is correct?

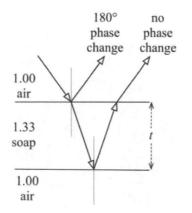

   (A) For constructive interference to occur for a given color, the path length in the film should be $t = \lambda/4$ of the wavelength for that color.
   (B) For constructive interference to occur for a given color, the path length in the film should be $t = \lambda/2$ of the wavelength for that color.
   (C) For destructive interference to occur for a given color, the path length in the film should be $t = 3\lambda/8$ of the wavelength for that color.
   (D) For destructive interference to occur for a given color, the path length in the film is of the wavelength for that color $t = 3\lambda/16$.

9. Two sources that are in phase are used to create a disturbance in a ripple tank, producing circular waves spreading outward from the sources. A light shining through the water to a paper on the floor beneath the ripple tank shows the pattern in the diagram below.

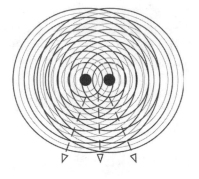

The pattern produced is similar to that observed in Young's double-slit experiment. Nodal lines shown in the diagram represent
(A) constructive interference of the water waves
(B) destructive interference of the water waves
(C) polarization of the light passing through the water
(D) dispersion of the light passing through the water

10. Light passing through an opening between two obstacles whose spacing is comparable in size to the wavelength of light illuminating the opening spreads out carrying energy with the wave.

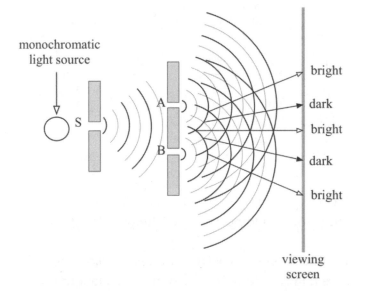

(A) A series of bright and dark fringes of the superposition of Huygens wavelets from each part of the slit have produced constructive and destructive interference some distance to the top and bottom of the slit, carrying energy outward from the central bright as indicated by the bright fringes.

(B) Most of the energy of the wave is carried in a very narrow region where a single band of light appears; very little is transferred around the obstacles.

(C) Light refracts as it passes through the opening, producing a series of bright and dark fringes, as shown in the diagram, carrying energy with it as it refracts.

(D) As the light passes through the opening, polarization of the wave occurs causing the electrical field vector, $\vec{E}$ and the magnetic field vector $\vec{B}$ to separate, carrying energy to the right and to the left of the opening between the obstacles reaching distances far away from the opening.

11. The intensity of a beam of electromagnetic radiation with an oscillating electric field vector $\vec{E}$ and magnetic field vector $\vec{B}$ is passed through a filter as shown in the diagram.

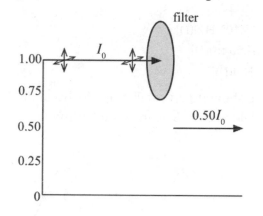

The beam is

(A) linearly polarized since the intensity of the incident beam is reduced to $0.5I_0$

(B) partially polarized with a reduction in the intensity of both the electrical field vector $\vec{E}$ and magnetic field vector $\vec{B}$

(C) unpolarized, but the filter absorbed half of the energy, converting it to internal energy in the filter

(D) unpolarized since the intensity dropped to $0.5I_0$. If it were linearly polarized, I would be zero

12. The representation of the electromagnetic wave shown below is a graph of its electric field $\vec{E}$–vector as a function of time. The magnetic field $\vec{B}$ component is not shown.

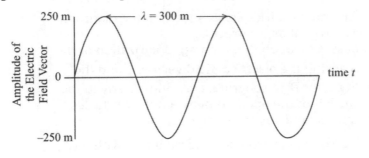

The correct equation relating the waveform shown above is

(A) $x = (250 \text{ m}) \sin[(2\pi)(3 \times 10^3 \text{ m})(t)]$

(B) $x = (250 \text{ m}) \sin[(2\pi)(1 \times 10^6 \text{ Hz})(t)]$

(C) $x = (300 \text{ m}) \cos[(2\pi)(250 \text{ m})(t)]$

(D) $x = (300 \text{ m}) \cos[(500 \text{ Hz})(t)]$

13. An electromagnetic wave showing an oscillating electrical field vector $\vec{E}$ and magnetic field vector $\vec{B}$ is indicated in the diagram below.

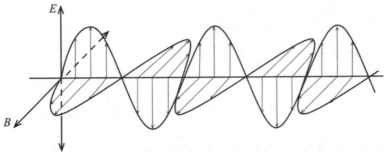

Which of the following diagrams gives a correct representation of the electromagnetic wave as it passes through a polarizer?

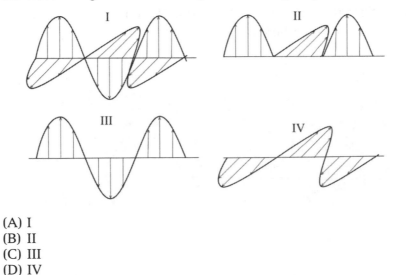

(A) I

(B) II

(C) III

(D) IV

14. In a single-slit experiment, increasing the width of the slit, *d*, from a fraction of a wavelength to a wavelength results in
    (A) increasing the diffraction pattern
    (B) narrowing the diffraction pattern
    (C) no change in the diffraction pattern
    (D) reversing the diffraction pattern.

Question 15

Directions: For the question below, <u>two</u> of the suggested answers will be correct. You must select <u>both</u> correct choices to earn credit. No partial credit will be earned if only one correct answer is selected. Select the two that are best in each case and then enter both of the appropriate answers in the corresponding space on the answer sheet.

15. Which of the following statements are true of both of the waveforms shown below?

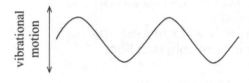

They both
    (A) transfer energy and momentum from one part of the wave to another without transferring matter as the disturbance moves through the medium
    (B) have properties associated with their motion such as wavelength, frequency, wave speed, and amplitude that remain constant as they travel through a medium of uniform density
    (C) can travel in solids, liquids, gases and vacuum with constant speed dependent of the density of the medium
    (D) can show reflection and refraction, but superposition only applies to transverse wave forms

FREE-RESPONSE PROBLEMS

1. A student conducts an interference experiment using a laser source of monochromatic light of wavelength = 635 nm.
    (a) The light is incident on a double slit having a separation of *d* = 0.04 mm. At what angle from the central maximum will the second-order
        i. maximum occur?
        ii. minimum occur?
    (b) The light is incident on a single slit of separation, *a* = 0.04 mm. At what angle will the second-order
        i. maximum occur?
        ii. minimum occur?
    (c) If the screen is 1.50 m from the double slits, what is the linear separation between the first-order maximum and the fourth-order maximum?

(d) The student places the double-slit film in water ($n = 1.33$) and illuminates it with monochromatic light of $\lambda_{air} = 635$ nm. What is the angle from the central maximum of the second order maximum?

2. Monochromatic light of wavelength = 630 nm is directed on a diffraction grating ruled with 300 lines per mm. Determine the
   (a) angle for the first-order maxima
   (b) angle for the third-order maxima
   (c) angle between the first- and third-order maxima
   (d) maximum number of orders that can be observed

3. Design an experiment to determine the wavelength of light from a coherent source such as a laser pointer falling on a diffraction grating in enough detail that another student could perform your experiment and duplicate your results.
   (a) Make a diagram of your experimental set up, labeling all the equipment you will use in your experiment.
   (b) What measurements will you take and how will you use them to determine the wavelength of the source of coherent light used in your experiment?
   (c) What assumptions did you make and how might these assumptions affect your results?
   (d) What determines the maximum number of orders that are seen in the experiment?

4. (a) Why is it possible for radio waves to diffract around buildings when visible light waves that are also electromagnetic radiation traveling with the same velocity do not?
   (b) You leave the cafeteria early to ask your teacher about an assignment while another class is in session. How is it possible that you can hear the conversation in the room while you are standing in the hall away from the open door in the room?

Answers

MULTIPLE-CHOICE QUESTIONS

1. **A** In a double-slit interference pattern, when the separation, d, between the slits is decreased, the width of the fringes increases.
   $$y_{bright} = \frac{\lambda L}{d}.$$
   (*College Physics* 9th ed. pages 825–830/10th ed. pages 836–840)
   (L.O. 6.C.2.1, 6.C.3.1)

2. **B** For destructive interference to occur in between two waves in a Young's double slit experiment producing a dark fringe, the path length must be an odd multiple of $\lambda/2$.

If the order number m = 0, then the path difference $\delta = \lambda/2$; if the order number is $m = 1$, the path difference is $\delta = 3\lambda/2$, etc.
(*College Physics* 9th ed. pages 825–830/10th ed. pages 836–840)
(L.O. 6.C.2.1, 6.C.3.1)

3. **D** The smaller the wavelength the closer the fringe patterns are together $y_{bright} = \dfrac{m\lambda L}{d}$.

The correct ranking is blue, green, orange, red.
(*College Physics* 9th ed. pages 825–830/10th ed. pages 836–840)
(L.O. 6.C.2.1, 6.3.C.1, 6.E.1.1)

4. **B** As the width of the slit in a single-slit diffraction pattern is increased, the pattern narrows. The central band becomes narrower and the secondary bands move closer to the central band.
(*College Physics* 9th ed. pages 836–839/10th ed. pages 847-850)
(L.O. 6.C.2.1)

5. **D** Light of all wavelengths is reduced in speed in glass, but violet light with a wavelength of $\lambda \cong 400 \text{ nm}$, which is refracted the greatest amount, travels more slowly than red light, $\lambda \cong 650 \text{ nm}$, which is refracted least. This effect is called *dispersion*.
(*College Physics* 9th ed. pages 771–774/10th ed. pages 782–785)
(L.O. 6.E.3.3)

6. **A** The frequency of light in the prism is determined from $v = \lambda f$. Since red is refracted the least, its speed is the greatest. Since its speed in the prism is the largest, its frequency is the smallest.
(*College Physics* 9th ed. pages 771–774/10th ed. pages 782–785)
(L.O. 6.E.3.3)

7. **D** The narrower the slit the light passes through, the more the diffracted light is spread out. The central maximum is widest in C so this is the narrowest slit. The correct order from widest to narrowest is D > A > B > C.
(*College Physics* 9th ed. pages 836–839/10th ed. pages 847–850)
(L.O. 6.E.3.1)

8. **A** The ray of light in the diagram traveling from air to the soap bubble undergoes reflection and refraction due to a speed change at the upper boundary. The ray is reflected 180° out of phase at the upper surface of the soap bubble (acts as a fixed boundary since n in the soap bubble is greater than n in air) producing a path difference of $\lambda/2$ between the reflected and refracted rays at the upper surface. The ray striking the lower surface and reflected back to the upper surface is reflected in phase since the ray interacting at the lower surface travels from the soap bubble to air and there is no phase change at the lower boundary (free boundary). In order to cause constructive interference of the two

rays from the upper and lower boundary, the ray in the soap bubble must travel a distance t equal to $\lambda/4$ down and $\lambda/4$ back to the upper surface to be in phase with the ray at the upper surface. Thus the minimum thickness of the film must be $\lambda/4$.
(*College Physics* 9th ed. pages 830–834/10th ed. pages 841–845)
(L.O. 6.E.3.1, 6.E.3.3)

9. **B** The nodal lines indicate regions were no displacement from the equilibrium occurs. Therefore it is destructive interference, corresponding to a dark fringe in a Young's double-slit experiment.
(*College Physics* 9th ed. page 826/10th ed. page 837)
(L.O. 6.C.1.1)

10. **A** When the width of the opening between obstacles is comparable to the wavelength of light illuminating the opening, the wave spreads out around the obstacles carrying energy with it. This is very much like water waves in a pond bending around an opening in a barrier, carrying energy to the other end of a pond or being able to hear sound coming from the other side of an open door.
(*College Physics* 9th ed. pages 825–829/10th ed. pages 836–840)
(L.O. 6.C.4.1)

11. **A** Since the filter reduces the intensity of the beam from I_0 to $0.5I_0$, one of the components of the transverse electromagnetic radiation is not transmitted by the filter (called a polarizer). The beam is linearly polarized along the direction of one of the field vectors the electric field vector $\vec{E}$.
(*College Physics* 9th ed. pages 842–844/10th ed. pages 854–856)
(L.O. 6.A.1.3)

12. **B** The wave is a sine wave with amplitude of ±250 m and a wavelength $\lambda = 300$ m. The basic form of the equation is $x = A\sin 2\pi ft$. The frequency can be determined from inspection since $c = \lambda f$, the frequency is 1×10^6 Hz.
(*College Physics* 9th ed. page 743/10th ed. page 753)
(L.O. 6.B.3.1)

13. **A** Electromagnetic waves with an oscillating electric field vector $\vec{E}$ and magnetic field vector $\vec{B}$ have random planes of vibration before they pass through a polarizer. The polarizer will transmit the EM waves that vibrate in the same plane—linearly or plane polarized.
(*College Physics* 9th ed. pages 743, 842–844/10th ed. pages 753, 854–856)
(L.O. 6.B.3.1)

14. **B** As the slit opening d increases, the pattern narrows. The central band becomes narrower and the secondary bands move closer to the central band.
(*College Physics* 9th ed. pages 836–839/10th ed. pages 847–850)
(L.O. 6.E.3.1)

15. **A and B** Both waveforms transfer energy as they move through the medium. It is the energy that causes each particle in the wave to oscillate about the equilibrium position as the wave front advances through the medium. In a medium of uniform density, $v = \lambda f$ will give the relationship among the three. Amplitude is related to energy; the more energy the greater the particle will move in its oscillation from the equilibrium position. Transverse waves such as electromagnetic waves, unlike longitudinal waves, can travel in vacuum. Superposition applies to all waveforms. (*College Physics* 9th ed. pages 461–462, 474, 742–744, 824–825/10th ed. pages 470–472, 482, 753–755, 835–836) (L.O. 6.A.1.2)

FREE-RESPONSE PROBLEMS

1. (a) i. The angle for the second-order maximum is given by

$$d\sin\theta_{bright} = (m\lambda) \qquad \text{where } m = 0, \ \pm 1, \ \pm 2, \ ...$$

Solving for θ

$$\theta_{bright} = \sin^{-1}\left(\frac{m\lambda}{d}\right) = \sin^{-1}\left[\frac{2(6.35\times10^{-7}\text{m})}{4.0\times10^{-5}\text{m}}\right] = \textbf{1.82°}$$

   ii. The angle for the second-order minimum is given by

$$d\sin\theta_{dark} = \left(m + \frac{1}{2}\right)\lambda \qquad \text{where } m = 0, \ \pm 1, \ \pm 2, \ ...$$

The second order minimum occurs at

$$\theta_{dark} = \sin^{-1}\left(\frac{1.5\lambda}{d}\right) = \sin^{-1}\left[\frac{1.5(6.35\times10^{-7}\text{m})}{4.0\times10^{-5}\text{m}}\right] = \textbf{1.36°}$$

   (b) The equation for part (a) i. $\sin\theta_{bright} = \dfrac{m\lambda}{d}$ and part

   (b) i. $\sin\theta_{dark} = \dfrac{m\lambda}{a}$ have the same form, *but* they do not mean the same thing. In part (a) the equation describes the *bright* regions in a two-slit interference pattern where *d* is the separation of the slits A and B.
   In part (b), the equation describes the *dark* regions in a single-slit interference pattern where *a* is the single-slit width.

   i. $a \sin\theta_{bright} = \left(m + \dfrac{1}{2}\right)\lambda \qquad \text{where } m = 0, \ \pm 1, \ \pm 2, \ ...$

   Solving for θ

$$\theta_{bright} = \sin^{-1}\left(\frac{1.5\lambda}{a}\right) = \sin^{-1}\left[\frac{1.5(6.35\times10^{-7}\text{m})}{4.0\times10^{-5}\text{m}}\right] = \textbf{1.36°}$$

   ii. $\theta_{dark} = \sin^{-1}\left(\dfrac{m\lambda}{a}\right) = \sin^{-1}\left[\dfrac{2(6.35\times10^{-7}\text{m})}{4.0\times10^{-5}\text{m}}\right] = \textbf{1.82°}$

(c) The linear separation is given by

$$y_{bright} = \frac{\lambda L m}{d} \text{ and } \Delta y = (y_4 - y_1) = \frac{6.35 \times 10^{-7}\text{m} \times 1.5\text{m} \times (4-1)}{4.0 \times 10^{-5}\text{m}} =$$

0.071 m

(d) The angle for the second-order maximum is

$$\lambda_n = \frac{\lambda}{n} = \frac{635 \text{ nm}}{1.33} = 477 \text{ nm}$$

$$\theta = \sin^{-1}\left(\frac{m\lambda}{d}\right) = \sin^{-1}\left[\frac{2(4.77 \times 10^{-7}\text{m})}{4.0 \times 10^{-5}\text{m}}\right] = \textbf{1.37}°$$

(*College Physics* 9th ed. pages 839–842/10th ed. pages 626–630)

2. (a) First, we need to find d

$$d = \frac{1}{300 \text{ mm}^{-1}} = 3.33 \times 10^{-6}\text{m}$$

The angle for the first-order maxima is

$$\theta_1 = \sin^{-1}\left(\frac{m\lambda}{d}\right) = \sin^{-1}\left[\frac{1(6.30 \times 10^{-7}\text{m})}{3.33 \times 10^{-6}\text{m}}\right] = \textbf{10.9}°$$

(b) The angle for the third-order maxima is

$$\theta_3 = \sin^{-1}\left(\frac{m\lambda}{d}\right) = \sin^{-1}\left[\frac{3(6.30 \times 10^{-7}\text{m})}{3.33 \times 10^{-6}\text{m}}\right] = \textbf{34.6}°$$

(c) The angle between the first- and third-order maxima is
$$\Delta\theta = 34.6° - 10.9° = \textbf{23.7}°$$

(d) The maximum number of orders that can be observed:
The maximum number of orders occurs when $\theta = 90°$ since
$\sin 90° = 1$

$$m = \frac{d}{\lambda} = \frac{3.33 \times 10^{-6}\text{m}}{6.30 \times 10^{-7}\text{m}} = \textbf{5.28}$$

> You *cannot* have a partial order. The maximum number of orders that can be observed under the given conditions is 5.

(*College Physics* 9th ed. pages 839–842/10th ed. pages 851–854)

3. (a) Design of the experimental procedure:
   - Record the ruling on the diffraction grating.
   - Determine the spacing, d, between the rulings of the diffraction grating in the experiment. Record d in data chart.
   (Note to student: The ruling is provided on the diffraction grating or can be obtained from your teacher. For example, if the grating is marked 100 lines/mm, the spacing between the lines is the reciprocal of the ruling—in this case the spacing is 10^{-5} m/line.)

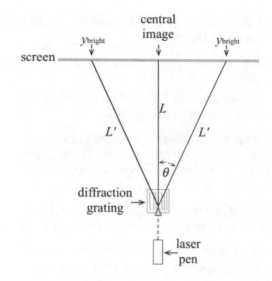

- Measure the distance L from the diffraction grating to the screen. (White paper taped to a wall or a whiteboard.) Record.
- Project the laser pointer so that the light passing through the diffraction grating falls on the white paper, producing the central image and orders to the left and right of the central image.
- Mark the position of the central image on the white paper.
- Mark the positions of the first order images right and left from the central image on the white paper.
- Continue marking for the second and third order images right and left from the central image.
- Mark other order images if you can obtain them using your diffraction grating.

(b) The wavelength of the laser light is determined from

$m\lambda = d\sin\theta_{bright}$ where $m = 0,\ \pm1,\ \pm2,...$ If the distance from

the grating is large enough, the $\tan\theta_{bright} = \dfrac{y_{bright}}{L}$ can be

substituted for $\sin\theta_{bright}$ and eliminate the use of a protractor in the experiment.

Measurement will include the distance from the grating to the screen locating the central image. Distance from the central image to each order image will be measured as y_{bright} and recorded in the data chart.

The distance to the right and the left of the central bright image will be averaged for each order seen and marked.

Calculate the wavelength of the laser pointer's light by

substitution into $m\lambda = d\sin\theta_{bright}$ or $m\lambda = \dfrac{d(y_{bright})}{L}$.

(c) The laser pointer does not produce one specific wavelength, but a narrow range. The range for a red laser pointer is 630 nm to 670 nm. For green, the range is 500 nm to 550 nm. Error should be calculated from the range, not a specific number as marked on some inexpensive pointers.

Substitution of $\tan\theta_{bright}$ for $\sin\theta_{bright}$ will introduce error if the angle is greater than 5°.

(d) The maximum angle of deviation is 90°. If the second order is seen at 76° there will be no third-order image.

** Alternatives to the experiment may use a mercury vapor lamp as the source of a discrete spectrum of light since the wavelengths in the mercury vapor spectrum are known to one decimal place.

Discharge tubes that produce discrete spectrums, such as hydrogen, helium, and mercury can be used in the experiment.

A showcase bulb will produce a continuous spectrum and it will be difficult to analyze a specific wavelength even if a colored cellophane filter is wrapped around the bulb.
(*College Physics* 9th ed. pages 839–842/10th ed. pages 851–854)
(L.O. 6.C.2.1, 6.C.3.1)

4. (a) The requirement for diffraction of Huygens wavelets is the opening through which the plane waves pass to be about the same size as the wavelength of the wave passing through the opening. If the opening is small, the wavelet cannot reproduce a straight wave front, some spreads out, and diffracts through the opening.

In the case of radio waves, the wavelength λ is about 10^3 m to about 10^{-2} m whereas visible light has a wavelength, λ, ranging from 400 nm to 700 nm. For visible light, the opening around buildings is just too large to cause diffraction.

(b) Compressional or longitudinal sound waves diffract in the same manner as transverse waveforms. When sound waves pass through an aperture, such as a door, or past the edge of an obstacle, they always bend to some degree into a region not directly exposed to the sound or light source. Diffraction is the ability of waves to bend around edges and obstacles placed in their path. In order to have waves diffract around the edges of an open door, the size of the opening must be about the same size as the wave. For human speech, the wavelengths for sound waves are about 1 m, close to the size of the open door.
(*College Physics* 9th ed. pages 747–748, 836–839/10th ed. pages 757–759, 847–850)
(L.O. 6.C.2.1, 6.E.1.1)

18

ATOMIC AND QUANTUM PHYSICS

PLANCK'S QUANTUM THEORY

(*College Physics* 9th ed. pages 911–913/10th ed. pages 923–925)

In 1903, Max Planck theoretically showed that light streams from light sources as tiny lumps of energy that he called *quanta* and each quantum of light have an energy related to the frequency of the light. That relationship is

$$E = hf$$

where h is called Planck's constant and has a value $h = 6.63 \times 10^{-34}$ J·s, and f is the frequency of the light. Planck suggested that light was made of particles that carried energy. For the previous two hundred years science thought that light was made of electromagnetic waves. Planck thought that quanta were associated with electromagnetic waves that acted as a carrier.

SAMPLE PROBLEM 1

Determine the energy of a single quantum of yellow light that has a wavelength of 590 nm. Express the answer in both J and eV. Quantum is the singular form of quanta.

Solution to Problem 1

First we write the Planck equation $E = hf$. Recall that wavelength and frequency are related by $c = \lambda f$ or $f = c/\lambda$. Substitute for frequency in the Planck equation and

$$E = \frac{hc}{\lambda} = \frac{\left(6.63 \times 10^{-34}\ \text{J} \cdot \text{s}\right)\left(3 \times 10^8\ \text{m}/\text{s}\right)}{590 \times 10^{-9}\ \text{m}} = \mathbf{3.37 \times 10^{-19}\ J}$$

Converting J to eV we need a conversion factor

$$3.37 \times 10^{-19}\ \text{J} \times \frac{1\ \text{eV}}{1.602 \times 10^{-19}\ \text{J}} = \mathbf{2.10\ eV}$$

Sample Problem 2

A quanta of infrared light carries an energy of 0.90 eV. What is the wavelength of the associated electromagnetic wave? What is the frequency?

Solution to Problem 2

First, convert eV to J as $0.90\ \text{eV} \times \dfrac{1.602 \times 10^{-19}\ \text{J}}{1\ \text{eV}} = 1.44 \times 10^{-19}\ \text{J}$

Next, write the expanded form of Planck's equation $E = \dfrac{hc}{\lambda}$ and solve for wavelength.

$$\lambda = \frac{hc}{E} = \frac{\left(6.64 \times 10^{-34}\ \text{J} \cdot \text{s}\right)\left(3 \times 10^8\ \text{m}/\text{s}\right)}{1.44 \times 10^{-19}\ \text{J}} = \mathbf{1.38 \times 10^{-6}\ m}$$

The major questions of the early part of the twentieth century were: is light a wave? Is light a particle? Is light both?

Special Relativity and Mass-Energy Equivalence

(*College Physics* 9th ed. pages 888–896, 899–902/10th ed. pages 900–908, 911–915)

During the spring of 1905, Albert Einstein published a series of papers that gave the scientific community both a jolt and an entirely new way of seeing the universe. Einstein's discovery was the *special theory of relativity*. A few of the major points in special relativity are relativistic mass, time dilation, relativistic length, and the equivalency of mass and energy. There are others, but they hold no importance to an AP Physics 2 course.

Einstein showed that everything in the universe has a speed limit, the speed of light, *c*. No material object or particle can travel at or beyond the speed of light. Only light can travel at the speed of light. As bodies accelerate faster and faster approaching near light speed, strange things happen. We say strange because we do not observe these in our everyday world. Material objects increase in mass as they approach the speed of light, and acquire *relativistic mass m*. All material bodies have rest mass m_0. It is the mass of a body when at rest on the surface of the Earth. The value *c*, of course, is the speed of light, 3×10^8 m/s, and v is the speed of the body relative to an observer at rest. Relativistic mass is calculated from

$$m = \frac{m_0}{\sqrt{1 - \dfrac{v^2}{c^2}}}$$

At a relativistic speed v of 86.6% c, a 2.0 kg body that was initially at rest will have a relativistic mass of 4.0 kg. Where did the body get the extra 2.0 kg of mass? It is actually the mass of the kinetic energy the body acquired as it was accelerated to $0.886c$. The relativistic mass equation has been verified many times over since the 1940s and the invention of particle accelerators. It is very common at places like CERN and Fermi Lab to accelerate particles like protons to $0.999c$ and slightly beyond.

Einstein also showed that time changes as clocks travel near the speed of light. Time intervals, Δt, undergo a relativistic effect. The faster a body travels, the slower its clocks run. The value Δt_0 is a time interval relative to the clock of an observer at rest. A subatomic particle called a muon is quite unstable and decays into an electron and something called an antineutrino. Muons have a lifetime of 2.21 μs when at rest in a laboratory on the Earth. When muons are given speeds of 86.6% c in particle accelerators, they are observed to "live" for 4.42 μs as is predicted by the relativistic time dilation equation

$$\Delta t = \frac{\Delta t_0}{\sqrt{1 - \dfrac{v^2}{c^2}}}$$

Experimentally, the muon does live for 4.42 μs when traveling at $0.866c$.

Length also undergoes relativistic change as a body travels very close to the speed of light. The oddity here is that the change, which is a *relativistic contraction*, occurs only in the direction of motion. Relativistic length, L, is determined from

$$L = L_0 \sqrt{1 - \frac{v^2}{c^2}}$$

In the equation, L_0 is the length of the body relative to the observer at rest. A 1.00 meter rod traveling at $0.866c$ would have a length of 0.50 m.

Before special relativity, physicists and chemists had always considered mass and energy as separate quantities that had to be conserved separately. Special relativity considers mass and energy to be the same thing but in two different forms; mass can be converted into energy and energy can be converted into mass. Energy is measured in J and mass in kg. Einstein found that the conversion factor between them to be the speed of light squared.

$$E = mc^2$$

A very tiny mass can yield a very large quantity of energy. The usual SI unit of energy is the joule, J, but as was pointed out earlier, there is another way of expressing energy that is convenient in studying quantum, atomic and nuclear physics, and that is in terms of the electron volt, eV. When an electron falls through a potential difference of one volt, work is done on the electron and that quantity of work is 1.602×10^{-19} J . Once again, we define the electron volt as

$$1 \text{ eV} = 1.602 \times 10^{-19} \text{ J}$$

or better yet

$$1 \text{ MeV} = 1.602 \times 10^{-13} \text{ J}$$

Sample Problem 3

Calculate the rest-mass energy of an electron in both joules and MeV.

Solution to Problem 3

Write the Einstein mass-energy relationship $E = mc^2$ and make substitution.

$$E = \left(9.11 \times 10^{-31} \text{ kg}\right)\left(3.00 \times 10^{8} \ \frac{\text{m}}{\text{s}}\right)^{2} = 8.20 \times 10^{-14} \text{ J}$$

Converting to MeV

$$8.20 \times 10^{-14} \text{ J} \times \frac{1 \text{ eV}}{1.602 \times 10^{-19} \text{ J}} \times \frac{1 \text{ Mev}}{1 \times 10^{6} \text{ eV}} = 0.51 \text{ MeV}$$

Is the reverse true? Can energy be converted into matter? Under certain conditions the answer is yes.

Sample Problem 4

A gamma ray photon passes very close to a $^{238}_{92}\text{U}$ where the photon is converted into an electron pair, an electron and a positron. What maximum wavelength can the gamma ray have and what is its frequency?

Solution to Problem 4

Two electrons, the electron and its anti particle, are created in the process.

$$\gamma \rightarrow e^- + e^+$$

Maximum wavelength implies minimal energy and that means there is just enough energy for the pair creation.

Rest-mass energy of the pair $E = 2m_e c^2$

Energy of the photon $E = \dfrac{hc}{\lambda}$

$$2m_e c^2 = \frac{hc}{\lambda}$$

$$2\lambda m_e c = h$$

$$\lambda = \frac{h}{2m_e c}$$

$$\lambda = \frac{6.63 \times 10^{-34} \text{ J} \cdot \text{s}}{2 \left(9.11 \times 10^{-31} \text{ kg}\right) \left(3.00 \times 10^{8} \text{ } \frac{\text{m}}{\text{s}}\right)} = 1.21 \times 10^{-12} \text{ m}$$

Frequency is related to wavelength by

$$c = \lambda f$$

$$f = \frac{c}{\lambda}$$

$$f = \frac{3.00 \times 10^{8} \text{ } \text{m/s}}{1.21 \times 10^{-12} \text{ m}} = 2.48 \times 10^{20} \text{ Hz}$$

SAMPLE PROBLEM 5

The reverse process to particle-anti particle pair creation is pair annihilation. Determine the minimum energy, in joules, released when a proton annihilates an anti proton to form two identical gamma ray photons.

SOLUTION TO PROBLEM 5

$$p^{+} + \overline{p}^{-} \rightarrow \gamma + \gamma$$

The energy release is

$$E = mc^2 = 2m_p c^2$$

$$E = 2\left(1.67 \times 10^{-27} \text{kg}\right)\left(3 \times 10^{8} \text{ m/s}\right)^{2} = 3.01 \times 10^{-10} \text{ J}$$

THE PHOTOELECTRIC EFFECT

(*College Physics* 9th ed. pages 913–916/10th ed. pages 926–929)

In his papers on special relativity, Einstein stated that light is emitted in the form of particles (Planck's quanta) he called photons, and each photon carries energy $E = hf$. Einstein suggested a solution to a problem that had baffled scientists for a number of decades. When certain types of light irradiated metallic surfaces, the surfaces acquired positive electrical charge. Einstein stated that photons struck surface electrons and were absorbed by them. Surface electrons are bound by an energy we call the work function, ϕ. If the incoming photons had enough energy, not only would surface electrons leave the surface of the metal, but they would leave with a kinetic energy

$$K = hf - \phi$$

SAMPLE PROBLEM 6

A potassium wafer is irradiated with monochromatic ultraviolet light of λ = 250 nm and intensity of 2.00 W/m². Photoelectrons are emitted from the surface of the metal. If potassium has a work function of ϕ = 2.21 eV

(a) what is the maximum kinetic energy of the photoelectrons?

(b) what is the rate of photoelectron emission from the surface of the potassium if the surface is 40% efficient as an emitter?

SOLUTION TO PROBLEM 6

(a) First, write the Einstein photoelectric equation

$$K = hf - \phi$$

$$K = \frac{hc}{\lambda} - \phi$$

$$K = \frac{\left(6.63 \times 10^{-34}\ \text{J} \cdot \text{s}\right)\left(3.00 \times 10^{8}\ \frac{\text{m}}{\text{s}}\right)}{\left(250 \times 10^{-9}\ \text{m}\right)} - 2.21\ \text{eV} \times \frac{1.602 \times 10^{-19}\ \text{J}}{1\ \text{eV}}$$

$$K = 4.42 \times 10^{-19}\ \text{J}$$

Alternate Solution

(a) Express h in terms of $\text{eV} \cdot \text{s}$

$$h = 6.63 \times 10^{-34}\ \text{J} \cdot \text{s} \times \frac{1.00\ \text{eV}}{1.602 \times 10^{-19}\ \text{J}} = 4.14 \times 10^{-15}\ \text{eV} \cdot \text{s}$$

$$K = hf - \phi$$

$$K = \frac{hc}{\lambda} - \phi$$

$$K = \frac{\left(4.14 \times 10^{-15}\ \text{eV} \cdot \text{s}\right)\left(3 \times 10^{8}\ \frac{\text{m}}{\text{s}}\right)}{\left(250 \times 10^{-9}\ \text{m}\right)} - 2.21\ \text{eV}$$

$$K = 2.76\ \text{eV}$$

As a check

$$4.42 \times 10^{-19}\ \text{J} \times \frac{1.00\ \text{eV}}{1.602 \times 10^{-19}\ \text{J}} = 2.76\ \text{eV}$$

(b) Since the light is monochromatic, each photon carries the same energy.

$$E = \frac{hc}{\lambda}$$

$$E = \frac{\left(6.63 \times 10^{-34}\ \text{J} \cdot \text{s}\right)\left(3.00 \times 10^{8}\ \frac{\text{m}}{\text{s}}\right)}{250 \times 10^{-9}\ \text{m}}$$

$$E = 7.96 \times 10^{-19}\ \frac{\text{J}}{\text{photon}}$$

Only 40% of the radiation falling on the surface of the potassium is effective for photoelectrons.

$$2.00 \frac{\text{W}}{\text{m}^2} \times 0.40 = 0.80 \frac{\text{J}}{\text{m}^2 \cdot \text{s}}$$

For each effective photon there is one photoelectron.

$$0.80\frac{\text{J}}{\text{m}^2 \cdot \text{s}} \times \frac{1 \text{ photon}}{7.95 \times 10^{-19} \text{ J}} = \mathbf{1.01 \times 10^{18}} \frac{\textbf{photoelectrons}}{\textbf{m}^2\textbf{s}}$$

X-RAYS

(College Physics 9th ed. pages 916–920/10th ed. pages 929–933)

Although X-rays secured their name from "X = unknown," it is now well established that they are high-energy electromagnetic waves of very short wavelength. Bombarding a heavy metal target with high-energy electrons in an X-ray tube generates continuous X-rays. The high-energy electrons are abruptly stopped and a major portion of the kinetic loss is converted into electromagnetic radiation, X-rays.

SAMPLE PROBLEM 7

A 50.0 kV X-ray tube is used to generate continuous X-rays.

(a) Calculate the kinetic energy of one of the electrons accelerated across the 50.0 kV potential difference immediately before it impacts the anode.

(b) What is the wavelength of the maximum energy X-ray produced in the tube?

SOLUTION TO PROBLEM 7

(a) The kinetic energy of the electron is

$$K = \frac{1}{2}mv^2 = Ve$$

$$K = \left(5.00 \times 10^4 \text{ V}\right)e$$

$$K = \mathbf{5.00 \times 10^4 \text{ eV}}$$

(b) Maximum X-ray energy implies that 100% of the kinetic energy of the electron is converted to electromagnetic radiation.

$$h = 6.63 \times 10^{-34} \text{ J} \cdot \text{s} = 4.14 \times 10^{-15} \text{ eV} \cdot \text{s}$$

$$K = E = \frac{hc}{\lambda}$$

$$\lambda = \frac{hc}{E}$$

$$\lambda = \frac{\left(4.14 \times 10^{-15} \text{ eV} \cdot \text{s}\right)\left(3.00 \times 10^8 \frac{\text{m}}{\text{s}}\right)}{\left(5.00 \times 10^4 \text{ eV}\right)}$$

$$\lambda = \mathbf{2.48 \times 10^{-11} \text{ m}}$$

While studying X-rays in 1913, William Bragg and his son, Lawrence, discovered a way to measure X-ray wavelengths by using salt crystals as a three-dimensional diffraction grating. He not only verified that X-rays were a form of electromagnetic radiations of very small wavelength, he also discovered a way to measure inner atomic distance in solids. Bragg showed that a plane of atoms in a crystal, called a Bragg plane, reflected X-rays much like a mirror reflects visible light.

In a crystal, the Bragg planes are spaced a distance, *d*, apart.

THE COMPTON EFFECT

(*College Physics* 9th ed. pages 920–922/10th ed. pages 933–935)

While making a spectroscopic study of scattered X-rays in 1923, Arthur H. Compton discovered a new phenomenon now know as the *Compton effect*. Compton proved conclusively that an X-ray may collide with an electron and bounce off with reduced energy in another direction. This is analogous to the collision between two billiard balls. His experiment demonstrated that photons had momentum. Light behaves as both a wave and as a stream of particles.

EARLY ATOMIC THEORY

(*College Physics* 9th ed. pages 934–935/10th ed. pages 947–948)

In the fall of 1897 J.J. Thomson experimentally discovered negatively charged electrons. The electrons were removed from electrically neutral atoms that had to contain an equal amount of positive charges. According to the plum-pudding model of Thomson, the positive charges were uniformly distributed within an atom with electrons symmetrically arranged throughout.

Ernest Rutherford, Ernest Marsden, and Hans Geiger, in 1911, conducted a series of experiments in which they directed a beam of positively charged alpha particles into thin gold foils. Rutherford found that most alpha particles went straight through the foils without being deflected; however, a small number of the incident alpha particles were deflected at very large angles. To account for these observations, Rutherford argued that all positive charges (containing 99.9% of the mass of the atom) were concentrated at the very center of the spherical atom. He called this region the atomic nucleus and suggested that the electrons rotated about the nucleus in circular orbits. His planetary or nuclear atomic model implied that the atom itself is practically all empty space.

ATOMIC SPECTRA OF HYDROGEN

(*College Physics* 9th ed. pages 935–937/10th ed. pages 948–950)

When a sample of a low-density atomic gas or a simple molecular gas is heated or excited electrically and the spectra of these glowing gases are directed into a spectrometer, a series of discrete colored lines are observed. The line spectra are different for each element and provide a unique way of identifying the elements present in the sample of a material. No two elements have the same atomic spectrum. The spectrometer not only separates atomic spectral lines, it also measures the wavelength of these lines.

Line spectra served as the key to understanding atomic structure since the structure must be able to explain line spectra and predict their wavelengths.

In 1884, the Swiss schoolteacher Johann Balmer noticed that wavelengths of all the lines in the visible spectrum of hydrogen could be calculated from a simple but yet remarkable empirical equation, the Balmer equation

$$\frac{1}{\lambda} = R_H \left(\frac{1}{2^2} - \frac{1}{n^2} \right)$$

where n had the integral values, $n = 3$, 4, 5, …. The constant R_H is called the Rydberg-Ritz constant and has a value of $R_H = 1.0978 \times 10^7$ m^{-1}. The series of visible lines in the spectrum of mono atomic hydrogen is called the *Balmer series*.

Over the following years additional sets of spectral lines were discovered for hydrogen; the *Lyman series* in the ultraviolet in 1916, the *Paschen series* in the near infrared, the *Brackett series* in the middle infrared in 1922, and the *Pfund series* in the far infrared in 1924. The wavelengths for all five series can be calculated by using a modified version of the Balmer equation

$$\frac{1}{\lambda} = R_H \left(\frac{1}{m^2} - \frac{1}{n^2} \right)$$

Where:

$m = 1 =$ Lyman series

$m = 2 =$ Balmer series

$m = 3 =$ Paschen series

$m = 4 =$ Brackett series

$m = 5 =$ Pfund series

and $m < n$ and both m and n are integers.

THE BOHR THEORY OF THE HYDROGEN ATOM

(*College Physics* 9th ed. pages 937–941/10th ed. pages 950–954)

The Rutherford planetary model of the atom could not explain the spectral lines emitted by the atom or why the spectral equations worked at all. The Rutherford model predicted a continuous spectrum to be emitted by atoms. And there was another major problem; an orbiting electron should radiate electromagnetic radiation according to Maxwell's electromagnetic theory. As a result, an orbiting electron within the confines of an atom should spiral inward and eventually fall into the nucleus. The Rutherford model was not a model for a stable atom.

Niels Bohr received his doctoral in 1911 in Copenhagen, and the same year he traveled to England to study with J. J. Thomson and Ernest Rutherford. From Rutherford's description of the atom, it was evident to Bohr that the atom had to consist of a heavy nucleus about which, and a great distance away, electrons would revolve. Bohr proposed a remarkable set of postulates as the basis for a new atomic model.

In 1912, Bohr developed a mathematical description of the hydrogen atom. Hydrogen consists of a nucleus, a single proton, and a lone orbiting electron. Bohr assumed the electron traveled about the nucleus in a circular orbit of radius, r. But the orbiting electron should radiate electromagnetic energy and spiral into the nucleus. To get around this, Bohr made a second assumption that the electron did not radiate energy while in a circular orbit. He went a step further and stated that the angular momentum of the orbiting electron is *quantized*. The electron can be found only in specific orbits that Bohr called *stationary states*. According to Bohr, the angular momentum of the electron is

$$L = mvr = \frac{nh}{2\pi}$$

The quantity n is called the *principal quantum number*. It can only be an integer and take on values of $n = 1, 2, 3, \ldots$. Since the electron travels a curved path and experiences a centripetal force, Bohr looked for the cause and showed that it was the electrical attraction between the positive proton and orbiting negative electron.

$$\frac{mv^2}{r} = \frac{ke^2}{r^2}$$

Bohr postulated that when a hydrogen atom is given outside energy, the electron absorbs that energy and moves to an outside orbit where it remains circling the nucleus for a time period on the order of 1×10^{-8} s. The electron then makes a *quantum jump* to a lower orbit emitting a photon.

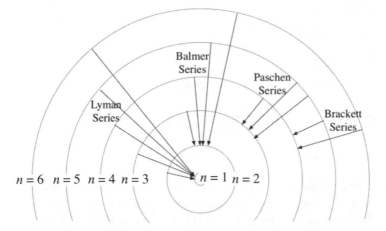

The Bohr Atom and a Description of the Origin of the Lyman, Balmer, Paschen, and Brackett Series of Spectral Series.

In the above diagram, which is not to scale, all members of the Lyman series are emitted when electrons jump from some excited state to the $n = 1$ orbit, which is also called the *ground state*. The Balmer series is due to excited electrons jumping from various outer states to the $n = 2$ orbit or the second energy level. Similarly, the Paschen series is emitted during jumps ending in the $n = 3$ orbit and the Brackett series by jumps ending in the $n = 4$ orbit.

The total energy, E, of the electron in any of the Bohr orbits is the sum of its kinetic energy, K, and the electrical potential energy, U and

$$E = K + U = \frac{1}{2}mv^2 + \left(-\frac{ke^2}{r}\right)$$

Combining the three above equations to find expressions for the radius, r, of a Bohr orbit, the speed of an electron, v, in any of Bohr orbits, the orbital frequency, f, and the energy of the electron in any orbit is left as an exercise for the student.

Deriving these Bohr equations and inserting the constants involved leads us to a set of simplified relationships.

The radius of any of the Bohr orbits: $\qquad r = \left(5.292 \times 10^{-11}\,\text{m}\right) n^2$

The speed of an electron in a Bohr orbit: $\qquad v = \dfrac{2.188 \times 10^6 \ \text{m}/_{\text{s}}}{n}$

The orbital frequency of the electron: $\qquad f = \dfrac{6.580 \times 10^{15} \ \text{rev}/_{\text{s}}}{n^3}$

The energy of the electron in a Bohr orbit: $\qquad E = -\dfrac{13.61 \ \text{eV}}{n^2}$

SAMPLE PROBLEM 8

Consider an electron in the ground state of a hydrogen atom.

(a) What equivalent current does the orbiting electron generate?

(b) What is the angular frequency?

(c) Determine the magnetic flux density at the center of the atom.

(d) What centripetal acceleration does the electron experience?

(e) Find the centripetal force acting on the electron.

(f) Calculate the electrostatic force on the electron.

SOLUTION TO PROBLEM 8

(a) The moving electron of charge $q = e$ generates a current as it orbits the nucleus. The current is: $I = \dfrac{q}{T} = \dfrac{e}{T}$. To find the current we need the period, T, of a single orbit. Since we know the frequency, f, for the electron in the $n = 1$ orbit, we find the period from $f = \dfrac{1}{T}$, current is found by

$$I = \frac{e}{T} = ef = \left(1.602 \times 10^{-9} \ \text{C}\right)\left(6.58 \times 10^{15} \ \text{s}^{-1}\right) = \ \textbf{1.05} \times \textbf{10}^{-3} \ \textbf{A}$$

(b) Angular frequency is found by

$$\omega = 2\pi f = 2\pi \left(6.58 \times 10^{15} \ \text{s}^{-1}\right) = \ \textbf{4.13} \times \textbf{10}^{16} \ \textbf{rad}/_{\textbf{s}}$$

(c) The magnetic flux density at the center of a circular loop is found by

$$B = \frac{\mu_0 I}{2r} = \frac{\mu_0 \left(1.05 \times 10^{-3} \text{ A}\right)}{2\left(5.29 \times 10^{-11} \text{ m}\right)} = \mathbf{12.47 \text{ T}}$$

(d) Centripetal acceleration is found by

$$a_c = \frac{v^2}{r} = \frac{\left(2.19 \times 10^6 \text{ m}\!/\!_s\right)^2}{\left(5.29 \times 10^{-11} \text{ m}\right)} = \mathbf{9.07 \times 10^{22}} \text{ m}\!/\!_{s^2}$$

(e) The centripetal force on the electron is found by

$$F_c = ma_c = \left(9.11 \times 10^{-31} \text{ kg}\right)\left(9.07 \times 10^{22} \text{ m}\!/\!_{s^2}\right) = \mathbf{8.26 \times 10^{-8} \text{ N}}$$

(f) Electrostatic force on the electron is found by

$$F = k\frac{e^2}{r^2} = k\left(\frac{e}{r}\right)^2 = k\left(\frac{1.60 \times 10^{-19} \text{ C}}{5.29 \times 10^{-11} \text{ m}}\right)^2 = \mathbf{8.24 \times 10^{-8} \text{ N}}$$

SAMPLE PROBLEM 9

An electron in the $n = 3$ orbit in a hydrogen atom makes a quantum jump to the $n = 2$ orbit.

(a) What energy does the electron lose in making this jump?

(b) What wavelength of light is produced in this jump?

(c) What color of light is produced?

(d) Use the Balmer equation and calculate the wavelength of the light produced.

SOLUTION TO PROBLEM 9

(a) Using the energy-level diagram, the energy lost as the electron jumps from $n = 3$ to $n = 2$ is

$$\Delta E = E_2 - E_3 = (-1.51 \text{ eV}) - (-3.40 \text{ eV}) = \mathbf{1.89 \text{ eV}}$$

(b) Depending upon the energy units used

$$h = 6.63 \times 10^{-34} \text{ J} \cdot \text{s} = 4.14 \times 10^{-15} \text{ eV} \cdot \text{s}$$

$$E = hf = \frac{hc}{\lambda} \text{ and}$$

$$\lambda = \frac{hc}{\Delta E} = \frac{\left(4.14 \times 10^{-15} \text{ eV} \cdot \text{s}\right)\left(3 \times 10^8 \text{ m}\!/\!_s\right)}{1.89 \text{ eV}} = \mathbf{6.57 \times 10^{-7} \text{ m}}$$

(c) A wavelength of 656 nm corresponds to **red light**.

(d) $$\frac{1}{\lambda} = R_H\left(\frac{1}{m^2} - \frac{1}{n^2}\right) = \left(1.098 \times 10^7 \text{ m}^{-1}\right)\left(\frac{1}{2^2} - \frac{1}{3^2}\right) = 1.525 \times 10^6 \text{ m}^{-1}$$

$$\lambda = \frac{1}{1.526 \times 10^6 \text{ m}^{-1}} = \mathbf{6.55 \times 10^{-7} \text{ m}}$$

The actual wavelength of the first line of the Balmer series is 6.563×10^{-7} m.

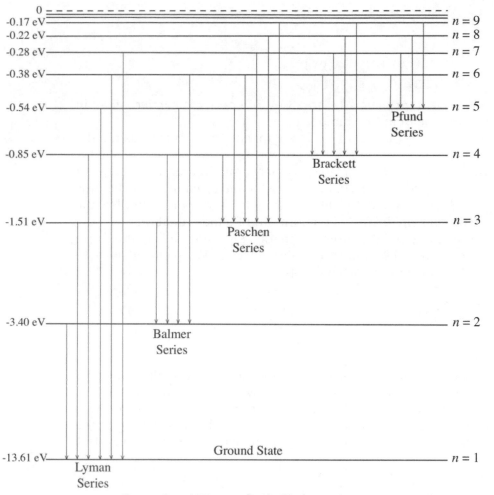

Energy-Level Diagram for the Hydrogen Atom

A convenient way to describe the transitions between orbits or stationary states is in terms of energy-level diagrams. In these the energy levels are plotted, but not to scale, as illustrated above. The transitions are shown by arrows that run from the initial excited state of the atom to a final state.

SAMPLE PROBLEM 10

Consider an excited hydrogen atom with an electron in the $n = 7$ energy-level. The electron undergoes a quantum jump to the $n = 3$, Use the diagram and determine the energy carried away by the photon created in the jump.

SOLUTION TO PROBLEM 10

Find the energy difference

$$\Delta E = E_{final} - E_{initial}$$
$$= E_{n=3} - E_{n=7}$$
$$= (-1.51 \text{ eV}) - (-0.28 \text{ eV})$$
$$- -1.23 \text{ eV}$$

The negative sign means that 1.23 eV of energy is carried away in the transition, the quantum jump.

Of course one could find wavelength and frequencies using the diagram.

It was soon found that the Balmer equation and subsequent modifications were only partially successful in calculating wavelengths of spectral lines emitted by other elements. The more complex the atom, the greater the failure of the Bohr and Balmer equations.

The Bohr model of the atom, although now replaced by the more powerful *quantum mechanics*, remains an effective pictorial way to introduce the concept of energy-levels.

DE BROGLIE WAVES

(*College Physics* 9th ed. pages 922–925/10th ed. pages 935–938)

In 1924, Louis de Broglie made the suggestion that this dual particle-wave character of light should apply as well to moving objects. His suggestion was based on the general observation that nature often reveals a physical or a mathematical symmetry. His reasoning that the wavelength, λ, and the momentum, p, of a particle must be related by the equation

$$\lambda = \frac{h}{p} = \frac{h}{mv}$$

The de Broglie equation states as the momentum of a particle increases, the *de Broglie wavelength* decreases. The equation is simplicity itself, yet has become one of the most important in modern-day physics. De Broglie's hypothesis was experimentally proven correct in 1927.

SAMPLE PROBLEM 11

Determine the de Broglie wavelength of a 27°C thermal neutron. The mass of the neutron is 1.67×10^{-27} kg .

SOLUTION TO PROBLEM 11

The de Broglie wavelength is given by $\lambda = \dfrac{h}{mv}$. Before we find the wavelength we need to find v. The kinetic energy of the neutron is related to temperature by

$$K = \frac{1}{2}mv^2 = \frac{3}{2}kT$$

$$mv^2 = 3kT$$

$$v^2 = \frac{3kT}{m}$$

$$v = \sqrt{\frac{3kT}{m}}$$

$$v = \sqrt{\frac{3\left(1.38 \times 10^{-23}\ \dfrac{\text{J}}{\text{K}}\right)(273 + 27)\text{K}}{1.67 \times 10^{-27}\ \text{kg}}}$$

$$v = 2.73 \times 10^3\ \frac{\text{m}}{\text{s}}$$

$$\lambda = \frac{h}{mv}$$

$$\lambda = \frac{6.63 \times 10^{-34}\ \text{J} \cdot \text{s}}{\left(1.67 \times 10^{-27}\ \text{kg}\right)\left(2.73 \times 10^3\ \dfrac{\text{m}}{\text{s}}\right)} = \mathbf{1.45 \times 10^{-10}\ m}$$

QUANTUM MECHANICS

(College Physics 9th ed. pages 942–945/10th ed. pages 955–958)

Classical physics, the physics of Newton, is said to be *deterministic*. If we know the position, velocity, momentum, and kinetic and potential energies of an object at some particular time, its future position, velocity, momentum, and kinetic and potential energies can be precisely determined if the force acting on the object is known. On the other hand, quantum mechanics is *probabilistic*. We are only able to find the probability that an electron may be at a region in space. Quantum mechanics predicts with a high probability that ordinary objects behave as classical physics predict. But according to quantum mechanics, electrons do not exist in well-defined circular orbits. They spread out in space to form a probability cloud. The cloud roughly indicates the size of the atom but an atom does not have distinct boundaries. The cloud is a result of the wave nature of electrons and can be interpreted as a probability distribution of electrons.

Quantum mechanics deals with the microscopic world of atoms, electrons, and photons. The theory covers all quantum phenomena from blackbody radiation to the structure of atoms and molecules. It is accepted as the fundamental theory underlying physical processes.

Classical physics produces accurate results for the motion of ordinary bodies. For objects moving at high speeds we must use special relativity. When dealing with the microscopic world of atoms and particles, we must use quantum mechanics.

ATOMIC AND QUANTUM PHYSICS: STUDENT OBJECTIVES FOR THE AP EXAM

- You should have an understanding of the basics of Planck's quantum theory.
- You should know and use Planck's quantum equation to solve problems.
- You should have an understanding of relativistic mass, time, and length.
- You should know and use the mass-energy relationship in problem solving.
- You should know and use the photoelectric effect equation and be able to apply it to graphical solutions.
- You should have an understanding of the Compton scattering effect.
- You should have an understanding of the origins of atomic spectra.
- You should have an understanding of the Bohr hydrogen atom.
- You should have an understanding of the de Broglie wave-particle dualism concept.
- You should be able to solve multiple-choice questions/problems with a calculator.

MULTIPLE-CHOICE QUESTIONS

1. An electron in a hydrogen atom drops from an energy state of –0.56 eV to an energy state of –3.40 eV, emitting a photon of electromagnetic radiation as it drops. The energy of this photon is
   (A) 3.96 eV because it cannot transition between allowed energy levels unless it has the total energy associated with these levels
   (B) 3.40 eV because it can only reach this state if it radiates the energy at this level
   (C) 2.86 eV because energy must be conserved in the drop between allowed states
   (D) 0.56 eV because this is the maximum energy the electron received as it was boosted to a higher state

2. The probability of finding an electron in the hydrogen atom is greatest in a region where

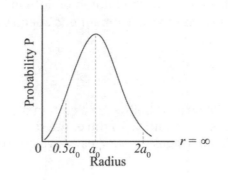

(A) $n <$ Bohr radius, a_0

(B) $n >$ Bohr radius, a_0

(C) $n =$ Bohr radius, a_0

(D) $n =$ Bohr radius, $2a_0$

3. Compton scattering produces a shift in the wavelength of the incident photon when it collides with an electron. The interaction is
   (A) elastic with a decrease in the wavelength of the scattered photon
   (B) elastic with an increase in the wavelength of the scattered photon
   (C) inelastic with a decrease in the wavelength of the scattered photon
   (D) inelastic with an increase in the wavelength of the scattered photon

4. According to the classical wave model of light, light travels as a continuous wave. In this model, the intensity of the wave depends on amplitude not on frequency. Experimental observations showed that when electromagnetic radiation struck the surface of certain metals, electrons were ejected from the surface. This can be explained by
   (A) electromagnetic radiation is both wave and particle in nature; the energy of the radiation is contained in packets called photons associated with frequency which can transfer both energy and momentum
   (B) electromagnetic radiation is a wave in nature; the energy transfer taking some measureable time to transfer enough energy to free an electron
   (C) electromagnetic radiation is both wave and particle in nature; the energy of the radiation is contained in packets called photons associated with amplitude of the intensity of the wave which can transfer both energy and momentum
   (D) the fact that Newton's corpuscular theory was correct and that light consists of extremely small particles moving at high velocity

5. An electron in the hydrogen atom dropped from an energy level of −1.51 eV to −3.61 eV producing a photon of light whose frequency is given by $\Delta E = hf$. If the frequency of the photon of light is 5.39×10^{14} hz, what is its range in the electromagnetic spectrum?
   (A) infrared
   (B) ultraviolet
   (C) visible
   (D) X-ray

6. An energy-level diagram is illustrated below for a certain atom. Rank the transitions for the wavelength λ of the emitted electromagnetic radiation from longest to shortest wavelengths.

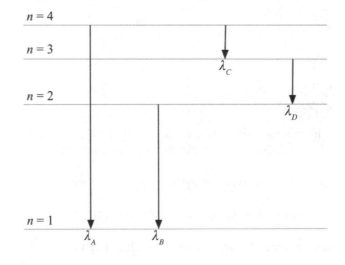

   (A) $\lambda_C > \lambda_D > \lambda_B > \lambda_A$
   (B) $\lambda_A > \lambda_B > \lambda_D > \lambda_C$
   (C) $\lambda_A > \lambda_B > \lambda_C > \lambda_D$
   (D) $\lambda_D > \lambda_C > \lambda_B > \lambda_A$

7. What is the de Broglie wavelength of an electron traveling with velocity of 0.300 c?
   (A) 8.08×10^{-12} m
   (B) 2.42×10^{-12} m
   (C) 3.97×10^{-14} m
   (D) 1.32×10^{-15} m

8. Bohr's theory of the hydrogen atom requires that the angular momentum of the electron be quantized. The de Broglie wave-particle duality shows that the electron has a wave character given by $\lambda = \dfrac{h}{p}$, thus the electron in allowed orbits forms a standing wave in the orbit. These standing waves are whole number multiples of the
   (A) frequency of the permitted radiation emitted or absorbed by the electron
   (B) wavelength associated with electron's motion
   (C) angular momentum of the electron
   (D) circumference of the orbit

9. The emission of a photoelectron from the surface of a certain metal as it is illuminated by light of a certain frequency and intensity is the indication that the electron
   (A) has absorbed the energy of several photons and after sufficient time will be able to leave the surface of the metal
   (B) will leave the surface of the metal with a de Broglie wavelength equal to the wavelength of the light illuminating the surface
   (C) will leave with excess kinetic energy if the light illuminating the surface has enough intensity to overcome the binding energy of the electron to the metal
   (D) will leave with excess kinetic energy if the light illuminating the surface has enough energy associated with the photon to overcome the binding energy of the electron to the metal

10. An electron and a proton are moving in the x direction with a speed of either $0.10c$ or $0.30c$ as shown in the illustration below.

$0.1c$	$0.1c$	$0.3c$	$0.3c$
e^-	p^+	e^-	p^+
A	B	C	D

    Rank the de Broglie wavelengths associated with the particles from longest wavelength to shortest wavelength.
    (A) $D > B > C > A$
    (B) $B > D > A > C$
    (C) $C > D > A > B$
    (D) $A > C > B > D$

11. A graph of the maximum kinetic energy of the photoelectrons emitted as a function of the frequency of the incident light from the surface of a certain metal plate is shown for data obtained in a photoelectric effect experiment. The range of the electromagnetic radiation needed to produce the photoelectron from this metal was in what part of the electromagnetic spectrum?

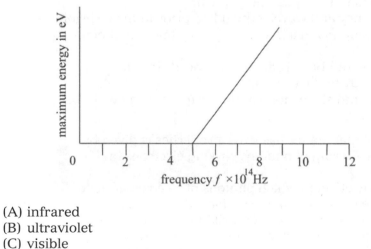

(A) infrared
(B) ultraviolet
(C) visible
(D) X-ray

12. A person on the Earth observes a clock on a spacecraft through the Earth-to-Satellite communication system making a comparison to an identical clock in his laboratory. The person on Earth states
   (A) both clocks record the same time since both clocks are in the Earth's gravitational field
   (B) the clock on the spacecraft runs slower since the spacecraft has a higher orbital velocity than the rotational speed of the Earth
   (C) the clock on the spacecraft runs faster since the spacecraft has a higher orbital velocity than the rotational speed of the Earth
   (D) the clock on the spacecraft alternately runs faster and slower as the spacecraft moves between the sun and the Earth

13. In the energy-level diagram illustrated below for a certain atom, four transitions are shown. Rank the transitions for the frequency of the emitted electromagnetic radiation from largest to smallest.

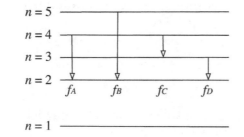

   (A) $f_A > f_B > f_C > f_D$
   (B) $f_C > f_D > f_A > f_B$
   (C) $f_A = f_B = f_D > f_C$
   (D) $f_B > f_A > f_D > f_C$

14. An X-ray photon collides with an electron at rest in a crystal, causing the electron to be ejected from the crystal with a gain in kinetic energy as the photon is deflected from its path. If the collision is considered to be elastic then the photon must carry momentum away from the crystal moving with
   (A) the same frequency and wavelength it had prior to the collision
   (B) a smaller wavelength and a larger frequency that it had before the collision
   (C) the same wavelength but a reduction in speed since it transferred energy to the electron
   (D) a larger wavelength since momentum is carried away with the deflected photon

15. Experimental proof that matter has wave properties is given by
   (A) the Compton scattering of photons striking electrons in crystals
   (B) the photoelectric effect in which photons of electromagnetic radiation eject electrons from the surface of a material
   (C) diffraction of low energy electrons striking crystals as they exhibit de Broglie waves associated with their velocity
   (D) transitions of electrons in the Bohr atom when they absorb or radiate electromagnetic radiation

FREE-RESPONSE PROBLEMS

1. Physics students performed a photoelectric experiment in which they determined the relationship between the electrical stopping potential, V_s, needed to stop the photoelectron with the maximum kinetic energy and the frequency of light illuminating the surface. To make evaluation of their data easier, they converted each electrical stopping potential into energy units in joules by multiplying each V_s by the charge on an electron, 1.6×10^{-19} C.

K_{max} (1.6×10^{-19} J)	frequency ($f \times 10^{15}$ hz)
0.00	0.50
3.31	1.00
5.51	1.25
6.62	1.50
9.94	2.00
12.6	2.25
13.3	2.50
16.6	3.00

(a) Plot the data points on the graph given below.

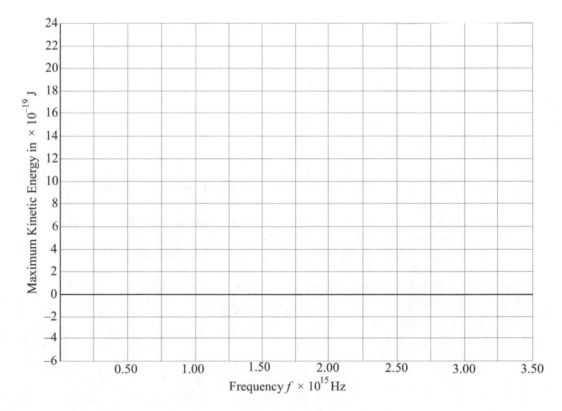

(b) What is the physical significance of the slope of the line?
(c) Determine the threshold frequency from the graph.
(d) What does the y-intercept of the graph represent?

2. A certain metal has a work function of 3.00 eV. When illuminated by light of intensity I_0 and frequency f_0, the maximum kinetic energy of the photoelectrons is 2.00 eV.
   (a) Doubling the intensity from I_0 to $2I_0$ results in

   _____ increasing the kinetic energy of the photoelectrons

   _____ decreasing the kinetic energy of the photoelectrons

   _____ no change in the kinetic energy of the photoelectrons

   Justify your answer.
   (b) Doubling the frequency from f_0 to $2f_0$ results in

   _____ increasing the maximum kinetic energy of the photoelectrons

   _____ decreasing the maximum kinetic energy of the photoelectrons

   _____ no change in the maximum kinetic energy of the photoelectrons

   Justify your answer.
   (c) Explain without mathematics how you can determine the threshold frequency for this metal.

3. The first four energy levels of a Bohr-like atom are given below.

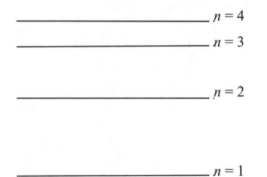

   _____ $n = 4$

   _____ $n = 3$

   _____ $n = 2$

   _____ $n = 1$

   (a) What are the possible transitions that will produce unique spectral lines?
   (b) How many of these transitions will be in the visible part of the spectrum?
   (c) What are the possible wavelengths in the visible part of the spectrum?
   (d) What is the energy difference in the transition from $n = 3$ to the $n = 2$?

4. An electron is placed in the electric field shown below and then released from rest at the surface of the negative plate. The potential difference across the plates is 50.0 V.

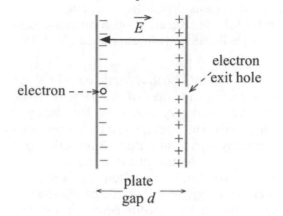

(a) What is its gain in kinetic energy as it accelerates across the plate gap d and exits the plates through the hole in the positive plate?
(b) What is its increase in momentum upon exiting the field?
(c) Determine the de Broglie wavelength associated with the momentum of the electron.
(d) Would the electron cause diffraction if it interacted with a crystal whose spacing between layers is 0.10 nm?
_____ would cause diffraction
_____ would not cause diffraction
_____ not enough information is given
Justify your answer.

Answers

MULTIPLE-CHOICE QUESTIONS

1. **C** The energy of the photon in transition is determined from $E = E_i - E_f$. The energy of the photon $E = -0.54 \text{ eV} - (-3.40 \text{ eV})$ is 2.86 eV. Energy must be conserved in the transitions between allowed energy levels.
    (*College Physics* 9th ed. pages 937–940/10th ed. pages 950–953)
    (L.O. 5.B.8.1)

2. **C** The probability of finding an electron in the hydrogen atom is in a region where there are n de Broglie wavelengths fitting into the circumference of the electron orbit. This probability would be greatest where the electron in closest to the nucleus i.e. the ground state, $n = 1$. The electron with excess energy in any permitted orbit will drop to this ground state, radiating energy in the electromagnetic spectrum.
    (*College Physics* 9th ed. pages 937–940/10th ed. pages 950–954)
    (L.O. 7.C.1.1, 7.C.2.1)

3. **B** The photon carries both momentum and energy that must be conserved in the collision. Thus the collision is elastic. The photon transfers momentum and energy to the electron and therefore the energy of the photon must decrease. Since the frequency decreases, the wavelength of the scattered photon must increase. (*College Physics* 9th ed. pages 920–922/10th ed. pages 933–935) (L.O. 5.D.1.6)

4. **A** Electromagnetic radiation exhibits both a particle and a wave nature. The photoelectric effect is an aspect of the particle nature in which the energy of the radiation is related to its frequency by $E = hf$. The very small discrete wave packets are called photons of light. The photons carry energy and momentum; interaction of the photon and matter will change these quantities. In the photoelectric effect, when the photon is absorbed, its momentum drops to zero and if sufficient energy to overcome binding of the electron to the surface is absorbed, the photoelectron moves from the surface with some maximum kinetic energy determined by the frequency of the photon. (*College Physics* 9th ed. pages 913–916/10th ed. pages 926–929) (L.O. 6.F.3.1)

5. **C** The energy drop produces a frequency that is in the visible part of the spectrum.

Since $c = \lambda f$, then $\dfrac{3.00 \times 10^8 \text{ m}/\text{s}}{5.39 \times 10^{14} \text{ hz}} = 5.56 \times 10^{-7}\text{m} = 556 \text{ nm}$.

(*College Physics* 9th ed. pages 920–922/10th ed. pages 950–954) (L.O. 5.B.8.1)

6. **A** The largest drop is the electromagnetic radiation that has the greatest frequency and thus the smallest wavelength. The energy is related to the wavelength by $\Delta E = hf = \dfrac{hc}{\lambda}$.

(*College Physics* 9th ed. pages 920–922/10th ed. pages 950–954) (L.O. 5.B.8.1)

7. **A** The velocity of the electron is $0.300c = 9.00 \times 10^7 \text{ m}/\text{s}$. The de Broglie wavelength is

$$\lambda = \frac{h}{mv} \quad \lambda = \frac{\left(6.63 \times 10^{-34} \text{ J} \cdot \text{s}\right)}{\left(9.11 \times 10^{-31} \text{ kg}\right)\left(9.00 \times 10^7 \text{ m}/\text{s}\right)} = 8.08 \times 10^{-12} \text{ m}$$

(*College Physics* 9th ed. pages 922–924/10th ed. pages 935–937) (L.O. 1.D.1.1)

8. **D** The Bohr theory requires that an integer multiple of the electron's wavelength equal the orbital circumference of the electron in that radius. (*College Physics* 9th ed. pages 937–938/10th ed. pages 951–952) (L.O. 7.C.2.1)

9. **D** The emission of a photoelectron from the surface of a certain metal requires that the photon of light has sufficient energy to overcome the forces binding the electron to the surface. If the photon carries energy in excess of the binding energy, the

photoelectron will leave the surface with excess kinetic energy. $K = hf - \phi$
(*College Physics* 9th ed. pages 913–916/10th ed. pages 926–929)
(L.O. 6.F.3.1)

10. **D** The de Broglie wavelength is determined from $\lambda = \dfrac{h}{mv}$. The slower the particle moves, the longer the de Broglie wavelength. A more massive particle will have a shorter wavelength. Thus both electrons will have longer wavelengths than the protons. The proton traveling at $0.30c$ will have the shortest wavelength.
(*College Physics* 9th ed. pages 937–938/10th ed. pages 935–937)
(L.O. 6.G.1.1)

11. **C** The threshold frequency obtained from the graph is 5×10^{14} hz.
Since $c = \lambda f$, the wavelength is $\lambda = \dfrac{3.0 \times 10^8 \text{ m}/\text{s}}{5 \times 10^{14} \text{ hz}} = 600$ nm. This puts it in the range of visible light.
(*College Physics* 9th ed. pages 913–916/10th ed. pages 926–929)
(L.O. 6.F.3.1)

12. **B** The statement of time dilation is that moving clocks run slow relative to a stationary clock. Thus the person on the Earth observing a clock in the spacecraft will indicate that because of the orbital velocity of the space craft is greater than the rotational speed of the Earth, the clock on the spacecraft is running slower.
(*College Physics* 9th ed. pages 890–895/10th ed. pages 902–906)
(L.O. 6.D.3.1)

13. **D** The greatest energy for the electromagnetic radiations are for the longest transitions. Since $E = hf$, the highest energy has the highest frequency and shortest wavelength. The correct ranking is $f_B > f_A > f_D > f_C$.
(*College Physics* 9th ed. pages 920–922/10th ed. pages 950–954)
(L.O. 7.C.4.1)

14. **D** Momentum must be conserved in a collision. The momentum of the X-ray photon is given by $\vec{p} = \dfrac{hf}{c} = \dfrac{h}{\lambda}$. Since momentum is transferred to the electron which gains kinetic energy in the collision then $\dfrac{h}{\lambda} = \dfrac{h}{\lambda'} + m_e v$. The X-ray photon is electromagnetic radiation moving with a velocity of c, thus the wavelength must decrease.
(*College Physics* 9th ed. pages 920–921/10th ed. pages 933–934)
(L.O. 5.D.1.6)

15. **C** X-rays passing through a crystal produce diffraction patterns. Low energy electrons with a de Broglie wavelength in the order of magnitude of X-rays will produce a diffraction pattern similar to the one observed with X-rays. This is the experimental evidence that confirmed de Broglie's matter waves.
(*College Physics* 9th ed. pages 922–924/10th ed. pages 935–936)
(L.O. 6.G.2.1)

FREE-RESPONSE PROBLEMS

1. (a) The graph of the points is shown below.

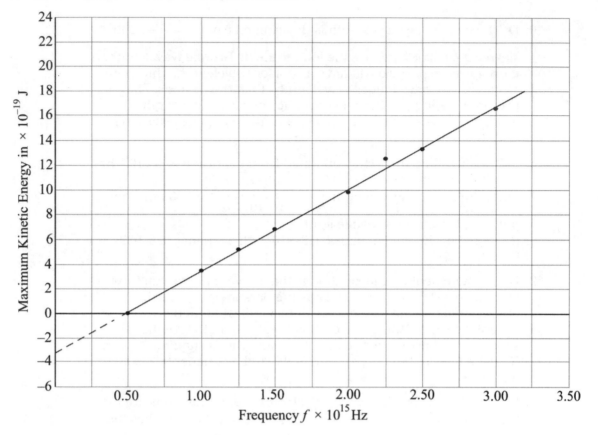

Maximum Kinetic Energy in $\times 10^{-19}$ J (y-axis)

Frequency $f \times 10^{15}$ Hz (x-axis)

(b) The slope of the line is Planck's constant.

$$h = \frac{\left(13.25 \times 10^{-19} \text{ J} - 3.31 \times 10^{-19} \text{ J}\right)}{\left(2.50 \times 10^{15} \text{ Hz} - 1.00 \times 10^{15} \text{ Hz}\right)} = \mathbf{6.63 \times 10^{-34} \text{ J} \cdot \text{s}}$$

(c) The y-intercept will give the work function for the material. The intercept gives $\phi \cong 3.5 \times 10^{-19}$ J.

Calculations from a substitution of data points

into $K_{max} = hf - \phi$ produces a work function

$\phi = \left(6.624 \times 10^{-34} \text{ J} \cdot \text{s}\right)(2.00 \times 10^{15} \text{ Hz}) - 9.94 \times 10^{-19} \text{ J} = \mathbf{3.31 \times 10^{-19} \text{ J}}$

(*College Physics* 9th ed. pages 913–916/10th ed. pages 926–929)
(L.O. 6.F.3.1)

2. (a) Correct line checked is

_____√____ no change in the kinetic energy of the photoelectrons

The maximum kinetic energy is independent of the intensity of light. Changing the intensity of the light just produces a greater number of photoelectrons per unit time, increasing the current so that a photoelectric blub will be brighter.

(b) Correct line checked is

_____√_____ increasing the kinetic energy of the photoelectrons

Increasing the frequency means more energy is added to the photoelectron since the energy of the incident photon is given by $E = hf$.

(c) The threshold frequency can be determined from setting the kinetic energy in the photoelectric equation to zero. The binding energy holding the electron to the metal has been overcome. Then, since the kinetic energy is zero, the work function is equal to the product of Planck's constant times the threshold frequency. Converting the work function from electron volts into joules by multiplying by the change of the electron will have consistent units for the division of the work function by Planck's constant. This will give the frequency in Hertz.

(*College Physics* 9th ed. pages 913–916/10th ed. pages 926–929)
(L.O. 6.F.3.1)

3. (a) There are 6 transitions that will produce unique spectral lines.
   $n = 4$ to $n = 1$
   $n = 3$ to $n = 1$
   $n = 2$ to $n = 1$
   $n = 4$ to $n = 3$
   $n = 4$ to $n = 2$
   $n = 3$ to $n = 2$

   (b) Two of the transitions will be in the visible part of the spectrum
   $n = 4$ to $n = 2$
   $n = 3$ to $n = 2$

   (c) The wavelengths can be calculated from $\dfrac{1}{\lambda} = R_H \left(\dfrac{1}{n_f^2} - \dfrac{1}{n_i^2} \right)$.

   Substitution of $n = 4$ to $n = 2$ produces

   $$\frac{1}{\lambda} = \left(1.097 \times 10^7 \text{ m}^{-1}\right)\left(\frac{1}{2^2} - \frac{1}{4^2} \right) = \textbf{486 nm}$$

   $$\frac{1}{\lambda} = \left(1.097 \times 10^7 \text{ m}^{-1}\right)\left(\frac{1}{2^2} - \frac{1}{3^2} \right) = \textbf{656 nm}$$

   (d) Since $\Delta E = hf$ yields, $\Delta E = \dfrac{hc}{\lambda}$.

   Then substitution gives

   $$\Delta E = \frac{\left(6.624 \times 10^{-34} \text{ J} \cdot \text{s}\right)\left(3.00 \times 10^8 \text{ m}\!\big/\!\text{s}\right)}{656 \times 10^{-9} \text{ nm}} = \textbf{3.02} \times \textbf{10}^{-19} \textbf{ J}$$

   The answer may also be written in eV

   $$\frac{3.02 \times 10^{-19} \text{ J}}{1.609 \times 10^{-19} \text{ J}\!\big/\!\text{eV}} = \textbf{1.89 eV}$$

(*College Physics* 9th ed. pages 920–922/10th ed. pages 950–954)
(L.O. 5.B.8.1)

4. (a) The electron gains kinetic energy given by $W = \Delta K = q\Delta V$.
   The gain in $\Delta K = e(50.0\text{ V}) = \mathbf{50.0\,eV}$ or
   $$\left(1.609 \times 10^{-19}\text{ C}\right)\left(50.0\,^{J}\!/_{C}\right) = \mathbf{8.05 \times 10^{-18}\ J}.$$

   (b) The momentum of the electron is $\vec{p} = m\vec{v}$ since it starts from rest.

   Solving for the velocity from $\Delta K = \dfrac{1}{2}mv^2$. Thus $v = \sqrt{\dfrac{2\Delta K}{m}}$

   $$v = \sqrt{\frac{2\left(8.05 \times 10^{-18}\text{ J}\right)}{9.11 \times 10^{-31}\text{ kg}}} = 4.21 \times 10^6\ ^{m}\!/_{s}.$$

   The momentum

   $$p = \left(9.11 \times 10^{-31}\text{ kg}\right)\left(4.21 \times 10^6\ ^{m}\!/_{s}\right) = \mathbf{3.83 \times 10^{-24}\ ^{kg \cdot m}\!/_{s}}$$

   (c) The de Broglie wavelength is $\lambda = \dfrac{h}{mv} = \dfrac{h}{\vec{p}}$

   $$\lambda = \frac{6.624 \times 10^{-34}\text{ J} \cdot \text{s}}{3.83 \times 10^{-24}\ ^{kg \cdot m}\!/_{s}} = \mathbf{1.73 \times 10^{-10}\ m}$$

   The de Broglie wavelength is **0.173 nm**

   (d) Correct line checked is
   _____√_____ would cause diffraction
   In order to cause diffraction of the crystal by the electron, the de Broglie wavelength must be approximately the size of the layer separation. Since the layers separation is given as 0.10 nm and the de Broglie wavelength for this problem is 0.244 nm, the electron would produce a diffraction pattern similar to one produced by X-ray diffraction of the crystal.
   (*College Physics* 9th ed. pages 937–938/10th ed. pages 935–937)
   (L.O. 6.G.1.1, 6.G.2.1, 6.G.2.2)

19

NUCLEAR PHYSICS

THE ATOMIC MASS UNIT

(College Physics 9th ed. page 958/10th ed. page 972)

In the study of nuclear physics, the masses of nuclei and nucleons are expressed in terms of the *unified atomic mass unit*, u, where a neutral C-12 atom is defined to be precisely 12.000 000 u. The unified atomic mass unit is $\frac{1}{12}$ of the mass of the C-12 atom. It is advantageous to express the unified atomic mass unit in terms of its rest-mass energy.

AP Tip

Calculations involving nuclear reactions involve working with masses expressed to six decimal places. Set your calculators to deal with six decimal places calculations. The usual rules for significant figures are not followed here.

SAMPLE PROBLEM 1

What is the rest mass energy, in MeV, of the unified mass unit, u?

SOLUTION TO PROBLEM 1

In terms of SI mass, the unified atomic mass unit, u, is defined as

$$1.000\ 000\ \text{u} = 1.660540 \times 10^{-27}\ \text{kg}$$

Write the Einstein mass-energy relationship

$$E = mc^2$$

$$E = \left(1.660540 \times 10^{-27} \text{ kg}\right)\left(2.997924 \times 10^8 \ \frac{\text{m}}{\text{s}}\right)^2$$

$$E = 1.492419 \times 10^{-10} \text{ J} \times \frac{1.00 \text{ MeV}}{1.602218 \times 10^{-13} \text{ J}}$$

1.00 u = 931.494 MeV

AP Tip

Use this conversion factor, $931.494 \ \dfrac{\text{MeV}}{\text{u}}$, to all three decimal places when determining the energy in nuclear reactions.

NUCLEI AND NUCLEONS

(College Physics 9th ed. pages 957–960/10th ed. pages 971–974)

Atomic nuclei are composed of nucleons. Only nucleons are found in the nucleus and these are protons and neutrons. Electrons are extra-nuclear in their nature and are never present in the nucleus. The proton population of a nucleus is the atomic number, Z. The total nucleon population is called the mass number, A, and the neutron population, N, is then $N = A - Z$.

Nuclear species are symbolically expressed as $^A_Z X$. The O-16 nuclear symbol is then $^{16}_8 O$. The O-16 nucleus contains 16 nucleons, 8 of which are protons and 8 are neutrons.

Nuclei of the same element that have different neutron populations are called isotopes. C-12, $^{12}_6 C$, and C-13, $^{13}_6 C$, are isotopes.

NUCLEAR BINDING ENERGY

(College Physics 9th ed. pages 960–962/10th ed. pages 974–976)

The rest mass of a nucleus is less than all of the rest masses of its constituent nucleons. The decrease in mass is due to the fact that negative energy is required to hold nucleons together in the nucleus. The binding energy, B, is found by taking the differences between the rest-mass energies of the constituent nucleons and the rest-mass energy of the final nucleus, M_A.

AP Tip

Tabulations of masses of isotopes are atomic masses and not nuclear masses. The electrons are included but this is not a problem. In determining energies, initial values are subtracted from final values eliminating the electron masses.

SAMPLE PROBLEM 2

Calculate both the binding energy and the binding energy per nucleon of the $^{16}_{8}O$ nucleus.

SOLUTION TO PROBLEM 2

The mass of a hydrogen atom is 1.007 825 u, the neutron is 1.008 665 u, and O-16 is 15.994 915 u.

The mass of the hydrogen atom, H, is used and not the mass of the proton. In the subtraction below, all electron masses are eliminated from the final answer.

The binding energy of a nucleus of Z protons and N neutrons is defined as

$$B = (Zm_H + Nm_n - M_A) \times 931.494 \frac{\text{MeV}}{\text{u}}$$

$$B = \left[(8 \times 1.007\ 825\ \text{u}) + (8 \times 1.008\ 665\ \text{u}) - (15.994\ 915\ \text{u}) \right] \times \left(931.494 \frac{\text{MeV}}{\text{u}} \right)$$

$$B = \textbf{127.62 MeV}$$

The binding energy per nucleon is the binding energy divided by the nucleon population.

$$\frac{B}{A} = \frac{127.619\ \text{MeV}}{16\ \text{nucleons}} = \textbf{7.98} \frac{\textbf{MeV}}{\textbf{nucleon}}$$

SAMPLE PROBLEM 3

A gamma ray photon is used to photo disintegrate a deuteron into a proton and a neutron as: $^{2}_{1}H + \gamma \rightarrow {}^{1}_{1}H + {}^{1}_{0}n$. Calculate the minimum energy of the photon and the frequency of the associated electromagnetic wave.

SOLUTION TO PROBLEM 3

Minimum energy implies the proton and neutron are at rest after the disintegration.

$$E = (m_H + m_n - M_D) \times 931.494 \frac{\text{MeV}}{\text{u}}$$

$$E = (1.007\ 825\ \text{u} + 1.008\ 665\ \text{u} - 2.014\ 102\ \text{u}) \times 931.494 \frac{\text{MeV}}{\text{u}}$$

$$= \textbf{2.22 MeV}$$

$$E = hf$$

$$f = \frac{E}{h}$$

$$f = \frac{(2.22 \text{ MeV})\left(\dfrac{1.60 \times 10^{-13} \text{ J}}{1.00 \text{ MeV}}\right)}{6.63 \times 10^{-34} \text{ J} \cdot \text{s}} = 5.36 \times 10^{20} \text{ Hz}$$

Notice that when a neutron and a proton come under the strong nuclear force, they merge to become a deuteron: ${}^1_0\text{n} + {}^1_1\text{H} \rightarrow {}^2_1\text{H} + 2.224 \text{ MeV}$. The energy will be released as a 2.22 MeV gamma ray having a frequency of 5.36×10^{20} Hz.

RADIOACTIVITY

(*College Physics* 9th ed. pages 962–971/10th ed. pages 976–985)

Discovery has its own chain reaction. The discovery of X-rays by Becquerel in 1895 set the stage for Becquerel's discovery of radioactivity a year later. Over the next decade a number of scientists investigated radioactivity and eventually unraveled its mysteries. Of all of the known nuclei, just under 300 are stable, while nearly five times that number are unstable—radioactive. In the lightest nuclei the number of protons and neutrons are about equal $(Z \approx N)$. As the number of protons and neutrons increases in higher Z nuclei, the number of neutrons becomes greater than the proton population $(N > Z)$. Increased neutron population in a heavier nucleus serves to buffer the repulsive Coulomb force between protons. A point is reached where there are too many neutrons in a nucleus and the nucleus becomes unstable—radioactive. Radioactive nuclei stabilize themselves by undergoing radioactive decay. There are several modes of radioactive decay.

Alpha decay is a spontaneous nuclear reaction that takes place in heavy, neutron-rich (too many neutrons) radioactive nuclei ($Z > 61$). A parent nucleus X emits an alpha particle ${}^4_2\text{He}$ or ${}^4_2\alpha$ and forms a daughter nucleus Y. The nuclear reaction for this decay is

$$ {}^A_Z\text{X} \rightarrow {}^4_2\text{He} + {}^{A-4}_{Z-2}\text{Y} $$

SAMPLE PROBLEM 4

Write the balanced alpha decay reactions for ${}^{239}_{94}\text{Pu}$, ${}^{238}_{92}\text{U}$, ${}^{230}_{90}\text{Th}$, ${}^{222}_{86}\text{Rn}$, and ${}^{214}_{84}\text{Po}$.

SOLUTION TO PROBLEM 4

$$ {}^{239}_{94}\text{Pu} \rightarrow {}^4_2\text{He} + {}^{235}_{92}\text{U} $$

$$ {}^{235}_{92}\text{U} \rightarrow {}^4_2\text{He} + {}^{231}_{90}\text{Th} $$

$$ {}^{230}_{90}\text{Th} \rightarrow {}^4_2\alpha + {}^{226}_{88}\text{Ra} $$

$$ {}^{222}_{86}\text{Rn} \rightarrow {}^4_2\text{He} + {}^{218}_{84}\text{Po} $$

$$ {}^{218}_{84}\text{Po} \rightarrow {}^4_2\alpha + {}^{214}_{82}\text{Pb} $$

Notice that each alpha decay results in a new nucleus two atomic numbers lower on the periodic table.

AP Tip

The alpha particle is a helium nucleus and its nuclear notation is commonly expressed either as ^4_2He or $^4_2\alpha$. The student should be familiar with both notations.

Energy, called the Q-value, is released in the alpha decay process, $^A_Z\text{X} \rightarrow {^4_2}\text{He} + {^{A-4}_{Z-2}}\text{Y} + Q$. Alpha decay can only take place if $Q > 0$ and

$$Q > (M_X - M_Y - M_\alpha) \times 931.494 \frac{\text{MeV}}{\text{u}}$$

The Q-value is calculated by

$$Q = (M_X - M_Y - M_\alpha) \times 931.494 \frac{\text{MeV}}{\text{u}}$$

SAMPLE PROBLEM 5

Calculate the Q-value for the alpha decay of Ra-226.

SOLUTION TO PROBLEM 5

First, write the balanced nuclear reaction for Ra-226.

$$^{226}_{88}\text{Ra} \rightarrow {^{222}_{86}}\text{Rn} + {^4_2}\alpha + Q$$

From an atomic mass table

$$M_{Ra} = 226.025\ 406\ \text{u}$$
$$M_{Rn} = 222.017\ 574\ \text{u}$$
$$M_\alpha = 4.002\ 603\ \text{u}$$

Now calculate the Q-value

$$Q = (M_X - M_Y - M_\alpha) \times 931.494 \frac{\text{MeV}}{\text{u}}$$

$$Q = (226.025\ 406\ \text{u} - 222.017\ 574\ \text{u} - 4.002\ 603\ \text{u}) \times 931.494 \frac{\text{MeV}}{\text{u}}$$

$$= \textbf{4.87 MeV}$$

The alpha particle carries away nearly 4.8 MeV of the Q-value as kinetic energy where the recoiling Rn-222 nucleus carries away approximately 0.1 MeV.

Negative beta decay takes place in neutron-rich (too many neutrons), radioactive nuclei. The process is complex and involves the creation of a beta particle and antineutrino by the weaker interaction and intermediate W⁻ and Z⁰ bosons. Very basically a neutron is converted into a proton with the emission of the beta particle and antineutrino. A parent nucleus X decays by emitting a beta particle $^0_{-1}\text{e}$ or $^0_{-1}\beta$, an antineutrino $^0_0\bar{\nu}$, and forms a daughter nucleus Y. The nuclear reaction for this decay process is

$$^A_Z\text{X} \rightarrow {^0_{-1}}\text{e} + {^0_0}\bar{\nu} + {^A_{Z+1}}\text{Y}$$

The beta particle is an electron. Note that electrons (beta particles) do not exist in the nucleus; the beta particle and antineutrino are created in the decay process. Both leave the surface of the nucleus at near the speed of light.

SAMPLE PROBLEM 6

Write balanced reactions for the beta decay of:

$$^{239}_{92}U, \ ^{239}_{93}Np, \ ^{90}_{38}Sr, \ ^{14}_{6}C, \text{ and } ^{3}_{1}H.$$

SOLUTION TO PROBLEM 6

$$^{239}_{92}U \ \rightarrow \ ^{0}_{-1}e + ^{0}_{0}\bar{\nu} + ^{239}_{93}Np$$

$$^{239}_{93}Np \ \rightarrow \ ^{0}_{-1}e + ^{0}_{0}\bar{\nu} + ^{239}_{94}Pu$$

$$^{90}_{38}Sr \ \rightarrow \ ^{0}_{-1}\beta + ^{0}_{0}\bar{\nu} + ^{90}_{39}Y$$

$$^{14}_{6}C \ \rightarrow \ ^{0}_{-1}e + ^{0}_{0}\bar{\nu} + ^{14}_{7}N$$

$$^{3}_{1}H \ \rightarrow \ ^{0}_{-1}\beta + ^{0}_{0}\bar{\nu} + ^{3}_{2}He$$

Each beta decay results in a new nucleus one atomic number higher on the periodic table.

AP Tip

The beta particle is an electron and its nuclear notation is commonly expressed either as $^{0}_{-1}e$ or $^{0}_{-1}\beta$. You should be familiar with both notations.

Positron decay takes place in neutron-poor (too few neutrons) radioactive nuclei. These nuclei are not found in nature—they are artificially made in nuclear laboratories. The positron process is complex and involves the creation of a positron (electron antiparticle) and neutrino by the weaker interaction and intermediate W^+ and Z^0 bosons. Basically, a proton is converted into a neutron with the emission of the positron and neutrino. A parent nucleus X decays by emitting a positron particle $^{0}_{+1}e$ or $^{0}_{+1}\beta$, a neutrino $^{0}_{0}\nu$, and forms a daughter nucleus Y. The nuclear reaction for this decay is

$$^{A}_{Z}X \ \rightarrow \ ^{0}_{+1}e + ^{0}_{0}\nu + ^{A}_{Z-1}Y$$

The positron is an anti-electron. Note that positrons do not exist in the nucleus; the positron and neutrino are created in the decay process. Both leave the surface of the nucleus at near the speed of light.

SAMPLE PROBLEM 7

Write the positron decay reactions for $^{53}_{26}Fe, \ ^{33}_{17}Cl, \ ^{28}_{15}P, \ ^{14}_{8}O, \text{ and } ^{11}_{6}C.$

SOLUTION TO PROBLEM 7

$$^{53}_{26}\text{Fe} \rightarrow {}^{0}_{+1}\text{e} + {}^{0}_{0}\nu + {}^{53}_{25}\text{Mn}$$

$$^{33}_{17}\text{Cl} \rightarrow {}^{0}_{+1}\text{e} + {}^{0}_{0}\nu + {}^{33}_{16}\text{S}$$

$$^{28}_{15}\text{P} \rightarrow {}^{0}_{+1}\beta + {}^{0}_{0}\nu + {}^{28}_{14}\text{Si}$$

$$^{14}_{8}\text{O} \rightarrow {}^{0}_{+1}\text{e} + {}^{0}_{0}\nu + {}^{14}_{7}\text{N}$$

$$^{11}_{6}\text{C} \rightarrow {}^{0}_{+1}\beta + {}^{0}_{0}\nu + {}^{11}_{5}\text{B}$$

Each positron decay results in a new nucleus one atomic number lower on the periodic table.

AP Tip

The positive beta particle or positron is an antielectron and its nuclear notation is commonly expressed either as ${}^{0}_{+1}\text{e}$ or ${}^{0}_{+1}\beta$. You should be familiar with both notations.

The nucleons of a nucleus that has undergone alpha or some form of beta decay are left in an excited state. To stabilize itself, the excited nucleus discards the excitation energy as a gamma ray photon γ. The excited state is short-lived and emits a gamma ray in about 10^{-8} s. A star (*) indicates an excited state, and both the daughter and the parent nucleus have the same nucleon and proton populations. The nuclear reaction for this decay process is

$$^{A}_{Z}\text{X}^{*} \rightarrow {}^{A}_{Z}\text{Y} + \gamma$$

SAMPLE PROBLEM 8

Write the nuclear reactions for the gamma emission of: $^{53}_{25}\text{Mn}^{*}$, $^{33}_{16}\text{S}^{*}$, $^{28}_{14}\text{Si}^{*}$, $^{14}_{7}\text{N}^{*}$, and $^{11}_{5}\text{B}^{*}$.

SOLUTION TO PROBLEM 8

$$^{53}_{25}\text{Mn}^{*} \rightarrow {}^{53}_{25}\text{Mn} + \gamma$$

$$^{33}_{16}\text{S}^{*} \rightarrow {}^{33}_{16}\text{S} + \gamma$$

$$^{28}_{14}\text{Si}^{*} \rightarrow {}^{28}_{14}\text{Si} + \gamma$$

$$^{14}_{7}\text{N}^{*} \rightarrow {}^{14}_{7}\text{N} + \gamma$$

$$^{11}_{5}\text{B}^{*} \rightarrow {}^{11}_{5}\text{B} + \gamma$$

RADIOACTIVE HALF-LIFE

(*College Physics* 9th ed. pages 963–965/10th ed. pages 977–979)

In the study of radioactivity a question immediately comes to mind that concerns the lifetime of a nucleus. What is the lifetime of a nucleus and how long does it last? The term *lifetime* is both apt and appropriate because in the disintegration of a nucleus by particle emission, the original nucleus, called the parent, vanishes and is replaced by a newly produced successor called the daughter nucleus. Exactly when the parent nucleus will expire and the new daughter nucleus takes its place is unpredictable; the disintegration of any one atom may occur within the next second, or not for another million years.

The study of radioactive decay is statistical by nature and requires large groups of nuclei. The rate at which radioactive nuclei decay is associated with a decay constant, λ, unique to any particular radioactive isotope. Each radioisotope has its own decay constant. Radioisotopes lessen with time. The rapidity of decay of a particular sample of a radioisotope is measured by the *half-life*, $T_{\frac{1}{2}}$, defined as the time period over which the number of parent nuclei at the beginning of the period is reduced by a factor of one-half. Half-life is defined in terms of λ as

$$T_{\frac{1}{2}} = \frac{0.693}{\lambda}$$

Starting with N_0 parent nuclei, $\frac{1}{2}N_0$ are left after a time period of $T_{\frac{1}{2}}$, $\frac{1}{4}N_0$ remain after a time period of $2T_{\frac{1}{2}}$, $\frac{1}{8}N_0$ after $3T_{\frac{1}{2}}$, etc.

Another quantity that measures how rapidly a sample radioisotope decays is by the *average* or *mean lifetime*, $\overline{T}$, of the nucleus

$$\overline{T} = \frac{1}{\lambda} = \frac{T_{\frac{1}{2}}}{\ln 2}$$

Sample Problem 9

Tritium, H-3, has a half-life period of 12.5 years.

(a) What is the decay constant of tritium?

(b) Find the mean lifetime of a nucleus of tritium.

Solution to Problem 9

(a) $T_{\frac{1}{2}} = \dfrac{0.693}{\lambda}$ and $\lambda = \dfrac{0.693}{T_{\frac{1}{2}}} = \dfrac{0.693}{12.5 \text{ y}} = \mathbf{5.54 \times 10^{-2} \text{ y}^{-1}}$

(b) $\overline{T} = \dfrac{1}{\lambda} = \dfrac{1}{5.54 \times 10^{-2} \text{ y}^{-1}} = \mathbf{18.05 \text{ y}}$

Regardless of the types of particles emitted, all nuclear decays obey the same radioactive decay law. If there are N_0 parent nuclei present initially, the number N of parent nuclei still remaining after time t is given by

$$N = N_0 e^{-\lambda t}$$

The above decay law is a statistical law. It yields the expected number N of parent nuclei that survive after a period of time, t.

Since the quantity of radioactive material is determined by the number of nuclei present, an equation similar to the one above can be used to calculate the mass, m, of remaining material after time period, t, when the initial mass, m_0 is given.

$$m = m_0 e^{-\lambda t}$$

Notice that both of the above equations are exponential in terms of the natural exponent e.

The number of decays per unit time taking place in a radioactive sample at any instant is called the *activity, A.*

$$A = \lambda N_0 e^{-\lambda t} = \lambda N$$

The SI unit of activity is called the *becquerel, Bq,* and it is defined as 1 becquerel = 1 Bq = 1 disintegration per second. A more common unit that is used to express the activity of a sample of radioisotope is the *curie, Ci,* and it is defined as 1 curie = 1 Ci = 3.700×10^{10} disintegrations per second.

SAMPLE PROBLEM 10

A radioactive material has a decay constant of 4.20×10^3 reciprocal second and starts with 30.0×10^6 nuclei.

(a) How many nuclei remain after 1.20 ms?

(b) In Ci, what is the initial activity of the material?

SOLUTION TO PROBLEM 10

(a) $N = N_0 e^{-\lambda t} = \left(30.0 \times 10^6 \text{ nuclei}\right) e^{-\left(4.20 \times 10^3 \text{ s}^{-1}\right)\left(1.20 \times 10^{-3} \text{ s}\right)}$

$$N = \left(30.0 \times 10^6 \text{ nuclei}\right) e^{-(5.04)} = \mathbf{1.92 \times 10^5 \text{ nuclei}}$$

(b) $A_0 = \lambda N_0 = \left(4.20 \times 10^3 \text{ s}^{-1}\right)\left(30.0 \times 10^6 \text{ nuclei}\right)$

$$A_0 = \left(1.26 \times 10^{11} \frac{\text{disintegrations}}{\text{s}}\right)\left(\frac{1 \text{ Ci}}{3.700 \times 10^{10} \text{ disintegrations/s}}\right)$$

$$= \mathbf{3.41 \text{ Ci}}$$

NUCLEAR REACTIONS

(*College Physics* 9th ed. pages 971–972/10th ed. pages 985–987)

An excellent source of neutrons is a mixture of radium and beryllium. To understand the mechanism involved we need to consider the following nuclear reactions.

$$^{226}_{88}\text{Ra} \rightarrow \,^{222}_{86}\text{Rn} + \,^4_2\text{He}$$

$$^9_4\text{Be} + \,^4_2\text{He} \rightarrow \,^{12}_6\text{C} + \,^1_0\text{n}$$

Alpha particles from the radium strike beryllium nuclei producing neutrons. The neutrons produced are not monoenergetic.

Most nuclear reactions are carried out in nuclear physics laboratories using high-energy particle accelerators.

SAMPLE PROBLEM 11

Tritium, H-3 nuclei, are bombarded with deuterons, H-2, producing helium nuclei, He-4, and neutrons. This type of nuclear reaction is usually represented as

$$X + x \rightarrow Y + y$$

The symbol X represents the target nucleus, x is the projectile, Y is the resulting nucleus, and y represents the fragment. The Q-value of the reaction is calculated using

$$Q = \left[(M_X + m_x) - (M_Y + m_y)\right] \times 931.494 \frac{MeV}{u}$$

Calculate the reaction Q-value for $^3_1H + ^2_1H \rightarrow ^4_2He + ^1_0n + Q$. Note that the projectile and fragment particles are given in the nuclear reaction.

SOLUTION TO PROBLEM 11

The reaction could also be written as $X(x,y)Y$ or $^3_1H(d, n)^4_2He$.
First, find the reaction Q-value

$M_{H\text{-}3}$	= 3.016 049 u		$M_{He\text{-}4}$	= 4.002 603 u
m_d	= 2.014 102 u		m_n	= 1.008 665 u
$M_{H\text{-}3} + m_d$	= 5.030 151 u		$M_{He\text{-}4} + m_n$	= 5.011 268 u

$$Q = \left[(M_X + m_x) - (M_Y + m_y)\right] \times 931.494 \frac{MeV}{u}$$

$$Q = \left[(5.030\ 151\ u) - (5.011\ 268\ u)\right] \times 931.494 \frac{MeV}{u} = \textbf{17.59 MeV}$$

The reaction Q-value is positive, indicating that energy is in excess by 17.59 MeV.

SAMPLE PROBLEM 12

Consider the alpha-neutron nuclear reaction $^{27}_{13}Al(\alpha,n)^{30}_{15}P$. Calculate the reaction Q-value.

SOLUTION TO PROBLEM 12

First, write the alpha-neutron nuclear reaction

$$^{27}_{13}Al + ^4_2He \rightarrow ^{30}_{15}P + ^1_0n + Q$$

Calculate the Q-value

M_{Al}	= 26.981 535 u		M_P	= 29.978 320 u
m_α	= 4.002 603 u		m_n	= 1.008 665 u
$M_{Al} + m_\alpha$	= 30.984 138 u		$M_P + m_n$	= 30.986 985 u

$$Q = \left[(M_X + m_x) - (M_Y + m_y)\right] \times 931.494 \frac{MeV}{u}$$

$$Q = \left[(30.984\ 138\ u) - (30.986\ 985\ u)\right] \times 931.494 \frac{MeV}{u} = \textbf{-2.65 MeV}$$

$Q < 0$ making the reaction endoergic. Such nuclear reactions cannot take place spontaneously. Energy in excess of 2.65 MeV must be added to the system to induce nuclear reaction.

NUCLEAR FISSION

(College Physics 9th ed. pages 982–986/10th ed. pages 996–1000)

Hahn and Strassman discovered nuclear fission in 1938. When a slow or thermal neutron enters a nucleus of fissionable material, like $^{235}_{92}U$ or $^{239}_{94}Pu$, the neutron is captured and the nucleus splits—fissions with a large release of energy. Uranium U-235 and plutonium Pu-239 are fissionable materials. Chemical reactions liberate energies on the order of several electron volts, eV, where nuclear fission releases energies on the order of 180 MeV. When nuclear fission occurs, two fission fragments A and B are formed along with several neutrons and a large Q-value. We can write the fission reaction as

$$^{235}_{92}U + {}^1_0n \rightarrow A + B + x{}^1_0n + Q$$

or as

$$^{239}_{94}Pu + {}^1_0n \rightarrow A + B + x{}^1_0n + Q$$

The fission fragments are asymmetric.

SAMPLE PROBLEM 13

A thermal neutron is used to initiate nuclear fission in a stationary U-235 nucleus. Calculate the Q-value for

$$^{235}_{92}U + {}^1_0n \rightarrow {}^{144}_{56}Ba + {}^{89}_{36}Kr + 3{}^1_0n + Q.$$

SOLUTION TO PROBLEM 13

The thermal neutron has an energy less than 0.1 eV. Since the energy released in a single fission far exceeds 100 MeV, the energy of the incoming thermal neutron is ignored in the calculations.

In this problem, the masses of the fission fragments are only given to four decimal places and we will calculate with the given masses.

M_U	= 235.0439 u	M_{Ba}	= 143.9605 u
m_n	= 1.0087 u	M_{Kr}	= 88.8640 u
		$3m_n$	= 3.0261 u
$M_U + m_n$	= 236.0526 u	$M_{Ba} + M_{Kr} + 3m_n$	= 235.8506 u

$$Q = \left[(M_U + m_n) - (M_{Ba} + M_{Kr} + 3m_n)\right] \times 931.494 \frac{MeV}{u}$$

$$Q = \left[(236.0526\ u) - (235.8506\ u)\right] \times 931.494 \frac{MeV}{u} = \textbf{188.16 MeV}$$

The fission fragments and fission neutrons share the 188.16 MeV as kinetic energy. Fissionable materials have a high density and the fission fragments are quickly stopped, transforming their energy into thermal energy. Nuclear fission releases gigantic quantities of heat.

The isotope Pu-239 does not exist in nature but is made in a type of nuclear reactor called a breeder reactor. The uranium isotope U-238 does not participate in slow neutron induced nuclear fission. In the breeder reactor U-238 absorbs a neutron and forms the short-lived U-239 isotope. U-239 is a beta emitter and forms element 93 that is also a short-lived beta emitter. The end product is Pu-239.

Sample Problem 14

Ignoring the Q-values, write the nuclear reactions for the formation of Pu-239 from U-238 in the breeder reactor.

Solution to Problem 14

Write the reaction for the absorption of the neutron by U-238

$$^{238}_{92}U + ^{1}_{0}n \rightarrow ^{239}_{92}U$$

The beta decay is

$$^{239}_{92}U \rightarrow ^{0}_{-1}e + ^{0}_{0}\bar{\nu} + ^{239}_{93}Np$$

and the next beta decay

$$^{239}_{93}Np \rightarrow ^{0}_{-1}e + ^{0}_{0}\bar{\nu} + ^{239}_{94}Pu$$

Thermonuclear Fusion

(*College Physics* 9th ed. pages 986–988/10th ed. pages 1000–1003)

Nuclear fission is a nuclear reaction in which massive, fissionable nuclei, when they absorb a neutron, split into two fission fragments with the release of several neutrons and energy on the order of 180 MeV per fission. Nuclear fusion is a nuclear process in which light nuclei fuse or join in a more massive nucleus with an energy release on the order of 10 to 20 MeV per fusion.

Light nuclei have to collide before they fuse. Surrounding each nucleus is an electrostatic coulomb barrier that repels other nuclei. High kinetic energy and great pressure are required by colliding nuclei to overcome the electrostatic barriers. Light nuclei heated to millions of degrees have such kinetic energies to bring nuclei into direct contact allowing fusion reactions. These nuclear reactions are called thermonuclear fusion reactions.

Thermonuclear fusion reactions are the reactions that drive stars and fuel the fireball of a thermonuclear device—a hydrogen bomb. Lithium-6 deuteride is a fuel used in thermonuclear devices.

Sample Problem 15

Under extreme temperature and pressure Li-6 and deuterium, H-2, will undergo thermonuclear fusion as: $^{6}_{3}Li + ^{2}_{1}H \rightarrow ^{4}_{2}He + ^{4}_{2}He + Q$. Calculate the reaction Q-value.

SOLUTION TO PROBLEM 15

Write the nuclear reaction

$$_3^6\text{Li} + {}_1^2\text{H} \rightarrow {}_2^4\text{He} + {}_2^4\text{He} + Q$$

Calculate the reaction Q-value

M_{Li}	= 6.015 122 u	M_{He}	= 4.002 603 u
m_d	= 2.014 102 u	m_{He}	= 4.002 603 u
$M_{Li} + m_d$	= 8.029 224 u	$M_{He} + m_{He}$	= 8.005 206 u

$$Q = \left[(M_X + m_x) - (M_Y + m_y) \right] \times 931.494 \, \frac{\text{MeV}}{\text{u}}$$

$$Q = \left[(8.029\ 224 \text{ u}) - (8.005\ 206 \text{ u}) \right] \times 931.494 \, \frac{\text{MeV}}{\text{u}} = \textbf{22.37 MeV}$$

NUCLEAR PHYSICS: STUDENT OBJECTIVES FOR THE AP EXAM

- ▨ You should know and use the mass-energy relationship.
- ▨ You should know and understand the symbols for atomic number Z, neutron number N, and mass number A and be able to use them correctly in radioactive decay and binding energy problems.
- ▨ You should know the processes for (a) alpha, (b) beta, and (c) gamma decay and be able to balance nuclear reactions.
- ▨ You should understand the meaning of radioactive half-life.
- ▨ You should know how to find the activity of a radioactive material.
- ▨ You should be able to calculate Q-value values in nuclear reactions.
- ▨ You should be able to calculate the binding energy of nuclei.
- ▨ You should know the difference between nuclear fission and fusion and be able to balance their nuclear reactions.

MULTIPLE-CHOICE QUESTIONS

1. A nucleus of $_{14}^{30}\text{Si}$ contains

	protons	neutrons
(A)	14	30
(B)	14	16
(C)	30	14
(D)	30	16

2. In the nuclear reaction $_{88}^{224}\text{Ra} \rightarrow {}_{86}^{220}\text{Rn} + ?$ The particle(s) ejected

   (A) is an alpha particle, $_2^4\text{He}$

   (B) is an alpha particle, $_2^4\text{He}$, and a conservation particle, the anti-neutrino $\bar{\nu}$

   (C) is an alpha particle, $_2^4\text{He}$, and a conservation particle, the neutrino, ν

   (D) are two deuterons

3. A certain radioactive isotope has a half-life of 2.40 days. If the initial mass is the sample is 6.00 μg, what is the mass of the remaining isotope after 5 half-lives?
   (A) 1.50 μg
   (B) 0.750 μg
   (C) 0.375 μg
   (D) 0.188 μg

4. In the nuclear decay, $^{239}_{93}\text{Np} \rightarrow {}^{239}_{94}\text{Pu} + \bar{\nu} + ?$, the missing particle is:
   (A) $^{4}_{2}\text{He}$
   (B) $^{1}_{0}\text{n}$
   (C) e^{-}
   (D) e^{+}

5. Calculate the binding energy released in the formation of the $^{7}_{3}\text{Li}$ nucleus.

   Mass of the proton is 1.007 276 (u)

   Mass of the neutron is 1.008 665 (u)

   Mass of the $^{7}_{3}\text{Li}$ nuclei is 7.016 004 (u)
   (A) 41.6 MeV
   (B) 37.7 MeV
   (C) 36.4 MeV
   (D) 32.5 MeV

6. What is the missing particle in the following nuclear reaction?

   $$^{27}_{13}\text{Al} + {}^{4}_{2}\text{He} \rightarrow {}^{30}_{15}\text{P} + ?$$
   (A) proton
   (B) deuteron
   (C) alpha particle
   (D) neutron

7. Consider the following nuclear fission reaction,
   $^{235}_{92}\text{U} + {}^{1}_{0}\text{n} \rightarrow {}^{102}_{42}\text{Mo} + {}^{130}_{50}\text{Sn} + ?$. What is the missing quantity?
   (A) $^{4}_{2}\text{He}$
   (B) $2\left({}^{1}_{1}\text{H}\right)$
   (C) $^{4}_{0}\text{n}$
   (D) $4\left({}^{1}_{0}\text{n}\right)$

8. The conservation laws that govern all nuclear reactions include the conservation of
   (A) charge and momentum
   (B) charge and mass-energy
   (C) mass-energy and momentum
   (D) charge, mass-energy, and momentum

9. The half-life of a radioactive material is the time for the number of unstable nuclei of a given isotope of an element to decrease by a

factor of 2. After 3 half-lives, the amount of radioactive isotope remaining is

(A) $\frac{1}{8}$ of the initial amount

(B) $\frac{1}{6}$ of the initial amount

(C) $\frac{1}{4}$ of the initial amount

(D) $\frac{1}{3}$ of the initial amount

10. Consider the following two-step nuclear reactions, first the β^- decay of $^{137}_{55}\text{Cs}$

   $^{137}_{55}\text{Cs} \rightarrow {}^{137}_{56}\text{Ba}^* + \beta^- + \bar{\nu}$ followed by the decay

   $^{137}_{56}\text{Ba}^* \rightarrow {}^{137}_{56}\text{Ba} + ?$ The unknown particle, ?, is

   (A) α

   (B) β^+

   (C) γ

   (D) n

11. An alpha decay occurring from the parent isotope of $^{238}_{92}\text{U}$ initially at rest forms the daughter isotope $^{234}_{90}\text{Th}$. In the process, the alpha particle, $^{4}_{2}\text{He}$, recoils from the thorium nucleus $^{234}_{90}\text{Th}$. The velocity of the center of mass of the system

   (A) moves with the recoiling parent $^{238}_{92}\text{U}$ as the alpha particle moves away from the parent in the decay

   (B) moves in the direction of the thorium isotope since it is much larger

   (C) remains at rest since momentum is conserved in the process and before the decay, the parent $^{238}_{92}\text{U}$ was at rest

   (D) moves in the direction of the alpha particle since it is smaller and carries the majority of the kinetic energy

12. Carbon dating is a way that scientists use to date organic material, since the ratio of $^{14}_{6}\text{C}$ to $^{12}_{6}\text{C}$ molecules in our atmosphere is constant. All living things have the same ratio. When they die, they no longer absorb $^{14}_{6}\text{C}$. The decay of the $^{14}_{6}\text{C}$ isotope produces which of the following particles?

   (A) α

   (B) β^-

   (C) β^+

   (D) γ

13. The fission of a heavy isotope into two smaller fission fragments is generally initiated by using a thermal neutron since the neutron is
    (A) unstable outside the nucleus with a half-life of about 10.4 minutes
    (B) electrically neutral and will not have a Coulombic barrier as it is absorbed by the heavy isotope
    (C) about the same size as the fissionable nucleus so that it can cause the nucleus to fragment easily
    (D) basically massless and will not transfer much energy into the heavy isotope

14. The number of neutrons in the atom of $^{11}_{5}$B is
    (A) 0
    (B) 5
    (C) 6
    (D) 11

15. The mass of a stable nucleus is less than the sum of the constituent protons and neutrons that make up that nucleus. The difference is accounted for by
    (A) the protons and the neutrons that are arranged in the nucleus energy levels much like the electrons on their energy levels outside the nucleus
    (B) binding energy , $E = \Delta mc^2$, produced by the mass defect between the nuclear mass and the constituent protons and neutrons holding the nucleus together against spontaneous decay
    (C) differences between the Z and the A numbers
    (D) the devices that are used to measure mass in the nuclear range that are inaccurate

FREE-RESPONSE PROBLEMS

1. Given the spontaneous decay reaction

    $$^{232}_{92}U \rightarrow {}^{228}_{90}Th + {}^{4}_{2}He + Q$$

    (a) Calculate the Q-value for the reaction.
    (b) Is this decay possible? Justify your answer.
    (c) Determine the binding energy of the U-232 nucleus.
    (d) Find the binding energy per nucleon given that the mass of the U-232 = 232.037 156 u , Th-228 = 228.028 741 u , He-4 = 4.002 603 u, H = 1.007 825 u, and the neutron = 1.008 665 u.

2. Balance the following nuclear reactions. Justify your answers.
    (a) $^{14}_{7}N + {}^{4}_{2}He \rightarrow {}^{1}_{1}H + ?$
    (b) $^{2}_{1}H + {}^{12}_{6}C \rightarrow ? + {}^{10}_{5}B$
    (c) $^{1}_{1}H + {}^{1}_{0}n \rightarrow \gamma + ?$
    (d) $^{6}_{3}Li + {}^{1}_{1}H \rightarrow {}^{4}_{2}He + ?$
    (e) $^{2}_{1}H + {}^{3}_{1}H \rightarrow {}^{3}_{2}He + ? + ?$

3. Write complete nuclear reactions for the following question (a) to (e). Justify your answers as to the correct equation for each.

   (a) beta decay of $^{14}_{6}\text{C}$

   (b) gamma emission of $^{9}_{4}\text{Be}^{*}$

   (c) alpha decay of $^{240}_{94}\text{Pu}$

   (d) positron decay of $^{11}_{6}\text{C}$

   (e) nuclear fusion of two deuterons, $^{2}_{1}\text{H}$

4. Ra-226 has an atomic mass of 226 g/mol and a half-life of 1620 y.

   (a) Calculate the decay constant of Ra-226 in reciprocal seconds, s^{-1}.

   (b) Find the number of nuclei of Ra-226 in a 1.0 mg sample of the material.

   (c) What is the activity of the 1.0 mg sample expressed in curie?

Answers

MULTIPLE-CHOICE QUESTIONS

1. **B** An atom of an element is denoted as $^{A}_{Z}\text{X}$, Z is the proton number and A is the mass number. The atomic number gives the sum of the protons and neutrons in the isotope of the element. In this case there are 14 protons and 30 – 14 or 16 neutrons.
   (*College Physics* 9th ed. pages 957–958/10th ed. pages 971–972)
   (L.O. 1.A.2.1)

2. **A** The decay is an alpha decay. Charge and mass must balance in the equation thus $^{224}_{88}\text{Ra} \rightarrow \, ^{220}_{86}\text{Rn} + ?$ (There is no other particle emitted with the alpha particle.)
   (*College Physics* 9th ed. pages 965–966/10th ed. pages 979–980)
   (L.O. 1.A.5.1)

3. **D** Half-life is the time that it takes for half of the given number of radioactive nuclei to decay. $N = N_0 e^{-\lambda t}$ is the equation for the number of radioactive atoms present under going decay. (Count rate R in disintegrations /sec dps or activity A could be used as well.) Since the half-life is related to the decay constant $T_{1/2} = \dfrac{0.692}{\lambda}$, the equation can be written as $N = N_0 e^{-0.693t/T_{1/2}}$. The substitution into this equation gives $N = 6.00 \ \mu g \left(e^{-0.693(12.0\text{ d})/2.4\text{ d}} \right)$ then

   $N = 6.00 \ \mu g \left(e^{-3.465} \right) = 0.1876 \ \mu g$. An alternate method of doing this without the equations used above is as follows.

$T_{1/2}$ in days	Sample size in μg
0	6.00
2.40	3.00
4.80	1.50
7.20	0.750
9.60	0.375
12.0	0.1857

which gives 0.188 μg answer D.

(*College Physics* 9th ed. pages 962–963/10th ed. pages 977–978)
(L.O. 7.C.3.1)

4. **C** In a nuclear reaction, the Z number as well as the A number must be conserved.

In terms of the Z number, $93 \rightarrow 94 + 0 - 1$ thus the particle must have a charge (Z number) of –1. (The antineutrino $\bar{\nu}$ is a conservation particle with zero charge and "zero" mass and is required for conservation of energy as well as spin.)

Conservation of mass number A gives $239 \rightarrow 239 + 0 + 0$. Thus the particle missing in the equation must be a beta particle e^-. The beta particle can also be written as β^- or $_{-1}^{0}\beta$.

(*College Physics* 9th ed. pages 967–969/10th ed. pages 981–983)
(L.O. 7.C. 3.1)

5. **B** In the $_3^7\text{Li}$ nuclei there are 3 protons and 4 neutrons. The mass of the individual particles gives 3(1.007 276 u) + 4 (1.008 665 u) = 7.056 488 (u).

The mass defect Δm = 7.056 488 (u) − 7.016 004(u) = 0.040 484(u).

The binding energy in MeV's is $\Delta m \left(931.5 \ \dfrac{\text{MeV}}{\text{u}} \right)$. In the formation of $_3^7\text{Li}$, the binding energy is $0.040\ 484 \ \text{u} \left(931.5 \ \dfrac{\text{MeV}}{\text{u}} \right) = 37.7 \ \text{MeV}$.

(*College Physics* 9th ed. pages 960–962/10th ed. pages 974–976)
(L.O. 4.C.4.1)

6. **D** In any nuclear reaction, both the Z number and the A number must be conserved.

$_{13}^{27}\text{Al} + {_2^4}\text{He} \rightarrow {_{15}^{30}}\text{P} + ?$. The Z number is $13 + 2 = 15 + 0$. The A number is $27 + 4 = 30 + 1$.

The particle has a mass A = 1 and Z = 0, thus it is a neutron $_0^1\text{n}$.

(*College Physics* 9th ed. pages 971–972/10th ed. pages 985–986)
(L.O. 5.C.1.1)

7. **D** In any nuclear reaction, both the Z number and the A number must be conserved.

   $^{235}_{92}U + ^{1}_{0}n \rightarrow ^{102}_{42}Mo + ^{130}_{50}Sn + ?$ The Z number is 92 = 42 + 50 + 0.

   The particle must be a neutron. The A number gives 235 + 1 = 102 + 130 + 4.

   Since the mass is 4 atomic mass units and the charge is zero, there must be 4 neutrons to complete the reaction.
   (*College Physics* 9th ed. pages 982–984/10th ed. pages 996–997)
   (L.O. 5.G.1.1)

8. **D** Momentum is conserved in all interactions. Charge must be conserved in all nuclear reactions. Conservation of mass-energy is also conserved in nuclear reactions. In nuclear reactions $E = mc^2$ relates the conversions between mass and energy.
   (*College Physics* 9th ed. pages 960–961, 965–969, 971–973, 982–983, 986–987/10th ed. pages 974–975, 979–983, 996–998, 1000–1001)
   (L.O. 1.C.4.1, 5.G.1.1)

9. **A** After one half-life the amount that remains is $\frac{1}{2}$. After 2 half-lives, the amount remaining is $\frac{1}{2} \times \frac{1}{2} = \frac{1}{4}$. This can be written as $\left(\frac{1}{2}\right)^2$. After three half-lives this would be $\left(\frac{1}{2}\right)^3 = \frac{1}{8}$.
   (*College Physics* 9th ed. pages 962–963/10th ed. pages 977–978)
   (L.O. 7.C.3.1)

10. **C** In all nuclear reactions Z and A numbers must balance. The Z numbers for Barium remain as 56 and the mass number A, as 137. This reaction indicates that $^{137}_{56}Ba^*$ is in an excited state and decayed to a more stable state by giving off energy in the form of a gamma ray, γ.
    (*College Physics* 9th ed. pages 962–963/10th ed. pages 977–978)
    (L.O. 5.G.1.1)

11. C The alpha decay of $^{238}_{92}U \rightarrow ^{234}_{90}Th + ^{4}_{2}He$ results in two new particles, $^{234}_{90}Th$ and $^{4}_{2}He$. Since the initial momentum of the system was zero, the total momentum after decay is also zero to conserve momentum. This means that the velocity of center of mass of the system will also be zero.
    (*College Physics* 9th ed. pages 962–963/10th ed. pages 977–978)
    (L.O. 5.G.1.1)

12. **C** The decay is β^-. There are six protons in the nucleus of $^{14}_{6}C$ and 8 neutrons. The neutron is transformed into a proton that remains in the nucleus thus increasing the Z number to 7 and producing nitrogen. The reaction is $^{14}_{6}C \rightarrow ^{14}_{7}N + \beta^- + \bar{\nu}$
    (*College Physics* 9th ed. pages 967–968/10th ed. pages 981–982)
    (L.O. 5.C.1.1)

13. **B** The neutron has no charge and will not be deflected by the orbital electrons or the positively charged nucleus–there is no

Coulombic barrier for the neutron. When it is absorbed into the nucleus (easier to capture a slow moving neutron), all of its initial energy will be used to disturb the nucleus. Thus $_0^1n + _{92}^{235}U \rightarrow \ _{92}^{236}U^*$ then fission into two smaller fission fragments, several additional neutron.
(*College Physics* 9th ed. pages 982–983/10th ed. pages 996–1000)
(L.O. 5.G.1.1)

14. **C** In the $_5^{11}B$ nucleus there are $A - Z$ neutrons. $11 - 5 = 6$ neutrons.
(*College Physics* 9th ed. pages 957–958/10th ed. pages 971–972)
(L.O. 1.A.2.1)

15. **B** The total energy of a bound system is less than the energy of its separated nucleons. This difference is the Δm of the system converted into binding energy produced in the formation of the nucleus. It is calculated from $E = mc^2$.
(*College Physics* 9th ed. pages 960–962/10th ed. pages 974–976)
(L.O. 4.C.4.1)

FREE-RESPONSE PROBLEMS

1. (a) Write the nuclear reaction for the spontaneous alpha decay of U-232

$$_{92}^{232}U \ \rightarrow \ _{90}^{228}Th + _2^4He + Q$$

The required masses are

$M_{U\text{-}232} = 232.037\ 156$ u
$M_{Th\text{-}228} = 228.028\ 741$ u
$M_\alpha \quad = \quad 4.002\ 603$ u
$M_H \quad = \quad 1.007\ 825$ u
$M_n \quad = \quad 1.008\ 665$ u

Calculating the Q-value

$$Q = (M_{U\text{-}232} - M_{Th\text{-}228} - M_\alpha) \times 931.494 \ \frac{\text{MeV}}{\text{u}}$$

$$Q = (232.037\ 156 \text{ u} - 228.028\ 741 \text{ u} - 4.002\ 603 \text{ u}) \times 931.494 \ \frac{\text{MeV}}{\text{u}}$$

$$Q = 5.41 \text{ MeV}$$

(b) The Q-value is positive, $Q > 0$, making the alpha decay of U-232 possible.

(c) The U-232 nucleus has $Z = 92$ protons and $N = 140$ neutrons. The binding energy is

$$B = \left(Zm_H + Nm_n - M_A\right) \times 931.494 \ \frac{\text{MeV}}{\text{u}}$$

$$B = \left[(92 \times 1.007\ 825 \text{ u}) + (140 \times 1.008\ 665 \text{ u}) - (232.037\ 156 \text{ u})\right]\left(931.494 \ \frac{\text{MeV}}{\text{u}}\right)$$

$$B = \mathbf{1766.0 \text{ MeV}}$$

(d) The binding energy per nucleon is the binding energy divided by the nucleon population.

$$\frac{B}{A} = \frac{1766.0 \text{ MeV}}{232 \text{ nucleons}}$$

$$\frac{B}{A} = 7.61 \frac{\textbf{MeV}}{\textbf{nucleon}}$$

(*College Physics* 9th ed. pages 957–958, 960–962, 965–966/10th ed. pages 971, 974–976, 979–982)
(L.O. 4.C.4.1, 5.B.11.1, 5.C.1.1)

2. Nuclear reactions:

    In any nuclear reaction, the Z number as well as the A number must be conserved.

    (a) $^{14}_{7}\text{N} + ^{4}_{2}\text{He} \rightarrow ^{1}_{1}\text{H} + ^{17}_{8}\text{O}$

    The Z number is $7 + 2 = 1 + 8$; the A number is $14 + 4 = 1 + 17$; thus the missing nuclei is $^{17}_{8}\text{O}$.

    (b) $^{2}_{1}\text{H} + ^{12}_{6}\text{C} \rightarrow ^{4}_{2}\text{He} + ^{10}_{5}\text{B}$

    The Z number is $1 + 6 = 2 + 5$; the A number is $2 + 12 = 4 + 10$. The missing nucleus is $^{4}_{2}\text{He}$ or α.

    (c) $^{1}_{1}\text{H} + ^{1}_{0}\text{n} \rightarrow \gamma + ^{2}_{1}\text{H}$

    The gamma ray, γ has zero charge and zero mass. Conservation of Z number gives $1 + 0 = 0 + 1$. Conservation of A number is $1 + 1 = 0 + 2$. The unknown in the reaction is $^{2}_{1}\text{H}$. This is a deuteron and may be written as D in the reaction.

    (d) $^{6}_{3}\text{Li} + ^{1}_{1}\text{H} \rightarrow ^{4}_{2}\text{He} + ^{3}_{2}\text{He}$

    In this reaction, conservation of charge, Z gives $3 + 1 = 2 + 2$. The A number is determined as $6 + 1 = 4 + 3$. The unknown is an isotope of helium, $^{3}_{2}\text{He}$. It is <u>not</u> an alpha particle.

    (e) $^{2}_{1}\text{H} + ^{3}_{1}\text{H} \rightarrow ^{3}_{2}\text{He} + ^{1}_{0}\text{n} + ^{1}_{0}\text{n}$

    Conservation of Z number is $1 + 1 = 2 + 0$. A number is $2 + 3 = 3 + 2$. The only particle that could satisfy this equation is the neutron, $^{1}_{0}\text{n}$. There are two neutrons emitted. They are written separately or as $2\left(^{1}_{0}\text{n}\right)$. It is <u>not</u> written as $^{2}_{0}\text{n}$.

(*College Physics* 9th ed. pages 971–972/10th ed. pages 986–987)
(L.O. 5.C.1.1, 5.G.1.1)

3. Nuclear decays

    (a) $^{14}_{6}\text{C} \rightarrow ^{0}_{-1}\beta + ^{0}_{0}\bar{\nu} + ^{14}_{7}\text{N}$ or $^{14}_{6}\text{C} \rightarrow ^{0}_{-1}\text{e} + ^{0}_{0}\bar{\nu} + ^{14}_{7}\text{N}$

    For Z, the charge, $6 = -1 + 7$; and A requires $11 = 0 + 0 + 11$ since there are two particles emitted in a beta negative decay: the beta particle and the conservation particle, the antineutrino

(b) $^{9}_{4}\text{Be}^{*} \rightarrow {}^{9}_{4}\text{Be} + \gamma$

This reaction indicates that $^{9}_{4}\text{Be}^{*}$ is in an excited state and decayed to a more stable state by giving off energy in the form of a gamma ray, γ, which has $Z = 0$, and $A = 0$.

(c) $^{240}_{94}\text{Pu} \rightarrow {}^{236}_{92}\text{U} + {}^{4}_{2}\alpha$ or $^{240}_{94}\text{Pu} \rightarrow {}^{236}_{92}\text{U} + {}^{4}_{2}\text{He}$

Substitution for Z is $94 = 92 + 2$, A produces $240 = 236 + 4$. No other particle is emitted with the alpha particle.

(d) $^{11}_{6}\text{C} \rightarrow {}^{0}_{+1}\beta + {}^{0}_{0}\nu + {}^{11}_{5}\text{B}$ or $^{11}_{6}\text{C} \rightarrow {}^{0}_{+1}e + {}^{0}_{0}\nu + {}^{11}_{5}\text{B}$

For Z, the charge, $6 = +1 + 5$; and A requires $11 = 0 + 0 + 11$ since there are two particles emitted in a beta positive or positron decay: the beta particle and the conservation particle, the neutrino.

(e) $^{2}_{1}\text{H} + {}^{2}_{1}\text{H} \rightarrow {}^{4}_{2}\text{He}$

In a fusion reaction, one heavier nuclide is produced. Thus A gives $2 + 2 = 4$, and Z gives $1 + 1 = 2$, which is $^{4}_{2}\text{He}$ or α.

(*College Physics* 9th ed. pages 965–969/10th ed. pages 979–983)
(L.O. 5.C.1.1, 5.G.1.1, 7.C.3.1)

4. (a) To find the decay constant of the material we write $T_{1/2} = \dfrac{0.693}{\lambda}$

and

$$\lambda = \frac{0.693}{T_{1/2}} = \frac{0.693}{1620 \text{ y}} \times \frac{1 \text{ y}}{3.16 \times 10^{7} \text{ s}} = 1.35 \times 10^{-11} \text{ s}^{-1}$$

(b) Next, we need to determine the number of nuclei in the sample.

$$N_0 = \left(1.0 \times 10^{-3} \text{ g}\right) \left(\frac{6.023 \times 10^{23} \text{ nuclei}/\text{mol}}{226 \text{ g}/\text{mol}}\right) = 2.66 \times 10^{18} \text{ nuclei}$$

(c) The activity of the sample is

$$A_0 = \lambda N_0 = \left(1.35 \times 10^{-11} \text{ s}^{-1}\right)\left(2.66 \times 10^{18} \text{ nuclei}\right) = 3.60 \times 10^{7} \text{ dis}/\text{s} = 3.60 \times 10^{7} \text{ Bq}$$

and

$$3.60 \times 10^{7} \text{ Bq} \times \frac{1 \text{ Ci}}{37 \times 10^{9} \text{ Bq}} = 9.73 \times 10^{-4} \text{ Ci}$$

(*College Physics* 9th ed. pages 962–965/10th ed. pages 976–979)
(L.O. 7.C.3.1)

AP® Tables of Information

Information

Constants and Conversion Factors

Proton mass, $m_p = 1.67 \times 10^{-27}$ kg

Neutron mass, $m_n = 1.67 \times 10^{-27}$ kg

Electron mass, $m_e = 9.11 \times 10^{-31}$ kg

Speed of light, $c = 3.00 \times 10^8$ m/s

Electron charge magnitude, $e = 1.60 \times 10^{-19}$ C

Couloub's law constant, $k = \dfrac{1}{4}\pi\varepsilon_0 = 9.0 \times 10^9$ N$\cdot$m^2 / C^2

Universal gravitational constant, $G = 6.67 \times 10^{-11}$ m^3 / kg$\cdot$s^2

Acceleration due to gravity at Earth's surface, $g = 9.8$ m/s^2

Unit Symbols

Unit Symbols								
meter,	m	kelvin,	K	joule,	J	volt,	V
kilogram,	kg	hertz,	Hz	watt,	W	ohm,	Ω
second,	s	newton,	N	coulomb,	C	degree Celsius,	°C
ampere,	A						

Prefixes

Factor	Prefix	Symbol
10^{12}	tera	T
10^9	giga	G
10^6	mega	M
10^3	kilo	k
10^{-2}	centi	c
10^{-3}	milli	m
10^{-6}	micro	μ
10^{-9}	nano	n
10^{-12}	pico	p

Values of Trigonometric Functions For Common Angles

θ	0°	30°	37°	45°	53°	60°	90°
$\sin\theta$	0	1/2	3/5	$\sqrt{2}/2$	4/5	$\sqrt{3}/2$	1
$\cos\theta$	1	$\sqrt{3}/2$	4/5	$\sqrt{2}/2$	3/5	1/2	0
$\tan\theta$	0	$\sqrt{3}/3$	3/4	1	4/3	$\sqrt{3}$	∞

The following conventions are used in this exam.

I. The frame of reference of any problem is assumed to be inertial unless otherwise stated.

II. Assume air resistance is negligible unless otherwise stated.

III. In all situations, positive work is defined as work done on a system.

IV. The direction of current is conventional current: the direction in which positive charge would drift.

V. Assume all batteries and meters are ideal unless otherwise stated.

ADVANCED PLACEMENT PHYSICS 1 EQUATIONS

Mechanics

$v_x = v_{x0} + a_x t$

$x = x_0 + v_{x0}t + \frac{1}{2}a_x t^2$

$v_x^2 = v_{x0}^2 + 2a_x(x - x_0)$

$\vec{a} = \dfrac{\sum \vec{F}}{m} = \dfrac{\vec{F}_{net}}{m}$

$\left|\vec{F}_f\right| \le \mu \left|\vec{F}_n\right|$

$a_c = \dfrac{v^2}{r}$

$\vec{p} = m\vec{v}$

$\Delta\vec{p} = \vec{F}\Delta t$

$K = \dfrac{1}{2}mv^2$

$\Delta E = W = F_{\parallel}d$

$\quad = Fd\cos\theta$

$P = \dfrac{\Delta E}{\Delta t}$

$\theta = \theta_0 + \omega_0 t + \dfrac{1}{2}\alpha t^2$

$\omega = \omega_0 + \alpha t$

$x = A\cos(2\pi ft)$

$\vec{\alpha} = \dfrac{\sum \vec{\tau}}{I} = \dfrac{\vec{\tau}_{net}}{I}$

$\tau = r_{\perp}F = rF\sin\theta$

$L = I\omega$

$\Delta L = \tau\Delta t$

$K = \dfrac{1}{2}I\omega^2$

$\left|\vec{F}_s\right| = k\left|\vec{x}\right|$

$U_s = \dfrac{1}{2}kx^2$

$\rho = \dfrac{m}{V}$

$\Delta U_g = mg\Delta y$

$T = \dfrac{2\pi}{\omega} = \dfrac{1}{f}$

$T_s = 2\pi\sqrt{\dfrac{m}{k}}$

$T_p = 2\pi\sqrt{\dfrac{\ell}{g}}$

$\left|\vec{F}_g\right| = G\dfrac{m_1 m_2}{r^2}$

$\vec{g} = \dfrac{\vec{F}_g}{m}$

$U_G = -\dfrac{Gm_1 m_2}{r}$

ε = acceleration
d = distance
E = energy
F = force
f = frequency
h = height
I = rotational inertia
K = kinetic energy
k = spring constant
L = angular
$\quad$ momentum
ℓ = length
m = mass
P = power
p = momentum
r = radius or
$\quad$ separation
T = period
t = time
U = potential energy
V = volume
v = speed
W = work done on a
$\quad$ system
x = position
α = angular
$\quad$ acceleration
μ = coefficient of
$\quad$ friction
θ = angle
τ = torque
ω = angular speed

Electricity

$\left|\vec{F}_E\right| = k\dfrac{|q_1 q_2|}{r^2}$

$I = \dfrac{\Delta q}{\Delta t}$

$R = \dfrac{\rho\ell}{A}$

$I = \dfrac{\Delta V}{R}$

$P = I\Delta V$

$R_s = \sum_i R_i$

$\dfrac{1}{R_p} = \sum_i \dfrac{1}{R_i}$

A = area
F = force
I = current
ℓ = length
P = power
q = charge
R = resistance
r = separation
t = time
V = electric potential
ρ = resistivity

Waves

$\lambda = \dfrac{v}{f}$

f = frequency
v = speed
λ = wavelength

Geometry and Trigonometry

Rectangle	$A = bh$	A = area
Triangle	$A = \dfrac{1}{2}bh$	C = circumference
		V = volume
Circle		S = surface area
$A = \pi r^2$		b = base
$C = 2\pi r$		h = height
Rectangular solid		ℓ = length
$V = \ell wh$		w = width
Right triangle		r = radius
$c^2 = a^2 + b^2$		
$\sin\theta = \dfrac{a}{c}$		Cylinder
		$V = \pi r^2 \ell$
$\cos\theta = \dfrac{b}{c}$		$S = 2\pi r\ell + 2\pi r^2$
		Sphere
$\tan\theta = \dfrac{a}{b}$		$V = \dfrac{4}{3}\pi r^3$
		$S = 4\pi r^2$

ADVANCED PLACEMENT PHYSICS 2 TABLE OF INFORMATION

Constants and Conversion Factors

Proton mass, $m_p = 1.67 \times 10^{-27}$ kg	Electron charge magnitude, $e = 1.60 \times 10^{-19}$ C
Neutron mass, $m_n = 1.67 \times 10^{-27}$ kg	1 electron volt, 1 $eV = 1.60 \times 10^{-19}$ J
Electron mass, $m_e = 9.11 \times 10^{-31}$ kg	Speed of light, $c = 3.00 \times 10^8$ m/s
Avogadro's number, $N_0 = 6.02 \times 10^{23}$ mol^{-1}	Universal gravitational constant,
Universal gas constant, $R = 8.31$ J / (mol · K)	$G = 6.67 \times 10^{-11}$ m^3 / kg · s^2
Boltzmann's constant, $k_B = 1.38 \times 10^{-23}$ J/K	Acceleration due to gravity at Earth's surface, $g = 9.8$ m/s^2

1 unified atomic mass unit, $\quad$ 1 $u = 1.66 \times 10^{-27}$ kg $= 931$ MeV / c^2	Coulomb's law constant, $\quad k = 1 / 4\pi\varepsilon_0 = 9.0 \times 10^9$ N · m^2/C^2
Planck's constant, $\quad h = 6.63 \times 10^{-34}$ J · s $= 4.14 \times 10^{-15}$ eV · s	Vacuum permeability, $\mu_0 = 4\pi \times 10^{-7}$ (T · m) / A
	Magnetic constant, $\quad k' = \mu_0 / 4\pi = 1 \times 10^{-7}$ (T · m) / A
$hc = 1.99 \times 10^{-25}$ J · m $= 1.24 \times 10^3$ eV · nm	1 atmosphere pressure,
Vacuum permittivity, $\quad \varepsilon_0 = 8.85 \times 10^{-12}$ C^2 / N · m^2	$\quad$ 1 atm $= 1.0 \times 10^5$ N/m^2 $= 1.0 \times 10^5$ Pa

Unit Symbols	meter,	m	mole,	mol	watt,	W	farad,	F
	kilogram,	kg	hertz,	Hz	coulomb,	C	tesla,	T
	second,	s	newton,	N	volt,	V	degree Celsius,	°C
	ampere,	A	pascal,	Pa	ohm,	Ω	electron volt,	eV
	kelvin,	K	joule,	J	henry,	H		

Prefixes

Factor	Prefix	Symbol
10^{12}	tera	T
10^9	giga	G
10^6	mega	M
10^3	kilo	k
10^{-2}	centi	c
10^{-3}	milli	m
10^{-6}	micro	μ
10^{-9}	nano	n
10^{-12}	pico	p

Values of Trigonometric Functions For Common Angles

θ	0°	30°	37°	45°	53°	60°	90°
$\sin\theta$	0	1/2	3/5	$\sqrt{2}/2$	4/5	$\sqrt{3}/2$	1
$\cos\theta$	1	$\sqrt{3}/2$	4/5	$\sqrt{2}/2$	3/5	1/2	0
$\tan\theta$	0	$\sqrt{3}/3$	3/4	1	4/3	$\sqrt{3}$	∞

The following conventions are used in this exam.

I. The frame of reference of any problem is assumed to be inertial unless otherwise stated.

II. In all situations, positive work is defined as work done <u>on</u> a system.

III. The direction of current is conventional current: the direction in which positive charge would drift.

IV. Assume all batteries and meters are ideal unless otherwise stated.

V. Assume edge effects for the electric field of a parallel plate capacitor unless otherwise stated.

VI. For any isolated electrically charged object, the electric potential is defined as zero at infinite distance from the charged object.

ADVANCED PLACEMENT PHYSICS 2 EQUATIONS

Mechanics

$$v_x = v_{x0} + a_x t$$

$$x = x_0 + v_{x0}t + \tfrac{1}{2}a_x t^2$$

$$v_x^2 = v_{x0}^2 + 2a_x(x - x_0)$$

$$\vec{a} = \frac{\sum \vec{F}}{m} = \frac{\vec{F}_{net}}{m}$$

$$\left|\vec{F}_f\right| \le \mu \left|\vec{F}_n\right|$$

$$a_c = \frac{v^2}{r}$$

$$\vec{p} = m\vec{v}$$

$$\Delta \vec{p} = \vec{F}\Delta t$$

$$K = \frac{1}{2}mv^2$$

$$\Delta E = W = F_\parallel d$$

$$= Fd \cos \theta$$

$$P = \frac{\Delta E}{\Delta t}$$

$$\theta = \theta_0 + \omega_0 t + \frac{1}{2}\alpha t^2$$

$$\omega = \omega_0 + \alpha t$$

$$x = A \cos(\omega t)$$

$$= A \cos(2\pi f t)$$

$$x_{cm} = \frac{\sum m_i x_i}{\sum m_i}$$

$$\vec{\alpha} = \frac{\sum \vec{\tau}}{I} = \frac{\vec{\tau}_{net}}{I}$$

$$\tau = r_\perp F = rF \sin \theta$$

$$L = I\omega$$

$$\Delta L = \tau \Delta t$$

$$K = \frac{1}{2}I\omega^2$$

$$\left|\vec{F}_s\right| = k\left|\vec{x}\right|$$

$$U_s = \frac{1}{2}kx^2$$

$$\Delta U_g = mg\Delta y$$

$$T = \frac{2\pi}{\omega} = \frac{1}{f}$$

$$T_s = 2\pi\sqrt{\frac{m}{k}}$$

$$T_p = 2\pi\sqrt{\frac{\ell}{g}}$$

$$\left|\vec{F}_g\right| = G\frac{m_1 m_2}{r^2}$$

$$\vec{g} = \frac{\vec{F}_g}{m}$$

$$U_G = -\frac{Gm_1 m_2}{r}$$

ε = acceleration
d = distance
E = energy
F = force
f = frequency
h = height
I = rotational inertia
K = kinetic energy
k = spring constant

L = angular momentum
ℓ = length
m = mass
P = power
p = momentum
r = radius or separation
T = period
t = time
U = potential energy
v = speed
W = work done on a system
x = position
α = angular acceleration
μ = coefficient of friction
θ = angle
τ = torque
ω = angular speed

Electricity and Magnetism

$$\left|\vec{F}_E\right| = \frac{1}{4\pi\varepsilon_0}\frac{|q_1 q_2|}{r^2}$$

$$\vec{E} = \frac{\vec{F}_E}{q}$$

$$\left|\vec{E}\right| = \frac{1}{4\pi\varepsilon_0}\frac{|q|}{r^2}$$

$$\Delta U_E = q\Delta V$$

$$V = \frac{1}{4\pi\varepsilon_0}\frac{q}{r}$$

$$\left|\vec{E}\right| = \left|\frac{\Delta V}{\Delta r}\right|$$

$$\Delta V = \frac{Q}{C}$$

$$C = \kappa\varepsilon_0\frac{A}{d}$$

$$E = \frac{Q}{\varepsilon_0 A}$$

$$U_c = \frac{1}{2}Q\Delta V = \frac{1}{2}C(\Delta V)^2$$

$$I = \frac{\Delta Q}{\Delta t}$$

$$R = \frac{\rho\ell}{A}$$

$$P = I\Delta V$$

$$I = \frac{\Delta V}{R}$$

$$R_s = \sum_i R_i$$

$$\frac{1}{R_p} = \sum_i \frac{1}{R_i}$$

$$C_p = \sum_i C_i$$

$$\frac{1}{C_s} = \sum_i \frac{1}{C_i}$$

$$B = \frac{\mu_0}{2\pi}\frac{I}{r}$$

$$\vec{F}_M = q\vec{v} \times \vec{B}$$

$$\left|\vec{F}_M\right| = \left|q\vec{v}\right|\left|\sin\theta\right|\left|\vec{B}\right|$$

$$\vec{F}_M = I\vec{\ell} \times \vec{B}$$

$$\left|\vec{F}_M\right| = \left|I\vec{\ell}\right|\left|\sin\theta\right|\left|\vec{B}\right|$$

$$\Phi_B = \vec{B}\cdot\vec{A}$$

$$\Phi_B = \left|\vec{B}\right|\cos\theta\left|\vec{A}\right|$$

$$\varepsilon = -\frac{\Delta\Phi_B}{\Delta t}$$

$$\varepsilon = B\ell v$$

A = area
B = magnetic field
C = capacitance
d = distance

E = electric field
$\mathcal{E}$ = emf
F = force
I = current
ℓ = length
P = power
Q = charge
q = point charge
R = resistance
r = separation
t = time
U = potential (stored) energy
V = electric potential
v = speed
ρ = resistivity
θ = angle
Φ = flux

ADVANCED PLACEMENT PHYSICS 2 EQUATIONS

Fluid Mechanics and Thermal Physics

$$\rho = \frac{m}{V}$$

$$P = \frac{F}{A}$$

$$P = P_0 + \rho g h$$

$$F_b = \rho V g$$

$$A_1 v_1 = A_2 v_2$$

$$P_1 + \rho g y_1 + \frac{1}{2}\rho v_1^2$$

$$= P_2 + \rho g y_2 + \frac{1}{2}\rho v_2^2$$

$$\frac{Q}{\Delta t} = \frac{kA\,\Delta T}{L}$$

$$PV = nRT = Nk_B T$$

$$K = \frac{3}{2}k_B T$$

$$W = -P\Delta V$$

$$\Delta U = Q + W$$

h = depth
k = thermal conductivity
K = kinetic energy
L = thickness
m = mass
n = number of moles
N = number of molecules
P = pressure
Q = energy transferred to a system by heating
T = temperature
t = time
U = internal energy
V = volume
v = speed
W = work done on a system
y = height
ρ = density
A = area
F = force

Waves and Optics

$$\lambda = \frac{v}{f}$$

$$n = \frac{c}{v}$$

$$n_1 \sin \theta_1 = n_2 \sin \theta_2$$

$$\frac{1}{s_i} + \frac{1}{s_o} = \frac{1}{f}$$

$$|M| = \left|\frac{h_i}{h_o}\right| = \left|\frac{s_i}{s_o}\right|$$

$$\Delta L = m\lambda$$

$$d \sin \theta = m\lambda$$

d = separation
f = frequency or focal length
h = height
L = distance
M = magnification
m = an integer
n = index of refraction
s = distance
v = speed
λ = wavelength
θ = angle

Modern Physics

$$E = hf$$

$$K_{max} = hf - \phi$$

$$\lambda = \frac{h}{p}$$

$$E = mc^2$$

E = energy
f = frequency
K = kinetic energy
m = mass
p = momentum
λ = wavelength
ϕ = work function

Geometry and Trigonometry

Rectangle $A = bh$

Triangle $A = \frac{1}{2}bh$

Circle

$$A = \pi r^2$$

$$C = 2\pi r$$

Rectangular solid $V = \ell w h$

Right triangle

$$c^2 = a^2 + b^2$$

$$\sin \theta = \frac{a}{c}$$

$$\cos \theta = \frac{b}{c}$$

$$\tan \theta = \frac{a}{b}$$

A = area
C = circumference
V = volume
S = surface area
b = base
h = height
ℓ = length
w = width
r = radius

Cylinder

$$V = \pi r^2 \ell$$

$$S = 2\pi r \ell + 2\pi r^2$$

Sphere

$$V = \frac{4}{3}\pi r^3$$

$$S = 4\pi r^2$$

Part III

Practice Tests

AP® PHYSICS 1
PRACTICE EXAM A

AP PHYSICS 1
Section I
50 Multiple-Choice Questions
Time–90 Minutes

Note: To simplify calculations, you may use g = 10 m/s² in all problems.

Directions: Each of the questions or incomplete statements below is followed by four suggested answers or completions. Select the one that is best in each case.

1. Marks made on a timing tape every 0.02 s apart are shown below. Which diagram best illustrates uniform acceleration of the body attached to the timing tape?

I • • • • • • • •

II • • • • • • • • •

III • • • • •

IV • • • • • •

(A) I
(B) II
(C) III
(D) IV

2. An object has an initial velocity of 10.0 $\frac{m}{s}$. How long must it accelerate at a constant rate of 2.00 $\frac{m}{s^2}$ in order to have an average velocity equal to twice its initial velocity?
(A) 10.0 s
(B) 12.0 s
(C) 16.0 s
(D) 20.0 s

3. A graph of the velocity of four objects as a function of time is shown below.

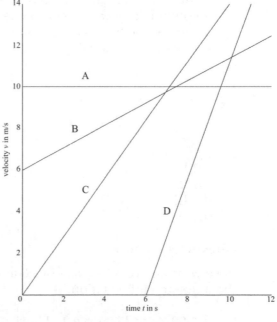

Rank the graphs for the accelerations from the greatest to the least.
(A) A > B > C > D
(B) B > C > D > A
(C) C > D > B > A
(D) D > C > B > A

GO ON TO NEXT PAGE

4. A 1.00 kg body and a 2.00 kg body are dropped simultaneously from the same height above the ground. In the absence of friction,
   (A) the 2.00 kg body reaches the ground first with the larger velocity since the gravitational force acting on it is larger
   (B) the 1.00 kg body reaches the ground first with the larger velocity since it has a smaller inertia and is easier to accelerate
   (C) they reach the ground at the same time with the same velocity since they are in the same gravitational field
   (D) they reach the ground at the same time, but the smaller body has the larger speed since it has the smaller inertia

5. A body is projected at some velocity v_0 at an angle θ above the horizontal. When the body is at the highest position in its flight, which of the following diagrams best represents the correct velocity and acceleration vectors for the body?

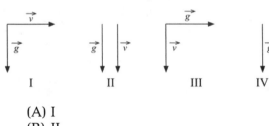

   I   II   III   IV

   (A) I
   (B) II
   (C) III
   (D) IV

Questions 6 and 7

Base your answers to questions 6 and 7 on the following information.

6. A 1.00 kg ball is projected horizontally from the roof of a building with a speed of 14.0 m/s. If the height of the building is 60.0 m and air resistance is negligible, the approximate time the ball is in the air is
   (A) 4.29 s
   (B) 3.50 s
   (C) 2.93 s
   (D) 1.76 s

7. As the ball in problem 6 falls freely under the influence of gravity to the Earth's surface, it will gain an equal amount of
   (A) momentum for each meter through which it falls
   (B) speed for each meter through which it falls
   (C) momentum during each second it falls
   (D) kinetic energy for each second it falls

Questions 8 and 9

Base your answers to questions 8 and 9 on the following information.

8. A hockey puck with a mass of 0.170 kg is sliding on ice at 10.0 m/s. Neglect friction on the surface of the ice. The hockey puck leaves the ice and moves onto a sidewalk around the ice rink. If the sidewalk has a coefficient of friction $\mu_k = 0.42$, identify which of the following choices below best represents the forces acting on the hockey puck when it moves onto the sidewalk.

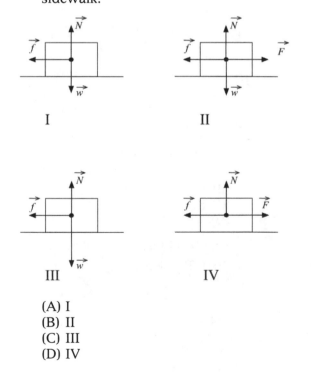

   I   II

   III   IV

   (A) I
   (B) II
   (C) III
   (D) IV

9. Using information from question 8, determine the distance the hockey puck will travel before coming to rest.
   (A) 12.1 m
   (B) 26.5 m
   (C) 71.5 m
   (D) 143 m

10. A 3.00 kg body is lifted 1.60 m above a floor and then moved a horizontal distance of 2.00 m. What is the work done by the gravitational force on the body?
    (A) –165 J
    (B) –118 J
    (C) –58.8 J
    (D) –47.0 J

11. A 2.00 kg body is dropped from a tall building. Ignoring friction,
    (A) its momentum remains constant since the only force acting on it is the force of gravity
    (B) only its momentum increases because of the external force of gravity
    (C) its momentum remains constant but its kinetic energy increases since the gravitational force does work on the body
    (D) both its momentum and the kinetic energy increase because of the external force of gravity

12. The momentum of a car rounding a curve at constant speed is
    (A) constant because its speed is constant
    (B) constant because the acceleration of the car is constant
    (C) not constant because there is an external force acting on the car to change its direction
    (D) not constant because there is no work done on the car by the external force

13. A body moves under the action of a variable force as shown in the graph below.

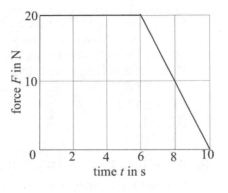

The change in the momentum of the body over the 10 s interval is closest to
(A) 100 N·s
(B) 120 N·s
(C) 160 N·s
(D) 200 N·s

14. A body initially moving to the right on a flat horizontal frictionless surface with a velocity of 1.20 $\frac{m}{s}$ is subjected to several forces as shown in the diagram for a period of 10.0 s.

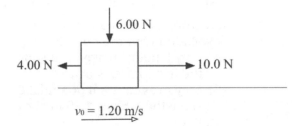

The momentum of the body will
(A) decrease because a force is applied to the body opposite to its initial motion during the 10.0 s interval
(B) increase because the net force is in the direction of the initial velocity
(C) remain constant since the net force acting on the body is zero during the 10.0 s interval
(D) be undetermined since the mass of the body is not given

15. A 1.80 kg box is held in place at the top of a 30° incline and then released. It slides down the incline which is 1.20 m in length. If the coefficient of kinetic friction between the box and the incline is 0.20, what is the work done by the frictional force on the box as it slides completely down the incline?
    (A) –3.67 J
    (B) –2.12 J
    (C) 2.12 J
    (D) 3.67 J

16. A 0.200 kg block is attached to a horizontal spring, $k = 150.0 \frac{N}{m}$ on a frictionless surface. The block-spring system is compressed 0.100 m then released. What is the maximum velocity of the system and where does it occur?
    (A) 7.50 m/s at ± A
    (B) 7.50 m/s at $x = 0$
    (C) 2.74 m/s at ± A
    (D) 2.74 m/s at $x = 0$

17. A 2.50 kg body slides across a frictionless, horizontal tabletop that is 1.20 m above the level of the floor with a speed of 2.10 $\frac{m}{s}$. Relative to the tabletop, the mechanical energy associated with the body is
    (A) only kinetic energy as it slides on the frictionless surface
    (B) only gravitational potential energy since the table is 1.20 m above the floor
    (C) the sum of the kinetic and the gravitational potential energy since the surface is frictionless
    (D) the difference between the kinetic energy and the gravitational potential energy

18. A 1.50 kg body slides off a frictionless horizontal tabletop that is 1.00 m above the floor with a speed of 2.00 $\frac{m}{s}$. As it strikes the ground, its energy is
    (A) 11.7 J
    (B) 14.7 J
    (C) 16.2 J
    (D) 17.7 J

19. A small body is attached to a horizontal spring that has been compressed to a position $x = -A$ and then released. The distance the body moves in one complete oscillation is
    (A) 4A
    (B) 2A
    (C) A/2
    (D) A/4

20. A block of ice sliding across a frozen pond at 3.00 $\frac{m}{s}$ enters a region of rough ice where a frictional force of 1.20 N acts. The kinetic energy of the block of ice as it enters the rough section
    (A) will increase because the force was applied in the direction of motion of the block
    (B) will decrease because the force was a frictional force applied opposite its motion
    (C) will remain constant since it is sliding on ice at 3.00 m/s
    (D) cannot be determined since the mass of the block of ice is not given in the problem

21. The period of a simple pendulum 1.20 m long at the surface of the Earth is 2.20 s. What is its period if it is taken to a planet whose mass is $3M_E$ and radius is $2R_E$?
    (A) 1.90 s
    (B) 2.25 s
    (C) 2.54 s
    (D) 3.11 s

22. Three masses $m_1 = 10.0$ kg, $m_2 = 20.0$ kg and $m_3 = 30.0$ kg are located on a horizontal line as shown below.

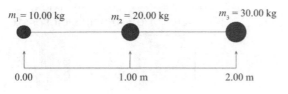

$m_1 = 10.00$ kg $m_2 = 20.00$ kg $m_3 = 30.00$ kg

0.00   1.00 m   2.00 m

The force on m_3 due to the other two masses is closest to
(A) 5.0×10^{-9} N to the left
(B) 4.0×10^{-8} N to the right
(C) 4.5×10^{-8} N to the left
(D) 5.8×10^{-8} N to the right

23. A person in a car at an intersection is waiting for the light to turn green when an ambulance sounding its siren with a frequency $f_0 = 1000$ Hz approaches the car from the rear of the vehicle at 15 $\frac{m}{s}$. As the ambulance approaches the car, the person in the car perceives
(A) a lower frequency because the wavelength between successive waves is shorter as the ambulance approaches the stationary car with a velocity relative to the person in the car
(B) a higher frequency because the wavelength between successive waves is shorter as the ambulance approaches the stationary car with a velocity relative to the person in the car
(C) no change in frequency since the person is stationary with respect to the ambulance
(D) a frequency that decreases and then increases as the ambulance approaches and then recedes because the distance between the successive waves decreases and then increases as the ambulance passes the car

24. A projectile shot with some velocity $\vec{v}_0$ at an angle θ with respect to the horizontal, explodes when it is at a distance h above the ground.

Explosion

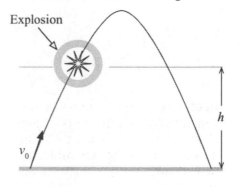

Which of the four illustrations best indicates the path of the fragments?

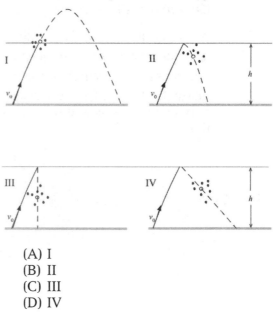

(A) I
(B) II
(C) III
(D) IV

GO ON TO NEXT PAGE

25. A beam of gas molecules is incident on a barrier at 30° relative to the horizontal surface as shown.

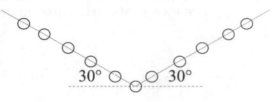

Each molecule of a mass m and a speed v strikes the barrier and is reflected elastically. What is the total change in momentum of the gas molecules in the beam containing n particles during this event?

(A) nmv

(B) $2nmv$

(C) $nmv(\sin 30°)$

(D) $nmv(\cos 30°)$

26. A body is lifted in the gravitational field associated with a planet of radius $2R_E$ and mass $3M_E$. Which of the graphs below best represents the relationship between the mass and the elevation that it is lifted?

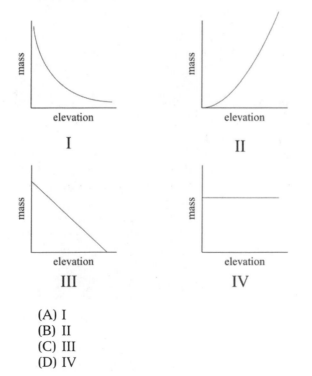

(A) I

(B) II

(C) III

(D) IV

27. A 2.00 kg block sliding across a frictionless surface strikes a spring whose spring constant is 15.0 $\frac{N}{m}$ compressing it 0.12 m. The initial velocity of the block is closest to

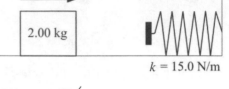

(A) 0.22 $\frac{m}{s}$

(B) 0.33 $\frac{m}{s}$

(C) 0.57 $\frac{m}{s}$

(D) 0.95 $\frac{m}{s}$

28. A set of horizontal rods have their axis of rotation at the left end of the rod and forces are applied to the rods as shown. Rank the forces from the greatest torque acting on the rods to the least.

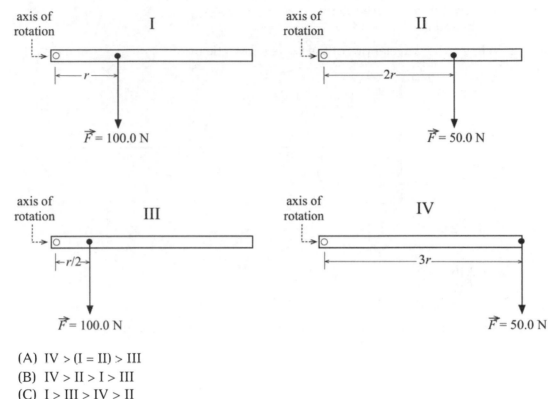

(A) IV > (I = II) > III
(B) IV > II > I > III
(C) I > III > IV > II
(D) I > II > III > IV

29. A figure skater with arms extended starts spinning on ice at $\omega_0 = 1.50\ \mathrm{rad/s}$. When the skater draws her arms in against her body,
(A) her angular momentum remains constant, but her kinetic energy increases since work is done by the skater pulling her arms inward
(B) her angular momentum increases, but her kinetic energy decreases since she changed her moment of inertia
(C) both her kinetic energy and the angular momentum increase since she did work in pulling her arms inward
(D) neither her kinetic energy nor the angular momentum increased since no torque was applied to her

30. A 1.50 kg block is attached to a spring of $k = 25.0\ \mathrm{N/m}$, that oscillates on a frictionless horizontal surface with an amplitude of 0.08 m. Doubling the
(A) mass of the block and the amplitude without changing the spring constant will increase the period of vibration by a factor of 2
(B) mass of the block and the amplitude without changing the spring constant will increase the period of vibration by a factor of $\sqrt{2}$
(C) spring constant and the amplitude while holding the mass constant will increase the period of vibration by a factor of 2
(D) spring constant and the amplitude while holding the mass constant will increase the period of vibration by a factor of $\sqrt{2}$

GO ON TO NEXT PAGE

31. A 2.50 kg mass hung at rest on the end of a spring held vertically from a support rod stretches the spring 0.065 m. When the spring-mass system is set into vibration, the frequency of oscillation is

   (A) 0.624 Hz
   (B) 1.96 Hz
   (C) 3.92 Hz
   (D) 12.3 Hz

32. What is the wavelength of the wave shown below?

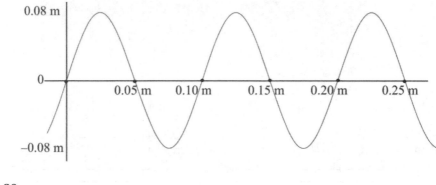

   (A) 0.20 m
   (B) 0.16 m
   (C) 0.10 m
   (D) 0.05 m

33. A wave moving through a medium is shown in the graph below.

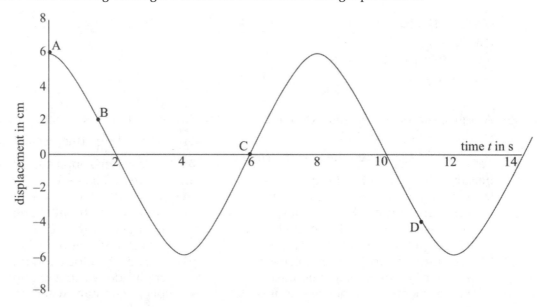

   Rank the magnitude of the displacement of the labeled points in the waveform shown from greatest to least.
   (A) D > C > B > A
   (B) A > D > B > C
   (C) C > A > B > D
   (D) C > B > D > A

34. A standing wave is set up in a string as shown below.

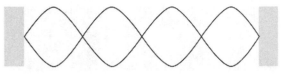

The waveform has
(A) 5 nodes and 4 antinodes
(B) 4 nodes and 5 antinodes
(C) 4 nodes and 3 antinodes
(D) 3 nodes and 4 antinodes

35. One end of a string is attached to a 60.0 Hz electrically driven tuning fork, the other end passes over a frictionless pulley to a known weight. The distance of the string between the tuning fork and the pulley is 1.00 m long. Observation of the string shows that the standing wave vibrates in 4 loops under the known weight. The speed of the wave in the string is
(A) 15.0 m/s
(B) 30.0 m/s
(C) 60.0 m/s
(D) 120 m/s

36. Two forces are applied to a wheel and axle as shown. $\vec{F_1} = 25.0$ N is applied to the outer cylinder of radius $r_1 = 0.300$ m. $\vec{F_2} = 40.0$ N is applied to the inner cylinder of radius $r_2 = 0.100$ m.

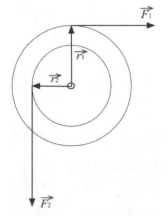

The net torque acting on the body is
(A) 3.50 N·m clockwise
(B) 3.50 N·m counterclockwise
(C) 11.5 N·m clockwise
(D) 11.5 N·m counterclockwise

37. Two charges $q_1 = 9.00 \times 10^{-9}$ C and $q_2 = -5.00 \times 10^{-9}$ C are located 0.01 m apart in air. The force acting between them is
(A) 4.05×10^{-3} N and is attractive
(B) 4.05×10^{-3} N and is repulsive
(C) 4.05×10^{-5} N and is attractive
(D) 4.05×10^{-5} N and is repulsive

38. Electrical charge that is transferred in the process of conduction when a charging wand touches an isolated body can produce charges on the body equal to multiples of
(A) $\pm 0.25e$
(B) $\pm 0.5e$
(C) $\pm e$
(D) $\pm 1.5e$

39. A small particle carrying a static charge is considered to be positive when it has
(A) dipole properties
(B) excess protons
(C) a deficiency of electrons
(D) a deficiency of protons

40. A flat disk with a moment of inertia I_0 is rotating with an angular velocity ω_0 when a small piece of modeling clay drops vertically on the edge of the disk. The angular velocity of the system will
(A) increase because the modeling clay imparted a torque on the disk in the same direction of the initial angular velocity of the disk
(B) decrease because the modeling clay imparted a frictional force on the disk which was opposite the initial motion of the disk
(C) decrease because the moment of inertia of the system increased from I_0 to $I_0 + I_{clay}$
(D) remain constant because no net torque was applied to the disk when the small piece of clay dropped vertically on the disk

GO ON TO NEXT PAGE

41. In the circuit shown below, the current in the 30 Ω resistor is closest to

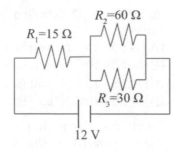

(A) 0.11 A
(B) 0.23A
(C) 0.34 A
(D) 0.44 A

42. A negatively charged wand is brought near but does not touch an isolated neutral electroscope. Which of the drawings best indicates the correct arrangement of charges induced on the electroscope?

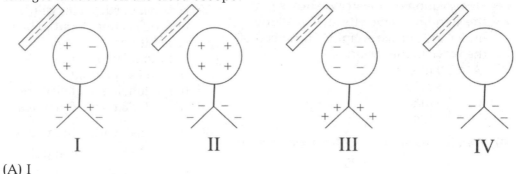

(A) I
(B) II
(C) III
(D) IV

43. Torques are applied to a cylinder as shown for 5.00 s. What is the change in the angular momentum of the cylinder?

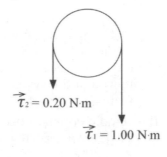

(A) 0.80 N · m · s clockwise
(B) 4.00 N · m · s clockwise
(C) 6.00 N · m · s clockwise
(D) 8.00 N · m · s clockwise

44. A circuit is shown below.

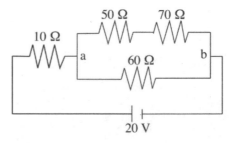

Rank the electrical potential difference across the resistors from highest to lowest.

(A) $V_{70\,\Omega} > V_{60\,\Omega} > V_{50\,\Omega} > V_{10\,\Omega}$

(B) $V_{10\,\Omega} > V_{60\,\Omega} > \left(V_{50\,\Omega} = V_{70\,\Omega}\right)$

(C) $V_{60\,\Omega} > V_{70\,\Omega} > V_{50\,\Omega} > V_{10\,\Omega}$

(D) $\left(V_{60\,\Omega} = V_{70\,\Omega} = V_{50\,\Omega}\right) > V_{10\,\Omega}$

45. A circuit consists of two resistors in a series connected to a 9.0 V battery.

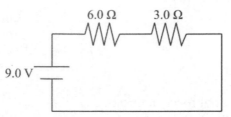

Which of the graphs drawn show the correct energy changes within the circuit?

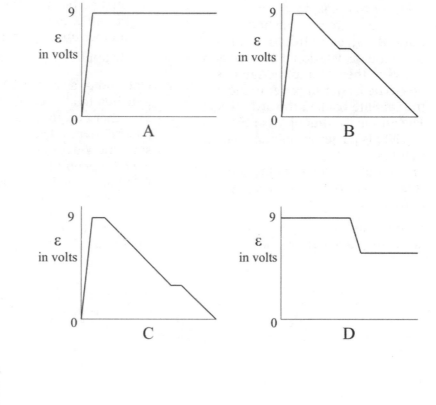

(A) A
(B) B
(C) C
(D) D

Questions 46 to 50

Directions: For each of the questions or incomplete statements below, <u>two</u> of the suggested answers will be correct. For each of these questions, you must select <u>both</u> correct answers to earn credit. No partial credit will be earned if only one answer is selected. Select the two that are best in each case and then enter both of the appropriate answers in the corresponding space on the answer sheet.

46. A particle of mass m moving in a straight line on smooth frictionless surface experiences an increase in velocity. This increase in velocity indicates
(A) the presence of a force with a component in the same direction as the direction of the velocity vector
(B) that there is no net force acting on the mass
(C) that work was done on the body increasing its kinetic energy
(D) only the momentum of the body increases

GO ON TO NEXT PAGE

47. A satellite travels in an orbit around the sun as shown below.

   (A) The gravitational force acting on the satellite at point **A** is greater than the gravitational force acting on the satellite at point **B** because it is closer to the sun.
   (B) The force acting on the body at point **B** is greater than at point **A** since the gravitational force acting between the sun and the satellite has to be larger in order to move the satellite back in toward the sun.
   (C) The angular momentum of the satellite is larger at point **A** than at point **B**.
   (D) The angular velocity of the satellite is larger at point **A** because the body is closer to the sun.

48. A graph of the force applied to a body versus its displacement is shown below.

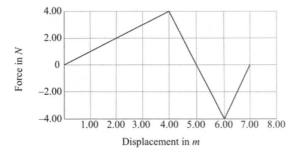

   (A) The kinetic energy of the body over the displacement of 7.00 m will increase since the net work on the body is positive.
   (B) The kinetic energy of the body will decrease since negative forces acted on the body.
   (C) The momentum of the body will increase since the total work done by the variable force was positive.
   (D) The momentum of the body will not change because the force was variable. In order to change the momentum, a constant force must be applied. $\vec{F}_{\text{constant}} \cdot \Delta t = m\Delta\vec{v}$.

49. One end of a wire, 1.20 m long, is attached to a mechanical oscillator and the other end to a known weight passing over a frictionless pulley. A standing wave is set up in the wire with a wave speed of 180 m/s. When the first harmonic is produced in the wire,
   (A) there are two complete waves in the region between the end points of the wire
   (B) there is ½ of a complete wave in the region between the end points of the wire
   (C) the frequency of the wave is 75 Hz
   (D) the frequency of the wave is 300 Hz

50. The mechanical waveforms shown in the diagrams below are to be used to answer this question concerning the vibration of the particles in the waves and the direction of the wavefront advancing through the medium.

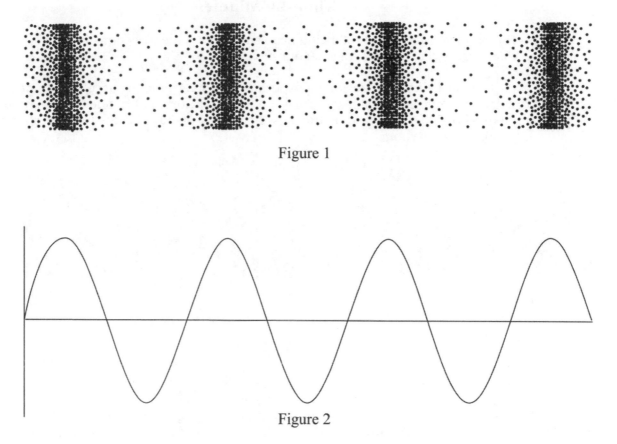

Figure 1

Figure 2

(A) In a transverse wave, the particles move back and forth parallel to the direction of propagation of the wave disturbance illustrated in Figure 1.

(B) In a longitudinal wave, the particles move back and forth parallel to the direction of propagation of the wave disturbance illustrated in Figure 1.

(C) In a transverse wave, the particles oscillate about the equilibrium position perpendicular to the direction of propagation of the wave disturbance as illustrated in Figure 2.

(D) In a longitudinal wave, the particles oscillate about the equilibrium position perpendicular to the direction of propagation of the wave disturbance as illustrated in Figure 2.

STOP
END OF SECTION I

IF YOU FINISH BEFORE TIME IS CALLED, YOU MAY CHECK YOUR WORK ON THIS SECTION. DO NOT GO ON TO SECTION II UNTIL YOU ARE TOLD TO DO SO.

AP PHYSICS 1
Section II
5 Free-Response Questions
Time–90 Minutes

Directions: Solve each of the following problems. Unless the directions indicate otherwise, respond to all parts of each question.

1. Your teacher tells you to design an experiment to determine the acceleration due to gravity using the equipment she places on the laboratory tables. She tells you to use a total mass of 500 g to 1000 g on the mass hangers. You have access to other standard equipment in the room.

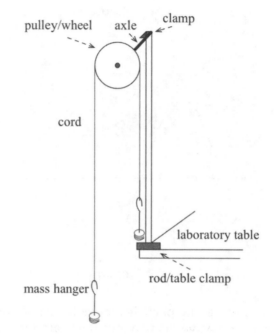

(a) Design a laboratory experiment in enough detail that another student could duplicate your experiment and obtain the same results.

(b) What measurements will you take and how will you use them to answer the question posed?

(c) If you plot a graph, what will you plot and how will you use the graph to determine an experiment value for the acceleration due to gravity?

(d) What assumption(s) did you make in the experiment and how might they affect your results?

2. A uniform rod, whose moment of inertia is $I = \frac{1}{3}mL^2$ about its end, is supported at the left end as shown.

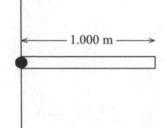

(a) What is the initial angular acceleration of the rod when it is released in terms of g and L?

(b) When the rod is held is placed on a pivot located at $\frac{L}{4}$ as shown, its new moment of inertia becomes $I = \frac{7}{48}mL^2$. The rod is then released.

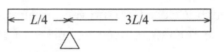

The initial angular acceleration of the rod when released, compared to the angular acceleration in part (a), will

_____ increase

_____ decrease

_____ remain constant

Justify your answer

(c) A uniform meterstick, whose weight is 0.980 N, is placed on a pivot at the 0.250 m mark. What is the direction and the point of application of a 1.50 N force that will place the meterstick in equilibrium?

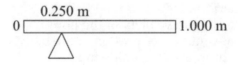

GO ON TO NEXT PAGE

3. A circuit shown below consists of four lamps $R_A = R_B = R_C$ and $R_D = 2R_A$.

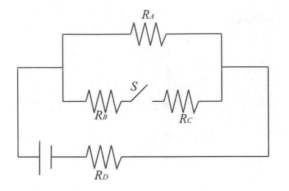

(a) When the switch S between R_B and R_C is opened the current in the circuit would be
_____ greater than when the switch is closed
_____ the same as when the switch is closed
_____ less than when the switch is closed
Explain your reasoning.

(b) When the switch is closed, the power consumed in R_A would be
_____ greater than the power consumed in R_B
_____ the same as the power consumed in R_B
_____ less than when the power consumed in R_B
Justify your reasoning without calculations.

(c) When the switch is closed, rank the brightness of the lamps from brightest to least bright.
Explain your ranking without calculations.

4. A 1.53 kg body is attached to a spring whose spring constant is $k = 15.0 \ \dfrac{N}{m}$ and oscillates on a flat frictionless surface with an amplitude of vibration of 0.120 m.
(a) What is the period of vibration?
(b) What is the maximum velocity of the body?
(c) What is the maximum acceleration of the body?
(d) Complete the graphs of the following:
    i.   displacement of the body versus time for at least two cycles of the subsequent simple harmonic motion using the grid below

ii. velocity of the body versus time for two cycles of it motion

iii. acceleration of the body versus time for two cycles of it motion

5. A 2.00 kg block is released from the top of a frictionless ramp as shown in the drawing below.

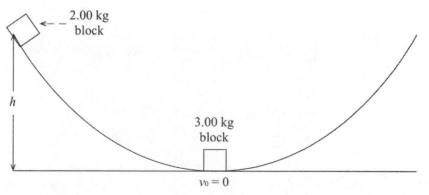

2.00 kg block

h

3.00 kg block

$v_0 = 0$

(a) The 2.00 kg block collides completely inelastically with a 3.00 kg block at rest at the bottom of the ramp.
   i. Explain without using a mathematical solution how you can determine the velocity of the 2.00 kg body at the instant of impact with the 3.00 kg body.
   ii. Explain without using a mathematical solution how you can determine the height on the second ramp the masses will rise before coming to rest.

GO ON TO NEXT PAGE

(b) In a second collision, the 2.00 kg block makes a perfectly elastic collision with the 3.00 kg block again at rest. The height the 3.00 kg block rises on the second ramp is

_____ higher than the height the blocks reached in part (a)

_____ the same height as reached in part (a)

_____ lower than the height reached in part (a)

Justify your answer.

END OF EXAMINATION

Answers

ANSWER KEY FOR MULTIPLE-CHOICE QUESTIONS

1. C	11. D	21. C	31. B	41. B
2. A	12. C	22. C	32. C	42. B
3. D	13. C	23. B	33. B	43. B
4. C	14. B	24. A	34. A	44. C
5. A	15. A	25. A	35. B	45. C
6. B	16. D	26. D	36. A	46. A & C
7. C	17. A	27. B	37. A	47. A & D
8. A	18. D	28. A	38. C	48. A & C
9. A	19. A	29. A	39. C	49. B & C
10. D	20. B	30. B	40. C	50. B & C

EXPLANATIONS FOR THE MULTIPLE-CHOICE ANSWERS

1. **C** Tape III indicates that the distance between the dots is increasing as time increases. Tapes II and IV show increases and decreases in the spacing of the dots and would give a variable acceleration for each tape. Tape I indicates that speed is fairly constant and thus has no acceleration.
   (*College Physics* 9th ed. pages 34–37/10th ed. pages 38–40)
   (L.O. 3.A.1.1)

2. **A** If the body is uniformly accelerated, the average velocity is $\vec{v}_{avg} = \dfrac{\vec{v}_f + \vec{v}_0}{2}$. For this question the average velocity is twice the initial velocity 10.0 $\frac{m}{s}$ or 20.0 $\frac{m}{s}$. If the average is 20.0 $\frac{m}{s}$, then the final must be 30.0 $\frac{m}{s}$. Then using $\vec{v}_f = \vec{v}_0 + \vec{a}t$, the time is
   $$\frac{\left(30.0 \ \frac{m}{s} - 10.0 \ \frac{m}{s}\right)}{2.00 \ \frac{m}{s^2}} = 10.0 \text{ s}$$
   (*College Physics* 9th ed. pages 34–37/10th ed. pages 38–40)
   (L.O. 3.A.1.1)

3. **D** The acceleration is the slope of the line. Line A indicates a constant velocity and therefore zero acceleration. The slopes of the other three indicate that D has the greatest slope in the times indicated followed by C and B in that order.
   (*College Physics* 9th ed. pages 34–37/10th ed. pages 38–40)
   (L.O. 3.A.1.1)

4. **C** In the absence of friction, they reach the ground at the same time with the same velocity since they are in the gravitational field of the Earth. The gravitational acceleration is the same for both.
(*College Physics* 9th ed. pages 43–47/10th ed. pages 44–49)
(L.O. 3.A.1.1)

5. **A** The body moves in the gravitational field of the Earth, whose acceleration points downward. In the absence of friction, the horizontal velocity remains constant, but at maximum height, the vertical component of the initial velocity is zero. The two vectors are perpendicular to each other.
(*College Physics* 9th ed. pages 43–47, 63–71/10th ed. pages 44–49, 65–73)
(L.O. 3.B.2.1)

6. **B** The body is projected with a horizontal velocity that in the absence of friction is constant. It starts from rest in the vertical direction, so its time of flight is given by $y = \frac{1}{2}\vec{a}t^2$. Substitution into the equation is $-60.0 \text{ m} = \frac{1}{2}\left(-9.80 \frac{\text{m}}{\text{s}^2}\right)t^2$. Solving gives the time as 3.50 s.
(*College Physics* 9th ed. pages 63–71/10th ed. pages 65–73)
(L.O. 3.A.1.1)

7. **C** Since the ball accelerates uniformly, increasing its speed by $9.80 \frac{\text{m}}{\text{s}}$ each second, it would therefore follow that the ball's momentum in the vertical direction would also increase uniformly by the same amount each second. The magnitude of the momentum is $\left|\Delta\vec{p} = m\Delta\vec{v}\right|$.
College Physics 9th ed. pages 168–169/10th ed. pages171–172)
(L.O. 3.D.2.2)

8. **A** The correct free body diagram for the hockey puck when it moves on to the sidewalk is I. A frictional force acts between the hockey puck and the sidewalk slowing the hockey puck. Since the frictional force is parallel to the surfaces in contact, the vectors that represent the weight and the normal are equal in magnitude, $\Sigma\vec{F}_y = 0$ and opposite in direction.
(*College Physics* 9th ed. pages 106–109/10th ed. pages 108–111)
(L.O. 3.B.2.1)

9. **A** When the hockey puck leaves the ice and moves onto the sidewalk, the net force acting on it is friction $\vec{f}_k = m\vec{a}$. Expanding the equation $-\mu_k m\vec{g} = m\left(\frac{v_f^2 - v_0^2}{2x}\right)$ then $-(0.42)\left(9.80 \frac{\text{m}}{\text{s}^2}\right) = \frac{-\left(10.0 \frac{\text{m}}{\text{s}}\right)^2}{2x}$. The distance the hockey puck travels is 12.1 m.

The distance traveled may also be determined from the reduction of the kinetic energy as the frictional force acts on the hockey

puck. This is determined from the Work-Kinetic Energy Theorem, $W_f = \Delta K$. Since the frictional force is opposite to the distance the hockey puck travels we can write $-f \cdot x = \dfrac{1}{2}m\left(v_f^2 - v_0^2\right)$ and solve for the distance the hockey puck travels. Substitution follows as is prior solution, as shown above.
(*College Physics* 9th ed. pages 89–90, 105–108, 125–127/10th ed. pages 91–92, 108–111, 141–143)
(L.O. 3.B.1.3, 4.C.1.1)

10. **D** The work done by the gravitational force on the body elevated in the field is negative since the direction of the force is opposite to the displacement. $W = \vec{F}_g \vec{x}(\cos 180°)$. The work done is $\left(9.80 \text{ m}\!\Big/\!_{s^2}\right)(1.60 \text{ m})\cos 180° = -47.0 \text{ J}$. The gravitational force does no work on the body as it is moved horizontally 2.00 m since the gravitational force is perpendicular to the displacement.
(*College Physics* 9th ed. pages 124–126/10th ed. pages 128–130)
(L.O. 4.C.1.1)

11. **D** The downward velocity increases, and therefore both the kinetic energy and the momentum increase because the gravitational force is in the same direction as its velocity during the time that it falls.
(*College Physics* 9th ed. pages 168–169/10th ed. pages 171–172)
(L.O. 3.D.2.2, 3.E.1.1)

12. **C** A frictional force acts on the car toward the center of the curve producing an acceleration that will change the direction of the car while maintaining its speed. Since the impulse provided by the centripetal force acts on the car $\vec{F}\Delta t = m\Delta\vec{v}$, the speed is constant but not the velocity. The velocity changes direction and thus the momentum (which is a vector pointing in the direction of the car's velocity) changes.
(*College Physics* 9th ed. pages 168–169, 207–211/10th ed. pages 171–172, 211–214)
(L.O. 3.D.2.2)

13. **C** The area under the force versus time graph is the change in the momentum of the body. The total area is the sum of the two areas under the curve that will give the change in momentum, $A_1 = 20 \text{ N}(6 \text{ s}) = 120 \text{ N}\cdot\text{s}$ and $A_2 = \dfrac{1}{2}(20 \text{ N})(4 \text{ s}) = 40 \text{ N}\cdot\text{s}$.

The total area is $160 \text{ N}\cdot\text{s}$.
(*College Physics* 9th ed. pages 168–169/10th ed. pages 171–172)
(L.O. 4.B.2.1)

14. **B** The net force applied to the body in the direction of motion is 6.00 N. The normal to the surface will increase because a vertical force of 6.00 N is applied to the body, but will not produce a change in the horizontal forces acting on the body since the surface is frictionless.
(*College Physics* 9th ed. pages 168–169/10th ed. pages 171–172)
(L.O. 3.D.2.2)

15. **A** The work done by friction is negative $W_f = -f\Delta x$ because the angle between the frictional force vector and the displacement of the box as it moves is 180° and the cosine of 180° is –1. The friction acting on the box is found by solving $f_k = \mu_k N = \mu_k mg\cos 30°$. Solving for the frictional force gives

    $f_k = 0.20(1.80 \text{ kg})\left(9.80 \text{ }^m\!\!/_{s^2}\right)\cos 30° = 3.06 \text{ N}$. The work done by friction is then, $W_f = -3.06 \text{ N}(1.20 \text{ m}) = -3.67 \text{ J}$.

    (*College Physics* 9th ed. pages 125–127/10th ed. pages 141–143)
    (L.O. 5.B.3.3)

16. **D** The block has maximum velocity as it passes though the equilibrium position.

    Its velocity determined from conservation of energy $U_s + K$ is a constant since the surface is frictionless. $\frac{1}{2}kx_i^2 + \frac{1}{2}mv_i^2 =$

    $\frac{1}{2}kx_f^2 + \frac{1}{2}mv_f^2$. Substitution into the equation is $\frac{1}{2}\left(150.0 \text{ } \frac{N}{m}\right)$

    $(0.100 \text{ m})^2 = \frac{1}{2}(0.200 \text{ kg})v^2$. Solving gives $v = 2.74 \frac{m}{s}$.

    (*College Physics* 9th ed. pages 437–439, 441–443/10th ed. pages 449–453)
    (L.O. 3.B.3.1, 5.B.3.2, 5.B.3.3, 5.B.4.2)

17. **A** Since the reference position is the tabletop, the body has no gravitational potential energy, it possess only kinetic energy.
    (*College Physics* 9th ed. pages 129–130, 132/10th ed. pages 132–133, 135)
    (L.O. 5.B.1.1)

18. **D** Conservation of energy applies $K_i + U_i = K_f + U_f$

    $\frac{1}{2}(1.50 \text{ kg})\left(2.00 \text{ } \frac{m}{s}\right)^2 + (1.50 \text{ kg})\left(9.80 \text{ } \frac{m}{s^2}\right)(1.00 \text{ m}) = 17.7 \text{ J}$.

    (*College Physics* 9th ed. pages 129–130, 132/10th ed. pages 132–133, 135)
    (L.O. 4.C.1.1)

19. **A** After one complete cycle, the body has returned to its initial position. It moves from $-A$ to $+A$ and back, a distance of $4A$.
    (*College Physics* 9th ed. page 442/10th ed. page 452)
    (L.O. 3.B.3.1)

20. **B** Negative work is done on the block of ice by the frictional force. Since there is no other force applied to the block of ice in the direction of motion, the kinetic energy will decrease. $W_f = \Delta K$

    (*College Physics* 9th ed. pages128–130/10th ed. pages 131–133)
    (L.O. 3.E.1.1)

21. **C** The gravitational acceleration on the planet is $\dfrac{\vec{g}_E}{\vec{g}_P} = \dfrac{M_E / R_E^2}{3M_E / (2R_E)^2}$.

Solving gives the ratio $\dfrac{\vec{g}_E}{\vec{g}_P} = \dfrac{4}{3}$. The acceleration on the planet is

$\dfrac{3\vec{g}_E}{4} = \vec{g}_P$, then the period of the pendulum is

$T_P = 2\pi \sqrt{\dfrac{1.20 \text{ m}}{7.35 \text{ m}/\text{s}^2}} = 2.54 \text{ s}$.

(*College Physics* 9th ed. pages 214–217, 451–453/10th ed. pages 219–222, 460–461)
(L.O. 2.B.2.2, 3.B.3.1)

22. **C** The gravitational force between the masses is a force of attraction. The net force on m_3 is toward the left. Its magnitude is calculated from $\left|\vec{F}_{13}\right| + \left|\vec{F}_{23}\right| = \left|\vec{F}_{net}\right|$.

$\left|\vec{F}_{13}\right| = 6.67 \times 10^{-11} \dfrac{\text{N} \cdot \text{m}^2}{\text{kg}^2} \left(\dfrac{10.00 \text{ kg} \cdot 30.00 \text{ kg}}{(2.00 \text{ m})^2}\right)$

$= 4.00 \times 10^{-8}$ to the left

$\left|\vec{F}_{23}\right| = 6.67 \times 10^{-11} \dfrac{\text{N} \cdot \text{m}^2}{\text{kg}^2} \left(\dfrac{20.00 \text{ kg} \cdot 30.00 \text{ kg}}{(1.00 \text{ m})^2}\right)$

$= 5.00 \times 10^{-9}$ to the left

then $\left|\vec{F}_{net}\right| = 5.0 \times 10^{-9} \text{ N} + 4.0 \times 10^{-8} \text{ N} = 4.5 \times 10^{-8} \text{ N}$ to the left.

(*College Physics* 9th ed. pages 214–217/10th ed. pages 219–222)
(L.O. 3.C.1.1)

23. **B** The perceived shift in frequency occurs due to relative motion between the stationary observer and the moving ambulance. The wave fronts crowd together as waves produced by the siren on the moving ambulance approach waves that were already traveling in the medium. As the apparent wavelength decreases, the perceived frequency increases.
(*College Physics* 9th ed. pages 482–485/10th ed. pages 491–494)
(L.O. 6.B.1.1)

24. **A** The center-of-mass of the fragments of the projectile after the explosion will follow the trajectory of the projectile had it not exploded. The explosion was a chemical process inside of the projectile and no net force was applied to it.
(*College Physics* 9th ed. pages 63–64, 241–244/10th ed. pages 65–67, 246–249)
(L.O. 5.D.3.1)

25. **A** The net change in momentum arises from the change in the horizontal and vertical components of the momentum when an

impulse $\vec{F}\Delta t = \Delta \vec{p}$ is applied. Solving for the change of momentum in the y direction, $\Delta \vec{p}_y = n(m\vec{v}\sin 30°) - n(-m\vec{v}\sin 30°) = n(2m\vec{v}\sin 30°)$. In the x direction, $\Delta \vec{p}_x = n(m\vec{v}\cos 30°) - n(m\vec{v}\cos 30°) = 0$. The change in momentum is thus $\Delta \vec{p} = \Delta \vec{p}_x + \Delta \vec{p}_y = 0 + n(2m\vec{v}\sin 30°) = nm\vec{v}$.
(*College Physics* 9th ed. pages 172–184/10th ed. pages 170–175)
(L.O. 3.D.2.1)

26. **D** As the body is lifted in a gravitational field the mass of the body will not change as it is lifted.
(*College Physics* 9th ed. pages 92–93/10th ed. pages 95–96)
(L.O. 2.B.1.1, 2.B.2.1)

27. **B** Conservation of energy applies $K_i + U_{s_i} = K_f + U_{s_f}$. The equation is written as $\frac{1}{2}mv_i^2 = \frac{1}{2}kx_f^2$. The initial velocity of the block is $v = \sqrt{\dfrac{(15.0 \text{ N}/_{\text{m}})(0.12 \text{ m})^2}{2.00 \text{ kg}}} = 0.33 \text{ m}/_{\text{s}}$.
(*College Physics* 9th ed. pages 140–143/10th ed. pages 143–145)
(L.O. 4.C.1.1)

28. **A** Torque is defined as $|\vec{\tau}| = |\vec{F}|\vec{r}\sin \theta$. (In all cases the angle is 90 °). IV has the largest torque since it has the longest moment arm and its torque is $3r(50 \text{ N})$. Both figure I and II have the same value $r(100 \text{ N})$, and III has the least with a value of $r(50 \text{ N})$.
(*College Physics* 9th ed. pages 236–239/10th ed. pages 241–244)
(L.O. 3.F.1.2)

29. **A** There is no outside torque applied to the skater, thus her angular momentum is constant. Reducing her moment of inertia by bringing her arms in toward her body increases her angular velocity. The skater does work as she pulls her arms inward thus increasing the kinetic energy.
(*College Physics* 9th ed. pages 257–259/10th ed. pages 262–265)
(L.O. 3.E.1.1, 5.E.1.1)

30. **B** The period of oscillation for a spring-mass system does not depend on the amplitude of vibration. It does depend on the mass of the body attached to the spring and the spring constant. $T = 2\pi\sqrt{\dfrac{m}{k}}$. Doubling the mass without changing the spring constant will change the period of vibration by a factor of the $\sqrt{2}$.
(*College Physics* 9th ed. pages 446–447/10th ed. pages 454–455)
(L.O. 3.B.3.1)

31. **B** The spring constant is determined from the restoring force which is equal to the weight of the mass at rest on the end of the spring stretching it 0.065 m. $\vec{F}_g = m\vec{g}$. The restoring force is 24.5 N. The spring constant is then found by substitution into

$\left|\vec{F}_s\right| = -k\left|\vec{x}\right|$. The spring constant is $k = 24.5\ \text{N}/0.065\ \text{m} = 377\ \text{N}/\text{m}$. Solving the equation, the frequency is then,

$$f = \frac{1}{2\pi}\sqrt{\frac{377\ \text{N}/\text{m}}{2.50\ \text{kg}}} = 1.96\ \text{Hz}.$$

(*College Physics* 9th ed. pages 437, 446–447/10th ed. pages 446, 454–455)
(L.O. 3.B.3.4)

32. **C** The wavelength of the wave is the distance between two points on a wave that have the same amplitude and the same phase (particles on the wave form are moving in the same direction).
(*College Physics* 9th ed. pages 458–459/10th ed. pages 466–467)
(L.O. 6.A.4.1)

33. **B** The displacement of a point on a wave is the is the distance of the vibrating particle from the equilibrium position and is measured above and below the equilibrium. In the wave shown, point A is at maximum amplitude and has the largest displacement. Since the question asked for the magnitude of the displacement, point D is ranked above point B. Point C is at the equilibrium and thus its displacement is zero.
(*College Physics* 9th ed. pages 458–459/10th ed. pages 466–467)
(L.O. 6.A.3.1)

34. **A** There is a standing wave set up in the string due to interference between the incident waves and the reflected waves. This standing wave has nodes at the fixed boundaries. There are two complete waves in the diagram thus there are 5 nodes and 4 antinodes.
(*College Physics* 9th ed. pages 489–493/10th ed. pages 498–503)
(L.O. 6.D.1.1, 6.D.3.2)

35. **B** There are 4 loops in the standing wave which are two complete waves in the region. The string is 1.00 m long and the wavelength is $\lambda = 1.00\ \text{m}/2 = 0.500\ \text{m}$. The velocity of the wave can be calculated from $v = \lambda f$. The velocity is $60.0\ \text{Hz}(0.500\ \text{m}) = 30.0\ \text{m}/\text{s}$.

(*College Physics* 9th ed. pages 458, 489–493/10th ed. pages 467, 498–503)
(L.O. 6.D.4.2)

36. **A** The net torque acting on the cylinder (where we define the clockwise direction to be negative) is $\Sigma\vec{\tau} = -(25.0\ \text{N})(0.300\ \text{m}) + (40.0\ \text{N})(0.100\ \text{m}) = -3.5\ \text{N}\cdot\text{m}$. Since the net torque is negative, the rotation is clockwise.
(*College Physics* 9th ed. pages 236–239/10th ed. pages 241–244)
(L.O. 3.F.1.3)

37. **A** Coulomb's Law gives the magnitude of the force acting between the charges $\left|\vec{F}_E\right| = k\dfrac{q_1 q_2}{r^2}$. The magnitude of the force is

$$9 \times 10^9 \, \frac{\text{N} \cdot \text{m}^2}{\text{C}^2} \frac{(9.00 \times 10^{-9} \, \text{C})(5.00 \times 10^{-9} \, \text{C})}{(0.01 \, \text{m})^2} = 4.05 \times 10^{-3} \, \text{N}.$$ Since the charges are opposite in sign, the force is attractive.
(*College Physics* 9th ed. pages 517–519/10th ed. pages 527–530)
(L.O. 3.C.2.1)

38. **C** The charge on the electron, e, has one value, e. Only whole number of charges $\pm e$, $\pm 2e$, $\pm 3e$, etc. are transferred.
(*College Physics* 9th ed. pages 515–516/10th ed. pages 525–526)
(L.O. 1.B.3.1)

39. **C** A static charge on the surface of a small particle is positive when there is a deficiency of electrons on its surface.
(*College Physics* 9th ed. pages 515–516/10th ed. pages 525–526)
(L.O. 1.B.1.1)

40. **C** Conservation of angular momentum applies. The small piece of modeling clay is a point mass and in the inelastic collision with the rotating disk I_0 the moment of inertia of the system increases to $I_0 + I_{clay}$, thus the angular velocity must decrease.
(*College Physics* 9th ed. pages 257–259/10th ed. pages 262–265)
(L.O. 5.E.1.1)

41. **B** The parallel branch consists of a 30 Ω resistor and a 60 Ω resistor. The equivalent resistance for this part of the circuit is $\frac{1}{R} = \frac{1}{30 \, \Omega} + \frac{1}{60 \, \Omega}$ or 20 Ω. The equivalent of 20 Ω is in series with the 15 Ω resistor for a total of 35 Ω for the circuit. Solving $V = IR$ will give the total current for the circuit. $\frac{12 \, \text{V}}{35 \, \Omega} = 0.34 \, \text{A}$. Kirchhoff's junction rule applies. The current, 0.34 A will divide in the parallel branch with the 30 Ω resistor carrying $\frac{2}{3} I_{total}$ or 0.23 A. (The equivalent resistance is 20 Ω for the parallel branch: the division of current is $\frac{20 \, \Omega}{30 \, \Omega} I_{total} = \frac{2}{3} I_{total}$ for the 30 Ω resistor and $\frac{20 \, \Omega}{60 \, \Omega} I_{total} = \frac{1}{3} I_{total}$ for the 60 Ω resistor.)
(*College Physics* 9th ed. pages 625–626/10th ed. pages 636–637)
(L.O. 5.C.3.3)

42. **B** The only charge that can move on the surface of the isolated conductor is the negative charge. Due to the electrostatic repulsion between the negative charge on the wand and the electrons on the electroscope, the electrons will move to the leaves of the electroscope and the charge on the surface will be positive. The leaves of the electroscope will have identical excess negative charge.
(*College Physics* 9th ed. pages 515–516/10th ed. pages 525–526)
(L.O. 1.B.1.2)

43. **B** The change in the angular momentum can be determined from

$$\Sigma \vec{\tau} = \frac{\Delta \vec{L}}{\Delta t} .$$

The two torques applied to the cylinder give a net torque of $-1.00 \text{ N} \cdot \text{m} + 0.200 \text{ N} \cdot \text{m} = -0.800 \text{ N} \cdot \text{m}$. The change in the angular momentum is then $-4.00 \text{ N} \cdot \text{m} \cdot \text{s}$. Rotation in a clockwise manner is defined as negative.
(*College Physics* 9th ed. pages 257–259/10th ed. pages 262–265)
(L.O. 4.D.3.1)

44. **C** In the circuit, the upper parallel branch consists of two resistors of 70 Ω and 50 Ω is in series producing a resistance in the upper branch of 120 Ω. This 120 Ω equivalent is in parallel with the 60 Ω resistance in the lower branch. The resistance for the parallel part of the circuit is found from $\dfrac{1}{R} = \dfrac{1}{120\ \Omega} + \dfrac{1}{60\ \Omega}$. The parallel branch has a total equivalent resistance of 40 Ω. This 40 Ω resistance is in series with a 10 Ω resistance for a total resistance in the circuit of 50 Ω. The total current in the circuit and thus in the 10 Ω resistor is found from $V = IR$. The total current in the circuit is $\dfrac{20 \text{ V}}{50\ \Omega} = 0.4 \text{A}$.

Kirchhoff's loop rule applies. The electrical potential difference is greatest over the parallel part of the circuit since it has the largest resistance, $V = IR$. The electrical potential difference across the 60 Ω resistor is the largest. The sum of the electrical potential differences across the two resistors in the upper branch has to equal the electrical potential difference across the lower branch. The electrical potential difference will be larger across the 70 Ω resistance since it has a larger resistance than the 50 Ω. Even though the entire current transits the 10 Ω resistance, it has the lowest electrical potential difference since it is the smallest resistance in the circuit.
(*College Physics* 9th ed. pages 625–626/10th ed. pages 636–637)
(L.O. 5.B.9.3)

45. **C** Kirchhoff's loop rule applies. Electrical energy developed in the battery is delivered to the external circuit (Connections from the battery and the resistors are ideal conductors). The electrical potential difference across the ends of the resistor multiplied by the current in the resistor is the power dissipated in the resistor or the work per unit time. The conventional current flows into the 6.0 Ω resistor and passes through an ideal conductor into the 3.0 Ω resistor where the rest of the energy developed by the battery is dissipated.
(*College Physics* 9th ed. pages 625–626/10th ed. pages 636–637)
(L.O. 5.B.9.1)

46. **A** and **C** Newton's Second law $F = ma$ applies; in order to increase the velocity of the mass m, a force with a component in the direction of the initial velocity vector must act on the mass, m. This force acting through a displacement will do work on the mass m increasing its kinetic energy and its momentum. The Work-Kinetic Energy Theorem indicates that $W = \Delta K$.
(*College Physics* 9th ed. pages 89–90, 129–131/10th ed. pages 91–92, 132–133)
(L.O. 3.B.1.4, 4.C.2.1)

47. **A** and **D** The gravitational force of attraction between the sun and the satellite is given by $\vec{F} = G\dfrac{M_s m}{r^2}$. The force is larger at point A since the distance is smaller. The speed of the satellite is largest at point A since no net torque acts on the satellite, thus its angular momentum must be conserved. Angular momentum is given as $L = I\omega$. The satellite is a point mass relative to the sun; $I = mr^2$ and angular velocity can be expressed as $\omega = \dfrac{v}{r}$. Substitution into $I = mr^2$ gives $I = \left(mr^2\right)\dfrac{v}{r} = mvr$. The velocity is dependent on the distance r from the sun $mv_A r_A = mv_B r_B$.
(*College Physics* 9th ed. pages 214–217, 257–259/10th ed. pages 219–222, 262–264)
(L.O. 3.C.1.2, 5.E.1.1)

48. **A** and **C** The work done on a body is the area under the curve. Since the net area is positive, the work done is positive, and the kinetic energy will increase. Since the kinetic energy increases, the momentum will also increase. The correct momentum equation is $\vec{F}_{\text{average}} \cdot \Delta t = m\Delta \vec{v}$.
(*College Physics* 9th ed. pages 129–131, 152–154, 168–169/10th ed. pages 132–134, 155–157, 171–172)
(L.O. 3.F.1.4, 4.B.2.1)

49. **B** and **C** The first harmonic is the fundamental wave set up in a string or a wire. The fixed ends are consecutive nodes thus the wavelength is $\lambda = 2L$. The distance between the nodes is half the wavelength. For the wire 1.20 m long, the wavelength is 2.40 m. and the wave speed in the wire is 180 m/s. The frequency of vibration can be calculated from $v = \lambda f$ $180\,\dfrac{\text{m}}{\text{s}} = (1.20\ \text{m})f$. The frequency is 75 Hz.
(*College Physics* 9th ed. pages 489–494/10th ed. pages 498–501)
(L.O. 6.C.1.1, 6.D.4.2)

50. **B** and **C** In a transverse wave, the particles move perpendicular to the direction of the wave disturbance in the medium as in Figure 2. In a longitudinal wave, the particles move back and forth, parallel to the direction of the wave front advance through the medium as in Figure 1.
(*College Physics* 9th ed. pages 456–457/10th ed. pages 465–466)
(L.O. 6.A.1.2)

ANSWERS TO FREE-RESPONSE PROBLEMS

QUESTION 1

(a) The acceleration due to gravity can be determined from the acceleration of a multi-mass system accelerated by a net force by determining the time t taken by the masses on the hanger to move a distance h.

Set up masses on the mass hangers so that the mass hangers move up and down at constant speed when given a slight push. Record the total mass.

Transfer a mass from the ascending side m_2 to the descending side m_1. The net force of the system will be the difference in weight between the two hangers.

Start the experiment with the ascending mass on the floor. Measure the distance between the mass hangers and the floor. Release the descending mass.

Time the masses hangers as they move, stopping the timer when the descending mass has reached the floor. Record the net force and the time.

Repeat for at least two more trials.

Determine the average of these times and calculate the acceleration of the system using $x = v_0 t + \frac{1}{2} at^2$.

Transfer additional mass from the ascending side to the descending side. Repeat the steps above, again making at least three separate determinations of the time.

Continue transferring mass until you have made several different runs. **(5 points)**

(b) Measurement of the height the mass hangers move and the time for each trial will permit the calculation of the acceleration of the system using $x = v_0 t + \frac{1}{2} at^2$. Comparison of the acceleration for each trial can be obtained by $\Sigma \vec{F}_y = (m_1 + m_2)\vec{a}_y$. **(2 points)**

(c) Plot a graph of the acceleration for each experiment run vs. $\dfrac{(m_1 - m_2)}{(m_1 + m_2)}$. The slope of the line is the experimental value for the acceleration due to gravity, $\vec{g}$. Compare the experimental value to the accepted value. **(3 points)**

(d) Assuming the pulley/wheel to be frictionless will change the experimental value determined for $\vec{g}$ because friction will supply a net torque to the pulley/wheel causing the pulley/wheel to have an angular acceleration. The pulley/wheel is not massless, but has a value M which gives it a moment of inertia I.   **(2 points)**
(*College Physics* 9th ed. pages 36–38, 89–90, 105–107, 109–111, 236–239, 247–248/10th ed. pages 38–41, 91–92, 111–112, 241–244, 253–254)
(L.O. 3.A.1.1, 2.B.1.1, 3.A.1.2, 3.A.1.3, 3.B.1.1)

QUESTION 2

(a) The torque acting on the meterstick is $\tau = Fr\sin\theta$. The F is $\perp$ to the moment arm r and thus θ is 90°. The torque acting on the meterstick is $\tau = \dfrac{mgL}{2}$.   **(1 point)**

Since the moment of inertia is given in the problem, $I = \dfrac{1}{3}mL^2$.

Substitution into the torque equation $\vec{\tau} = I\vec{\alpha}$ is $\dfrac{mgL}{2} = \dfrac{1}{3}mL^2\alpha$.

           (1 point)

The initial angular acceleration is $\alpha = \dfrac{3}{2}\dfrac{g}{L}$.   **(1 point)**

(b) The correct line checked is ____√____ **increase.**   **(1 point)**

The torque acting on the meterstick is one-half of the initial torque since the moment arm is reduced by 2. The new torque is $\tau = \dfrac{mgL}{4}$.

Changing the location of the point of rotation changes the moment of inertia. Both the torque and the moment of inertia have reduced in value, but the moment of inertia is much smaller and thus the initial angular acceleration is larger when the stick is released.   **(2 points)**

Mathematically, $\dfrac{mgL}{4} = \dfrac{7}{48}mL^2\alpha$. The angular acceleration is now $\dfrac{12}{7}\dfrac{g}{L}$.

(c) To set the meterstick into rotational equilibrium, the net torque on the system must be zero.

The moment arm for the weight of the meterstick is the distance from the pivot point to center-of-mass of the meterstick. Since the meterstick is uniform, the center-of-mass is at the 0.500 mark. Thus its moment arm is $(0.500\text{ m} - 0.250\text{ m}) = 0.250\text{ m}$.

Substitution into the $\Sigma\tau = 0$ equation is $(0.980\text{ N})(0.250\text{ m}) =$ $(1.50\text{ N})r$. $r = 0.1633\text{ m} = \mathbf{0.163\text{ m}}$ mark on the meterstick and is directed downward. **(2 points)**
(*College Physics* 9th ed. pages 236–239, 240–243, 248–251/10th ed. pages 241–244, 245–249, 253–255)
(L.O. 3.F.1.1, 2.F.1.5, 3.F.2.1, 3.F.3.2, 4.A.1.1)

QUESTION 3

(a) The correct line checked is ___√___ less than when the switch is closed. **(1 point)**

When the switch is open, $R_T = R_A + 2R_A = 3R_A$.

When the switch is closed, $\dfrac{1}{R_A} + \dfrac{1}{2R_A} = \dfrac{1}{R_T}$, which gives the parallel arrangement a resistance of $\dfrac{2}{3}R_A$. Then this resistance is in series with R_D. The total resistance when the switch is closed is $2R_A + \dfrac{2}{3}R_A = R_T = 2.67R_A$. Since the resistance is smaller with the switch closed, the current is larger. **(2 points)**

When the switch is open, the current is smaller.

Justification to (a) without mathematics.

When the switch is open, the resistance of the lamps is the sum of R_A and R_B. When the switch is closed, there are two paths in the parallel arrangement. The resistance in the parallel arrangement is less than the resistance of R_A. The equivalent resistance of the parallel arrangement and R_D is less than the equivalent resistance when the switch is open. Thus the current is greater when the switch is closed than when the switch is open. **(2 points)**

(b) The correct line checked is ___√___ greater than the power consumed in R_B **(1 point)**

When the switch is closed, the resistance in the lower branch is twice as large as the resistance in the upper branch. The current in the upper branch is larger than the current in the lower branch by a factor of 2. Since power is the product of current squared times resistance, the power consumed in R_A **is four times larger** than the power consumed in R_B. **(2 points)**

Alternate solution for (b) Kirchhoff's loop rule applies. The electrical potential difference across the resistance in the upper branch is equal to the sum of the electrical potential differences across the two resistors in the lower branch. Since power is the square of the electrical potential difference divided by the resistance, R_A has the larger power consumption. The power developed in R_A is four times the power in R_B.

(c) The ranking for the brightness of the lamps is $\mathbf{D > A > (B = C)}$
(1 point)

The brightness of the lamps is proportional to the current passing through the lamps. All the current passes through R_D. The other lamps are in a parallel arrangement; Kirchhoff's junction rule applies, with the current in the upper branch greater than the current in the lower branch containing the two lamps $R_B = R_C$. **(2 points)**

(*College Physics* 9th ed. pages 617–628/10th ed. pages 628–638)
(L.O. 5.B.9.3, 5.C.3.1, 5.C.3.3)

QUESTION 4

(a) The period of vibration is found from $T = 2\pi\sqrt{\dfrac{m}{k}}$. Substitution into the equation and solving, the period is $T = 2\pi\sqrt{\dfrac{1.53 \text{ kg}}{15.0 \text{ N/m}}} = 2.00 \text{ s}$.

(1 point)

(b) The maximum velocity occurs when the body passes through the equilibrium position. Since the surface is flat and frictionless, the mechanical energy is conserved.

$$\frac{1}{2}mv^2 = \frac{1}{2}kA^2 \qquad v^2 = \frac{\left(15.0 \text{ N/m}\right)(0.120 \text{ m})^2}{1.53 \text{ kg}}.$$ The maximum velocity is $\mathbf{0.376 \dfrac{m}{s}}$.

(1 point)

(c) The maximum acceleration occurs at the amplitude A and points toward equilibrium. Its magnitude is determined from $kx = ma$.

The maximum acceleration is $\dfrac{\left(15.0 \text{ N/m}\right)(0.120 \text{ m})}{1.53 \text{ kg}} = \mathbf{1.18 \text{ m/s}}$.

(1 point)

(d) The graphs are as follows:

    i. displacement versus period of the oscillation   **(2 points)**

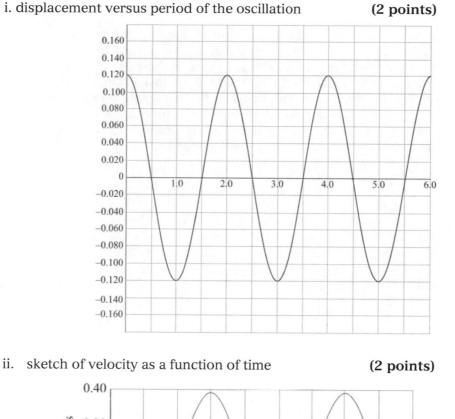

    ii. sketch of velocity as a function of time   **(2 points)**

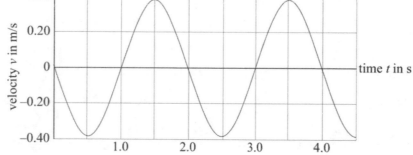

    iii. The acceleration as a function of time

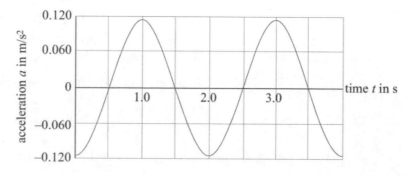

    (2 points)

(*College Physics* 9th ed. pages 438, 441–444, 446, 449/10th ed.
pages 447, 449–452, 455, 458, 628–638)
(L.O. 3.B.3.1, 3.B.3.4, 5.B.3.1, 5.B.3.2, 5.B.4.2)

QUESTION 5

(a) i. Conservation of energy applies. Since the surface of the ramp is frictionless, the sum of the initial kinetic energy and gravitational potential energy is equal to the sum of the final kinetic energy and potential energy. At the highest point on the first ramp, the two kg block is stationary and has no kinetic energy. At the bottom of the first ramp, the two kg block has zero gravitational potential energy. Setting the initial gravitational potential energy equal to the final kinetic energy will let you solve for the velocity just before impact. **(2 points)**

ii. Conservation of momentum applies for the completely inelastic collision. Setting up and solving for the velocity of the composite body will give the needed value to solve for the height the composite mass rises on the second ramp. Kinetic energy is not conserved in the inelastic collision, but kinetic energy after the collision is converted into gravitational potential energy after the collision. Solving this will give the height on the second ramp. **(2 points)**

(b) The correct line checked is __√__ higher than the distance the blocks reached in part (a) **(1 point)**

Solving for the velocity of the 2.00 kg block just before impact from

$$\frac{1}{2}(2.00 \text{ kg})v^2 = (2.00 \text{ kg})\left(9.80 \ \frac{m}{s^2}\right)(1.50 \text{ m})$$ gives the 2.00 kg block

a velocity of $5.42 \ \frac{m}{s}$. The velocity of the composite is obtained from solving the conservation of momentum equation. $(2.00 \text{ kg})\left(5.42 \ m/s\right) = (5.00 \text{ kg})v$. The velocity of the composite is $2.17 \ m/s$. Then the height is found as

$$\frac{1}{2}(5.00 \text{ kg})\left(2.17 \ m/s\right)^2 = (5.00 \text{ kg})\left(9.80 \ \frac{m}{s^2}\right)h.$$

The height up the second ramp is 0.24 m.

The collision with the 3.00 kg block is perfectly elastic. The velocity of each block is found from $m_1(v_{1i} - v_{1f}) = m_2(v_{2f})$ since the 3.00 kg block is initially at rest. Knowing that the collision is perfectly elastic and that coefficient of restitution is given as $\varepsilon = \frac{\text{relative rate of separation}}{\text{relative rate of approach}}$. Since it is perfectly elastic

$1 = \frac{v_{2f} - v_{1f}}{v_{1i}}$ (again the 3.00 kg body was at initially at rest). Thus

$5.42 \ m/s - v_{2f} = v_{1f}$. Substituting in to the momentum equation is

$2.00 \text{ kg}\left(5.42 \ m/s - \left(v_{2f} - 5.42 \ m/s\right)\right) = (3.00 \text{ kg})v_{2f}$

$0.667\left(5.42 \ m/s - v_{2f} + 5.42 \ m/s\right) = v_{2f}$

$7.26 \frac{m}{s} - 0.667 v_{2f} = v_{2f}$. The velocity of the 3.00 kg block is $4.35 \frac{m}{s}$.

Then conservation of energy after the collision for the 3.00 kg block moving up the second ramp is $\frac{1}{2}(3.00 \text{ kg})\left(4.35 \frac{m}{s}\right)^2 = (3.00 \text{ kg})\left(9.80 \frac{m}{s^2}\right)h$ gives a height of **0.960 m** which is higher than the height reached by the composite. **(4 points)**
(*College Physics* 9th ed. pages 135–136, 175–181/10th ed. pages 141–143,179–185)
(L.O. 4.C.1.1, 5.A.2.1, 5.B.3.2, 5.B.4.2, 5.D.1.3, 5.D.2.3, 5.D.2.5)

AP® PHYSICS 1
PRACTICE EXAM B

AP PHYSICS 1
Section I
50 Multiple-Choice Questions
Time–90 Minutes

Note: To simplify calculations, you may use $g = 10$ m/s^2 in all problems.

Directions: Each of the questions or incomplete statements below is followed by four suggested answers or completions. Select the one that is best in each case.

1. A car moves in one dimension along the x-axis. A velocity vs. time graph shows its motion over a period of 12.0 s.

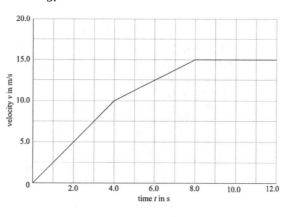

What is the car's displacement during the time interval 0–12 seconds?
(A) 90 m
(B) 100 m
(C) 110 m
(D) 130 m

2. A 2.00 kg body is supported by two cables attached to the ceiling as shown in the diagram. The tension in each cable is

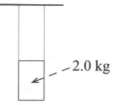

(A) 19.6 N
(B) 9.80 N
(C) 4.90 N
(D) 1.00 N

3. A 20.0 N force acts on two blocks moving them horizontally across a frictionless floor. What force does the 6.00 kg block exert on the 4.00 kg block?

(A) 20.0 N
(B) 16.0 N
(C) 12.0 N
(D) 8.00 N

GO ON TO NEXT PAGE

657

4. A basketball of mass m attached to a massless cord is used as a pendulum. The basketball is large enough that the force of air resistance $\vec{R}$ cannot be ignored. The basketball swings from point A to point B as shown in the diagram below.

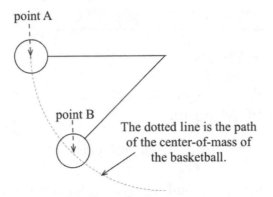

The dotted line is the path of the center-of-mass of the basketball.

Which of the following is the correct free-body diagram of the forces acting on the center-of-mass of the basketball at point B?

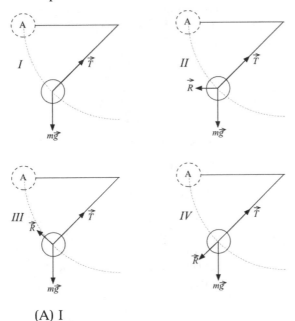

(A) I
(B) II
(C) III
(D) IV

5. A 0.20 kg sphere and a 0.40 kg sphere are dropped simultaneously from the top of a tower. When they reach the ground
(A) they have the same acceleration and the same kinetic energy
(B) the larger sphere has a larger acceleration and a larger kinetic energy than the smaller sphere
(C) the smaller sphere has the same acceleration and a smaller kinetic energy than the larger sphere
(D) they have the same kinetic energy but the larger sphere has the larger acceleration

6. In the diagram shown a 5.00 kg mass is supported by two cables $\vec{T}_1$ and $\vec{T}_2$. What is the tension in $\vec{T}_1$

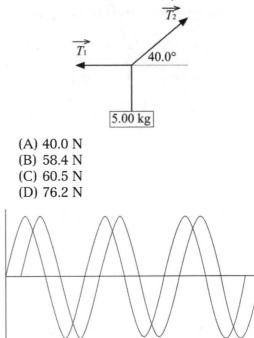

(A) 40.0 N
(B) 58.4 N
(C) 60.5 N
(D) 76.2 N

7. Two waves travel through the same medium with a phase difference of 90° as shown above. As the waves travel over time, the resulting waveform will
(A) vary in both amplitude and frequency
(B) be constant in amplitude and frequency
(C) vary in amplitude while maintaining constant frequency
(D) be constant in amplitude only

8. A small charge is located in the hollow center of an uncharged thin conducting ring.

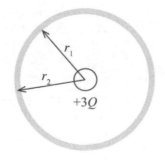

The charge on the outer surface r_2 is

(A) $+3Q$

(B) $-3Q$

(C) $+1.5Q$

(D) $-1.5Q$

9. Four identical blocks with the same initial velocity $\vec{v}_i$ experience a force as they move a distance on a frictionless surface in the right (+x direction). At the end of the displacement, the blocks have some final velocity $\vec{v}_f$. The magnitude of the force $\left|\vec{F}\right|$ acting on the blocks is the same.

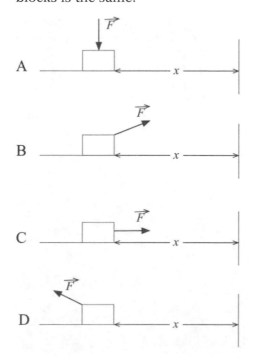

Rank the work done on the blocks by the applied force from the greatest amount of work to the least. Positive work is to be ranked higher than negative work.

(A) $C > B > D > A$

(B) $C > B > A > D$

(C) $B > D > A > C$

(D) $C > A > (B = D)$

10. A block moving at a constant speed of 1.20 m/s to the right enters a rough region where a frictional force acts on it.

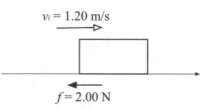

A graph of the block's velocity as a function of time is shown.

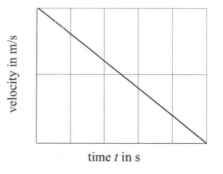

The velocity as a function of time graph suggests that

(A) the acceleration of the block is positive and constant and the graph of the displacement vs time is parabolic, opening upward

(B) the acceleration of the block is positive and constant and the graph of the displacement vs time is parabolic, opening downward

(C) the acceleration of the block is negative and constant and the graph of the displacement vs time is parabolic, opening upward

(D) the acceleration of the block is negative and constant and the graph of the displacement vs time is parabolic, opening downward

GO ON TO NEXT PAGE

11. A block is at rest on a level tabletop. Which of the following statements is the correct statement describing the reaction to the pull of gravity on the book?

The force of the
(A) Earth pulling on the book
(B) table pushing on the book
(C) book pulling on the Earth
(D) book pushing on the table

12. A 10.0 kg block is uniformly accelerated to the right on a horizontal surface as shown below, where the coefficient of friction μ_k between the block and the surface is 0.010.

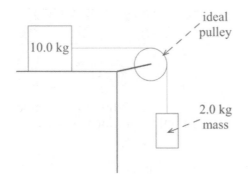

Which of the following is the correct free-body diagram for the 10.0 kg block?

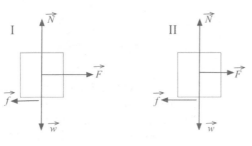

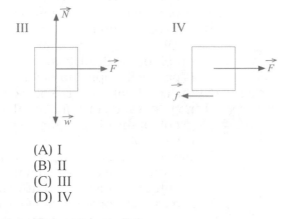

(A) I
(B) II
(C) III
(D) IV

13. Two blocks connected by a light metal rod, as shown in the diagram, are moved a distance to the right along the frictionless floor by a force F that acts at some angle θ below the horizontal. The kinetic energy of the blocks

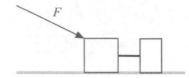

(A) remains the same since the force is applied to only the larger block
(B) increases because the force applied to the two blocks will increase the velocity of the center-of-mass increasing the kinetic energy
(C) decreases since the force is applied to only one block
(D) remains constant because the force acts downward below the horizontal and cannot change the velocity of the center-of-mass

14. Three cars A, B, and C, are pulled to the right by a 30.0 N force.

The mass of each car is 0.500 kg. Neglecting friction, determine the tension in the rope between cars A and B.
(A) 5.00 N
(B) 10.0 N
(C) 20.0 N
(D) 30.0 N

15. A 100 N block is placed on a scale and is connected to a 20 N weight by a massless rope which passes over an ideal pulley as shown.

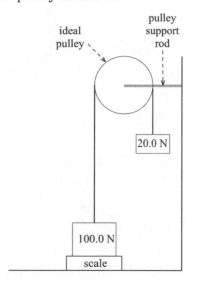

The normal force exerted on the block by the scale is
(A) 60 N
(B) 80 N
(C) 100N
(D) 120 N

Question 16

Use the diagram below to answer question 16 which shows a 3.00 kg block moving on the +x axis with a speed of 4.00 $\frac{m}{s}$ colliding with and sticking to a 1.00 kg block moving in the opposite direction with a speed of 2.00 $\frac{m}{s}$. The surface is frictionless.

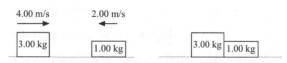

16. The speed of the composite system after the collision is
(A) 3.50 $\frac{m}{s}$
(B) 2.50 $\frac{m}{s}$
(C) 3.33 $\frac{m}{s}$
(D) 4.66 $\frac{m}{s}$

17. An elevator car is rising at a constant velocity. Consider the following statements.
  I. The upward force on the elevator is constant.
  II The kinetic energy of the elevator is constant.
  III. The gravitational potential energy of the elevator is constant.
  IV The acceleration of the elevator is constant.
  V. The kinetic plus the gravitational potential energies of the elevator are constant.
Which of following choices is correct?
(A) All five statements I to V are true.
(B) Only statements II and V are true.
(C) Only statements I, II, and IV are true.
(D) Only statements I, II, and III are true.

18. A 0.05 kg bullet with an initial velocity of 400 $\frac{m}{s}$ strikes a 500 kg block at rest on a horizontal frictionless surface and emerges with a final velocity of 200 $\frac{m}{s}$.

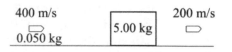

What is the velocity of the block after the interaction with the block?
(A) 2.0 $\frac{m}{s}$
(B) 3.0 $\frac{m}{s}$
(C) 4.0 $\frac{m}{s}$
(D) 6.0 $\frac{m}{s}$

GO ON TO NEXT PAGE

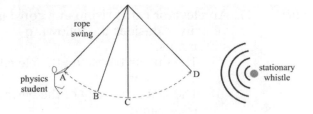

19. A physics student swings on a rope from point A to point D as shown in the diagram above. Points A and D are the highest positions of the swing and point C is the lowest position on the swing. Somewhere in front of the student a stationary whistle is blowing. At which position will the student hear the highest sound frequency from the whistle?
    (A) At B when moving toward A
    (B) At B when moving toward C
    (C) At C when moving toward B
    (D) At C when moving toward D

20. A student uses a spring scale and a balance to determine the "weight" of an object at ground floor of a building and later at the 100th floor of the same building. Which of the following is the correct answer concerning the readings for the "weight"?
    (A) The readings on both the spring scale and the balance are the same.
    (B) The readings on both the spring scale and the balance are different.
    (C) The reading for the spring scale is the same, but the reading on the balance is different.
    (D) The reading for the spring scale is different, but the reading for the balance is the same.

21. A 1.00 kg mass attached to a horizontal massless string is released from rest at point A, as shown in the diagram below.

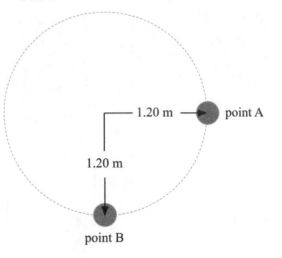

The mass then swings through a sector of a vertical circle of 1.20 m radius to point B. The moment of inertia of the 1.00 kg mass is $I = mr^2$. At point B, the angular momentum of the mass is
    (A) $4.12 \dfrac{kg \cdot m^2}{s}$
    (B) $4.43 \dfrac{kg \cdot m^2}{s}$
    (C) $4.85 \dfrac{kg \cdot m^2}{s}$
    (D) $5.82 \dfrac{kg \cdot m^2}{s}$

22. A particle of mass m is moving to the right along the +x axis with a velocity of 10.0 $\dfrac{m}{s}$ when it suddenly breaks apart into two unequal pieces. One piece of mass $\dfrac{m}{3}$ continues in the forward direction with a velocity of 20.0 $\dfrac{m}{s}$. What is the velocity of the second piece?
    (A) $-10.0 \dfrac{m}{s}$
    (B) $5.00 \dfrac{m}{s}$
    (C) $10.0 \dfrac{m}{s}$
    (D) $15.0 \dfrac{m}{s}$

Questions 23 and 24

Use the diagram below to answer questions 23 and 24.

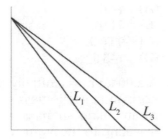

23. Three identical blocks at placed at the top of three frictionless inclines of lengths L_1, L_2 and L_3. The heights of all three inclines are the same. Rank the speed of the blocks at the bottom of the inclines from largest to smallest. The block sliding down L_1 has a speed of v_1. Blocks sliding down L_2 and L_3 have speeds of v_2 and v_3 respectively.
    (A) $v_1 > v_2 > v_3$
    (B) $v_3 > v_2 > v_1$
    (C) $v_1 = v_2 = v_3$
    (D) $v_1 > v_3 > v_2$

24. Equal amounts of frictional forces are applied to each identical body on the three ramps shown in problem 23. The blocks start from rest and slide down the ramp. Rank the speed at the bottom of the incline from greatest to least.
    (A) $v_1 > v_2 > v_3$
    (B) $v_3 > v_2 > v_1$
    (C) $v_1 = v_2 = v_3$
    (D) $v_1 > v_3 > v_2$

25. A variable resultant force F acts upon a 0.100 kg block initially at rest. The block is accelerated to speed v after being displaced 0.200 m by the force. Calculate the speed v of the block. The graph given below shows the force as a function of displacement x.

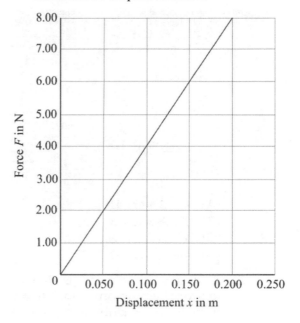

(A) 1.00 m/s
(B) 2.00 m/s
(C) 3.00 m/s
(D) 4.00 m/s

26. A 100 kg body is lifted to a position that is 1.50 Earth Radii, R_E, above the surface of the Earth. The weight of the body at that location is
    (A) 157 N
    (B) 437 N
    (C) 543 N
    (D) 980 N

GO ON TO NEXT PAGE

27. Four blocks experience the forces shown in the diagram below for 0.10 s. Rank the blocks in order of their change in momentum from the largest to the smallest.

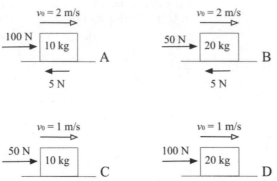

(A) A > B > C > D
(B) D > A > C > B
(C) A > D > B > C
(D) A > C > D > B

28. A force vs. time graph is shown for the net force acting on a block that is moving to the right along the + x axis.

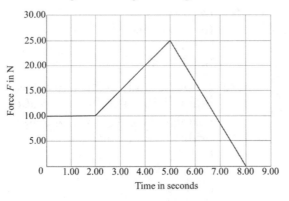

The momentum of the block over the 8.00 s interval will
(A) increase because the variable force acting on the block is always positive
(B) decrease because the slope of the line is negative between 5.00 s and 8.00 s
(C) decrease because the force decreases from 25.00 N to 0.00 N at 8.00 s
(D) increase from 0 to 5.00 s and then it will decrease in the interval between $t = 5.00$ s to 8.00 s

29. A 4.00 kg body is lifted vertically 1.20 m and then carried horizontally a distance of 2.50 m. The work done by the gravitational force is closest to
(A) −47.0 J
(B) −51.0 J
(C) −98.0 J
(D) −145 J

30. A 2.00 kg mass initially at rest on a horizontal frictionless surface is struck by an unknown mass m initially traveling to the right with a speed of 0.300 m/s. The collision is a totally elastic collision with the 2.00 kg mass moving to the right with a speed of 0.200 m/s while the unknown mass m moves to the left with a speed of 0.100 m/s. What is the mass m of the unknown object?
(A) 0.500 kg
(B) 1.00 kg
(C) 1.20 kg
(D) 1.80 kg

Questions 31 and 32

Questions 31 and 32 refer to the waveform shown in the graph below.

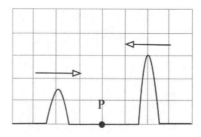

31. What is the amplitude of vibration of the wave in the graph?
(A) 0.08 m
(B) 0.16 m
(C) 2.0 m
(D) 4.0 m

32. What is the wavelength of the wave shown in the graph?
(A) 0.08 m
(B) 0.16 m
(C) 2.0 m
(D) 4.0 m

33. Two wave pulses approach each other on a string. What is the amplitude of the superimposed waveform at point P?

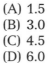

(A) 1.5
(B) 3.0
(C) 4.5
(D) 6.0

GO ON TO NEXT PAGE

34. A drive system consists of two pulleys connected by a drive belt. The radius of the output pulley $\vec{r}_o$ is twice the radius of the input pulley $\vec{r}_i$. The moment of inertia of the output pulley is also twice as large as the input pulley.

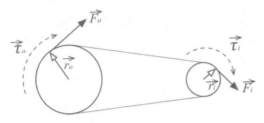

The belt wraps around both pulleys and rotates in a clockwise direction without slipping.
(A) The output pulley has twice the angular velocity of the input pulley since it has twice the radius.
(B) The angular velocity of the output pulley is the same as the angular velocity of the input pulley since the belt rotating connects them.
(C) The output pulley has half the angular velocity of the input pulley since it has twice the radius.
(D) The smaller pulley has twice the angular velocity since it has half the radius and half the moment of inertia and linear momentum must be conserved.

35. A cylinder is initially rotating about a frictionless axle in a counterclockwise direction at $4.00 \ \text{rad}/_s$ when $\vec{\tau}_1$ and $\vec{\tau}_2$ are applied to the cylinder as shown.

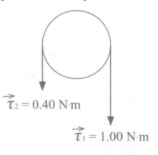

$\vec{\tau}_2 = 0.40$ N·m

$\vec{\tau}_1 = 1.00$ N·m

The cylinder will rotate with
(A) increasing angular speed since both of the torques are applied tangent to the cylinder pointing downward
(B) decreasing angular speed because $\vec{\tau}_1 > \vec{\tau}_2$ and $\vec{\tau}_1$ is applied opposite the initial direction of rotation causing the cylinder to come to rest
(C) decreasing speed until it stops and then increasing speed as it changes its direction of rotation because $\vec{\tau}_1 > \vec{\tau}_2$ and $\vec{\tau}_1$ is applied opposite the initial direction of rotation
(D) increasing speed because $\vec{\tau}_1 > \vec{\tau}_2$ and $\vec{\tau}_1$ is applied in the initial direction of rotation

36. A 50.0 kg student stands 2.00 m from the central hub of a merry-go-round, whose moment of inertia is $I = 800 \ \text{kg} \cdot \text{m}^2$. The student and the merry-go-round system are initially rotating at $1.50 \ \text{rad}/_s$. What is the angular velocity of the system when the student walks to a position that is 1.00 m from the hub of the merry-go-round? (Consider the student to be a point mass with a moment of inertia of $I = mr^2$.)
(A) $1.50 \ \text{rad}/_s$
(B) $1.76 \ \text{rad}/_s$
(C) $2.36 \ \text{rad}/_s$
(D) $2.50 \ \text{rad}/_s$

37. A variable torque is applied to a rotating platform for 4.00 s as shown in the graph.

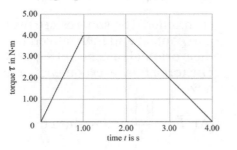

The increase in the angular momentum of the platform at the end of 4.00 s is
(A) 2.00 N·m·s
(B) 4.00 N·m·s
(C) 10.0 N·m·s
(D) 16.0 N·m·s

38. A tennis player hits a tennis ball with their racket, returning it to the player on the other side of the net. (Assume an elastic collision between the ball and the racket.) The racket increases the
(A) time the force is applied to the tennis ball, decreasing the change in momentum
(B) force applied to the tennis ball by reducing the time of contact, reducing the change in momentum
(C) force by decreasing the time, therefore increasing the change in momentum
(D) time of the impulse which reduces the force needed to change the direction of the ball, maintaining the magnitude of the momentum

39. A standing wave is set up in a wire that is 1.80 m long. The oscillator is electrically driven with a frequency of 120 Hz.

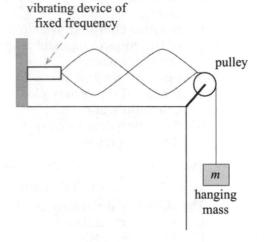

The speed of the wave in the wire is
(A) 66.7 m/s
(B) 133 m/s
(C) 108 m/s
(D) 216 m/s

40. A circuit is shown below. The 22.0 Ω resistor R_1 is in series with the parallel combination of R_2 equal to 12.0 Ω and R_3 equal to 24.0 Ω.

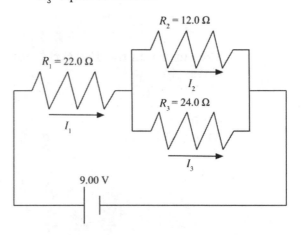

Rank the current in the resistors from the largest current to the smallest.
(A) $I_1 > I_2 > I_3$
(B) $I_1 > (I_2 = I_3)$
(C) $I_3 > I_1 > I_2$
(D) $I_2 > I_1 > I_3$

GO ON TO NEXT PAGE

41. A charging wand carrying a positive charge is brought near but does not touch an isolated neutral conducting sphere. During this action
    (A) the sphere gains a net positive charge
    (B) positive charge moves to the region of the sphere opposite to the charging wand
    (C) negative charge moves to the region of the sphere closest to the charging wand
    (D) the sphere loses positive charge due to repulsion

42. Two charges $q_1 = +6.50\ \mu C$ and $q_2 = -8.1\ \mu C$ are 0.100 m apart in air. The electrical force between them is
    (A) 47.4 N attractive
    (B) 47.4 N repulsive
    (C) 59.0 N attractive
    (D) 59.0 N repulsive

43. A circuit consists of three resistors as shown.

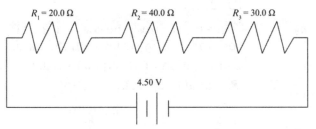

The current in the 15.0 Ω resistor is closest to
    (A) 6.67 A
    (B) 1.57 A
    (C) 0.600 A
    (D) 0.150 A

44. Two isolated spheres 0.100 m apart and carrying charges $q_1 = 5.00\ \mu C$ and $q_2 = -15.00\ \mu C$ exert a force $\left|\vec{F}_1\right|$ on each other. The spheres are brought into contact and then moved back in their original distance of separation. The force they exert on each other is now

    (A) $\left|\vec{F}_2\right| = \dfrac{\left|\vec{F}_1\right|}{2}$ and is attractive

    (B) $\left|\vec{F}_2\right| = \dfrac{\left|\vec{F}_1\right|}{2}$ and repulsive

    (C) $\left|\vec{F}_2\right| = \dfrac{\left|\vec{F}_1\right|}{3}$ and attractive

    (D) $\left|\vec{F}_2\right| = \dfrac{\left|\vec{F}_1\right|}{3}$ and repulsive

45. A circuit consists of three resistors as shown in the schematic below.

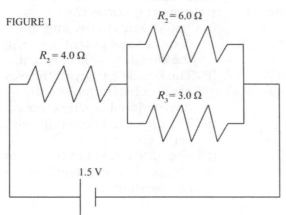

FIGURE 1

$R_2 = 6.0\ \Omega$

$R_2 = 4.0\ \Omega$

$R_3 = 3.0\ \Omega$

1.5 V

How will changing the circuit configuration change the current in the 4.0 Ω resistor?

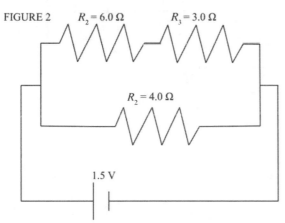

FIGURE 2 $R_2 = 6.0\ \Omega$ $R_3 = 3.0\ \Omega$

$R_2 = 4.0\ \Omega$

1.5 V

(A) The net resistance in the second arrangement is smaller, increasing the current in the circuit. Because the electrical potential difference across the parallel arrangement is the same, more current will go through the 4.0 Ω resistance in the lower branch.

(B) The entire current existed in the 4.0 Ω in the first arrangement. Current will divide in the parallel branch thus the current through the 4.0 Ω resistor will reduce.

(C) The 1.5 V battery was not changed therefore the current in the 4.0 Ω resistor will not change.

(D) The current in the 4.0 Ω resistor will be smaller since most of the current will go through the smaller 3.0 Ω resistor.

Questions 46 to 50

Directions: For each of the questions or incomplete statements below, <u>two</u> of the suggested answers will be correct. For each of these questions, you must select <u>both</u> correct answers to earn credit. No partial credit will be earned if only one correct answer is selected. Select the two that are best in each case and then enter both of the appropriate answers in the corresponding space on the answer sheet.

46. A 1.0 kg crate accelerates down an inclined plane at 0.60 $\frac{m}{s^2}$.

(A) Increasing the mass of the crate will decrease the acceleration down the plane since Newton's second law applies.

(B) Increasing the angle will increase the acceleration since the effective weight acting down the plane will increase.

(C) Increasing the angle will have no change on the acceleration since it will not change the net force.

(D) Increasing the mass will not change the acceleration down the plane since Newton's second law applies.

47. Students designed an experiment to measure the motion of a body using various pieces of standard laboratory equipment. Which of the following approaches will permit them to determine either the velocity or the acceleration of the body?

(A) A constant motion cart, a meterstick, and a stopwatch.

(B) An inclined plane, a block of unknown mass, and a platform balance.

(C) A glider on a tilted airtack, a protractor, and a photogate.

(D) A mass attached to a spring of known spring constant and a meterstick.

GO ON TO NEXT PAGE

48. A uniform rod, 1.00 long, is placed on a pivot at 0.60 m from the left end of the rod. In order for the rod to be in static equilibrium the sum of the
    (A) torques applied to the rod must be zero
    (B) forces applied to the rod must be zero
    (C) moment arms must be zero
    (D) frictional forces acting on the rod must be zero

49. Which of the graphs sketched below may apply to a body in translational equilibrium?

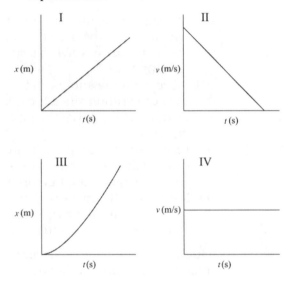

    (A) I
    (B) II
    (C) III
    (D) IV

50. An elevator car moves upward at a constant speed. Which of the following statements is correct?
    (A) The kinetic energy and the gravitational potential energy of the elevator car is constant.
    (B) The kinetic energy of the elevator car is constant but not the gravitational potential energy.
    (C) The upward force on the elevator car is constant.
    (D) The acceleration of the elevator car is equal to the gravitational acceleration.

STOP
END OF SECTION I

IF YOU FINISH BEFORE TIME IS CALLED, YOU MAY CHECK YOUR WORK ON THIS SECTION. DO NOT GO ON TO SECTION II UNTIL YOU ARE TOLD TO DO SO.

AP PHYSICS 1
Section II
5 Free-Response Questions
Time–90 Minutes

Directions: Solve each of the following problems. Unless the directions indicate otherwise, respond to all parts of each question.

1. A steel sphere of mass m_1 and radius r rolls down a ramp without slipping, making a glancing collision with an identical steel sphere, m_2 at rest on a peg at the edge of a table. The moment of inertia for a solid sphere is $I = \frac{2}{5}mr^2$. A side view of the ramp-spheres system is shown below.

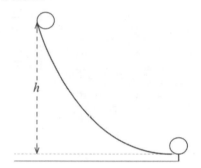

   (a) Explain without calculation how you would determine the velocity of m_1 before it collides with m_2.
   (b) If the height of the ramp is 0.300 m, what is the velocity of m_1 just before it collides with m_2?
   (c) As viewed from above, the two spheres undergo a glancing collision, leaving the table with the angles as shown below.

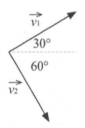

   The velocity of m_1 after the collision, $\vec{v}_1$ is 1.78 $\frac{m}{s}$. Determine the velocity of m_2.

   (d) If the collision takes place at the edge of a table that is 1.00 m high, which of the two spheres will land furthest from the base of the table? Explain your answer without a mathematical solution.

2. You are to design an experiment to determine the coefficient of kinetic friction μ_k between a block and a friction board in enough detail that another student can duplicate your experiment and produce the same results.
   (a) Explain your procedure and include a schematic diagram of your experiment.
   (b) What measurements will you take and how will you use them to determine the coefficient of kinetic friction μ_k?

GO ON TO NEXT PAGE

(c) If you plot a graph, what will you plot and how will you use the graph to determine the coefficient of kinetic friction μ_k?

(d) Can the normal force ever be
  i. greater than the weight of the body? If so, explain your answer.
  ii. less than the weight of the body? If so, explain your answer.

3. A planetary lander with an initial mass $m = 2.00 \times 10^4$ kg lands on a newly discovered planet whose radius is 1.10 R_E and mass is 0.900 M_E. During the descent to the planet, thrusters provide a constant upward thrust of 1.30×10^5 N over a period of 40.0 s to slow the lander.

(a) Using the information below, plot the data provided and draw a best fit line through the data points on the grid below.

V(m/s)	t(s)	Remarks
–20.0	0	Begin Timing
–16.0	10.0	Altitude H
–12.5	15.0	
–11.0	20.0	
–5.00	30.0	
0	40.0	$h = 0, v = 0$

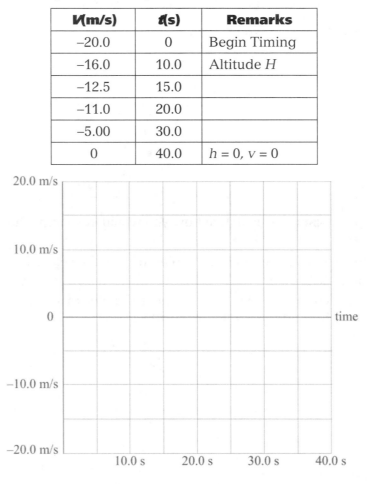

(b) Using the best fit line drawn on the graph, determine the acceleration of the lander during the descent.

(c) i. Explain how you would calculate the height of the lander when the timing begins at time $t = 0$ seconds.
  ii. Explain how you would calculate the height of the lander when it is at altitude H when $t = 10.0$ s.

(d) Explain how you would determine the weight of the lander when it reached the surface of the planet.

4. Students added weights to an elastic strap and measured the elongation after each addition of weight. When they unloaded the weights they obtained additional values for elongation. Their data is shown below for both loading and unloading the elastic strap.

Force (N)	Elongation (m) Loading	Force (N)	Elongation (m) Unloading
1.00	0.015	22.0	0.180
3.00	0.325	19.0	0.155
6.00	0.475	15.0	0.133
9.75	0.680	9.75	0.105
16.5	0.105	4.50	0.078
20.2	0.128	1.50	0.063
21.5	0.148	0.500	0.033
22.0	0.180		

(a) Plot the data on the grid below using dots ● for loading and ▲ for unloading.

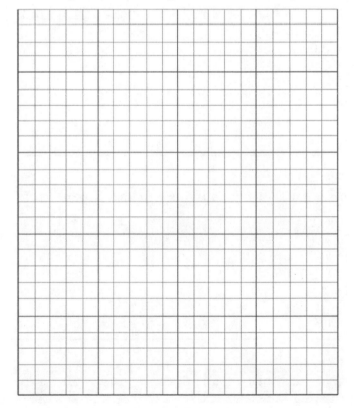

(b) Is the elastic strap a Hookean material? Explain your reasoning.
(c) i. What is the approximate area bounded by the loading and unloading readings?
   ii. What does this tell you about the work done?

GO ON TO NEXT PAGE

5. Two waves pulses approach each other as shown at time $t = 0$.

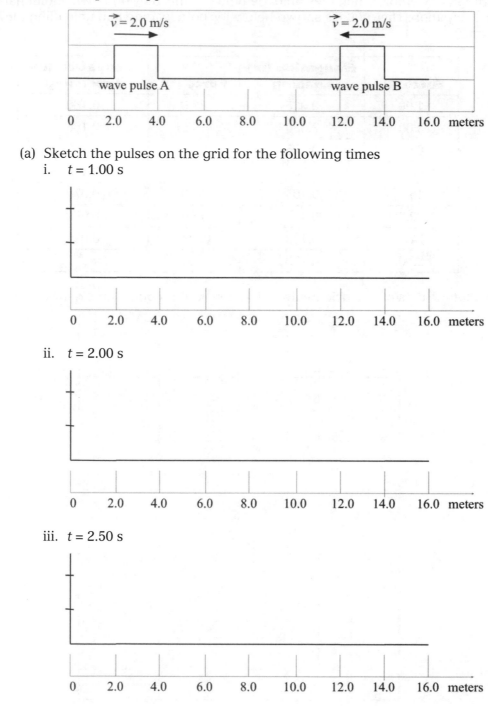

(a) Sketch the pulses on the grid for the following times
   i. $t = 1.00$ s

   ii. $t = 2.00$ s

   iii. $t = 2.50$ s

iv. $t = 3.00$ s

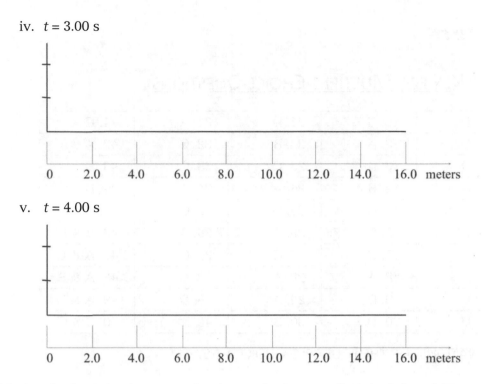

| | | | | | | | | |
| 0 | 2.0 | 4.0 | 6.0 | 8.0 | 10.0 | 12.0 | 14.0 | 16.0 meters |

v. $t = 4.00$ s

| | | | | | | | | |
| 0 | 2.0 | 4.0 | 6.0 | 8.0 | 10.0 | 12.0 | 14.0 | 16.0 meters |

(b) A pulse is set up in a rope that is attached to a wall on its left end. The pulse approaches the barrier as shown.

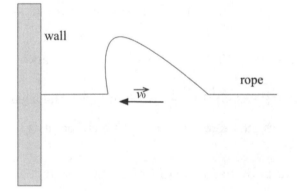

Draw the reflected pulse and describe any changes to the wave upon reflection.

END OF EXAMINATION

Answers

ANSWER KEY FOR MULTIPLE-CHOICE QUESTIONS

1. D	11. C	21. D	31. A	41. C
2. B	12. A	22. B	32. C	42. A
3. D	13. B	23. C	33. C	43. D
4. C	14. B	24. A	34. A	44. D
5. C	15. B	25. D	35. C	45. A
6. B	16. B	26. A	36. B	46. B & D
7. C	17. C	27. C	37. C	47. A & C
8. A	18. A	28. A	38. D	48. A & B
9. B	19. D	29. A	39. D	49. A & D
10. D	20. D	30. B	40. A	50. B & C

EXPLANATIONS FOR THE MULTIPLE-CHOICE ANSWERS

1. **D** The displacement of the car during the time shown on the graph is the area under the curve. There are 4 areas on the graph.

$$A_1 = \frac{1}{2}(4.0 \text{ s})\left(10.0 \text{ } \frac{m}{s}\right) = 20 \text{ m}. \quad A_2 (8.0 \text{ s} - 4.0 \text{ s})\left(10.0 \text{ } \frac{m}{s}\right) = 40 \text{ m}$$

$$A_3 = \frac{1}{2}(8.0 \text{ s} - 4.0 \text{ s})\left(15.0 \text{ } \frac{m}{s} - 10.0 \text{ } \frac{m}{s}\right) = 10 \text{ m} \quad \text{and} \quad \text{the} \quad \text{last}$$

area $A_4 = (12.0 \text{ s} - 8.0 \text{ s})\left(15.0 \text{ } \frac{m}{s}\right) = 60 \text{ m}$. The total area is 130 m.

(*College Physics* 9th ed. pages 41–42/10th ed. pages 43–44)
(L.O. 3.A.1.1)

2. **B** The 2.00 kg body has a weight given by $\vec{F}_g = m\vec{g}$. The weight of the 2.00 kg body is 19.6 N. Because the stationary body $\Sigma\vec{F} = 0$ is supported by two identical vertical cables, the tension in the cables is the same, 9.80 N.
(*College Physics* 9th ed. pages 88–89, 93, 99–100/10th ed. pages 90–91, 95, 101–102)
(L.O. 2.B.1.1, 3.A.3.1)

3. **D** The force acts on the two blocks giving them the same acceleration.

$$\Sigma\vec{F} = (m_1 + m_2)\vec{a}. \text{ The acceleration is } \vec{a} = \frac{20.0 \text{ N}}{10.0 \text{ kg}} = 2.00 \text{ } \frac{m}{s^2}.$$

The force accelerating the 6.00 kg block is $\vec{F} = (6.00 \text{ kg})\left(2.00 \text{ } \frac{m}{s^2}\right) = 12.0 \text{ N}$.

The reaction force the 4.00 kg block exerts on the 6.00 kg body is $20.0\,\text{N} - 12.0\,\text{N} = 8.00\,\text{N}$. The reaction force the 6.00 kg body exerts on the 4.00 kg body is 8.00 N.
(*College Physics* 9th ed. pages 95–97, 109–111/10th ed. pages 97–99, 111–112)
(L.O. 3.A.1.1, 3.A.4.1, 3.A.4.1)

4. **C** There are three forces acting on the center-of-mass of the basketball: the tension, the weight of the basketball and the resistive force of air resistance. The resistive force is tangent to the motion of the center-of-mass of the basketball.
(*College Physics* 9th ed. pages 88–90, 99–100/10th ed. pages 90–92, 101–102)
(L.O. 3.B.2.1)

5. **C** They are in the same gravitational field, therefore the gravitational force acting on them is the same. In the absence of air resistance, the gravitational potential energy mgh is converted into kinetic energy $K = \frac{1}{2}mv^2$. Then, since $mgh = \frac{1}{2}mv^2$, they hit the ground with the same velocity. The smaller body has the smaller kinetic energy since $K = \frac{1}{2}mv^2$.
(*College Physics* 9th ed. pages 43, 134–135/10th ed. pages, 45, 135–136)
(L.O. 3.A.1.1, 4.C.1.1)

6. **B** The weight $\vec{F}_g = m\vec{g}$ is 49.0 N in the vertical direction. It exerts a force of 49.0 N on the rope supporting it. Interactions between adjacent particles in the rope produce action-reaction pairs of 49.0 N before finally reaching the knot. The downward force at the knot of 49.0 N is resolved into components acting in the x and y direction in the cables $\vec{T}_1$ and $\vec{T}_2$.

There are two possible ways for determining the tension $\vec{T}_1$. Both involve the $\Sigma\vec{F}_y = 0$. $\vec{T}_2 \sin 40° = 49.0\,\text{N}$. Then $\vec{T}_2 = 76.2\,\text{N}$.

$\Sigma\vec{F}_x = 0$ results in finding $\vec{T}_1$.

$$\vec{T}_1 = \vec{T}_2 \cos 40° = (76.2\,\text{N})(\cos 40°) = 58.4\,\text{N}$$

The second solution is determined from $\tan 40° = \dfrac{\vec{T}_{2_y}}{\vec{T}_{2_x}}$. This will give $\vec{T}_{2_x}$.
(*College Physics* 9th ed. pages 93, 99–100/10th ed. pages 95, 101–102)
(L.O. 3.A.4.2, 3.A.4.3)

7. **C** As seen in the diagram, the waves are 90° out of phase, with the same frequency and wavelength. Since they are traveling in the same medium, the speed of the wave will not change. The superimposed waveform will vary in amplitude only.
(*College Physics* 9th ed. pages 461–463/10th ed. pages 470–472)
(L.O. 1.A.5.1, 6.D.1.1)

8. **A** The only charge that can move on the surface of the conductor, inner and outer radii, is the negative charge which will move toward the inner radius, attracted to the ++3Q charge at the center. Thus the charge on the outer surface is + +3Q. Electrostatic charge comes in discrete amounts of charge $\pm e,\ \pm 2e,\ \pm 3e \cdots$ which eliminates answers C and D.
    (*College Physics* 9th ed. pages 514–516/10th ed. pages 524–526)
    (L.O. 1.B.1.1, 1.B.1.2, 1.B.3.1)

9. **B** The work done on the blocks is equal to the change in the kinetic energy $\left(\vec{F}\cos\theta \right)\vec{x} = \frac{1}{2}m\left(\vec{v}_f - \vec{v}_0 \right)$. The blocks move in the positive x direction and at the end of the displacement the blocks have some final velocity $\vec{v}$. In figure A, the force does no work since it is $\perp$ to the displacement, $\cos 90° = 0$. In D, the force is opposite to the displacement and there is a reduction in the kinetic energy, since the work is negative and the velocity will be reduced. Since the force in B is applied at an angle θ, the force acting in the direction of the displacement will be smaller than the force applied in C.
    (*College Physics* 9th ed. pages 126, 129–131/10th ed. pages 129, 132–134)
    (L.O. 3.E.1.1)

10. **D** Since the slope of the linear velocity-time graph is negative, the acceleration is constant and negative. The graph of the velocity vs time has some initial positive value. Thus the displacement is parabolic, opening downward.
    (*College Physics* 9th ed. pages 30–31, 34–35, 37/10th ed. pages 31, 33, 36, and 38)
    (L.O. 4.A.2.1)

11. **C** By Newton's third law, for each action there is an equal but opposite reaction. Because we are told Earth pulls on the book, the reaction is the book pulling on the Earth.
    (*College Physics* 9th ed. pages 95–98/10th ed. pages 97–99)
    (L.O. 3.A.4.2)

12. **A** The correct free-body diagram for the forces acting on the 10.0 kg block indicates that the normal force, which is the reaction force exerted on the block from the surface, is in response to the downward force of the block and the surface. Since no other forces are exerted in the y-direction, the arrows representing the normal and the weight are equal in length. The block is accelerated to the right by the weight hanging from a cord passing over the pulley, and because it is accelerating, the tension in the rope is larger than the frictional force.
    (*College Physics* 9th ed. page 89–93, 95–97, 105–107, 109–111)/10th ed. pages 91–95, 97–99, 108–110, 111–113)
    (L.O. 3.A.4.3)

13. **B** The force acts on the center-of-mass of the two bodies in contact, increasing the velocity, since a component of the force and the displacement are in the same direction. Increasing the velocity increases the kinetic energy.
(*College Physics* 9th ed. pages 129–131, 241–244/10th ed. pages 132–134, 246–249)
(L.O. 4.C.2.2)

14. **B** Newton's second law applies. A net force applied to the total mass will produce an acceleration. $\Sigma\vec{F} = (m_1 + m_2 + m_3)\vec{a}$. The acceleration is $\dfrac{30.0 \text{ N}}{15.0 \text{ kg}} = 2.00 \dfrac{\text{m}}{\text{s}^2}$. Because the acceleration of all the cars is the same, the tension in the rope connecting cars A and B is $\Sigma\vec{F} = (5.00 \text{ kg})\left(2.00 \dfrac{\text{m}}{\text{s}^2}\right) = 10.0 \text{ N}$.
(*College Physics* 9th ed. pages 109–111/10th ed. pages 111–113)
(L.O. 3.A.3.1, 3.B.1.4)

15. **B** The normal force is determined by writing $\Sigma\vec{F}_y = 0$.
$\vec{N} - 100 \text{ N} + 20 \text{ N} = 0$.
The normal force is 80.0 N.
(*College Physics* 9th ed. pages 95–97, 99–100/10th ed. pages 97–99, 101–102)
(L.O. 3.A.4.1)

16. **B** In a perfectly inelastic (sticking) collision, the bodies move away with a common velocity since they form a composite mass. The equation for conservation of momentum for this question is $m_1 v_1 + m_2 v_2 = (m_1 + m_2)V$. Substitution into the equation is $(3.00 \text{ kg})\left(4.00 \text{ m}/\text{s}\right) - (1.00 \text{ kg})\left(2.00 \text{ m}/\text{s}\right) = (3.00 \text{ kg} + 1.00 \text{ kg})V$.
The final velocity is 2.50 m/s.
(*College Physics* 9th ed. pages 176–177/10th ed. pages 180–181)
(L.O. 5.D.2.5)

17. **C** Statement I is true because the question states the elevator car is rising with a constant velocity and is therefore not accelerating since $\vec{a} = \dfrac{\Delta\vec{v}}{\Delta t}$; thus statement IV is true. Statement II must be correct since the kinetic energy $K = \dfrac{1}{2}mv^2$ is dependent on the velocity that is not changing. As the elevator rises, the height increases, thus the potential energy increases, and the sum of the kinetic and gravitational potential energy must increase. Therefore statements III and V are not true.
(*College Physics* 9th ed. pages 99–101,135–138/10th ed. pages 101–104, 138–141)
(L.O. 3.A.1.1, 3.E.1.1, 4.A.2.1, 4.C.1.2)

18. **A** Conservation of momentum for this question gives $m_{\text{bullet}} V_{0_{\text{bullet}}} = m_{\text{bullet}} V_{f_{\text{bullet}}} + M_{\text{block}} V_{\text{block}}$. Substitution into the equation is $(0.050 \text{ kg})\left(400 \; \dfrac{\text{m}}{\text{s}}\right) = (0.050 \text{ kg})\left(200 \; \dfrac{\text{m}}{\text{s}}\right) + (5.00 \text{ kg})v$.

The velocity of the block is $\dfrac{10.0 \; \dfrac{\text{kg} \cdot \text{m}}{\text{s}}}{5.00 \text{ kg}} = 2.0 \; \dfrac{\text{m}}{\text{s}}$.

(*College Physics* 9th ed. pages 175–181/10th ed. pages 179–185)
(L.O. 5.A.2.1)

19. **D** The physics student is approaching the stationary source, so the frequency of the perceived sound will increase.
(*College Physics* 9th ed. pages 482–487/10th ed. pages 491–496)
(L.O. 6.B.5.1)

20. **D** The balance will measure the inertial mass of the body and thus will read the same on the ground floor and the 100th floor. The spring scale measures the gravitational mass and as the elevation in the building increases, the value for gravitational acceleration will decrease and the spring scale will give a different reading.
(*College Physics* 9th ed. pages 92–93, 214–217/10th ed. pages 95–96, 219–222)
(L.O. 1.C.3.1)

21. **D** The mass swings in a vertical circle with gravitational potential energy at the point of release converted into kinetic energy at the lowest point of the vertical circle. $\Delta U = \Delta K$. The velocity of the 1.00 kg mass is found by substitution into $mgh = \dfrac{1}{2}mv^2$. The velocity is $v = \sqrt{2\left(9.80 \; \dfrac{\text{m}}{\text{s}^2}\right)(1.20 \text{ m})} = 4.85 \; \dfrac{\text{m}}{\text{s}}$. The moment of Inertia of the 1.00 kg mass is given as $I = mr^2$, and the angular momentum gain is $\Delta \vec{L} = I \Delta \vec{\omega}$. The angular momentum is rewritten as $\Delta \vec{L} = mr^2 \dfrac{\vec{v}}{r} = m\vec{v}r = 1.00 \text{ kg} \left(4.85 \; \dfrac{\text{m}}{\text{s}}\right)(1.20 \text{ m}) = 5.82 \; \dfrac{\text{kg} \cdot \text{m}^2}{\text{s}}$.
(*College Physics* 9th ed. pages 135–138, 257–259/10th ed. pages 136–138, 262–265)
(L.O. 5.B.4.2, 5.E.1.1, 5.E.1.2)

22. **B** The mass of the second piece is $m - \dfrac{m}{3} = \dfrac{2}{3}m$. Conservation of momentum applies after the mass breaks up into two separate pieces.

$$m\left(10.0 \; \text{m}/\text{s}\right) = \dfrac{m}{3}\left(20.0 \; \text{m}/\text{s}\right) + \dfrac{2}{3}mv$$

$$\left(10.0 \; \text{m}/\text{s}\right) = \dfrac{1}{3}\left(20.0 \; \text{m}/\text{s}\right) + \dfrac{2}{3}v \text{ then } 3.33 \; \text{m}/\text{s} = \dfrac{2}{3}v$$

The velocity of the second piece is $5.00 \; \text{m}/\text{s}$.

(*College Physics* 9th ed. pages 172–175/10th ed. pages 176–179)
(L.O. 5.A.2.1)

23. **C** The Conservation of Energy applies to this problem since there is no friction between the blocks and the inclines. $mgh_i + \frac{1}{2}mv_i^2 = mgh_f + \frac{1}{2}mv_f^2$. The initial kinetic energy is zero as is the final gravitational potential energy (using the bottom of the inclines as the reference point for the gravitational potential energy). The three blocks reach the bottom of the inclines with the same speeds since the inclines have the same height.
(*College Physics* 9th ed. pages 135–138/10th ed. pages 141–143)
(L.O. 4.C.1.1)

24. **A** As the blocks move down the incline an identical frictional force acts. The work due to friction is negative because the force and the displacement are anti-parallel. Work of friction is dependent on path. The distance along incline L_3 is the greatest and along L_1 the least. Therefore the ranking for the speed at the bottom of the ramp is $v_1 > v_2 > v_3$. (The frictional force will reduce the kinetic energy in the system converting it into some other form internal energy, such as thermal energy or sound.)
(*College Physics* 9th ed. pages 138–140/10th ed. pages 141–143)
(L.O. 4.C.1.2)

25. **D** The solution is found by using the Work–Kinetic Energy Theorem.

$$W = \text{area under the curve} = \Delta K \text{ and } \frac{1}{2}\text{base} \times \text{altitude} = \frac{1}{2}mv^2.$$

Solving for v gives $v = \sqrt{\dfrac{(0.200 \text{ m})(8.00 \text{ N})}{(0.100 \text{ kg})}} = 4.00 \text{ m/s}.$

(*College Physics* 9th ed. pages 152–154/10th ed. pages 155–157)
(L.O. 5.B.5.3)

26. **A** The 100 kg body is lifted a distance of $R_E + 1.5R_E$ from the center of the Earth.

The acceleration due to gravity at that location is found from $\vec{g} = G\dfrac{M_E}{\left(R_E + 1.5R_E\right)^2}$. A ratio for the acceleration can be written as

$$\frac{\vec{g}_{\text{surface}}}{\vec{g}_{\text{altitude}}} = \frac{\left(R_E + 1.5R_E\right)^2}{R_E^2} = 6.25 . \ \vec{g}_{\text{saltitude}} = \frac{\vec{g}_{\text{surface}}}{6.25} = 1.57 \ \frac{\text{m}}{\text{s}^2} \ 45 \text{ N}$$

At that altitude, the 100 kg body has a weight $\vec{F}_g = m\vec{g}$ equal to 157 N.
(*College Physics* 9th ed. pages, 92–93, 214–217/10th ed. pages 95–96, 219–222)
(L.O. 2.B.1.1, 2.   B.2.1)

27. **C** The net forces are applied to the blocks for the same amount of time. The larger the impulse applied to the blocks, $\vec{F}\Delta t = \Delta \vec{p}$, the larger the change in momentum. The net force applied to block A is 100 N – 5 N = 95 N. The net force applied to block D is 100 N – 10

$N = 90$ N. The net force of B is 50 N – 5 N = 45 N and finally the net force on C is 50 N – 10 N = 40 N.
(*College Physics* 9th ed. pages 167–169/10th ed. pages 170–172)
(L.O. 4.B.2.1)

28. **A** The change in momentum is the area under the force vs. time graph. Since the variable force is always positive, there is an increase in momentum.
(*College Physics* 9th ed. pages 167–169/10th ed. pages 170–172)
(L.O. 4.B.2.2)

29. **A** $W = Fx \cos\theta$. The work done by the gravitational force on the body is negative since the force is opposite to the vertical displacement of the body. The gravitational force does no work as the body is moved horizontally since the angle between the force and the displacement is 90°.
(*College Physics* 9th ed. pages 124–126/10th ed. pages 128–130)
(L.O. 4.C.1.1)

30. **B** Conservation of momentum applies. Since the 2.00 kg body is initially at rest, the equation is $m\left(0.300 \ \text{m}/\text{s}\right) = (2.00 \ \text{kg})$ $\left(0.200 \ \text{m}/\text{s}\right) - m\left(0.100 \ \text{m}/\text{s}\right)$ because the unknown mass moves to the left after the collision. The unknown mass is then found as $m\left(0.400 \ \text{m}/\text{s}\right) = 0.400 \ \text{kg} \cdot \text{m}/\text{s}$. The unknown mass is 1.00 kg.
(*College Physics* 9th ed. pages 175–176, 179–180/10th ed. pages 176–177, 183–184)
(L.O. 5.D.1.3)

31. **A** The amplitude of the wave is the maximum displacement of the vibrating particles on the wave form from the equilibrium position. The amplitude of the wave from the graph is 0.08 m.
(*College Physics* 9th ed. pages 458–459/10th ed. pages 466–467)
(L.O. 6.A.3.1)

32. **C** The wavelength is the distance from a point on a wave to the next point that has the same amplitude and the same phase. (Moving in the same direction.)
(*College Physics* 9th ed. pages 458–459/10th ed. pages 466–467)
(L.O. 6.B.2.1)

33. **C** Superposition applies. The pulses approach each other and as they pass through each other at point P, their amplitudes add constructively.
(*College Physics* 9th ed. pages 461–463/10th ed. pages 470–472)
(L.O. 6.D.1.1)

34. **A** Angular momentum is conserved. $I_o \omega_o = \dfrac{I_o}{2} \omega_{\text{input pulley}}$. Thus the angular velocity of the input pulley must be equal to twice the velocity of the output pulley. $I_o \omega_o = \dfrac{I_o}{2}(2\omega_o)$.
(*College Physics* 9th ed. page 257–279/10th ed. pages 262–265)
(L.O. 4.D.3.1)

35. **C** The net torque applied to the cylinder acts to cause clockwise angular acceleration. The cylinder will decrease its speed in the counterclockwise direction, stop momentarily, and reverses it direction of rotation, moving clockwise.
(*College Physics* 9th ed. pages 236–239/10th ed. pages 241–244)
(L.O. 4.D.1.1)

36. **B** Conservation of angular momentum applies.
$$\left(I_{merry-go-round} + I_{0\ student}\right)\omega_0 = \left(I_{merry-go-round} + I_{f\ student}\right)\omega_f$$

$$\left(800\ kg \cdot m^2 + (50\ kg)(2.00\ m)^2\right)\left(1.50\ \frac{rad}{s}\right)$$
$$= \left(800\ kg \cdot m^2 + (50\ kg)(1.00\ m)^2\right)\omega_f$$

$$\left(1000\ kg \cdot m^2\right)\left(1.50\ \frac{rad}{s}\right) = \left(850\ kg \cdot m^2\right)\omega_f.$$

The final angular velocity is 1.76 $\frac{rad}{s}$.
(*College Physics* 9th ed. pages 257–260/10th ed. pages 262–266)
(L.O. 5.E.1.2)

37. **C** The change in the angular momentum is the area under the torque vs. time graph.
$$\Sigma\vec{\tau} = \frac{\Delta\vec{L}}{\Delta t}.$$
The area is
$$\frac{1}{2}(4.00\ N \cdot m)(1.00\ s) + (4.00\ N \cdot m)(1.00\ s) + \frac{1}{2}(4.00\ N \cdot m)(2.00\ s)$$
$$= 10.0\ N \cdot m \cdot s$$
(*College Physics* 9th ed. pages 257–259/10th ed. pages 262–265)
(L.O. 4.D.3.1)

38. **D** $\vec{F}\Delta t = m\Delta\vec{v}$. The tennis racket changes the direction of the momentum of the ball. The time of the impulse is increased, which reduces the force needed to maintain the magnitude of the momentum and change its direction.
(*College Physics* 9th ed. pages 167–169/10th ed. pages 170–172)
(L.O. 3.D.2.2)

39. **D** The standing wave in the wire has 3 nodes and two antinodes. Since the end points of a standing wave in a wire must be nodes, the wavelength is 1.80 m. The velocity of the wave in the wire is given by $v = \lambda f$. $v = (120\ Hz)(1.80\ m) = 216\ \frac{m}{s}$.
(*College Physics* 9th ed. pages 458, 489–493/10th ed. pages 467, 498–503)
(L.O. 6.D.4.2)

40. **A** Kirchhoff's junction rule applies. 0.300 A enters the junction and divides with R_2, being half as large as R_3 and getting twice the current as R_3 0.30 A.
(*College Physics* 9th ed. pages 617–627/10th ed. pages 628–638)
(L.O. 5.C.3.1)

41. **C** The charging wand is not in contact with the isolated sphere and charge cannot be transferred. The sphere cannot gain charge from the ground since it is isolated. The side of the sphere closest to the positive charging wand will be negative because the negative charge will move to the side of the sphere closest to the charging wand. (The only charge that can move on the sphere is the negative charge.)
(*College Physics* 9th ed. pages 513–515/10th ed. pages 523–527)
(L.O. 1.B.2.1)

42. **A** The electrical force acting between the two charges is found from $\left|\vec{F}_E\right| = \dfrac{kq_1q_2}{r^2}$.

Substitution gives

$$\left|\vec{F}_E\right| = \frac{\left(9 \times 10^9 \ \text{N} \cdot \text{m}^2\!/_{\text{C}^2}\right)\left(6.50 \times 10^{-6} \ \text{C}\right)\left(8.10 \times 10^{-6} \ \text{C}\right)}{(0.100 \ \text{m})^2}.$$

The magnitude of the force is $47.4 \ \text{N}$. Since the charges are $q_1 = +6.50 \ \mu\text{C}$ and $q_2 = -8.1 \ \mu\text{C}$, the force is attractive.
(*College Physics* 9th ed. pages 517–519/10th ed. pages 527–530)
(L.O. 3.C.2.1)

43. **D** The circuit is a simple series circuit. The total resistance in the circuit is $15.0 \ \Omega + 13.0 \ \Omega + 32.0 \ \Omega = 60.0 \ \Omega$. The current in the circuit from Ohm's law is $I = \dfrac{9.00 \ \text{V}}{60.0 \ \Omega} = 0.150 \ \text{A}$. Kirchhoff's junction rule will show the current in all three resistors is the same.
(*College Physics* 9th ed. pages 617–620, 625–627/10th ed. pages 628–630, 636–638)
(L.O. 5.C.3.1, 5.C.3.3)

44. **D** The charges $q_1 = 5.00 \ \mu\text{C}$ and $q_2 = -15.00 \ \mu\text{C}$ initially attract each other. When they touch, charge will move from q_2 to q_1. The net charge will be $-10.00 \ \mu\text{C}$ and will redistribute until both spheres have the same charge of $-5.00 \ \mu\text{C}$ and the force will therefore be repulsive. Since the product of the charges $q_1 \times q_2$ has been reduced by $\dfrac{1}{3}$, the force between them will be reduced by $\dfrac{1}{3}$.
(*College Physics* 9th ed. pages 514–515, 517–519/10th ed. pages 524–525, 527–530)
(L.O. 1.B.1.1, 1.B.1.2, 3.C.2.1)

45. **A** The net resistance in the first arrangement is larger than in the second arrangement. Therefore the total current is larger in the second configuration. The $4.0 \ \Omega$ resistor in the lower branch will receive the most current since it is in the branch with the least resistance.
(*College Physics* 9th ed. pages 617–627/10th ed. pages 628–638)
(L.O. 5.C.3.1)

46. **B** and **D** Newton's second law applies. A general equation for motion down the plane where there is no other force acting on the body is $m\vec{g}\sin\theta - \mu_k mg\cos\theta = ma$. Whether there is a frictional force or not, changing the mass of the body will not change the acceleration. Increasing the angle will increase the effective force down the plane $m\vec{g}\sin\theta$ and decrease the normal to the surface, decreasing the frictional force if a frictional force exists between the body and the surface of the plane on the body.
(*College Physics* 9th ed. pages 90, 101–107/10th ed. 92, 104–109)
(L.O. 2.B.1.1, 3.A.1.1)

47. **A** and **C** The speed of the constant motion cart can be determined from $V_{avg} = \dfrac{\Delta x}{\Delta t}$.

The acceleration of the glider can be determined by $v_f^2 = v_0^2 + 2ax$ from the tilted airtrack by solving. Starting from rest, the glider moves on the marked airtrack a given distance. The photogate will permit them to determine the final velocity.
(*College Physics* 9th ed. pages 27–29, 36–38/10th ed. pages 29, 38–40)
(L.O. 3.A.1.2)

48. **A** and **B** In order for an object to be in static equilibrium it must be in translational and rotational equilibrium. Thus $\Sigma\vec{\tau} = 0$ and $\Sigma\vec{F} = 0$ both apply.
(*College Physics* 9th ed. pages 88–89, 99–100, 240, 244–247/10th ed. pages 90–91, 101–103, 245, 249–252)
(L.O. 3.A.3.1, 3.F.1.1, 3.F.1.2)

49. **A** and **D** When the body is in equilibrium, either stationary or moving at a constant speed, the net force acting on it is $\Sigma\vec{F}_y = 0$. There is no acceleration. The slope of the distance-time graph gives velocity. The slope of graph I, $x = f(t)$ is constant and thus the velocity is constant. Graph IV, $v = f(t)$ is constant and has a slope of zero–no acceleration.
(*College Physics* 9th ed., pages 30–31, 34–35, 99–100/10th ed. pages 35–36, 101–103)
(L.O. 3.A.1.1, 4.A.2.1)

50. **B** and **C** The elevator is rising with constant speed, thus its kinetic energy is constant. It is increasing its height in a gravitational field, thus increasing its gravitational potential energy. There is no acceleration on the elevator car since it is rising at a constant speed and that means the force acting on the elevator car is constant.
(*College Physics* 9th ed. pages 36–37, 88–89, 99–100/10th ed. pages 33, 38, 90–91, 101–103)
(L.O. 3.A.1.1, 2.A.3.1, 4.C.1.2, 5.B.4.1)

ANSWERS TO FREE-RESPONSE QUESTIONS

QUESTION 1

(a) Conservation of energy will apply to the problem. The initial energy in the problem is only gravitational potential energy since the sphere is at rest at the top of the ramp. At the bottom of the ramp the energy is only kinetic if we consider the bottom of the ramp is the reference point for the initial gravitational potential energy. Since the sphere rolls without slipping down the ramp, the kinetic energy is both rotational and translational. The moment of inertia of the sphere is given and will be substituted for the moment of inertia I in the rotational kinetic energy equation. The angular velocity of the sphere divided by the radius will give the tangential velocity of the sphere. This will be substituted for ω in the rotational kinetic energy equation. All terms of the energy transformation equation contain the mass of the sphere and both terms for the kinetic energy contain the linear velocity. Elimination of the mass will give the solution for the velocity in terms of the height of the ramp and the acceleration due to gravity. **(4 points)**

(b) The conservation of energy equation pertaining to this situation may be written as $mgh = \frac{1}{2}mv^2 + \frac{1}{2}I\omega^2$. Substitution as above is

$$mgh = \frac{1}{2}mv^2 + \frac{1}{2}\left(\frac{2}{5}mr^2\right)\left(\frac{v}{r}\right)^2$$

The velocity is

$$v = \sqrt{\frac{10}{7}gh} \, .$$

$$v = \sqrt{\frac{10}{7}\left(9.80 \, \frac{\text{m}}{\text{s}^2}\right)(0.300 \text{ m})}$$

The velocity of m_1 as $v = \mathbf{2.05 \, \frac{m}{s}}$ **(3 points)**

(c) $\vec{P}_x = m_1 v_1 \cos\theta_1 + m_2 v_2 \cos\theta_2$. Because the each spheres has the same mass the substitution into the equation reduces to

$$2.05 \, \frac{\text{m}}{\text{s}} = 1.78 \, \frac{\text{m}}{\text{s}}\cos 30° + v_2 \cos 60°$$ **(3 points)**

$$v_2 = 0.96 \, \frac{\text{m}}{\text{s}}$$

(d) Both spheres start at rest in the vertical direction and drop the same distance to the floor. Therefore their time of flight is the same. The horizontal displacement is the product of the horizontal velocity multiplied by the time. Sphere m_1 has the larger horizontal velocity and therefore will land further from the base of the table.

(2 points)

(*College Physics* 9th ed. pages 63–67, 175–183, 203–204, 254–255/10th ed. pages 65–68, 179–185, 208–210, 259–261)

(L.O. 3.A.1.1, 4.C.1.1, 5.B.4.2, 5.D.1.5)

QUESTION 2

(a) The schematic for the block on the friction board is shown.
(1 point)

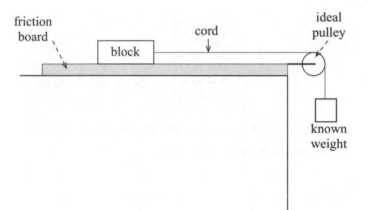

Record the mass of the block in kilograms. Convert the mass to weight in newtons by multiplying the mass by the acceleration due to gravity $\vec{W} = m\vec{g}$.

With the friction board horizontal, place the block at the far end of the board and pass a string from the block over the pulley to a mass hanger, making sure that the string is horizontal.

Adjust the load on the mass hanger so that the block will move at a constant speed after the block is started. Record the total mass, the mass hanger plus the load on the hanger. Convert this mass into newtons by using $\vec{W} = m\vec{g}$. Repeat the procedure at least three times and record the average frictional force.

Add masses to the block on the friction board. Added mass will increase the normal force acting on the block. Again adjust the load on the mass hanger so that the block will move at a constant speed after the block is started. Record the total mass, the mass hanger plus the load on the hanger. Convert this mass into newtons by using $\vec{W} = m\vec{g}$. Repeat the procedure at least three times and record the average frictional force.

Repeat the above procedure by increasing the mass on the friction block until you have several additional readings. **(3 points)**

(b) The measurements taken will be the mass added to the block plus the mass of the block and the mass on the cord connected to the weight hanger that passes over the pulley. These will be converted into newtons using $\vec{F}_g = m\vec{g}$ and will be used to plot the graph in Part (c). **(1 point)**

(c) The graph plotted will be the frictional force supplied by the force on the cord passing over the pulley vs. the normal force on the block from the surface. The slope of the line will give the coefficient of kinetic friction μ_k. **(2 points)**

(d) i.   The normal force can be greater than the weight of the body when a force acting at an angle below the horizontal is exerted on the body.

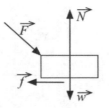

The equation for translational equilibrium in the y direction for a body moving horizontally is $\Sigma \vec{F}_y = \vec{N} - F_{applied}(\sin\theta) - W = 0$.

(2 points)

ii.   Two cases are common where the normal is less than the weight. The normal force can be less than the weight of the body when a force acting at an angle above the horizontal is exerted on the body. The equation for translational equilibrium in the y direction for a body moving horizontally is $\Sigma \vec{F}_y = \vec{N} + F_{applied}(\sin\theta) - W = 0$. **(2points)**

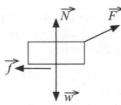

A body on an inclined plane moving under the action of forces applied parallel to the plane gives the equation for translational equilibrium in the y direction for a body moving parallel to the plane as $\Sigma \vec{F}_y = \vec{N} - W\cos\theta = 0$.

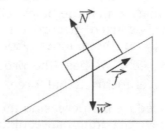

(1point)

(If the force is applied at some angle to a body on an inclined plane, the normal can be larger or smaller depending on how the force is applied. This is beyond the scope of AP Physics 1.)
(*College Physics* 9th ed. pages 95, 97–99/10th edition 95, 97–99, 101–103, 108–110)
(L.O. 2.B.1.1, 3.A.2.1, 3.A.4.1, 3.B.1.2, 3.B.2.1, 3.C.4.2)

QUESTION 3

(a) The correct graph is shown below.

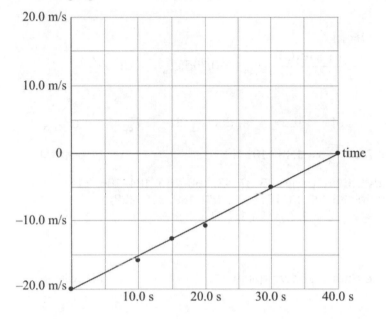

(3 points)

(b) The acceleration of the lander is the slope of the best-fit line. Taking two slope points from the line and not data points, the

$$\text{slope is } \vec{a} = \frac{-2.50\ \frac{m}{s} - \left(-12.5\ \frac{m}{s}\right)}{(35.0\ s - 15.0\ s)} = 0.50\ \frac{m}{s^2}$$

(2 points)

(c) i. The displacement is the area under the velocity-time graph. This will give the height of the lander when the thrusters were fired at $t = 0$ s.

ii. The displacement during the first 10.0 s is the sum of areas under the curve, the rectangular area bounded by the product of 10.0 s and –15.0 m/s as seen from the graph plus ½ of the product of 10.0 s times –5.0 m/s. The height of the lander would then be the displacement of the lander determined from part (c) i.–the displacement found in this part.

Alternate explanation from kinematics equations

Since the slope of the line gives the deceleration of the lander, the displacement for the first 10 s can be calculated either from the final velocity squared minus the initial velocity squared, then dividing that answer by twice the acceleration from the slope of the line. The height can also be determined by multiplying one half the slope of the line by the time squared and the subtraction that number from the product of the initial velocity times the time. In both cases the height H is the difference between the altitude when $t = 0$ and $t = 10$ s.

(1 point for any of the explanations listed)

(d) The acceleration due gravity on the surface of the planet is found from the ratio of the gravitational values between the Earth and the planet.

$$\frac{\vec{g}_{planet}}{\vec{g}_{Earth}} = \frac{(0.90 M_E) / (1.10 R_E)^2}{M_E / R_E^2} \quad \vec{g}_{planet} = 0.75 \vec{g}_{Earth} = 7.29 \ \text{m}/\text{s}^2 .$$

The weight of the lander is $\vec{F}_{\vec{g}_{Planet}} = m \vec{g}_{\ Planet}$

$$(2.00 \times 10^4 \ \text{kg}) \left(7.29 \ \frac{\text{m}}{\text{s}^2} \right) = 1.46 \times 10^5 \ \text{N} \qquad \textbf{(4 points)}$$

(*College Physics* 9th ed. pages 35–37, 42, 168–169, 184–186, 214–217/10th ed. pages 36–38, 43, 171–172, 188–189, 219–222)
(L.O. 2.B.1.1, 3.A.1.1, 3.A.1.3, 3.C.1.1, 3.D.2.2, 4.A.2.1)

QUESTION 4

(a) The graph of the data is shown below. **(4 points)**

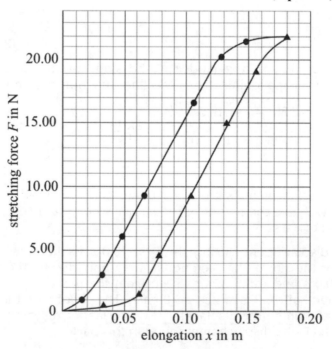

(b) The elastic strap is not a Hookean material. Hooke's law is a linear relationship between the force and the displacement of the material. **(1 point)**

(c) i. Counting blocks bounded by the lines will give an internal energy production of approximately 77 blocks. The area of each block is (1.00 N)(0.100 m) or 0.100 J. Approximately 8 J of energy was produced as internal energy in the stretching and the relaxing of the strap. **(2 points)**

ii. The area bounded by the loading and unloading of the strap represents the energy that was transferred to internal friction as the chemical bonds were stretched in the strap. This energy will leak to the environment as thermal energy. **(2 points)**
(*College Physics* 9th ed. pages 140, 146, 152–154, 437–442/10th ed. pages143, 149, 155–157, 445–450)
(L.O. 4.C.1.2, 5.A.2.1, 5.B.3.1, 5.B.3.3, 5.B.4.1, 5.B.5.3)

QUESTION 5

(a) The pulses shown for the times are

i. time $t = 1.0$ s

ii. time $t = 2.0$ s — the leading edges of the pulses start to move through each other with the same velocity and amplitude as at $t = 1.0$ s.

iii. time $t = 2.5$ s — the pulses have combined constructively giving an amplitude that is twice as great as the amplitude at $t = 1.0$ s and 2.0 s.

iv. time $t = 3.0$ s — the training edges of the pulse start to separate as the pulses move with their initial speeds in their original directions. The amplitude of each pulse is equal to their initial amplitude.

v. time $t = 4.0$ s — The pulses have separated and continue in their original directions with the same speed and the same amplitude. **(5 points)**

(b) The correct reflected pulse is **(1 point)**

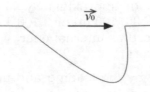

The wave pulse is reflected from a fixed barrier, the wall, and is inverted. It travels with the same speed since the medium (the rope) determines the speed of the pulse or the wave. **(1 point)** (*College Physics* 9th ed. pages 461–463/10th ed. pages 470–472) (L.O. 6.D.1.1, 6.D.2.1)

AP® PHYSICS 2
PRACTICE EXAM C

AP PHYSICS 2
Section I
50 Multiple-Choice Questions
Time–90 Minutes

Note: To simplify calculations, you may use $g = 10 \text{ m/s}^2$ in all problems.

Directions: Each of the questions or incomplete statements below is followed by four suggested answers or completions. Select the one that is best in each case.

1. Blood from a main vein ($r_{vein} = 1.00 \text{ mm}$) enters into ten narrow capillaries. The radius of each capillary is $r_{capillary} = 0.100 \text{ mm}$. The speed of the blood in the vein is 20.0 cm/s.

The speed of the blood in each of the capillaries is

(A) 5.00 cm/s

(B) 20.0 cm/s

(C) 100.0 cm/s

(D) 200 cm/s

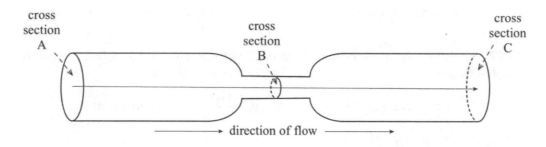

cross section A   cross section B   cross section C

→ direction of flow →

2. An ideal fluid moves smoothly through the tube shown above, moving from point A to point B and then to point C. The cross sectional area of A and C is the same.

Which of the following is the best choice?

(A) The pressure drops as the fluid moves through the tube. The pressure at A is larger than the pressure at B which is larger than the pressure at C.

(B) The pressure at points A and C are the same. The pressure at B is smaller than the pressure at A and C.

(C) The pressure at A is somewhat larger than the pressure at C. Both of the pressures at A and C are larger than the pressure at B.

(D) The pressure at points A, B, and C are the same since the fluid moves smoothly through the tube.

GO ON TO NEXT PAGE

693

3. An atom of $^{239}_{94}\text{Pu}$ undergoes a nuclear fission by a neutron as indicated in the reaction shown below.

$$^{239}_{94}\text{Pu} + ^{1}_{0}\text{n} \rightarrow ^{148}_{56}\text{Ba} + ^{90}_{38}\text{Sr} + ?$$

The missing particle is

(A) $^{2}_{0}\text{n}$

(B) $2\left(^{1}_{0}\text{n}\right)$

(C) $^{2}_{1}\text{H}$

(D) $2\left(^{1}_{1}\text{H}\right)$

4. A sample of an ideal gas undergoes an isothermal compression in a container. As a result there is an increase in the rate at which the molecules collide with the walls of the container going through a change in momentum during the collision. This produces

(A) an increase in the force exerted per unit area on the walls of the container and a corresponding increase in pressure

(B) an increase in the force exerted per unit area on the walls of the container and a corresponding decrease in pressure

(C) a decrease in the force since the time of interaction increases. This causes a drop in pressure

(D) a decrease in the time of interaction causing a corresponding decrease in pressure, since the force is smaller

5. The four spheres shown below are immersed in water. The volume V of each sphere is given.

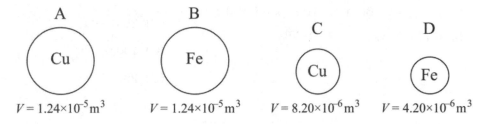

Rank the buoyant force acting on each sphere from the greatest magnitude to the least.

The density of copper is $\rho_{\text{Cu}} = 8.92 \times 10^3 \ \dfrac{\text{kg}}{\text{m}^3}$ and the density of iron is $\rho_{\text{Fe}} = 7.86 \times 10^3 \ \dfrac{\text{kg}}{\text{m}^3}$.

(A) $A > B > C > D$

(B) $A > C > B > D$

(C) $(A = B) > C > D$

(D) $B > A > D > C$

6. A concave mirror with a radius of curvature of 30.0 cm produces an upright image located 40.0 cm behind the mirror. What is the position of the object?
   (A) 10.9 cm
   (B) 12.8 cm
   (C) 17.1 cm
   (D) 21.8 cm

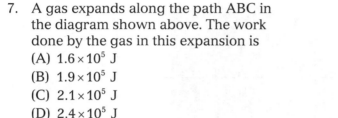

7. A gas expands along the path ABC in the diagram shown above. The work done by the gas in this expansion is
   (A) 1.6×10^5 J
   (B) 1.9×10^5 J
   (C) 2.1×10^5 J
   (D) 2.4×10^5 J

8. Water $\rho = 1000 \ \dfrac{\text{kg}}{\text{m}^3}$ enters the lower end of the tube with a velocity of $2.00 \ \dfrac{\text{m}}{\text{s}}$. With an input pressure at the lower end of the tube of 2.10×10^5 Pa, what is the pressure at the top of the tube?
   (A) 2.10×10^5 Pa
   (B) 1.92×10^5 Pa
   (C) 1.65×10^5 Pa
   (D) 1.47×10^5 Pa

9. Using the diagram below, identify the correct ranking for the electromagnetic waves listed from the longest wavelength to the shortest
   (A) Infrared Radiation > Ultraviolet Radiation > X-rays >Gamma rays
   (B) Ultraviolet radiation > Gamma rays >X-rays >Infrared radiation
   (C) Gamma rays> X-rays > Ultraviolet Radiation >Infrared Radiation
   (D) Ultraviolet radiation > Infrared radiation > Gamma rays >X-rays

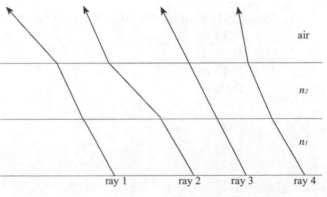

GO ON TO NEXT PAGE

10. Rays of light originate in the lower medium of index of refraction n_1. The rays pass into a medium of index of refraction of n_2 where $n_2 > n_1$ then into air where the index of refraction of air is less than the index of refraction of the other two mediums

$n_{air} < n_1 < n_2$. The ray that shows the correct path is
(A) Path 1
(B) Path 2
(C) Path 3
(D) Path 4

11. When a converging lens is placed in front of an object, its image is formed on the screen on the other side of the lens at a distance that is shown in the figure below.

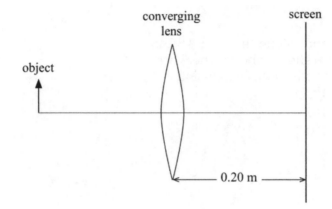

A diverging lens is then placed 0.05 m behind the converging lens. A new image is formed 0.30 m from the diverging lens on the screen as shown.

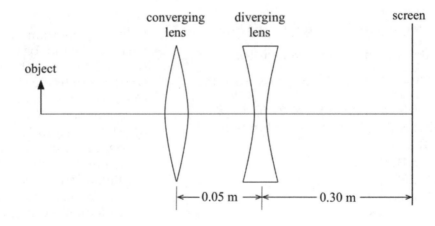

What is the focal length of the diverging lens?
(A) −0.15 m
(B) −0.30 m
(C) −0.45 m
(D) −0.60 m

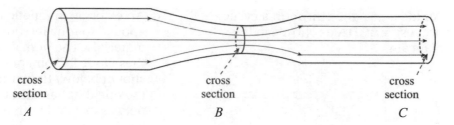

cross section A · cross section B · cross section C

12. The diagram above shows the flow of an ideal non-compressional fluid flowing through a tube of three different cross-sectional areas from the left to right. Which of the following statements concerning the velocity and pressure is correct for the areas shown?

(A) $v_A = v_B = v_c$ and $p_A = p_B = p_C$

(B) $v_A = v_B = v_c$ and $p_A \neq p_B \neq p_C$

(C) $v_A = v_B = v_c$ and $p_A \neq p_B \neq p_C$

(D) $v_A \neq v_B \neq v_c$ and $p_A \neq p_B \neq p_C$

13. A group of students obtained the following set of data from an experiment that was performed by increasing the pressure on a cylinder and recording the volume of the confined gas in the isothermal compression of the gas in the cylinder.

Pressure $(10^5$ Pa$)$	Volume $(10^{-3}$ m$^3)$
1.10	5.00
1.15	4.78
1.20	4.58
1.25	4.40
1.30	4.23
1.40	3.92
1.50	3.67

Which of the following graphs will best illustrate the correct plot of the data above?

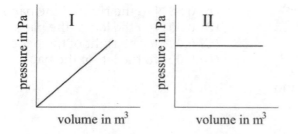

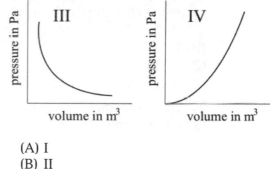

(A) I
(B) II
(C) III
(D) IV

14. A liquid in an insulated container is stirred and undergoes a rise in the temperature. Considering the liquid to be a system, then

(A) the temperature increased because work was done by the system

(B) there was an increase in the internal energy of the system

(C) there was no change in the internal energy of the system

(D) the work done by the system is equal to the work done by the system

GO ON TO NEXT PAGE

15. An ideal gas goes through a cyclic process ABCDA as shown in the diagram.

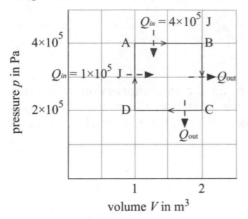

If the thermal energy entering the system along path AB is 5×10^5 J, what is the thermal energy that leaves the system during the cyclic process?
(A) 2×10^5 J
(B) 3×10^5 J
(C) 5×10^5 J
(D) 7×10^5 J

16. Two rays of light in air, red and violet fall on the same side of a glass prism as shown.

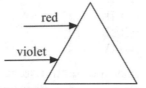

As the rays pass through and emerge from the prism the ray of
(A) red light will bend more than the ray of violet light because the violet light has a longer wavelength and higher frequency
(B) violet light will bend more than the ray of red light because the violet light has the shorter wavelength and higher frequency
(C) red light will bend more than the ray of violet light because the red light has a longer wavelength and higher frequency
(D) red light will bend more than the ray of violet light because the red light has the shorter wavelength and higher frequency

17. An external magnetic field has been applied to four ferromagnetic materials. The domains associated with these four ferromagnetic materials are shown below. Rank the materials for the one that has the strongest magnetic field associated with it to the one that has least magnetic field.

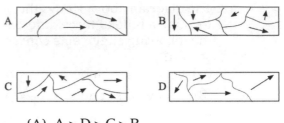

(A) $A > D > C > B$
(B) $A > B > C > D$
(C) $D > (C = B) > A$
(D) $(C = B) > D > A$

18. A wire that is 1.20 m long carrying a current of 5.00 A toward the top of the page is placed in a magnetic field of 0.100 T directed out of the page as shown. The force on the wire is

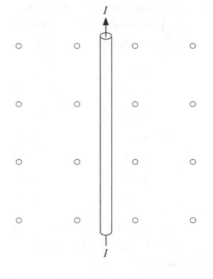

(A) 0.60 N to the right of the page
(B) 0.60 N to the left of the page
(C) 6.0 N to the right of the page
(D) 6.0 N to the left of the page

19. Two wires carry current of $I_1 = 4.0$ A and $I_2 = 8.0$ A. The wire carrying I_1 exerts a force $\left|\vec{F}_{12}\right|$ on the wire carrying current I_2. The wire carrying current I_2 exerts a force $\left|\vec{F}_{21}\right|$ on the wire carrying current I_1.

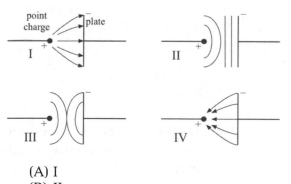

$I_1 = 4$ A $I_2 = 8$ A

The force between the wires is

(A) $\left|\vec{F}_{12}\right| = \left|\vec{F}_{21}\right|$ attractive

(B) $2\left|\vec{F}_{12}\right| = \left|\vec{F}_{21}\right|$ attractive

(C) $\left|\vec{F}_{12}\right| = 2\left|\vec{F}_{21}\right|$ repulsive

(D) $\left|\vec{F}_{12}\right| = \left|\vec{F}_{21}\right|$ repulsive

20. A positive point charge is located to the left of a plate containing negative charge as illustrated in the four diagrams below. Which one of the diagrams best indicates the electric field between the positive point charge and the negative plate?

point charge — plate

I

II

III

IV

(A) I
(B) II
(C) III
(D) IV

21. The gases in two containers A and B have the same volume and the same pressure. Container A has half the number of molecules as container B. Which of the following choices is the best answer?

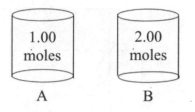

1.00 moles   2.00 moles

A   B

(A) The molecules in container A have a lower rms (root-mean-squared) speed than the molecules in container B because the temperature in container A is related to the temperature in B by $T_A = \dfrac{T_B}{2}$.

(B) The molecules in container A have a higher rms speed than the molecules in container B because the temperature in A is twice as high the temperature in B.

(C) The molecules in container A and B have the same rms speed since $\dfrac{p_1 V_1}{T_1} = \dfrac{p_2 V_2}{T_2}$ and the only difference is the number of moles in the containers.

(D) Since we do not know what gases are in the containers, we do not know which container has molecules with the higher rms speed.

GO ON TO NEXT PAGE

Questions 22 and 23

Use the circuit shown below is answer questions 22 and 23.

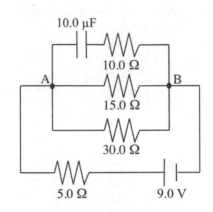

22. The current through the 15.0 Ω resistor when the circuit has reached steady-state is
    (A) 0.150 A
    (B) 0.200 A
    (C) 0.300 A
    (D) 0.400 A

23. What is the charge on the 10.0 μF capacitor when the circuit above has reached steady-state?
    (A) 30.0 μC
    (B) 45.0 μC
    (C) 60.0 μC
    (D) 90.0 μC

24. Four charges are arranged in a square as shown below. The electric field $\vec{E}$ is zero at

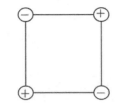

    (A) points on each side of the square midway between each pair of charges
    (B) the midpoint of the square
    (C) midway between the top two charges and midway between the bottom two charges
    (D) midway between the two charges on the left and midway between the two charges on the right

25. When monochromatic rays of red and blue light fall on a narrow slit producing a diffraction pattern
    (A) red light is diffracted more than blue light since it has the highest frequency
    (B) blue light is diffracted more than red light since it has the highest frequency
    (C) red light is diffracted more that blue light since it has the longest wavelength
    (D) blue light is diffracted more than red light since it has the longest wavelength

26. An object placed 30.0 m in front of a lens produces a real image that is three times the size of the object. What is the focal length of the lens?
    (A) 22.5 cm
    (B) 30.0 cm
    (C) 45.0 cm
    (D) 60.0 cm

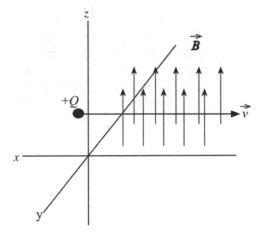

27. A positive charge $+Q$ moves along the $+x$ axis with some velocity $\vec{v}$ into a region where there is a magnetic field of strength $\vec{B}$ directed along the $+z$ direction as shown in the diagram. The direction of the force on the positive charge is in the
    (A) positive z direction
    (B) positive y direction
    (C) negative z direction
    (D) negative y direction

28. A dipole molecule is aligned along the x-axis with the positive end $q_1 = 8.00 \times 10^{-9}$ C at 0.200 m and the negative end $q_2 = -8.00 \times 10^{-9}$ C at −0.200 m.

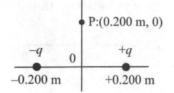

The magnitude and the direction of the electric field at $(0, 0.200\text{ m})$ is closest to

(A) $1.27 \times 10^3 \ \dfrac{\text{N}}{\text{C}}$ in the direction of the − x axis

(B) $1.27 \times 10^3 \ \dfrac{\text{N}}{\text{C}}$ along the + y axis

(C) $1.80 \times 10^3 \ \dfrac{\text{N}}{\text{C}}$ in the direction of the − x axis

(D) $1.80 \times 10^3 \ \dfrac{\text{N}}{\text{C}}$ along the + y axis

29. Three charges are located on a line. What is the electrostatic force on q_2 due to the other two charges?

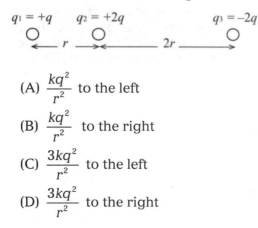

(A) $\dfrac{kq^2}{r^2}$ to the left

(B) $\dfrac{kq^2}{r^2}$ to the right

(C) $\dfrac{3kq^2}{r^2}$ to the left

(D) $\dfrac{3kq^2}{r^2}$ to the right

30. Consider the electrical circuit shown below. The battery has negligible internal resistance and its emf is $\varepsilon = 10$ V. Given $R_1 = R_2 = R_3 = R_4 = R_5 = 10\ \Omega$, what is the resistance of R_6 so that the power delivered by the battery is 10 W?

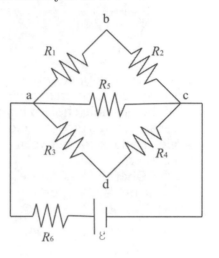

(A) 5 Ω
(B) 10 Ω
(C) 20 Ω
(D) 30 Ω

31. An electron, initially at rest, is placed in the region between two electrically charged parallel plates as shown below.

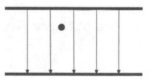

The direction of the force $|F_E|$ exerted on the electron by the field is best illustrated by which arrow?

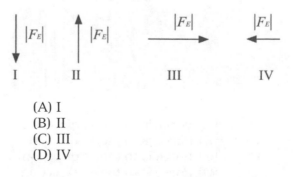

(A) I
(B) II
(C) III
(D) IV

GO ON TO NEXT PAGE

32. Two isolated identical spheres A and B containing charges as shown initially attract each other.

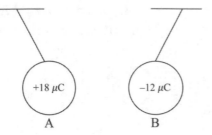

A piece of copper wire is connected to the spheres and then removed. Which of the possible choices indicating the resultant charge on A and B and the electrostatic for between them is correct?

	Charge on A	Charge on B	Result
(A)	$+6 \ \mu C$	$-6 \ \mu C$	attraction
(B)	$+6 \ \mu C$	$+6 \ \mu C$	repulsion
(C)	$+3 \ \mu C$	$-3 \ \mu C$	attraction
(D)	$+3 \ \mu C$	$+3 \ \mu C$	repulsion

33. A current carrying wire of infinite length carries a current I in the positive z direction as shown in the diagram below. A negative charge moves with some velocity $\vec{v}$ parallel to the wire in a region very close to the wire. What is the direction of the magnetic force on the charge due to the magnetic field created by the current carrying wire?

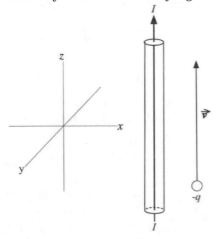

(A) Force is to the $-x$ direction
(B) Force is to the $+x$ direction
(C) Force is to the $-y$ direction
(D) Force is to the $+y$ direction

34. A proton is injected into the region between 2 parallel plates as shown with an initial velocity of $3.00 \times 10^5 \ \frac{m}{s}$.

Four possible paths are shown for the motion of the proton when it enters the region between the plates.

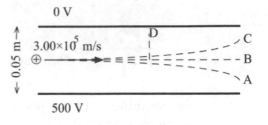

The proton
(A) follows path A because the gravitational force acts on the proton in the same manner that a projectile with some initial horizontal velocity will move in a gravitational field
(B) will move along path B since the horizontal velocity of the proton is constant in the region between the plates
(C) follows path C because the electrical force accelerates it toward the upper plate, but it has an initial velocity parallel to the plates so its path is parabolic
(D) follows path D directly upward to the upper plate because the electrical force accelerates it to the low potential end of the field

35. Rank the resistors in the circuit shown from the largest current in the given resistor to the smallest current.

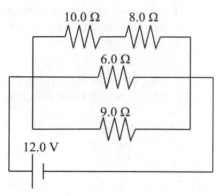

(A) $I_{6\,\Omega} > I_{8\,\Omega} > I_{9\,\Omega} > I_{10\,\Omega}$

(B) $I_{6\,\Omega} > I_{8\,\Omega} > I_{10\,\Omega} > I_{9\,\Omega}$

(C) $I_{10\,\Omega} = I_{8\,\Omega} > I_{9\,\Omega} > I_{6\,\Omega}$

(D) $I_{6\,\Omega} > I_{9\,\Omega} > (I_{8\,\Omega} = I_{10\,\Omega})$

36. The diagram below shows a standing wave pattern corresponding to the de Broglie wavelength for the electron in a particular orbit of the Bohr atom of hydrogen. The energy level occupied by this electron is

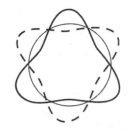

(A) $n = 1$
(B) $n = 2$
(C) $n = 3$
(D) $n = 4$

37. Identify the missing particle in the nuclear reaction show below.

$$^{23}_{11}\text{Na} + ? \rightarrow \ ^{20}_{10}\text{Ne} + \ ^{4}_{2}\text{He}$$

(A) $^{0}_{-1}e$

(B) $^{1}_{0}n$

(C) $^{1}_{1}H$

(D) $^{2}_{1}H$

38. Two conducting loops have a common vertical axis as shown below.

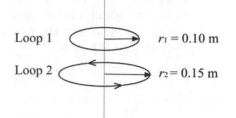

Loop 1 has a radius $r_1 = 0.10$ m and loop 2 has a radius $r_2 = 0.15$ m. Current in loop 2 (lower loop) is in the counterclockwise direction as viewed from above and increasing. The induced current in loop 1 as viewed from above is
(A) clockwise and increasing
(B) counterclockwise and increasing
(C) clockwise and decreasing
(D) counterclockwise and decreasing

39. A conducting rod ab of length 0.10 m is moving with a constant velocity of 10.0 m/s toward the right in a uniform magnetic field 0f 0.10 T directed vertically out of the page as shown in the figure.

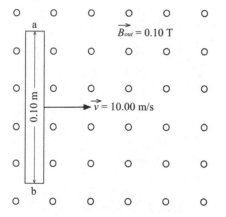

What is the electrical potential difference induced across the ends of the rod?
(A) 0.10 V and the top of the rod is positive
(B) 0.10 V and the bottom of the rod is positive
(C) 1.0 V and the top of the rod is positive
(D) 1.0 V and the bottom of the rod is positive

GO ON TO NEXT PAGE

40. An electric field $\vec{E}$ is directed to the right as shown in the diagram below. Four points, A, B, C, and D, are in the region produced by the field. Rank the points in the diagram from the greatest potential to the least.

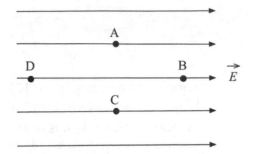

(A) $D > C > B > A$
(B) $B > C > A > D$
(C) $D > (A = C) > B$
(D) $A = B = C = D$

41. An energy level diagram is illustrated for a certain atom. Rank the transitions for the emitted electromagnetic radiation from longest wavelength to shortest wavelength.

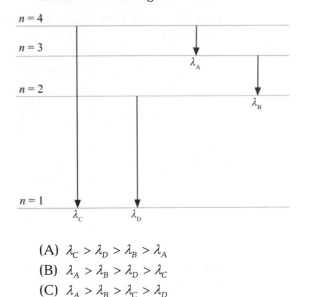

(A) $\lambda_C > \lambda_D > \lambda_B > \lambda_A$
(B) $\lambda_A > \lambda_B > \lambda_D > \lambda_C$
(C) $\lambda_A > \lambda_B > \lambda_C > \lambda_D$
(D) $\lambda_D > \lambda_C > \lambda_B > \lambda_A$

42. Electrons and positrons have the same mass $m = 0.000\,55$ u . When an electron and a positron come into direct contact they annihilate one another producing a pair of identical gamma ray photons.

$$_{-1}^{0}e + {}_{+1}^{0}e \rightarrow \gamma + \gamma$$

Each gamma ray carries away approximately how much energy?
(A) 0.5 MeV
(B) 1.0 MeV
(C) 2.0 MeV
(D) 25 MeV

43. The isotope C–14 is radioactive and decays as

$$_{6}^{14}C \rightarrow {}_{7}^{14}N + {}_{0}^{0-}\nu + ?$$

The unknown particle (?) needed to complete the decay equation is
(A) $_{+1}^{0}e$
(B) $_{-1}^{0}e$
(C) $_{0}^{1}n$
(D) $_{1}^{1}H$

44. The graph below shows the number of un-decayed nuclei as a function of time. The half-life of the radioactive isotope is approximately
    (A) 1 s
    (B) 2 s
    (C) 4 s
    (D) 10 s

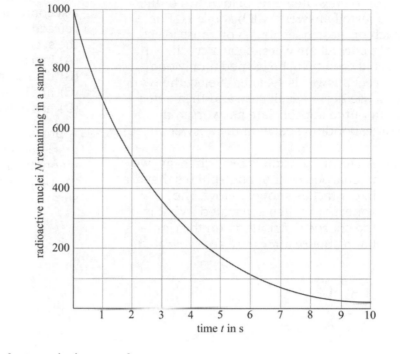

45. The surface of a photoemissive metal plate has a threshold frequency of 1.50×10^{15} Hz . When light of frequency 2.00×10^{15} Hz falls on this metal plate
    (A) an electron with zero velocity and a 0.50×10^{15} Hz photon are emitted from the surface
    (B) no electron is emitted from the surface
    (C) an electron is emitted with a speed of 0.750 c since the ratio of the frequencies is $\dfrac{1.50 \times 10^{15}}{2.00 \times 10^{15}} = 0.750$
    (D) an electron is emitted with a slightly lower speed since the new frequency is slightly larger than the threshold frequency

GO ON TO NEXT PAGE

Questions 46 to 50

Directions: For each of the questions or incomplete statements below, <u>two</u> of the suggested answers will be correct. For each of these questions, you must select <u>both</u> correct answers to earn credit. No partial credit will be earned if only one correct answer is selected. Select the two that are best in each case and then enter both of the appropriate answers in the corresponding space on the answer sheet.

46. A charging wand is brought near two uncharged conducting spheres that are in contact as shown below. The spheres are then separated. What is the charge distribution on the right-hand sphere after they are separated?

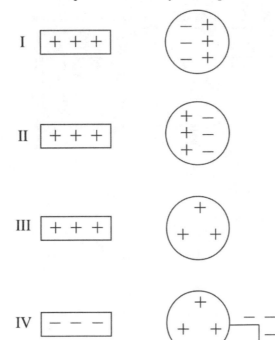

(A) I
(B) II
(C) III
(D) IV

47. An electron drops from $n = 3$ to $n = 2$ in the Bohr atom of hydrogen. As a result the
(A) energy of the electron increases
(B) force on the electron increases
(C) energy of the electron decreases
(D) force on the electron decreases

48. A 620 nm ray of light traveling in a medium whose index of refraction is 1.33 strikes the interface between it and a second medium with an index of refraction of 1.52 at an angle of 30°. In the second medium, the ray of light
(A) increases in speed
(B) decreases in speed
(C) has an increased wavelength
(D) has a decreased wavelength

49. A proton with a velocity of 6.0×10^5 m/s enters a region in which there is a magnetic field of 0.10 T directed into the page. The proton follows the path shown.

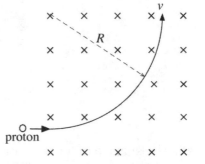

(A) The initial force on the proton is 9.6×10^{-15} N directed to the top of the page.
(B) The initial force on the proton is 9.6×10^{-15} N directed to right causing the velocity of the proton to increase.
(C) The momentum of the proton is constant because the magnetic force is perpendicular to the velocity of the proton. The speed is the same when it leaves the field.
(D) The momentum of the proton has changed since the direction of the velocity has changed.

50. Two rods of copper and aluminum are placed between two walls maintained at temperatures of 100 °C and 0 °C as shown in Figure 1, in which the two pieces of metal are connected between the walls in parallel and in Figure 2 where the two pieces of metal are in series between the walls.

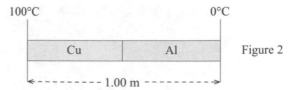

Figure 2

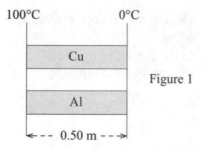

Figure 1

The rate at which thermal energy is conducted from one wall to the other is greater

(A) through Figure 2 than through Figure 1 since the rod connecting the two walls is longer

(B) through Figure 1 since the effective cross-sectional area is larger

(C) through Figure 1 since the change in the temperature ΔT is the same for both rods

(D) through Figure 2 since there is a smaller temperature difference ΔT between the ends of the copper rod and the aluminum rod

STOP
END OF SECTION I

IF YOU FINISH BEFORE TIME IS CALLED, YOU MAY CHECK YOUR WORK ON THIS SECTION. DO NOT GO ON TO SECTION II UNTIL YOU ARE TOLD TO DO SO.

AP PHYSICS 2
Section II
4 Free-Response Questions
Time–90 Minutes

Directions: Solve each of the following problems. Unless the directions indicate otherwise, respond to all parts of each question.

1. A 2.0 cm tall object O is placed 60 cm to the left of a thin converging lens A of focal length $f_A = 20$ cm as shown in the figure below.
   (a) Use two rays from the tip of the object O to locate the image.
       i.   Describe the type of image, its height and its position.

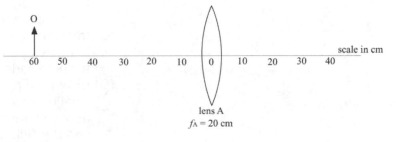

       ii. Explain how you will determine the size and magnification of the image.
   (b) A second converging lens B with a focal length $f_B = 20$ cm is placed 20 cm to the right of lens A as shown below.

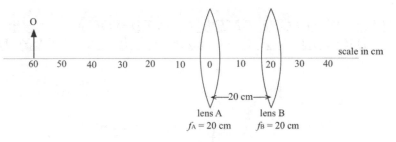

       i.   What is the location of the final image relative to lens B?
       ii. Describe the final image formed in terms of the type of image, its magnification and its location.
   (c) A concave mirror of $f_{Mirror} = 20$ cm is placed 40 cm to the right of lens A as shown.

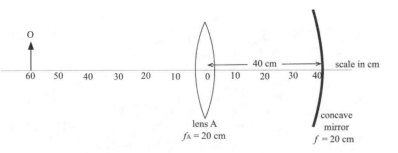

       i.   Explain how you will determine the type of image formed.
       ii. Explain where the final image will be formed.

2. When you walk into the classroom on a laboratory day, your teacher tells you that she attached one end of a coil of wire to simulate an internal resistance in an opaque box connected to a power supply. Using the equipment placed on the table, she tells you to design an experiment to determine the "internal resistance" of the power supply. On your laboratory table besides the power supply with internal resistance you have a voltmeter, a switch, a variable resistor in the range of 0.1 Ω to 110.0 Ω, and connecting wires. (The power supply was pre-set to give you a maximum value of 1.50 V.)

(a) Design an experiment in sufficient detail that another student could perform your experiment and obtain the same results. Include the schematic of your set up in your procedure.

(b) What measurements are you going to take in the experiment and how are you going to use the data from the measurements to determine the "internal resistance" attached to the power supply?

(c) When the switch is open, what is the value of the current in your circuit? What does this tell you about the value of the resistance R in the circuit?

(d) If you make a graph, what are you going to graph and how will your graph help you to answer the experimental question?
    i.   What does the intercept of the graph suggest?
    ii. Why does the voltmeter not indicate the exact emf of a cell?

(e) Another group of students was given a power supply with an identical coil of wire in an opaque box but a different set of equipment that they set wired in the schematic shown below.

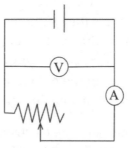

They plotted a graph of their data and came up with an internal resistance that had a higher value that your "internal resistance." What are some possible reasons to account for their higher value?

3. A loop of wire 20.0 cm by 20.0 cm enters a region where a magnetic field of 1.60 T is directed out of the page and confined in a square of dimensions 70.0 cm by 70.0 cm.

The loop of wire has a velocity of 10.0 cm/s perpendicular to the $\vec{B}$ field as shown in the diagram.

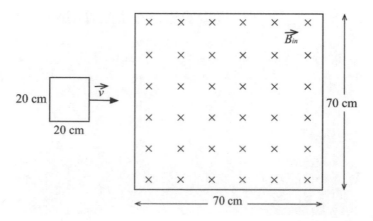

GO ON TO NEXT PAGE

(a) Explain, using the correct scientific terms, what happens to the emf induced in the loop as the loop first enters the field, travels through the field and then exits the field.

(b) Graph the emf as a function of time as the loop transits the field on the grid below.

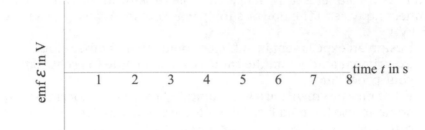

(c) If the loop of wire has a resistance of 40.0 Ω, what is the magnitude of the maximum induced current in the loop?

(d) Calculate the magnetic flux through the loop when the loop is completely immersed in the field.

4. (a) The isotope Pu-236 is an alpha emitter with a half-life of 2.86 years. It decays into U-232 as $^{236}_{94}\text{Pu} \rightarrow {}^{232}_{92}\text{U} + {}^{4}_{2}\text{He} + Q$. If the masses of the Pu-236, U-232, and the alpha particle are, respectively $M_{Pu} = 236.046\ 071\ \text{u}$, $M_U = 232.037\ 168\ \text{u}$, and $M_\alpha = 4.002\ 603\ \text{u}$, what is the Q-value for the decay?

(b) The alpha particles from the Pu-236 source are allowed to fall on a thin section of gold foil. An alpha particle, ^4_2He, comes within 80.0×10^{-15} m of a gold nucleus, $^{197}_{79}\text{Au}$. Assuming that both the gold nucleus and the alpha particle behave as point charges, determine the maximum electrostatic repulsive force between them at this distance.

(c) An alpha particle penetrates the electron cloud of a gold atom colliding with and ejecting the inner electrons of the 1st energy level creating vacancies. Explain what happens to these inner electron vacancies.

(d) The alpha particle is observed to have a momentum of 1.10×10^{-19} $\text{kg} \cdot \text{m} / \text{s}$ at 0°. What is the momentum of the U-232 nucleus?

(e) A sample of Pu-236 containing 4.00×10^{10} nuclei is prepared in a nuclear physics laboratory. How would you go about determining how many Pu-236 nuclei remain after 4 half-life periods?

END OF EXAMINATION

Answers

ANSWER KEY FOR MULTIPLE-CHOICE QUESTIONS

1. D	11. B	21. D	31. B	41. B
2. C	12. D	22. D	32. D	42. A
3. B	13. C	23. C	33. B	43. B
4. A	14. B	24. B	34. C	44. B
5. C	15. B	25. C	35. D	45. D
6. A	16. B	26. A	36. C	46. A & D
7. C	17. A	27. D	37. C	47. B & C
8. C	18. A	28. A	38. A	48. B & D
9. A	19. D	29. D	39. B	49. A & D
10. A	20. A	30. A	40. C	50. B & C

EXPLANATIONS FOR THE MULTIPLE-CHOICE ANSWERS

1. **D** The equation of continuity is $A_1 v_1 = A_2 v_2$. Since area is $A = \pi r^2$, we will write the equation as $r_1^2 v_1 = r_2^2 v_2$ substitution is

$$(0.100 \text{ cm})^2 \left(20.0 \ \frac{\text{cm}}{\text{s}}\right) = 10(0.010 \text{ cm})^2 v_2$$

Solving yields $200 \ \frac{\text{cm}}{\text{s}}$.

(*College Physics* 9th ed. pages 299–302/10th ed. pages 305–306)
(L.O. 5.B.10.3)

2. **C** The ideal fluid moves through the tube from a larger cross-section into a smaller one. The equation of continuity relates the velocity in the region $A_1 v_1 = A_2 v_2$. The fluid will flow faster in the constriction. Bernoulli's equation, a statement of conservation of energy, for the horizontal tube is. The $p + \frac{1}{2}\rho v^2 = \text{constant}$. The pressure in B is smaller than the pressure at A and C. But the pressure at A must be slightly higher that the pressure at C because the fluid is moving in the tube from point A to B then to C.
(*College Physics* 9th ed. pages 299–301/10th ed. pages 305–306)
(L.O. 5.B.10.4)

3. **B** In the fission of $^{239}_{94}\text{Pu}$ by a neutron, charge number and mass number must be conserved. For charge, $94 + 0 \rightarrow 56 + 38$. The missing particle must have a charge of 0. The mass numbers are $239 + 1 \rightarrow 148 + 90 + ?$ The mass needed to balance is 2. A neutron is correctly written as $^1_0 n$ thus 2 neutrons are required to complete the reaction $2\left(^1_0 n\right)$.
(*College Physics* 9th ed. pages 982–983/10th ed. pages 996–998)
(L.O. 5.G.1.1)

4. **A** This is an isothermal process. The pressure will increase as the volume decreases at constant temperature. Molecules will collide elastically with the walls of the container more frequently. Since this takes place over a very short period of time, the force must increase. The increased force per unit area on the walls of the container results in an increase in pressure.
    (*College Physics* 9th ed. pages 280, 345, 349–350/10th ed. pages 285, 350, 354–356)
    (L.O. 7.A.1.1)

5. **C** The buoyant force on the object is exerted on the object by the fluid. The magnitude of the buoyant force $\left|\vec{F}_B\right|$ is equal to the weight of the water displaced. Since spheres A and B have the same volume, they displace the same volume of water and the buoyant force on each is the same. The buoyant force is directed upward on all of the spheres.
    (*College Physics* 9th ed. pages 293–295/10th ed. pages 299–301)
    (L.O. 3.C.4.1)

6. **A** The focal length of the mirror is $f = \dfrac{R}{2} = \dfrac{30.0 \text{ cm}}{2} = 15.0 \text{ cm}$. The image formed is negative since it is formed behind the mirror. Substitution in $\dfrac{1}{f} = \dfrac{1}{p} + \dfrac{1}{q} = \dfrac{1}{15.0 \text{ cm}} = \dfrac{1}{p} + \left(-\dfrac{1}{40.0 \text{ cm}}\right)$. The object is located at 10.9 cm.
    (*College Physics* 9th ed. pages 793–795/10th ed. pages 804–806)
    (L.O. 6.E.4.2)

7. **C** The work done in the expansion of the gas along path ABC is the area under the pressure-volume curve. This is the sum of three areas. A_1 is the rectangular area of $\left(4.0 \times 10^5 \text{ Pa} - 0\right)$ $\left(0.8 \text{ m}^3 - 0.4 \text{ m}^3\right) = 1.6 \times 10^5 \text{ J}$. A_2 is the triangular area equal to $\dfrac{1}{2}\left(4.0 \times 10^5 \text{ Pa} - 1.0 \times 10^5 \text{ Pa}\right)\left(1.0 \text{ m}^3 - 0.8 \text{ m}^3\right) = 3.0 \times 10^4 \text{ J}$ and $A_3 = \left(1.0 \times 10^5 \text{ Pa} - 0\right)\left(1.0 \text{ m}^3 - 0.8 \text{ m}^3\right) = 2.0 \times 10^4 \text{ J}$. The net work is $2.1 \times 10^5 \text{ J}$.
    (*College Physics* 9th ed. pages 395–398 /10th ed. pages 402–405)
    (L.O. 5.B.7.3.)

8. **C** The equation of continuity $A_1 v_1 = A_2 v_2$ applies. Substitution into the equation is $\pi (0.120 \text{ m})^2 \left(2.00 \; \dfrac{\text{m}}{\text{s}}\right) = \pi (0.060 \text{ m})^2 v_2$. The exit velocity at the top is $8.00 \; \dfrac{\text{m}}{\text{s}}$.

    Bernoulli's equation for this problem is $p_1 + \dfrac{1}{2}\rho v_1^2 = p_2 + \dfrac{1}{2}\rho v_2^2 + \rho g h_2$. If we take the initial height h_1 as the reference point, $h_1 = 0$. Substitution into the equation is

$$2.10 \times 10^5 \text{ Pa} + \frac{1}{2}\left(1000 \text{ } \frac{\text{kg}}{\text{m}^3}\right)\left(2.00 \text{ } \frac{\text{m}}{\text{s}}\right)^2$$

$$= p_2 + \frac{1}{2}\left(1000 \text{ } \frac{\text{kg}}{\text{m}^3}\right)\left(8.00 \text{ } \frac{\text{m}}{\text{s}}\right)^2 + \left(1000 \text{ } \frac{\text{kg}}{\text{m}^3}\right)\left(9.80 \text{ } \frac{\text{m}}{\text{s}^2}\right)(1.50 \text{ m})$$

$$2.10 \times 10^5 \text{ Pa} + \frac{1}{2}\left(1000 \text{ } \frac{\text{kg}}{\text{m}^3}\right)\left(4.00 \text{ } \frac{\text{m}^2}{\text{s}^2}\right)$$

$$= p_2 + \frac{1}{2}\left(1000 \text{ } \frac{\text{kg}}{\text{m}^3}\right)\left(64.0 \text{ } \frac{\text{m}^2}{\text{s}^2}\right) + \left(1000 \text{ } \frac{\text{kg}}{\text{m}^3}\right)\left(9.80 \text{ } \frac{\text{m}}{\text{s}^2}\right)(1.50 \text{ m})$$

$$p_2 = 1.65 \times 10^5 \text{ Pa}$$

(*College Physics* 9th ed. pages 299–305/10th ed. pages 305–310)
(L.O. 5.B.10.1, 5.B.10.3)

9. **A** Gamma rays have a wavelength in the order of 10^{-12} m . X-Ray radiation is on the order of 10 nm to about 10^{-4} nm . Ultraviolet radiation covers a range of about 400 nm to about 0.6 nm, and infrared, "heat waves" are about 1 mm to around 700 nm.
(*College Physics* 9th ed. pages 746–749/10th ed. pages 757–759)
(L.O. 6.F.1.1)

10. **A** Light travels in a medium of uniform optical density in straight lines. The light traveling from n_1 to n_2, slows as it enters the optically slower substance, bending toward the normal (perpendicular). The ray of light traveling from n_2 into air, an optically slower medium will bend away from the normal.
(*College Physics* 9th ed. pages765–766/10th ed. pages 777–782)
(L.O. 6.E.3.1)

11. **B** For the diverging lens the object distance is –0.15 m and the image distance is 0.30 m . Using $\frac{1}{f} = \frac{1}{p} + \frac{1}{q}$ substitution is

$\frac{1}{f} = \frac{1}{0.30} + \frac{1}{-0.15}$ then $\frac{1}{f} = \frac{-2+1}{0.30 \text{ m}} = \frac{-1}{0.30 \text{ m}}$. The focal length of the diverging lens is –0.30 m .
(*College Physics* 9th ed. pages 805–811/10th ed. pages 816–822)
(L.O. 6. E.5.1)

12. **D** The fluid flows from region A into B. The area decreases in B and the speed increases from the equation of continuity $A_1 v_1 = A_2 v_2$. The fluid then flows into region C where the cross sectional area is larger than B but smaller than A. The speed will decrease, but will be faster than the speed in area A because the cross sectional is smaller than the one in A.

When the speed changes in the horizontal pipe, Bernoulli's equation, a statement of conservation of energy which relates the pressure plus the kinetic energy to a constant, will show that the pressures must be different in all three sections since the speed in these sections are different.
(*College Physics* 9th ed. pages 299–305/10th ed. pages 305–310)
(L.O. 5.B.10.4)

13. **C** Since the experiment was done at constant temperature this is an isothermal process. Boyle's law relates the relationship between the volume of the confined gas and its pressure. $p_1 V_1 = p_2 V_2$. A pressure–volume graph is hyperbolic.
(*College Physics* 9th ed. pages 345 and 407/10th ed. pages 355 and 417)
(L.O. 5.B.7.2)

14. **B** The system is insulated, therefore heat cannot flow either into or out of the system. Work was done on the system by stirring the liquid; therefore there is an increase in the internal energy of the system.
(*College Physics* 9th ed. 395–400/10th ed. pages 402–407)
(L.O. 5.B.3.1, 5.B.4.1)

15. **B** In a cyclic process the system returns to initial state conditions of pressure, volume, and temperature. Since the temperature returns to its initial value $\Delta U = 0$, and $Q = -W$. The net work done per cycle is the area bounded by the cycle. $W = -\left(4 \times 10^5 \text{ J} - 2 \times 10^5 \text{ J}\right)\left(2 \text{ m}^3 - 1 \text{ m}^3\right) = -2 \times 10^5 \text{ J}$. The thermal energy added along AB is $Q_{in} = 5 \times 10^5$ J. The thermal energy leaving the system is $Q_{out} = 5 \times 10^5 \text{ J} - 2 \times 10^5 \text{ J} = 3 \times 10^5 \text{ J}$.
(*College Physics* 9th ed. pages 396–397/10th ed. pages 403–404)
(L.O. 5.A.2.1, 5.B.4.1, 5.B.7.3)

16. **B** The angle of refraction of the light falling on the prism depends on the wavelength of the light. The index of refraction usually decreases with increasing wavelength. Violet light has a shorter wavelength and will have a higher angle of deviation (it will spread further from the original path). It will refract more than the ray of red light.
(*College Physics* 9th ed. pages 771–774/10th ed. pages 782–784)
(L.O. 6.F.1.1)

17. **A** The domains in the ferromagnetic material listed as A are aligned in somewhat the same direction by an external magnetic field, followed by the domains in D. While C and B are close, B is a little more random than the domains in C.
(*College Physics* 9th ed. pages 673–674/10th ed. pages 685–687)
(L.O. 4.E.1.1)

18. **A** The direction of the force on the current in the wire is given by using the right hand rule. The conventional current is toward the top of the page. The magnetic field is out of the page and therefore the force on the wire is toward the right.

The magnitude of the force is $\left|\vec{F}\right| = \left|\vec{B}\left(I\vec{L}\right)\right|\sin\theta$. Substitution into the equation is $\left|\vec{F}\right| = \left|0.10 \text{ T}\left(5.00 \text{ A} \cdot 1.2 \text{ m}\right)\right|\sin 90° = 0.60 \text{ N}$.
(*College Physics* 9th ed. pages 655–658/10th ed. pages 667–668)
(L.O. 2.D.1.1)

19. **D** Both wires carrying current produce magnetic fields that point into the page in the region between the two wires. This acts as if

two N poles of magnet were near each other causing a repulsive force. The forces the wires exert on each other are action-reaction pairs. They exert the same magnitude of force on each other. (*College Physics* 9th ed. pages 664–669/10th ed. pages 676–681) (L.O. 2.D.2.1, 3.A.4.2)

20. **A** The electric field points away from the positive point charge and toward the negative charge. Figure I illustrates the correct diagram. Five lines leave the positive charge and terminate on the negative plate, indicating the magnitude of the charges are the same. (*College Physics* 9th ed. pages 522–523, 526–528/10th ed. pages 532–533, 536–538) (L.O. 2.C.2.1)

21. **D** The rms speed of a gas molecule is given by $v_{rms} = \sqrt{\dfrac{3N_A kT}{M}}$.

The containers have the same volume and pressure but because they have a different number of moles of the gas, they have different temperatures. Knowing that $pV = NkT$ then $N_A kT_A = N_B kT_B$. Since container B has twice the number of moles as A it must have half the temperature if the pressure in A is to equal the pressure in B. (*College Physics* 9th ed. pages 351–353/10th ed. pages 357–358) (L.O. 7.A.2.1)

22. **D** At steady state, no current flows through the 10.0 Ω resistor in the top branch of the parallel network because the capacitor is fully charged. The resistance in the parallel branch without including the 10 Ω resistor is $\dfrac{1}{R} = \dfrac{1}{15.0\ \Omega} + \dfrac{1}{30.0\ \Omega}$. This gives a resistance of 10.0 Ω which is in series with a 5.00 Ω resistance for a total of 15.0 Ω.

The current from the battery that enters junction A is $I = \dfrac{9.00\ \text{V}}{15.0\ \Omega} = 0.600\ \text{A}$.

By Kirchhoff's junction rule, 15.0 Ω resistor has a current of 0.400 A and the 30.0 Ω resistor is 0.200 A. (*College Physics* 9th ed. pages 617–628/10th ed. pages 628–639) (L.O. 5.C.3.4, 5.C.3.7)

23. **C** When the circuit has reached steady state no current flows through the 10.0 Ω resistor. The entire electrical potential difference for the top branch is across the plates of the capacitor. The electrical potential difference across the parallel section of the circuit is $9.00\ \text{V} = (0.600\ \text{A})(5.00\ \Omega) + V_{parallel} = 6.00\ \text{V}$. Then $C = \dfrac{Q}{V}$.

The charge on the plates of the capacitor is $(10.0\ \mu\text{F})(6.00\ \text{V}) = 60.0\ \mu\text{F}$. (*College Physics* 9th ed. pages 562–563/10th ed. page 573) (L.O. 5.B.9.5, 5.C.3.7)

24. **B** $\vec{E}$ is zero wherever the net force acting on a test charge is zero. At the center of the square the two positive charges alone would produce a resultant electric field of zero, and the two negative charges alone would also produce a resultant electric field of zero. Thus, the resultant force acting on a test charge at the midpoint of the square will be zero.
(*College Physics* 9th ed. pages 522–523/10th ed. pages 532–533)
(L.O. 2.C.2.1)

25. **C** Diffraction is wavelength dependent. Shorter wavelengths, blue light, is diffracted the least. The red light with its longer wavelength is diffracted the most.
(*College Physics* 9th ed. pages 836–841/10th ed. pages 847–853)
(L.O. 6.C.2.1)

26. **A** Magnification of the image is given by $|M| = \dfrac{q}{p}$. The image distance, which is positive, is $3(30.0 \text{ cm}) = 90.0 \text{ cm}$. The equation $\dfrac{1}{f} = \dfrac{1}{p} + \dfrac{1}{q}$ will give the focal length of the convex lens (image is real). $\dfrac{1}{f} = \dfrac{1}{30.0 \text{ cm}} + \dfrac{1}{90.0 \text{ cm}} = \dfrac{1+3}{90.0 \text{ cm}}$. $f = 22.5 \text{ cm}$
(*College Physics* 9th ed. pages 805–811/10th ed. pages 816–822)
(L.O. 6.E.5.1)

27. **D** By the right hand rule, the force on the positive charge in in the negative y direction.
(*College Physics* 9th ed. pages 652–655/10th ed. pages 663–667)
(L.O. 3.A.2.1)

28. **A** The electric field points away from the positive charge and toward the negative charge. By symmetry the vertical components of the electric field are equal in magnitude and opposite in direction.

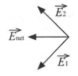

The net electric field at $(0, 0.200 \text{ m})$ is directed along the $-x$ axis and its magnitude is given by $\left|\vec{E}_{x_1}\right| + \left|\vec{E}_{x_2}\right| = \left|\Sigma\vec{E}_x\right|$ and thus since the dipole has the same magnitude of charge on its ends, $\left|\vec{E}\right| = \dfrac{2k_e q}{r^2}\cos 45°$. Since $r^2 = (0.200 \text{ m})^2 + (0.200 \text{ m})^2 = 0.080 \text{ m}^2$, the field strength is $2\dfrac{\left(9\times10^9 \ \dfrac{\text{N}\cdot\text{m}^2}{\text{C}^2}\right)(8.00\times10^{-9} \text{ C})}{(0.080 \text{ m}^2)}\cos 45°$. The magnitude of the field is $1.27\times10^3 \ \dfrac{\text{N}}{\text{C}}$.
(*College Physics* 9th ed. pages 522–525/10th ed. pages 532–535)
(L.O. 2.C.1.2, 2.C.2.1, 2.C.4.2)

29. **D** The Coulombic force on q_2 due to q_1 and q_3 is toward the right. The force between $\vec{F}_{12}$ is repulsive since both charges q_1 and q_2 are positive and will be toward the right. The force $\vec{F}_{23}$ between q_2 and q_3 is attractive and thus to the right. The magnitude of the force is $\dfrac{kq_1q_2}{r^2} + \dfrac{kq_2q_3}{(2r)^2}$. Substitution for the values of the charges $\dfrac{k(q)(2q)}{r^2} + \dfrac{k(2q)(2q)}{(2r)^2} = \dfrac{3kq^2}{r^2}$.
    (*College Physics* 9th ed. pages 517–519/10th ed. pages 527–529)
    (L.O. 2.C.1.2)

30. **A** Loop and junction rules apply. The resistance in the top and bottom branches are $R_{12} = 10.0\ \Omega + 10.0\ \Omega = 20.0\ \Omega$. $R_{34} = 10.0\ \Omega + 10.0\ \Omega = 20.0\ \Omega$. The resistance between junctions a and c is $\dfrac{1}{R_{1\to 5}} = \dfrac{1}{20.0\ \Omega} + \dfrac{1}{10.0\ \Omega} + \dfrac{1}{20.0\ \Omega}$. $R_{1\to 5} = 5.00\ \Omega$. The current can be determined from $I = \dfrac{P}{V} = \dfrac{10.0\ \text{W}}{10.0\ \text{V}} = 1.00\ \text{A}$. The potential difference across $R_{1\to 5} = 5.00\ \Omega$ is 5.00 V. This gives the potential difference across R_6 as $10.0\ \text{V} - 5.00\ \text{V} = 5.00\ \text{V}$. Since the current in the circuit is 1.00 A, the resistor R_6 is $5.00\ \Omega$.
    (*College Physics* 9th ed. pages 617–628/10th ed. pages 628–638)
    (L.O. 5.B.9.6, 5.C.3.5)

31. **B** The direction of the electric field in the region between the plates is downward from the upper plate toward the lower plate as shown by the field arrows. A positive charge will move in the direction of the field. The force on the electron is opposite to the field and will move the electron toward upper plate.
    (*College Physics* 9th ed. pages 522–524/10th ed. pages 532–534)
    (L.O. 2.C.1.1)

32. **D** When the copper wire connects A and B, negative charge will move and the net charge remaining between the two spheres will be $+6\ \mu C$. Negative charge will redistribute so that each sphere will have the same charge, $+3\ \mu C$, when the copper wire is removed. The force between the two spheres will then be repulsive.
    (*College Physics* 9th ed. pages 514–517/10th ed. pages 524–527)
    (L.O. 1.B.1.2)

33. **B** The wire creates a magnetic field to the right of the wire that is into the page wire. A charge moving parallel to the wire experiences a force by the right hand rule that is in the –x direction. However, the charge is negative, therefore the force acting on it is toward the right.
    (*College Physics* 9th ed. pages 652–654, 664–666/10th ed. pages 663–665, 676–677)
    (L.O. 3.C.3.1)

34. **C** The electric field between the plates accelerates the proton toward the upper plate. The force is perpendicular to the initial velocity of the proton; therefore the proton will follow a parabolic path toward the upper plate.
(*College Physics* 9th ed. pages 63–70, 522–523/10th ed. pages 65–71, 532–533)
(L.O. 2.C.1.1, 2.C.5.3)

35. **D** Kirchhoff's junction rule applies. The total current entering the junction divides as it branches into three separate paths. The branch with the smallest resistance $R = 6.0\ \Omega$ will have the largest current, followed the $9.0\ \Omega$ resistor. The two resistors in the top branch are in series and each has the same current.
(*College Physics* 9th ed. pages 617–627/10th ed. pages 628–638)
(L.O. 1.B.1.2)

36. **C** There are whole number multiples of the De Broglie wavelengths for the electron in a stable orbit of hydrogen. In the diagram there are 3 complete wavelengths. This gives $n = 3$ for the stable orbit.
(*College Physics* 9th ed. pages 922–924, 937–939/10th ed. pages 935–936, 950–953)
(L.O. 7.C.2.1)

37. **C** In any nuclear reaction charge and mass must be conserved. Conservation of charge is 11 + ? = 10 + 2. The missing particle has a charge of +1. Conservation of mass (A number) is 23 + ? = 20 + 4. The missing particle has a mass of +1. This is the proton ^1_1H.
(*College Physics* 9th ed. pages 957–958/10th ed. pages 971–972)
(L.O. 5.C.1.1, 5.G.1.1)

38. **A** The increasing current in the lower loop produces a magnetic field pointing upward from loop 2, which behaves like the north pole of a magnet approaching the upper loop. According to Lenz's law, this induces a current in the upper loop (loop 1) that will flow in the direction that will create a magnetic field to oppose what induced it. The current as viewed from above will be clockwise. Since the current in the lower loop is increasing, the current in the upper loop will also increase.
(*College Physics* 9th ed. pages 691–695/10th ed. pages 702–706)
(L.O. 4.E.2.1)

39. **B** The potential difference induced in the rod is determined by $\varepsilon = Blv$.

The electrical potential difference is $(0.10\ \text{T})(0.10\ \text{m})\left(10.0\ \tfrac{\text{m}}{\text{s}}\right) = 0.10\ \text{V}$. The direction of the field is out of the page and the velocity of the rod is toward the right. The force on the conventional charge carrier (positive) is therefore by the right-hand rule toward the bottom of the rod. The rod will act like a battery of $\varepsilon = 0.10\ V$ with the positive terminal at the bottom of the rod.
(*College Physics* 9th ed. pages 697–699/10th ed. pages 708–710)
(L.O. 3.C.3.1)

40. **C** The direction of the Electrical field is toward the right out from the positive end of the field. Since $\left|\vec{E}\right| = \dfrac{\Delta V}{\Delta r}$, the electrical potential will decrease from the left to the right in the field. Points A and C are on the same isoline and thus have the same electrical potential. Point D is closest to the positive end of the field and therefore has the highest electrical potential, and B is the least since it is to the right of the other points.
(*College Physics* 9th ed. pages 526–528, 552–553/10th ed. pages 536–538, 562–563)
(L.O. 2.E.2.3)

41. **B** The transition between $n = 4$ to $n = 1$ results in the radiation with the most energy and therefore the highest frequency and the shortest wavelength λ_C since $\Delta E = hf = \dfrac{hc}{\lambda}$. The lowest energy is the drop from $n = 4$ to $n = 3$ or λ_A. This is the lowest frequency and the longest wavelength. Correct ranking is $\lambda_A > \lambda_B > \lambda_D > \lambda_C$.
(*College Physics* 9th ed. pages 937–940/10th ed. pages 950–954)
(L.O. 6.F.1.1)

42. **A** In the annihilation process matter is converted into pure energy. The electron and the positron each produce one gamma ray photon.
The energy release is $0.000\ 55\ \text{u}\left(\dfrac{931\ \text{MeV}}{1\ \text{u}}\right) = 0.51\ \text{Mev}$
(*College Physics* 9th ed. pages 902–903/10th ed. pages 914–915)
(L.O. 4.C.4.1, 5.B.11.1)

43. **B** To conserve charge the unknown particle must have a -1 charge. This is response B, the electron. $^{14}_{6}\text{C} \rightarrow \,^{14}_{7}\text{N} + \,^{0}_{0}\overset{-}{\nu} + \,^{0}_{-1}\text{e}$. The total charge on the left-hand side of the reaction is $+6$ and on the right side it is $+7 - 1 = +6$.
(*College Physics* 9th ed. pages 967–968/10th ed. pages 981–982)
(L.O. 5.C.1.1)

44. **B** Half-life is the time for one half of the number of initial radioactive nuclei to decay to another isotope. The time on the curve where the number of remaining nuclei is one-half of the initial sample is 500. This occurs at $t = 2$ s.
(*College Physics* 9th ed. pages 962–964/10th ed. pages 977–979)
(L.O. 7.C.3.1)

45. **D** The photoelectron has a low speed since the difference between the threshold frequency needed to overcome the work function is 1.50×10^{15} Hz and the new frequency of 2.00×10^{15} Hz is 0.50×10^{15} Hz. This will give the photoelectron a lower energy, $3.31 \times \times 10^{-19}$ J and a lower speed.
(*College Physics* 9th ed. pages 913–916/10th ed. pages 926–928)
(L.O. 6.7.3.1)

46. **A** and **D**   The only charge that moves under electrostatic conditions is the negative charge. In A, negative charge will move to the side of the sphere closest to the charging wand leaving the opposite side of the sphere with a deficit of negative charge, hence a positive charge.

    In D, the sphere is connected to ground. Electrostatic repulsion between the negative charge on the charging wand and the sphere will cause some negative charge to move along the wire to the ground.
    (*College Physics* 9th ed. pages 515–516/10th ed. pages 524–527)
    (L.O. 1.B.1.1, 1.B.1.2, 1.B.2.3)

47. **B** and **C** The electron was boosted to $n = 3$ and s it drops back to $n = 2$ it radiates energy in the visible range of the electromagnetic spectrum $E = hf$. As it drops to a lower energy state, it is closer to the proton in the nucleus. Since r has decreased the electrical force between the proton and the electron has increased.
    (*College Physics* 9th ed. pages 517–519, 937–940/10th ed. pages 527–529, 950–954)
    (L.O. 3.A.3.4, 3.C.2.1, 6.F.1.1)

48. **B** and **D** As a wave travels from a medium of lower index of refraction to one of higher index of refraction, its speed decreases. Since the frequency of the wave does not change, the wavelength must decrease. $\lambda_1 n_1 = \lambda_2 n_2$.
    (*College Physics* 9th ed. pages 765–768/10th ed. pages 777–779)
    (L.O. 6.E.3.2, 6.E.3.3)

49. **A**   and   **D**   The   force   on   the   proton   is   given   by $\left|\vec{F}_B\right| = 0.10\ \text{T}\left(1.6 \times 10^{-19}\ \text{C}\right)\left(6.0 \times 10^5\ \dfrac{\text{m}}{\text{s}}\right)$.

    The force is $9.6 \times 10^{-15}\ \text{N}$. By the right-hand rule, the given direction of the magnetic field is toward the page and the velocity is to the right of the page. Therefore the force is initially to the top of the page. The magnetic force is a centripetal force acting on the charge continually changing its direction. Since the direction of the velocity vector has changed, its momentum has changed.
    (*College Physics* 9th ed. pages 652–654/10th ed. pages 663–664)
    (L.O. 2.D.1.1, 3.C.3.1)

50. **B** and **C** Thermal energy is conducted through the rods at a rate given by $\dfrac{Q}{\Delta t} = \dfrac{kA}{L}$. (Then conversion of temperatures from °C to K by adding 273 to each temperature.)

    Thermal energy will transit from the 373 K wall to the 273 K wall because molecules colliding with the rods have higher momentum and energy at the wall whose temperature is 373 K. Increasing the effective cross-sectional area in Figure 1 means there are more molecules/unit area transferring both energy and momentum to those particles, which have lower energies. Since the rate at which thermal energy is conducted depends on the temperature difference, the arrangement in Figure 1 has the same ΔT between the ends of each rod. In Figure 2, ΔT is smaller for each rod, the

effective cross-sectional area is less and there is a smaller rate of transfer of energy with increasing length.
(*College Physics* 9th ed. pages 375–380/10th ed. pages 380–384)
(L.O. 4.C.3.1, 5.B.6.1)

ANSWERS TO FREE-RESPONSE PROBLEMS

QUESTION 1

(a) As seen from the correct drawing, the image is

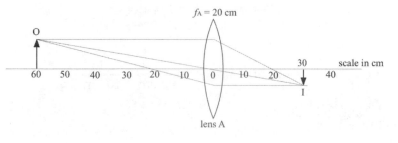

$f_A = 20$ cm

scale in cm

lens A

i. real, inverted, and smaller than the object. **(1 point)**

ii. The height of the image can be determined from the magnification of the image. The absolute value of the magnification $|M|$ is determined from the ratio of the image distance q to the object distance p. Since the drawing gives both p and q, the magnification is 1/2 and the image size is 1/2 the object size and will be 1 cm tall. **(1 point)**

(b) The image is determined from $\dfrac{1}{f} = \dfrac{1}{p} + \dfrac{1}{q}$. The object distance for the second lens B is 10 cm from the lens and is inverted.

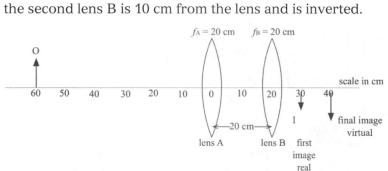

$f_A = 20$ cm $f_B = 20$ cm

scale in cm

—20 cm—

lens A   lens B   first
                          image
                          real

I   final image
      virtual

Solving for the position of the image of the first object $\dfrac{1}{20 \text{ cm}} = \dfrac{1}{10 \text{ cm}} + \dfrac{1}{q}$ then $\dfrac{1}{q} = \dfrac{1-2}{20 \text{ cm}}$.

The image is located 20 cm to the right of lens B at the 40 cm mark on the scale.

It is inverted, virtual, and the same size as the first object O.
(4 points)

(c) The first image from lens A in part (a) is 30 cm from the lens that places it 10 cm from the mirror. Since it is between the focal length and the mirror the image formed by the mirror will be virtual. Because the initial image was inverted, the image formed by the mirror will also be inverted.

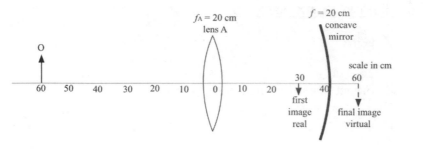

Using the equation $\frac{1}{f} = \frac{1}{p} + \frac{1}{q}$ the final image is $\frac{1}{20 \text{ cm}} = \frac{1}{10 \text{ cm}} + \frac{1}{q}$

solving $\frac{1}{q} = \frac{1-2}{20 \text{ cm}}$ and $q = -20 \text{ cm}$.

The initial image was half the size of the object. This image has a magnification of +2. The final image is virtual, inverted and the same size as the object, O, for the lens. **(4 points)**
(*College Physics* 9th ed. pages 793–800, 805–813/10th ed. pages 804–811, 816–824)
(L.O. 6.E.4.2, 6.E.5.1)

QUESTION 2

(a) One possible schematic diagram of the equipment set up is shown below.

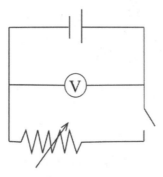

(1 Point)

Read the voltmeter with the switch open and record this value in the data table as the emf of the power supply, ε.

Since the power supply has been set to read 1.50 V by the teacher, adjust the resistance on the box to a value of 20.0 Ω. Close the switch and record the reading on the voltmeter and the variable resistance box. Open the switch. Repeat this procedure at least three times making sure that your readings are consistent.

Change the resistance on the variable resistance box and close the switch. Record the voltmeter reading and the resistance value for this set of readings. Repeat this reading procedure at least three times making sure your readings are consistent.

Repeat this step until you have five to six different resistance/voltmeter readings.

Adjust the resistance box to zero and record the voltmeter reading.
(4 points)

(b) The data taken and recorded will be the voltmeter reading in V and the resistance from the variable resistance box in Ω. The current in the circuit for each different reading will be calculated using

$$I = \frac{V}{R}.$$ **(1 point)**

(c) When the switch was opened, the reading on the voltmeter is the emf, ε, of the power supply and the current is zero. This indicates that the resistance in the circuit is infinite. **(1 point)**

(d) The graph plotted will be the terminal potential difference V_{TPD} in volts versus the current I for each different resistance value from the variable resistance box. The graph should look similar to the one below.

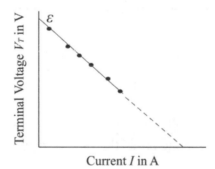

(2 points)

The slope of the line is the negative of the "internal resistance."

$$r = \frac{\varepsilon - V_{TPD}}{\Delta I}$$ **(1 point)**

(e) There are two meters in the second arrangement. Some current is always needed to operate the voltmeter. The second arrangement has an ammeter that should be a pure conductor, but will always suffer an IR drop across its ends.

There is no switch in the second arrangement, so that the circuit may have heated slightly changing the resistance of the coil of wire if the second group did not disconnect a lead wire between readings. However the switch in the first arrangement has resistance that is difficult to measure. **(2 points)**
(*College Physics* 9th ed. pages 616–629/10th ed. pages 627–638)
(L.O. 4.E.5.2, 5.B.9.6, 5.B.9.7, 5.B.9.8, 5.C.3.4)

QUESTION 3

(a) Before the loop enters the field, there is no magnetic flux through the loop. As the leading edge enters the field, the flux increases until the trailing edge of the loop is in the field. The flux decreases as the loop leaves the field.

Before the loop entered the field, there was no motional emf in the loop because there was no field present. As the right side of the loop enters the magnetic field, flux increases directed out of the page. According to Lenz's law, the induced current must be clockwise through the loop because it must produce a magnetic field that is directed into the page to counter the increase in flux out of the page. Since the current is clockwise, the induced emf is negative.

Once the loop is completely in the field the change in the magnetic flux is zero. This occurs because when the left edge of the loop enters the field, the induced emf in it cancels the motional emf present in the right side of the loop.

As the right side of the loop leaves the field, the flux outward begins to decrease. This sets up a counterclockwise current in the loop as it tries to maintain the magnetic field. **(6 points)**

(b) Setting up the graph requires the correct value for the emf on the vertical axis.

Solving for the magnitude of the emf $|\varepsilon| = \vec{B}\vec{L}\vec{v}$

$|\varepsilon| = (1.60 \text{ T})(0.200 \text{ m })\left(0.100 \ \dfrac{\text{m}}{\text{s}} \right) = 3.20 \times 10^{-2} \text{ V}$ **(1 point)**

Setting the correct time for the horizontal axis **(2 points)**

The time for the loop to completely enter the field and to leave the field is

$t = \dfrac{0.20 \text{ m}}{0.10 \ ^{\text{m}}\!/\!_{\text{s}}} = 2.0 \text{ s}$

The time for the leading edge to completely transit the field is

$t = \dfrac{0.70 \text{ m}}{0.10 \ ^{\text{m}}\!/\!_{\text{s}}} = 7.0 \text{ s}$

The correct graph is shown below.

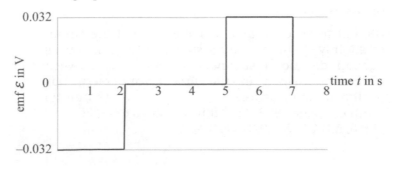

(c) $I = \dfrac{\varepsilon}{R} = \dfrac{3.20 \times 10^{-2} \text{ V}}{40.0 \text{ }\Omega} = 8.00 \times 10^{-4} \text{ A}$ **(1 point)**

(d) The magnetic flux when the loop is completely in the field is $\phi_M = \vec{B}A$.

$\phi_M = (1.60 \text{ T})(4.00 \times 10^2 \text{ m}^2) = 6.40 \times 10^{-2} \text{ Wb}$ **(1 point)**

(*College Physics* 9th ed. pages 591, 689, 691–699/10th ed. pages 601, 700, 702–710)
(L.O. 3.C.3.1, 4.E.2.1)

QUESTION 4

(a) The *Q*-value in an alpha decay reaction is given by:

$$Q = (M_{Pu} - M_U - M_\alpha)\left(931 \text{ }^{\text{MeV}}\!/\!_{\text{u}}\right)$$

$$Q = (236.046\ 071 \text{ u} - 232.037\ 168 \text{ u} - 4.002\ 603 \text{ u})\left(931 \text{ }^{\text{MeV}}\!/\!_{\text{u}}\right)$$

$$Q = 5.87 \text{ MeV}$$

(3 points)

(b) The electrostatic force is found by using Coulomb's Law.

Knowing the charge of proton is $e = 1.6 \times 10^{-19}$ C then

$$F = k\dfrac{q_{He}q_{Au}}{r^2}$$

$$= \left(9 \times 10^9 \text{ N}\cdot\text{m}^2\!/\!_{C^2}\right)\dfrac{(2e)(79e)}{\left(80.0 \times 10^{-15} \text{ m}\right)^2}$$

$$= 5.70 \text{ N}$$

(3 points)

(c) Electrons from outer electron shells fall into the vacancies in the inner shells. In large atoms such a gold, these "quantum jumps" are followed by the emission of photons that carry considerable energy. The photons produced when electrons jump from the 5th or 6th electron shells into the lowest electron shells are in the X-ray range. **(2 points)**

(d) By the Law of Conservation of Linear Momentum, the recoiling U-232 nucleus must be 1.10×10^{-19} $^{\text{kg}\cdot\text{m}}\!/\!_{\text{s}}$ at 180°. The total momentum before and after decay must be zero. **(2 points)**

(e) At the end of each half-life, one-half the remaining sample will remain. Half of a half of a half of a half means that one-sixteenth of the original sample will remain. **(2 points)**
(*College Physics* 9th ed. pages 172–173, 517–519, 937–940, 963–964, 971–973/10th ed. pages 176–177, 527–529, 950–954, 977–978, 986–987)
(L.O. 3.C.2.1, 4.C.4.1, 5.B.8.1, 5.B.11.1, 5.D.1.1, 5.G.1.1, 7.C.3.1)

AP® PHYSICS 2
PRACTICE EXAM D

AP PHYSICS 2
Section I
50 Multiple-Choice Questions
Time–90 Minutes

Note: To simplify calculations, you may use $g = 10 \text{ m/s}^2$ in all problems.

Directions: Each of the questions or incomplete statements below is followed by four suggested answers or completions. Select the one that is best in each case.

1. A convex lens produces a real image of an object that has a magnification of –4.0 when the object is placed 50.0 cm from the lens. What is the focal length of the lens?
    (A) 40 cm
    (B) 50 cm
    (C) 80 cm
    (D) 200 cm

Questions 2 and 3

Use the diagram of the pipe below to answer questions 2 and 3. The radius of the pipe at cross-section A is $r_A = 0.040 \text{ m}$ and at cross-section B is $r_B = 0.025 \text{ m}$. Water enters cross-section A with a speed of 5.00 m/s.

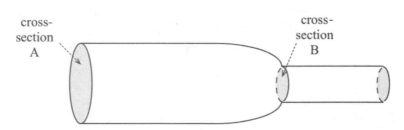

2. What is the volume flow rate of the water entering cross-section A of the pipe?
    (A) $1.06 \times 10^{-3} \text{ m}^3/\text{s}$
    (B) $2.33 \times 10^{-2} \text{ m}^3/\text{s}$
    (C) $2.51 \times 10^{-2} \text{ m}^3/\text{s}$
    (D) $6.28 \times 10^{-1} \text{ m}^3/\text{s}$

3. What is the speed of the water as it enters cross-section B of the pipe?
    (A) 1.60 m/s
    (B) 3.13 m/s
    (C) 8.00 m/s
    (D) 12.8 m/s

GO ON TO NEXT PAGE

727

4. Three resistors $R_1 = 20.0 \, \Omega$, $R_2 = 40.0 \, \Omega$, and $R_3 = 30.0 \, \Omega$ are connected to a 4.50 V power supply.

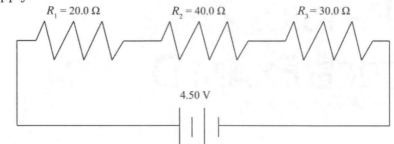

Which of the following graphs best represents the electrical potential difference across the ends of the elements in the circuit?

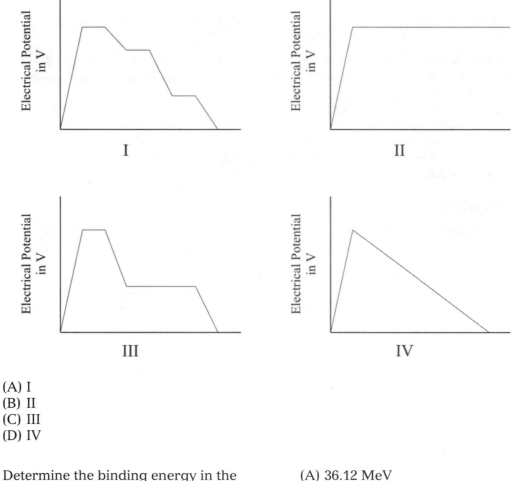

(A) I
(B) II
(C) III
(D) IV

5. Determine the binding energy in the formation of a $^{7}_{3}\text{Li}$ nucleus. The rest mass energies of $^{7}_{3}\text{Li}$ nucleus and the proton and neutron are
$^{7}_{3}\text{Li} = 6\,535.408 \text{ MeV}$
$^{1}_{1}\text{H} = 938.789 \text{ MeV}$
$^{1}_{0}\text{n} = 939.571 \text{ MeV}$

(A) 36.12 MeV
(B) 39.24 Mev
(C) 41.59 Mev
(D) 44.57 MeV

6. A sphere of mass 0.10 mg carries an electric charge of +1.00 μC. It is placed in the E-field existing between two parallel plates that are 0.05m apart.

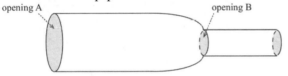

+1 μC ○   0.05 m

What are the magnitude and the direction of the electric field between the plates if the charge is to remain stationary?

(A) 980 $\dfrac{\text{N}}{\text{C}}$ directed upward

(B) 980 $\dfrac{\text{N}}{\text{C}}$ directed downward

(C) 100 $\dfrac{\text{N}}{\text{C}}$ directed upward

(D) 100 $\dfrac{\text{N}}{\text{C}}$ directed downward

7. Water flows smoothly through the horizontal pipe illustrated below.

opening A   opening B

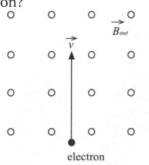

(A) The pressure at opening A is greater than at opening B because the velocity of the water is greater at opening B.

(B) The pressure at opening A is greater than at opening B because the velocity of the water is greater at opening A.

(C) The pressure at openings A and B is the same because the pipe is horizontal.

(D) The pressure is less at opening A than at opening B because the cross-sectional area at A is larger than at B.

8. The simple circuit shown below is used to evaluate the resistance of a resistor by the voltmeter-ammeter method.

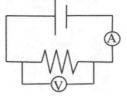

Which of the following graphs would indicate that the resistance of the element is non-ohmic?

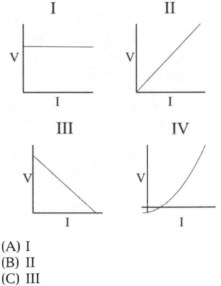

(A) I
(B) II
(C) III
(D) IV

9. An electron moves with velocity of 0.200 c in a magnetic field of strength 0.200 T. Which of the following choices gives the correct magnitude and the direction of the force acting on the electron?

(A) 1.92×10^{-12} N directed to the left
(B) 1.92×10^{-12} N directed to the right
(C) 9.60×10^{-12} N directed to the left
(D) 9.60×10^{-12} N directed to the right

GO ON TO NEXT PAGE

10. The probability of finding an electron in the hydrogen atom is greatest in a region where

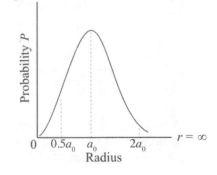

(A) $n >$ Bohr radius, $2a_0$
(B) $n =$ Bohr radius, $2a_0$
(C) $n <$ Bohr radius, a_0
(D) $n =$ Bohr radius, a_0

11. A charge of $+2q$ traveling along the $+x$-axis with a velocity $\vec{v}$ enters a region associated with an infinitely long wire carrying a current I parallel to the direction of the charge and positioned below the charge as shown below.

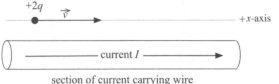

Which of the directions of the force vectors diagramed below is the correct direction of the force acting on the charge $+2q$ due to the current in the wire?

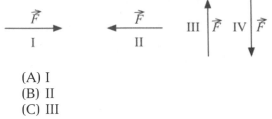

(A) I
(B) II
(C) III
(D) IV

12. Water of density 1000 kg/m^3 flows smoothly through the horizontal pipe drawn below.

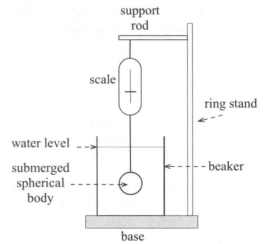

The water enters cross-section A with a speed of 4.00 m/s and a pressure $p_A = 2.05 \times 10^5$ Pa . If the radius $R_A = 2R_B$, what is the pressure p_B as the water enters cross-section B?
(A) 1.30×10^4 Pa
(B) 6.90×10^4 Pa
(C) 7.70×10^4 Pa
(D) 8.50×10^4 Pa

13. A 19.6 N sphere is suspended from a spring scale and immersed in water in a beaker as shown.

The spring scale reads 14.6 N when the body is placed in the water. The volume of the submerged body is closest to
(A) 5.1×10^{-4} m^3
(B) 5.0×10^{-3} m^3
(C) 1.5×10^{-3} m^3
(D) 2.0×10^{-3} m^3

14. Which of the following observations support the theory of Special Relativity?
    (A) The Doppler shift of red light indicating a star is receding
    (B) The bending of light near the sun observed during a total solar eclipse
    (C) The observation of a μ meson created in the upper atmosphere with a half-life about $2 \ \mu s$ reaching the Earth's surface
    (D) The diffraction of an electron from a crystal

15. A charge of $+2Q$ is brought to a point outside, but not touching, an isolated metal sphere. Which of the following statements best describes what will occur?

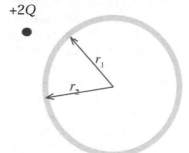

    $+2Q$

    (A) A positive charge of $+2Q$ is induced on the outer surface of the sphere.
    (B) A positive charge of Q is induced on the outer surface and a charge of $-Q$ is induced on the inner surface.
    (C) A negative charge of $-2Q$ is induced on the outer surface and a charge of $+Q$ is induced on the inner surface.
    (D) A negative charge of $-2Q$ is induced on the outer surface and a charge of $+2Q$ is induced on the inner surface.

16. A ray of polychromatic light composed of violet light and red light is incident on a cross glass plate 1.00 mm thick.

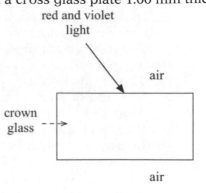

    red and violet light

    air

    crown glass

    air

    When the ray emerges from the other side of the plate both wavelengths of light will leave the plate at
    (A) the same point with the same speed
    (B) the same point but the violet light will travel faster since is has a smaller wavelength
    (C) different points with the same speed
    (D) different points but the violet light will travel faster since it has a smaller wavelength

17. Students were given an optical bench, a centimeter ruler, a 2.00 cm tall object and a curved mirror and asked to perform an experiment to determine the radius of curvature of the mirror. Part of their data is shown below.

p (cm)	q (cm)	$|M|$
40.0	13.3	0.33
30.0	15.0	0.50
20.0	20.0	1.00
5.00	−10.0	2.00

Their results lead them to conclude the mirror was
    (A) concave with a radius of curvature of +10.0 cm
    (B) concave with a radius of curvature of +20.0 cm
    (C) convex with a radius of curvature of −10.0 cm
    (D) convex with a radius of curvature of −20.0 cm

GO ON TO NEXT PAGE

18. A beam of monochromatic light from a point source shining on a small coin will cause shadows with a series of alternating light and dark bands found to border the shadow. Which of the following statements best describes what happens?
    (A) This occurs because light reflected from the surface of the coin will produce the bright bands when they meet at a single point.
    (B) Interference patterns are produced by the light reflected from the coin which is 180° out of phase with the incoming light.
    (C) A small amount of light bends around the edge of the geometric shadow of the coin diffracting into the shadow producing alternating light and dark bands.
    (D) The coin linearly polarizes the light in regions that are dark bordering the shadow.

19. A diffraction grating is used to determine the wavelength of light. In using the same grating illuminated by red light compared to blue light, the angle for the first-order maximum is greater for
    (A) red light than for blue light because red light has a smaller wavelength
    (B) red light than for blue light because red light has a longer wavelength
    (C) blue light than for red light since blue light has a smaller frequency
    (D) blue light than for red light since blue light has a higher frequency

20. An object is placed in front of three reflecting surfaces in sequence producing an upright image in all three. The image of the object in the first surface was smaller, the second image was the same size, and the third image was larger than the object. The correct sequence of mirrors is
    (A) convex, plane, concave
    (B) convex, concave, plane
    (C) plane, concave, convex
    (D) plane, convex, concave

21. A ray of light is directed into a calcite crystal as illustrated below. Which of the following statements best describes what will occur?

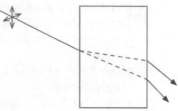

    (A) The two rays of light that emerge from the calcite crystal shows that the incident ray is both a particle and wave as indicated from the two rays that emerged from the crystal.
    (B) The calcite caused dispersion of the light into the visible colors of the electromagnetic spectrum.
    (C) Interference between the reflected ray at the surface of the crystal and the refracted ray in the crystal set up a diffraction pattern for the emerging light.
    (D) Different indexes of refraction exist for different planes of polarization and relate to the calcite crystal splitting the incident ray into two plane-polarized rays.

22. One mole of an ideal gas is confined in a fixed container. A pressure-temperature graph shown below indicates the response in the temperature due to changes in pressure.

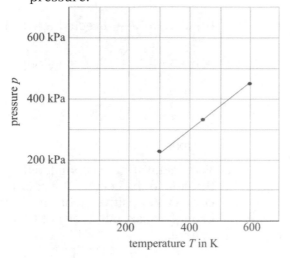

Extrapolation of the line on the graph will indicate

(A) the amount of work done by the gas as the pressure is reduced
(B) that as the pressure approaches zero, the temperature of the gas will become constant
(C) that as the pressure approaches zero, the temperature of the gas approaches absolute zero
(D) the pressure of the gas approaches zero because some of the molecules have solidified

23. Monochromatic light falls on a double slit in a diffraction experiment. The greatest separation of the maxima occurs when the monochromatic light source is

(A) green because it has the longest wavelength
(B) red because it has the longest wavelength
(C) green because it has the smallest frequency
(D) red because it has the larger frequency

24. A gas is taken through the cyclic process shown in the pV graph. What work is done on the gas?

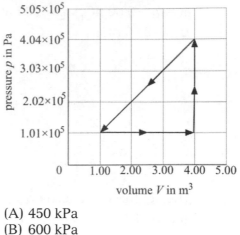

(A) 450 kPa
(B) 600 kPa
(C) 800 kPa
(D) 900 kPa

25. Glass prisms are used in many optical instruments in place of mirrors. Prisms can be used to change the direction of light beams by 90° because total internal reflection better preserves the brightness and the sharpness of light beams. In the diagram given below the line N–N is the normal.

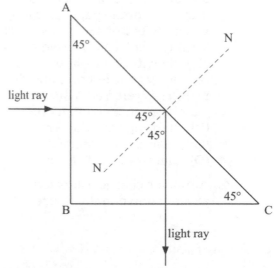

Which of the following best represents the minimum index of refraction for such a prism?

(A) 1.00
(B) 1.33
(C) 1.41
(D) 1.50

GO ON TO NEXT PAGE

26. Three charges are located on the vertices of an equilateral triangle as indicated in the diagram. The charges are $q_1 = 9.00$ nC, $q_2 = 9.00$ nC and $q_3 = -9.00$ nC.

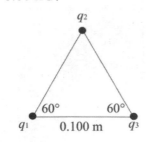

The net force of charge q_2 due to q_1 and q_3 is

(A) 7.28×10^{-5} N directed toward the right

(B) 14.6×10^{-5} N directed toward the right

(C) 18.1×10^{-5} N directed toward the right

(D) 24.3×10^{-5} N directed toward the right

27. Bringing a positively charged rod near a neutral piece of paper causes the attraction of the paper because its valence electrons and their nuclei are slightly displaced. The electrons move slightly within the paper toward the positively charged rod, and this process is referred to as

(A) charging by conduction

(B) charging by induction

(C) polarization of charge

(D) quantization of charge

28. A dipolar charge is located along the y-axis as shown in the figure below.

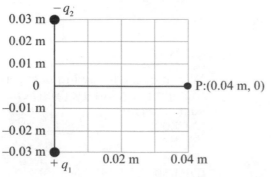

If the magnitude of each charge is 7.5×10^{-9} C, what is the electric field at point $P(0.04$ m, $0)$?

(A) $2.7 \times 10^4 \ \dfrac{\text{N}}{\text{C}}$ directed upward at $90°$

(B) $3.2 \times 10^4 \ \dfrac{\text{N}}{\text{C}}$ directed upward at $90°$

(C) $4.3 \times 10^4 \ \dfrac{\text{N}}{\text{C}}$ directed along the x-axis

(D) $5.4 \times 10^4 \ \dfrac{\text{N}}{\text{C}}$ directed along the x-axis

29. Two metal spheres connected by silk threads to the ceiling of a room are in contact. A positively charged wand is brought near, but does not touch either sphere.

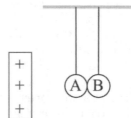

What are the charges on A and B?

(A) The left sides of both A and B are negative, the right sides of A and B are both positive.

(B) The left sides of both A and B are positive, the right sides of A and B are both negative.

(C) A is negative and B is positive.

(D) A is positive and B is negative.

30. Two charges are shown in the sketch. The charge q on the sphere on the right would be closest to

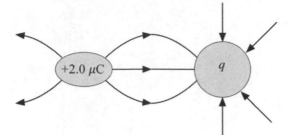

(A) –2.8 μC

(B) –2.0 μC

(C) –1.4 μC

(D) +2.0 μC

31. What is the current in the ammeter in the circuit shown?

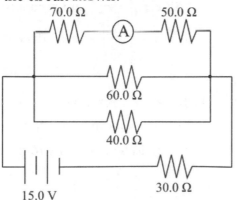

(A) 0.050 A

(B) 0.100 A

(C) 0.150 A

(D) 0.300 A

32. Two parallel plates, as shown in the diagram, are spaced by 0.04 m and have a potential difference of 1000 V existing between them. A proton is placed next to the positive plate and released from rest. What is the gain in the kinetic energy of the proton?

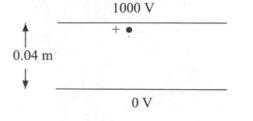

(A) 1.6×10^{-16} J

(B) 2.4×10^{-16} J

(C) 3.2×10^{-16} J

(D) 6.4×10^{-16} J

33. A student-designed experiment to evaluate Kirchhoff's junction rule is shown in the diagram below. An ammeter is placed in series with the 40 Ω resistor. The current in the ammeter is

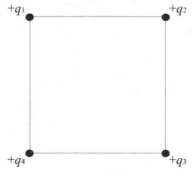

(A) 1.0 A

(B) 0.8 A

(C) 0.4 A

(D) 0.2 A

34. Four identical point charges of $+q$ are arranged at the corners of a square as shown in the diagram below.

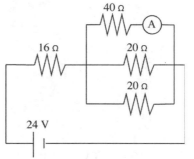

Which of the following vectors shows the direction of the net electrostatic force on $+q_3$ due to the other three charges?

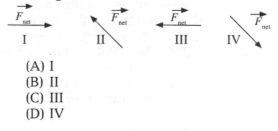

(A) I

(B) II

(C) III

(D) IV

GO ON TO NEXT PAGE

35. A proton of charge +e is moving to the right with a velocity of $\vec{v}$ in a magnetic field that directed into the page. What is the direction of the force acting on the proton? The magnetic force on the proton directs it

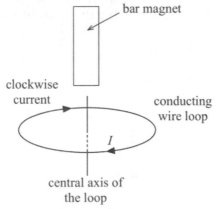

(A) to the top of the page
(B) to the bottom of the page
(C) into the page
(D) out of the page

36. A bar magnet is dropped into a loop of wire inducing a clockwise current in the loop as shown below.

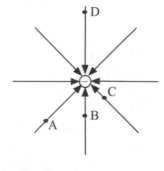

As the bar magnet approaches the loop, which pole is facing the loop?
(A) The North Pole of the magnet is moving toward the loop.
(B) The North Pole of the magnet is moving away from the loop.
(C) The South Pole of the magnet is moving away from the loop.
(D) The South Pole of the magnet is moving toward the loop.

37. Two wires carry currents $I_1 = 4.0$ A and $I_2 = 8.0$ A in the same direction as shown.

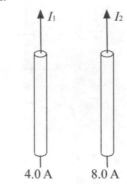

The force acting between the two wires is
(A) $\left|\vec{F}_{12}\right| = \left|\vec{F}_{12}\right|$ and is repulsive
(B) $2\left|\vec{F}_{12}\right| = \left|\vec{F}_{12}\right|$ and is repulsive
(C) $\left|\vec{F}_{12}\right| = \left|\vec{F}_{12}\right|$ and is attractive
(D) $2\left|\vec{F}_{12}\right| = \left|\vec{F}_{12}\right|$ and is attractive

38. Rank the strength of the electric field $\left|\vec{E}\right|$ surrounding the negative charge from highest intensity to the lowest intensity.

(A) $C > B > D > A$
(B) $C > B > A > D$
(C) $A > (B = C) > D$
(D) $D > A > B > C$

39. A metal surface is illuminated by light of a given frequency. If the light intensity falling on the metal is increased, the
    (A) work function for the metal will decrease
    (B) work function for the metal will increase
    (C) photoelectron current will decrease
    (D) photoelectron current will increase

40. The copper bar in the figure below has a mass of $m = 0.050$ kg. It slides freely on the frictionless metal strips 0.40 m apart on the edges of the frictionless incline. A current I flows through the strips and the bar, as indicated. There is a uniform vertical magnetic field of $\vec{B} = 0.20$ T directed into the loop. How large must the current I be if the bar is to remain motionless?

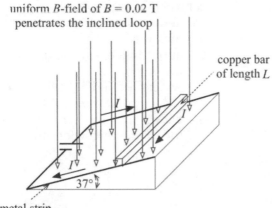

uniform B-field of $B = 0.02$ T penetrates the inclined loop

copper bar of length L

$37°$

metal strip

    (A) 3.1 A
    (B) 4.6 A
    (C) 5.3 A
    (D) 6.1 A

41. The wavelike characteristic of the electron is demonstrated in the
    (A) ejection of a photoelectron from a metal surface when illuminated with light of a wavelength less than the threshold wavelength
    (B) diffraction of the electron from a crystal
    (C) the Compton scattering of an electron from a crystal and the incident X-ray striking the crystal surface

(D) transition of the electron from an upper orbital state to a lower orbital state in the Bohr atom as the energy is emitted as a photon of light

42. What is the unknown particle(s) needed to complete the following nuclear reaction equation?
    $$^{235}_{92}U + ^{1}_{0}n \rightarrow ^{144}_{56}Ba + ^{89}_{36}Kr + ?$$
    (A) $^{4}_{2}He$
    (B) $^{3}_{0}n$
    (C) $3(^{1}_{0}n)$
    (D) $^{3}_{1}H$

43. What is the binding energy, Q, associated with the following nuclear reaction?
    $$^{3}_{1}H + ^{2}_{1}H \rightarrow ^{4}_{2}He + ^{1}_{0}n + Q$$

    The masses of the particles are:
    $^{3}_{1}H = 3.016\ 049$ u $^{2}_{1}H = 2.014\ 102$ u
    $^{4}_{2}He = 4.002\ 603$ u $^{1}_{0}n = 1.008\ 665$ u
    (A) 17.59 MeV
    (B) 0.190 MeV
    (C) 23.83 MeV
    (D) 0.256 MeV

44. In the decay of $^{222}_{86}Rn \rightarrow ^{218}_{84}Po + ?$ the missing particle is
    (A) $^{0}_{-1}\beta$
    (B) $^{0}_{+1}e$
    (C) $2(^{2}_{1}H)$
    (D) $^{4}_{2}He$

45. A 1.2×10^{-6} kg sample of Co-60 is prepared in a nuclear physics laboratory for use in a medical center. Co-60 has a half-life period of 5.24 years. What quantity will remain after 15.72 years?
    (A) 6.0×10^{-7} kg
    (B) 3.0×10^{-7} kg
    (C) 1.5×10^{-7} kg
    (D) 7.5×10^{-8} kg

GO ON TO NEXT PAGE

Questions 46 to 50

Directions: For each of the questions or incomplete statements below, <u>two</u> of the suggested answers will be correct. For each of these questions, you must select <u>both</u> correct answers to earn credit. No partial credit will be earned if only one correct answer is selected. Select the two that are best in each case and then enter both of the appropriate answers in the corresponding space on the answer sheet.

46. The kinetic energy of a photoelectron
    (A) increases with increasing wavelength of light beyond the threshold wavelength
    (B) depends on the intensity of light falling on the metal surface
    (C) increases with increasing frequency of light beyond the threshold frequency
    (D) depends on the nature of the surface being illuminated

47. A mole of an ideal gas is taken through a process ADCDA as shown.

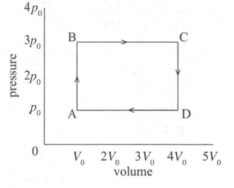

In the process, the net
    (A) change in the internal energy of the system is $6P_0V_0$
    (B) change in the entropy of the system is 0
    (C) thermal energy that crossed the boundaries is $6P_0V_0$
    (D) work done during the process was is 0

48. A container holds 0.10 moles of H_2 and 0.10 moles of O_2 in thermal equilibrium.
    (A) The O_2 molecules and the H_2 molecules have the same average kinetic energy since they are in thermal equilibrium.
    (B) The O_2 molecules and the H_2 molecules have different average kinetic energies since the O_2 molecule is more massive.
    (C) The O_2 molecules and the H_2 molecules have the same rms speed since they are in thermal equilibrium.
    (D) The O_2 molecules and the H_2 molecules have different rms speeds since the O_2 molecule is more massive.

49. In a single slit diffraction pattern the central maximum is
    (A) about the same width as the other maxima
    (B) about twice as wide as the other maxima
    (C) widest for red light because it has the longest wavelength
    (D) widest for blue light because it has the longest wavelength

50. One mole each of an ideal gas is confined in two identical cylinders. The temperature of cylinder 1 is $T_1 = 500 \text{ K}$, and the temperature of cylinder 2 is $T_2 = 300 \text{ K}$. The same amount of thermal energy Q_{in} is added to both cylinders as they undergo an isothermal expansion.

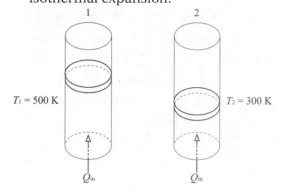

(A) The work done by the gas in cylinder 1 is greater than the work done by the gas in cylinder 2 since the temperature of the gas in cylinder 1 is higher.
(B) The work done by the gas in cylinder 1 is the same as the work done in cylinder 2 since the same amount of thermal energy was added to the cylinders during the isothermal expansion.
(C) The change in the entropy is the same in both cylinders since the same amount of thermal energy was added.
(D) The change in the entropy is smaller in cylinder 1 because it had a higher initial temperature.

STOP
END OF SECTION I

IF YOU FINISH BEFORE TIME IS CALLED, YOU MAY CHECK YOUR WORK ON THIS SECTION. DO NOT GO ON TO SECTION II UNTIL YOU ARE TOLD TO DO SO.

AP PHYSICS 2
Section II
4 Free-Response Questions
Time–90 Minutes

Directions: Solve each of the following problems. Unless the directions indicate otherwise, respond to all parts of each question.

1. An ideal gas has initial state conditions of $P_A = 2.00$ MPa, $V_A = 0.001$ m^3 and an internal energy $U_A = 20.0$ kJ. The gas is taken through the following steps:

    A → B the pressure is increased at constant volume to $P_B = 5.00$ MPa
    B → C the volume is increased isobarically until it reaches $V_C = 0.005$ m^3
    C → D the gas is compressed at constant volume to its initial pressure
    D → A the gas is isobarically returned to its initial volume
    (a) Graph the above steps on the Pressure-Volume graph shown below.

    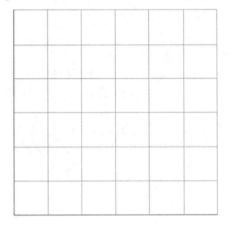

    (b) Explain how you will determine the amount of work done on each step and in the cycle without a mathematical solution.
    (c) i.   10 kJ of thermal energy enters the system along path A → B. What is the internal energy at point B?
        ii.   If the internal energy of the gas at point C is 70 KJ, how much thermal energy entered or left the system along the path B → C. Justify your answer. (Your answer may be mathematical.)
    (d) What is the net thermal energy entering or leaving the system as it returns to point A? Justify your answer.

2. Your teacher has set up on your laboratory table the apparatus shown below. In the set up a length of wire passes through several horseshoe magnets arranged with all their N poles aligned producing one large horseshoe magnet. (Support stands and clamps are not shown in the rendering.)

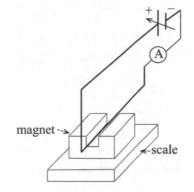

Your teacher tells you that you and your laboratory partners are to design an experiment to measure the magnetic field associted with the horseshoe magnets in the experimental setup shown in enough detail that another laboratory group could repeat your experiment and obtain the the same results. (You have access to other standard equipment in the room.)

(a) Explain in detail the design of your experiment.

(b) What measurements are you going to take and how are you going to use them to determine the strength of the magnetic field?

(c) If you plot a graph, what will you plot and how will the graph help you determine the strength of the magnetic field?

(d) Without a Tesla meter available in the room, how can you determine if the magnetic field $\vec{B}$ that you measured is consistent and accurate?

(e) i.   A wire carries current to the right of the page. Show the magnetic field around the wire.

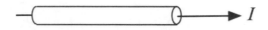

ii. The drawing below shows a wire carrying a current out of the page. Four compasses have been placed the same distance from the core of the wire. Indicate the correct direction of the field that will be produced surrounding the wire.

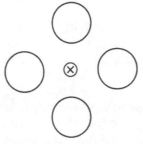

iii. The wire produces a magnetic field surrounding it. The electric field produced is

$\vec{E} = \vec{B}$ _____

$\vec{E} > \vec{B}$ _____

$\vec{E} < \vec{B}$ _____

$\vec{E} = 0$ _____

Justify your answer.

GO ON TO NEXT PAGE

3. (a) In the circuit shown below, initially both S_1 and S_2 are closed.
   Which resistor will dissipate the least power?
   Justify your answer without calculations.

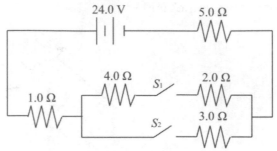

   (b) The switch S_1 connecting the 4.0 Ω resistor and the 2.0 Ω resistor is now
   opened. Which resistors will now dissipate the most power?

   Justify your answer without calculations.

   (c) Some time later, switch S_1 is removed and a 5.0 μF capacitor is placed in the
   circuit between the 4.0 Ω resistor and the 2.0 Ω resistor. Switch S_2 is closed.
   When steady state has been reached, rank the resistors for power dissapation
   from greatest to least. Justify your answer without calculations.

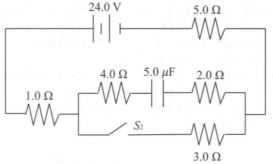

   (d) i.   Explain how you can determine the charge stored on the plates of the
            capacitor when the circuit has reached steady state.
       ii. What is the charge on the capacitor?
       iii. What difficulties might you encounter in trying to prove the resistive elements
            in the circuit obey Ohm's law?

4. (a) A narrow beam of electrons, in a vacuum, directed parallel to the page upward
   toward the top of the page is to be deflected 90° to the right. How would you
   accomplish this? Justify your answer using diagrams if necessary to help you with
   your justification.
   (b) The electron beam is homogeneous with each electron having energy of 100.0 eV.
       i.   What is the de Broglie wavelength associated with one of the electrons?
       ii. The beam strikes a crystal lattice with spacing between the crystal planes of
            0.263 nm. Explain, using the correct scientific terms, what occurs when the
            beam strikes the crystal.
   (c) A beam of electrons with energy of 1000 eV strikes a block of tungsten.
       i.   What happens to the electrons? Justify your answer.
       ii. What happens to the energy of the electrons as they impact the tungsten
            block? Justify your answer.

END OF EXAMINATION

Answers

ANSWER KEY FOR MULTIPLE-CHOICE QUESTIONS

1. A	11. D	21. D	31. A	41. B
2. C	12. D	22. C	32. A	42. C
3. D	13. A	23. B	33. D	43. A
4. A	14. C	24. A	34. D	44. D
5. B	15. D	25. C	35. A	45. C
6. A	16. C	26. A	36. D	46. C & D
7. A	17. B	27. C	37. C	47. B & C
8. D	18. C	28. B	38. B	48. A & D
9. A	19. B	29. C	39. D	49. B & C
10. D	20. A	30. A	40. B	50. B & D

EXPLANATIONS FOR THE MULTIPLE-CHOICE ANSWERS

1. **A** The magnification of an image is given by $|M| = \dfrac{q}{p}$. Solving for q in terms of p gives $4 = \dfrac{q}{p}$ therefore $4p = q$. The problem gives the distance for p as 50 cm; therefore, q is 200 cm. The focal length is related to the distances p and q by $\dfrac{1}{f} = \dfrac{1}{p} + \dfrac{1}{q}$.

   $\dfrac{1}{f} = \dfrac{1}{50 \text{ cm}} + \dfrac{1}{200 \text{ cm}}$. The focal length is 40 cm.
   (*College Physics* 9th ed. pages 805–809/10th ed. pages 816–820)
   (L.O. 6.E.5.1)

2. **C** The volume flow rate in any section is given by $R = Av$. The volume flow rate at end A is $\pi(0.040 \text{ m})^2 \left(5.00 \text{ } \frac{m}{s}\right) = 2.51 \times 10^{-2} \text{ } \frac{m^3}{s}$.
   (*College Physics* 9th ed. pages 299–301/10th ed. pages 305–307)
   (L.O. 5.F.1.1)

3. **D** The equation of continuity applies to this question.

   $A_1 v = A_2 v$ $\pi(0.040 \text{ m})^2 \left(5.00 \text{ } \frac{m}{s}\right) = \pi(.0250 \text{ m})^2 v_2$. The velocity at end B is 12.8 $\frac{m}{s}$.
   (*College Physics* 9th ed. pages 299–301/10th ed. pages 305–307)
   (L.O. 5.B.10.3)

4. **A** The resistors are in series $20.0 \, \Omega + 40.0 \, \Omega + 30.0 \, \Omega = 90.0 \, \Omega$. The current in the circuit and in each resistor is $I = \dfrac{4.50 \text{ V}}{90.0 \, \Omega} = 0.050 \text{ A}$. The electrical potential difference across the resistors in turn is $V_{20 \, \Omega} = (0.050 \text{ A})(20.0 \, \Omega) = 1.00 \text{ V}$. Repeating the calculations gives $V_{40.0 \, \Omega} = 2.00 \text{ V}$ and $V_{30.0 \, \Omega} = 1.50 \text{ V}$.
   (*College Physics* 9th ed. pages 617–628/10th ed. pages 628–638)
   (L.O. 5.B.9.8)

5. **B** The binding energy given off in the formation of ^7_3Li is equal to the difference between the sum of the rest mass energies of the 3 protons and 4 neutrons and the rest mass energy of ^7_3Li. $(3(938.789) + 4(939.571 \text{ Mev})) - 6535.408 \text{ Mev}$. The binding energy is 39.2 MeV.
   (*College Physics* 9th ed. pages 960–962/10th ed. pages 974–976)
   (L.O. 4.C.4.1, 5.C.1.1, 5.G.1.1)

6. **A** The net force acting on the charge must be zero. $\Sigma \vec{F} = 0$, $m\vec{g} = \vec{E}q$. Since the gravitational force in downward on the positive charge, the electric field is directed upward in the region of the plates i.e., the lower plate is positive.
$$|\vec{E}| = \frac{(0.10 \times 10^{-3} \text{ kg})(9.80 \text{ m}/\text{s}^2)}{1.00 \times 10^{-6} \text{ C}} = 980 \text{ N}/\text{C}$$
   (*College Physics* 9th ed. pages 522–524/10th ed. pages 532–534)
   (L.O. 2.B.1.1, 2.C.1.1, 2.C.1.2)

7. **A** The pressure is lower in constriction B because the velocity is greater. This is a direct application of Bernoulli's principle.
   (*College Physics* 9th ed. pages 302–305/10th ed. pages 307–310)
   (L.O. 5.B.10.4, 5.F.1.1)

8. **D** If a resistor obeys Ohm's Law, the graph of potential difference across the ends of the resistor versus the current is linear. Graph IV indicates that the resistance does not obey Ohm's law.
   (*College Physics* 9th ed. pages 596–597/10th ed. pages 605–607)
   (L.O. 5.B.9.7)

9. **A** The velocity of the electron is $0.200 \, c$ or (0.200) $(3.00 \times 10^8 \text{ m}/\text{s}) = 6.00 \times 10^7 \text{ m}/\text{s}$. The force on the electron is found from $|\vec{F}_B| = q\vec{v}\vec{B}\sin\theta$. Since the electron moves perpendicular to the field, by the right-hand rule the force on the electron is maximum and directed to the left of the page. (Opposite the direction of the force on a proton.) The magnitude of the force is $|\vec{F}_B| = (1.60 \times 10^{-19} \text{ C})(6.00 \times 10^7 \text{ m}/\text{s})(0.200 \text{ T}) = 1.92 \times 10^{-12} \text{ N}$.
   (*College Physics* 9th ed. pages 652–655/10th ed. pages 663–667)
   (L.O. 2.D.1.1, 3.A.2.1)

10. **D** The probability of finding an electron in the hydrogen atom is in a region where there are n de Broglie wavelengths fitting into the

circumference of the electron orbit. This probability would be greatest where the electron in closest to the nucleus (the ground state $n = 1$). This corresponds to the Bohr radius a_0.
(*College Physics* 9th ed. page 937–940/10th ed. page 950–954)
(L.O. 7.C.1.1, 7.C.2.1)

11. **D** The wire creates a magnetic field that is into the page below the wire and out of the page above the wire in the region where the $+2q$ charge is moving to the right.

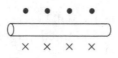

The force on the charge is given by the right-hand rule. The magnetic field is out of the page, the velocity is toward the right of the page, thus the force is toward the bottom of the page.
(*College Physics* 9th ed. pages 652–655, 664–666/10th ed. 663–667, 676–678)
(L.O. 2.D.2.1, 3.C.3.1)

12. **D** The equation of continuity applies to determine the speed of the water in the constriction. $A_1 v = A_2 v$ Since $R_A = 2R_B$, substitution

    is $(2R_B)^2 (4.00 \text{ m/s}) = (R_B)^2 v_B$. $\quad v_B = \dfrac{4R_B^2}{R_B^2}(4.00 \text{ m/s}) = 16.0 \text{ m/s}$.

    Bernoulli's equation $P_1 + \dfrac{1}{2}\rho v_1^2 + \rho g h_1 = P_2 + \dfrac{1}{2}\rho v_2^2 + \rho g h_2$ will give

    the pressure in the constriction. Since the pipe is horizontal then both terms involving $\rho g h$ will not apply. Substitution into the

    equation is then, $(2.05 \times 10^5 \text{ Pa}) + \dfrac{1}{2}\left(1000 \text{ kg/m}^3\right)\left(4.00 \text{ m/s}\right)^2 =$

    $P_2 + \dfrac{1}{2}\left(1000 \text{ kg/m}^3\right)\left(16.00 \text{ m/s}\right)^2$, then $(2.05 \times 10^5 \text{ Pa}) + 8.00 \times 10^3 \text{ Pa}$

    $= P_2 + 1.28 \times 10^5 \text{ Pa}$. This gives $P_2 = 8.50 \times 10^4 \text{ Pa}$.
    (*College Physics* 9th ed. pages 299–305/10th ed. pages 305–310)
    (L.O. 5.B.10.1)

13. **A** The buoyant force acting on the body immersed in water

    is $\left|\vec{B}\right| = \left|\vec{F}_g\right| - \left|\vec{W}_{\text{apparent}}\right|$.

    $\left|\vec{B}\right| = 19.6 \text{ N} - 14.6 \text{ N} = 5.00 \text{ N}$. The buoyant force acts upward and

    is the weight of the fluid that the object displaces. $\left|\vec{B}\right| = \rho_{\text{fluid}} V_{\text{fluid}} \vec{g}$.

    The volume of the fluid displaced and hence the volume of the

    object is found from $5.00 \text{ N} = \left(1000 \text{ kg/m}^3\right)\left(9.80 \text{ m/s}^2\right)V$. The

    volume is $5.1 \times 10^{-4} \text{ m}^3$.
    (*College Physics* 9th ed. pages 293–298/10th ed. pages 299–304)
    (L.O. 3.C.4.2)

14. **C** Time dilation is responsible for some of the mesons created in the Earth's upper atmosphere with a velocity near the speed of light being able reach the surface.
(*College Physics* 9th ed. pages 890–893/10th ed. pages 902–905)
(L.O. 1.D.3.1)

15. **D** Since the charge outside of the sphere is positive +2Q, a negative charge of –2Q will be induced on the outer surface. Since the only charge that can move in a conductor is the negative charge, this leaves a deficit of negative charge on the inner surface. The charge on the inner surface will be +2Q.
(*College Physics* 9th ed. pages 514–516/10th ed. pages 524–526)
(L.O. 1.B.1.1, 1.B.1.2, 1.B.2.3, 1.B.2.2)

16. **C** The rays travel with different speeds in the glass plates since the index of refraction is dependent on the wavelength of the light. They have been dispersed through the glass. When they emerge on the other side of the glass plate, they will be at different points. Since the medium in which they emerge is air, they will have the same speed.
(*College Physics* 9th ed. pages 771–774/10th ed. pages 782–785)
(L.O. 6.E.3.1)

17. **B** A convex mirror can only form an image that is virtual and smaller than the object. From the data, this is a concave mirror. Substitution into $\frac{1}{f} = \frac{1}{p} + \frac{1}{q}$ will give the focal length. Using any of the sets of data $\frac{1}{f} = \frac{1}{40.0 \text{ cm}} + \frac{1}{13.3 \text{ cm}}$ will give a focal length of +10.0 cm. Since the focal length is related to the radius of curvature by $f = \frac{R}{2}$ the radius of curvature for the mirror is +20.0 cm.
(*College Physics* 9th ed. pages 793–800/10th ed. pages 804–812)
(L.O. 6.E.4.1, 6.E.4.2)

18. **C** The diffraction of light is the ability of light to bend around obstacles in its path causing the light to spread into regions that would be in shadow. In the same manner that you can hear around corners, the sound wave diffracts around obstacles in its path.
(*College Physics* 9th ed. pages 836–837/10th ed. pages 847–848)
(L.O. 6.C.4.1)

19. **B** In the equation $m\lambda = d\sin\theta$. Both m and d are the same, thus as λ shifts and so does $\sin\theta$. Since red light has a wavelength of about 700 nm and blue light has a wavelength of about 450 nm, the angle for the red light is greater than the angle for blue light.
(*College Physics* 9th ed. pages 836–840/10th ed. pages 847–852)
(L.O. 6.F.1.1)

20. **A** In all cases, the image is virtual and upright. A convex mirror always produces a virtual upright image that is smaller than the object. The image in a plane mirror is always virtual, upright and the same size as the object. A concave mirror will produce a virtual

upright enlarged image when the object is between the focal point and the mirror.
(*College Physics* 9th ed. pages 790–800/10th ed. pages 801–812)
(L.O. 6.E.4.2)

21. **D** The incident ray falling on the calcite is unpolarized with light of vibrations in all directions. The calcite as well as quartz and tourmaline have different indexes of refraction for light waves with different planes of polarization. Sheets of these materials can be used to transmit light in only a single plane of oscillation, thus the transmitted light is plane polarized.
(*College Physics* 9th ed. pages 842–849/10th ed. pages 854–861)
(L.O. 6.A.1.3)

22. **C** As the pressure approaches zero, fewer collisions with the walls of the container occur because the average kinetic energy of the system approaches zero. Since the average v_{rms} corresponds to the kinetic energy, the temperature approaches zero as well.
(*College Physics* 9th ed. pages 334–335, 351–352/10th ed. pages 339–340, 357–358)
(L.O. 7.A.3.1)

23. **B** The separation of the maxima is wavelength dependent. Monochromatic red light has a wavelength on the order of about 700 nm and green light is about 495 nm to about 570 nm. Since red light has the longer wavelength, the distance between the maxima will be greatest for the red light.
(*College Physics* 9th ed. pages 747–748, 836–841/10th ed. pages 758–759, 847–852)
(L.O. 6.C.2.1)

24. **A** The work done in the cyclic process shown on the pV graph is the area bounded by the cycle. The work done is
$$\frac{1}{2}bh = \frac{1}{2}\left(4.04 \times 10^5 \text{ Pa} - 1.01 \times 10^5 \text{ Pa}\right)\left(4.00 \text{ m}^3 - 1.00 \text{ m}^3\right) = 450 \text{ kPa}.$$
(*College Physics* 9th ed. pages 397 and 408/10th ed. pages 404–405 and 416)
(L.O. 7.A.3.3)

25. **C** The incident light ray enters the prism normal to the surface AB. The ray then makes an angle of 45° with the normal N–N to side AC. The critical angle of the prism must be smaller than 45° if the ray is to be totally reflected at side AC and be turned through 90°. From $n_1 \sin\theta_c = n_2 \sin 90°$ and with $n_2 = 1.00$ we can write the minimum n_1 as $n_1 = \dfrac{1}{\sin 45°} = 1.41$.
(*College Physics* 9th ed. pages 771–775/10th ed. pages 782–784)
(L.O. 6.F.1.1)

26. **A** The force between q_1 and q_2 is repulsive because they are both positive charges. The force between q_2 and q_3 is attractive since they are unlike charges. $\left|\vec{F}_{12}\right| = \dfrac{kq_1q_2}{r_{12}^2}$. Substitution gives

$$|\vec{F}_{12}| = \frac{\left(9\times10^{9}\ \frac{\text{N}\cdot\text{m}^{2}}{\text{kg}^{2}}\right)\left(9.00\times10^{-9}\ \text{C}\right)^{2}}{\left(0.100\ \text{m}\right)^{2}} = 7.28\times10^{-5}\ \text{N}. \text{ Since } q_2 \text{ and}$$

q_3 have the same magnitude of charge then $|\vec{F}_{23}|$ is also 7.28×10^{-5} N.

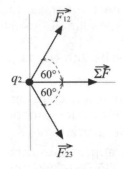

The vertical components of the forces are equal in magnitude and opposite in direction, giving a vector sum of zero. The resultant force is then $2|\vec{F}|\cos60° = 2\left(8.10\times10^{-6}\ \text{N}\right)\cos60° = 7.28\times10^{-5}\ \text{N}$.

(*College Physics* 9th ed. pages 517–522/10th ed. pages 527–532)
(L.O. 3.A.4.1, 3.C.2.3)

27. **C** The paper is neutral, but electrons can be slightly displaced from the lattice structure, attracted to the positively charged rod. This is referred to as polarization of charge.
(*College Physics* 9th ed. pages 514–516/10th ed. pages 524–526)
(L.O. 1.B.2.2)

28. **B** The direction of the electric field for the dipolar charges is shown at point P

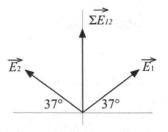

where the electric field intensity for $\vec{E}_2$ is directed toward the negative charge q_2. The electric field intensity $\vec{E}_1$ is directed away from the positive charge q_1. Since the magnitudes of the charges and the distances to point P are identical for both charges, the magnitude of the field strength is the same. The distance from the charges to point P can be determined from $r^2 = \left((0.03\ \text{m})^2 + (0.04\ \text{m})^2\right) = 2.5\times10^{-3}\ \text{m}^2$. The angle the field makes with the x-axis is found from $\tan\theta = \dfrac{0.03}{0.04} = 0.750$. The angle $\theta = 37°$.

Solving for $\left|\vec{E}\right|$ gives $\left|\vec{E}\right| = \dfrac{\left(9\times10^9 \ \dfrac{\text{N}\cdot\text{m}^2}{\text{C}^2}\right)\left(7.5\times10^{-9} \ \text{C}\right)}{2.5\times10^{-3} \ \text{m}^2}$

$= 2.7\times10^4 \ \dfrac{\text{N}}{\text{C}}$. The resultant electric field at point P is directed upward at 90° and is equal to $2\left|\vec{E}\right|\sin37°$

The field strength is $2\left(2.7\times10^4 \ \dfrac{\text{N}}{\text{C}}\right)\sin37° = 3.2\times10^4 \ \dfrac{\text{N}}{\text{C}}$.

(*College Physics* 9th ed. pages 522–526/10th ed. pages 532–538)
(L.O. 2.C.2.1, 2.C.4.1)

29. **C** The spheres are initially uncharged, containing equal amount of negative and positive charge. The wand causes some of the negative charge from both spheres A and B to move to sphere A, positioned closer to the positive wand. This gives sphere A a negative charge and sphere B a positive charge only as long as the positive charging wand is near.
(*College Physics* 9th ed. pages 514–516/10th ed. pages 524–526)
(L.O. 1.B.1.1, 1.B.2.2)

30. **A** Five electric field lines originate on the $+2.0 \ \mu\text{C}$ charge and seven lines terminate on q. The charge q is negative. The magnitude of q is $\dfrac{7}{5}(+2.0 \ \mu\text{C}) = 2.8 \ \mu\text{C}$.
(*College Physics* 9th ed. pages 526–528/10th ed. pages 536–538)
(L.O. 2.C.2.1, 5.C.2.1)

31. **A** In the upper branch of the parallel arrangement the series resistors have an equivalent resistance of $70.0 \ \Omega + 50.0 \ \Omega = 120.0 \ \Omega$. The net resistance for the three parallel branches is then $\dfrac{1}{R_{eq}} = \dfrac{1}{120.0 \ \Omega} + \dfrac{1}{60.0 \ \Omega} + \dfrac{1}{40.0 \ \Omega}$ which yields a resistance equal to $20.0 \ \Omega$. The total resistance for the circuit is the parallel equivalent of $20.0 \ \Omega$ plus the $30.0 \ \Omega$ external resistance of $50.0 \ \Omega$. The current in the circuit entering the junction is $I = \dfrac{15.0 \ \text{V}}{50.0 \ \Omega} = 0.300 \ \text{A}$. The electrical potential difference across the parallel set of resistors is $V = 0.300 \ \text{A}\,(20.0 \ \Omega) = 6.00 \ \text{V}$.

The current is the ammeter is then $I = \dfrac{6.00 \ \text{V}}{120.0 \ \Omega} = 0.050 \ \text{A}$
(*College Physics* 9th ed. pages 617–628/10th ed. pages 628–638)
(L.O. 5.C.3.4)

32. **A** The work done on the proton by the electric field in the region between the plates results in a change in ΔK. The work is

$W = \Delta K = Vq = Ve$. The gain in the kinetic energy is

$W = (1000 \ \dfrac{J}{C})(1.6 \times 10^{-19} \ C) = 1.6 \times 10^{-16} J$.

(*College Physics* 9th ed. pages 548–550/10th ed. pages 559–560)
(L.O. 5.B.5.5)

33. **D** Kirchhoff's junction rule applies the current into the junction, I_T = $I_1 + I_2 + I_3$. The largest resistor in the parallel branch will have the least current. The resistance in the parallel branch is found from $\dfrac{1}{40 \ \Omega} + \dfrac{1}{20 \ \Omega} + \dfrac{1}{20 \ \Omega} = \dfrac{1}{R_{eq}}$ and $R_{eq} = 8 \ \Omega$. The total resistance in the circuit is $16 \ \Omega + 8 \ \Omega = 24 \ \Omega$. The total current is 1.0 A. The current in the 40 Ω resistor is 0.2 A.
(*College Physics* 9th ed. pages 617–628/10th ed. pages 636–638)
(L.O. 5.C.3.3)

34. **D** The force between $+q_3$ and $+q_1$ is repulsive and directed along the diagonal of the square. The force between $+q_3$ and $+q_2$ is repulsive and directed along the –y-axis.

    The force between $+q_3$ and $+q_4$ is also repulsive and directed along the +x-axis. The magnitude of the forces acting between sets charges 2 and 3, and 3 and 4 $\left|\vec{F}_{23}\right|$ and $\left|\vec{F}_{43}\right|$ are equal. Resolving $\left|\vec{F}_{13}\right|$ into its x and y components produces equal magnitudes for these since the angle along the diagonal is 45°. The resultant of the x and y forces will give a resultant force 45° into the 4th quadrant.
(*College Physics* 9th ed. pages 517–526/10th ed. pages 517–522/10th ed. 527–532)
(L.O. 2.C.4.2, 3.A.2.1, 3.A.4.3, 3.C.2.1)

35. **A** The right hand rule will give the direction of the magnetic force acting on the proton. The velocity is toward the right while the magnetic field is directed into the page. The force on the proton is directed to top of the page.
(*College Physics* 9th ed. pages 652–655/10th ed. pages 663–666)
(L.O. 2.D.1.1)

36. **D** The current induced in the loop is the clockwise direction. By the right-hand rule, a clockwise current in the loop produces a magnetic field directed into the center of the loop to oppose what caused the current. The end of the magnet dropping into the loop is the South end of the magnet.
(*College Physics* 9th ed. pages 691–695/10th ed. pages 702–706)
(L.O. 3.C.3.1)

37. **C** By the right-hand rule the magnetic field around the wires is

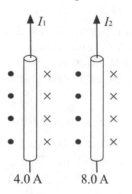

I_1 I_2

4.0 A   8.0 A

the same as if the North and South ends of a pair of magnets were brought near each other. The force is attractive. The force $\left|\vec{F}_{21}\right|$ exerted on the wire carrying current I_1 equals the force $\left|\vec{F}_{12}\right|$ on the wire carrying current I_2. These are action-reaction forces.
(*College Physics* 9th ed. pages 664–668/10th ed. pages 676–681)
(L.O. 2.D.2.1, 3.A.4.2)

38. **B** The electric field intensity $\left|\vec{E}\right|$ is an inverse square law.

$\left|\vec{E}\right| = k_e \dfrac{Q}{r^2}$. Ranking the magnitude of the field gives $C > B > A > D$.
(*College Physics* 9th ed. pages 522–523/10th ed. pages 532–533)
(L.O. 2.C.3.1)

39. **D** The work function is a characteristic of the metal and is not affected by the frequency or intensity of light falling on the surface. If a photoelectron is produced, increasing the intensity of light will increase the photoelectric current. If no photoelectron is produced, increasing the intensity will not produce one. Discrete packets of energy associated with the photon of light striking the metal is responsible for producing a photoelectron. It is the energy of the photon, not the amplitude of wave responsible for production of the photoelectrons. The amplitude of the wave and its intensity will increase a photoelectric current if one already exists.
(*College Physics* 9th ed. pages 913–916/10th ed. pages 926–928)
(L.O. 6.F.3.1, 6.G.1.1)

40. **B** If no motion is to occur, $\Sigma \vec{F} = 0$. The gravitational force must be opposite to the magnetic force, and $ILB\cos 37° = mg \sin 37°$ from which

$$
\begin{aligned}
I &= \frac{mg \sin 37°}{BL \cos 37°} \\
&= \frac{mg \tan 37°}{BL} \\
&= \frac{(0.050 \text{ kg})\left(9.8 \text{ }^{\text{m}}\!/_{\text{s}^2}\right)(\tan 37°)}{(0.20 \text{ T})(0.40 \text{ m})} \\
&= 4.6 \text{ A}
\end{aligned}
$$

(*College Physics* 9th ed. pages 655–657/10th ed. pages 667–670)
(L.O. 3.A.1.1, 3.C.3.1)

41. **B** The diffraction of the electron from a crystal experimentally confirmed that an electron-matter had wave properties. The diffraction occurs because of the wave nature of the electron.
(*College Physics* 9th ed. pages 922–925/10th ed. pages 935–938)
(L.O. 6.G.1.1, 6.G.2.1)

42. **C** The missing particles are $3\left(_0^1 n\right)$. In any nuclear reaction equation charge number and mass number must balance. Conservation of charge Z is $92+0 = 56+36$. The missing particle has zero charge. Conservation of mass A is $235 + 1 = 144+89+3$. Since the missing particle has charge of zero and a mass of 3, it is three neutrons that are correctly written as $3\left(_0^1 n\right)$.

(*College Physics* 9th ed. pages 957–958/10th ed. pages 971–972)
(L.O. 5.C.1.1, 5.G.1.1)

43. **A** The energy in the reaction is calculated from $E = mc^2$. The mass defect Δm is

$$\Delta m = (3.016\ 049\ u + 2.014\ 102\ u) - (4.002\ 603\ u + 1.008\ 665\ u)$$
$$= 0.018\ 883\ u$$

$$E = (931.5\ \frac{MeV}{u})(0.018\ 883\ u) = 17.59\ MeV$$

(*College Physics* 9th ed. pages 960–961/10th ed. pages 986–987)
(L.O. 5.B.11.1)

44. **D** In the alpha decay reaction, $_{86}^{222}Rn \rightarrow\ _{84}^{218}Po + ?$, charge and mass must balance. There are 88 protons in the parent nuclei and 86 protons in the daughter nucleus. The missing particle must have a charge of $+2q$. Mass must balance as well. The mass number for the parent is 222 and the mass number from the daughter is 218. That gives the missing particle a mass of 4. This is an alpha particle, $_2^4He$.
(*College Physics* 9th ed. pages 972–973/10th ed. pages 979–980)
(L.O. 5.C.1.1)

45. **C** 15.72 years/5.25 years = 3 half-life periods and the sequence is $\frac{1}{2}, \frac{1}{4}, \frac{1}{8}$. $\frac{1.2\times10^{-6}\ kg}{8} = 1.5\times10^{-7}\ kg$.
(*College Physics* 9th ed. pages 963–964/10th ed. pages 977–978)
(L.O. 7.C.3.1)

46. **C and D** The kinetic energy depends on the frequency of the light falling on the surface beyond the threshold frequency required to produce a photoelectron $E = hf$. The kinetic energy is dependent on the surface being illuminated since a certain amount of energy is needed to free the photoelectron from the surface, $E = hf - \phi$.
(*College Physics* 9th ed. page 913–916/10th ed. page 926–928)
(L.O. 1.D.1.1, 6.G.1.1)

47. **B** and **C** The process is a cyclic process, taking the working substance through a series of state changes and returning to the initial conditions of $p_0 V_0 T_0$. Since it returned to its initial temperature, the change in the entropy during the process ABCDA is zero. In the cyclic process since $\Delta U = 0$ the work done must equal the thermal energy added to the system.
(*College Physics* 9th ed. pages 398–399, 418–423/10th ed. pages 406–407, 426–431)
(L.O. 5.B.4.1, 5.B.7.1, 7.B.2.1)

48. **A** and **D** Since they are in thermal equilibrium, they have the same average kinetic energy. $K_{avg} = \frac{3}{2} k_B T$. They have different average speeds since they have different masses. $v_{rms} = \sqrt{\frac{3RT}{M}}$. The H_2 molecule will have the higher speed since its molar mass is 1/16 as large as O_2.
(*College Physics* 9th ed. pages 351–353/10th ed. pages 357–358)
(L.O. 7.A.2.1)

49. **B** and **C** The width of a single slit diffraction depends on the wavelength of light. Red light because it has a larger wavelength has a wider central maximum than blue light. The width of the central maximum is larger the other maxima regardless of the wavelength of light used in the diffraction and will increase in width as the width of the slit is reduced. Each maxima beyond the central maximum is reduced in intensity.
(*College Physics* 9th ed. pages 837–838/10th ed. pages 848–849)
(L.O. 6.C.2.1, 6.F.1.1)

50. **B** and **D** The work done in the isothermal expansion of the gas is equal to the amount of thermal energy added to each cylinder. The change in the internal energy was zero since the temperature did not change. $Q = W$. The entropy of the system will change since thermal energy was added and the gases occupied a greater volume, but the change in the entropy of cylinder 1 is smaller since it has the higher temperature. The change in entropy of the cylinders is given by $\Delta S = \frac{Q}{T}$.
(*College Physics* 9th ed. pages 407–410, 418–423/10th ed. pages 414–417, 426–431)
(L.O. 7.B.2.1)

ANSWERS TO FREE-RESPONSE PROBLEMS

QUESTION 1

(a) The correct graph of the process $A \to B \to C \to D \to A$ is shown below.

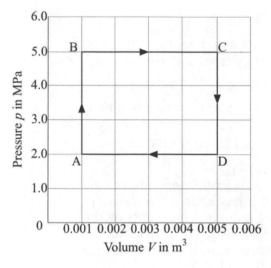

(3 points)

(b) The work done is the area under the curve. $A \to B$ is isochoric, there is no change in volume therefore the work done is zero along this path. $B \to C$ is isobaric so the work done is the product of the pressure and the volume change. Since work is defined as $W = -p\Delta V$ the work done on the gas along this path is negative. Along path $C \to D$, the volume again is constant, and therefore the work is zero. The work on the path $D \to A$ is given as $W = -p\Delta V$. Since the volume decreases along this path, the work on path $D \to A$ is positive. The net work is the sum of the work done on each path. **(4 Points)**

(c) i. The change in the internal energy on path $A \to B$ can be determined from the first law of thermodynamics $\Delta Q = \Delta U + \Delta W$. Along path $A \to B$, no work is done since the volume is constant. Thus the change in the internal energy is equal to the thermal energy that crosses the boundary. $U_B - U_A = Q_{A \to B}$ $U_B = 20.0 \text{ kJ} + 10.0 \text{ kJ} = \textbf{30.0 kJ}$ **(2 points)**

ii. The internal energy of the gas at point C is 70 kJ with an isobaric expansion in which the gas did work against the piston as the gas expanded. If the internal energy increased, then thermal energy entered the system. $\Delta Q = \Delta U + \Delta W$. $\Delta Q = (70.0 \text{ kJ} - 30.0 \text{ kJ}) - 5.00 \text{ MPa}(.005 \text{ m}^3 - 0.001 \text{ m}^3)$. The thermal energy crossing into the system is $\Delta Q = 40.0 \text{ kJ} - 20.0 \text{ kJ} = \textbf{20.0 kJ}$. **(2 points)**

(d) The net change in the thermal energy is equal to the net work that is done in the cycle, since the gas returns to its initial temperature and therefore to an internal energy at $U_A = 20.0 \text{ kJ}$. Thermal energy will enter the system. **(2 points)**
(*College Physics* 9th ed. pages, 395–403, 406–409/10th ed. pages 402–411, 413–416)
(L.O. 5.A.2.1, 5.B.4.1, 5.B.5.5, 5.B.7.1, 5.B.7.2, 5.B.7.3, 7.A.3.3)

QUESTION 2

(a) Determine the mass of the system before current exists in the wire. Record this value.

Connect a lead to the variable power supply and introduce a current in the circuit. When current exists in the wire the scale will read a different value. If the magnetic force produced by the wire is in the same direction as the gravitational force, the scale will indicate an increase in mass. If the magnetic force produced by the wire is opposite to the gravitational force, the scale will read a decrease in mass.

The net force is the difference between the two scale readings multiplied by the gravitational acceleration. $\Sigma\left|\vec{F}_{net}\right| = (\Delta m_{scale})\vec{g} = \left|\vec{F}_B\right|$.

Disconnect the lead.

Start the experiment by connecting a lead to the variable power supply and adjust the potential difference across the power supply to give a small current in the wire. Record the ammeter reading. Record the mass reading on the scale. Disconnect the lead.

Repeat this reading by connecting the lead wire to make sure your values are consistent.

Connect the lead to the power supply and increase the current in the circuit. Record the new values for the scale reading and the current.

Repeat the procedure for at least 6 more readings, recording both the mass indicated on the scale and the ammeter reading.

Measure the length of the wire in the U-shaped region of the magnets. **(3 points)**

(b) The measurements taken will be the initial mass, $m_{\text{zero current}}$, the mass, $m_{\text{with current}}$ when current exists in the loop and Δm, the difference between these two values. Convert this reading to force units $\Sigma\left|\vec{F}_{net}\right| = (\Delta m_{scale})\vec{g} = \left|\vec{F}_B\right|$.

The current in amperes will be recorded as well as the length of the wire in the U-shaped region. **(1 point)**

(c) The graph plotted should be force on the wire versus the current I the loop.

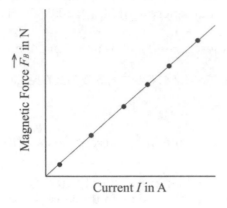

Current I in A

(1 point)

This graph should show a linear relationship between the force and the current.

The slope of the line is $\left|\dfrac{\vec{F}_B}{I}\right| \propto \vec{B}$. Since the length of the wire in the magnetic field has been measured, the strength of the field is then $\left|\dfrac{\vec{F}_B}{I\vec{L}}\right| = \vec{B}$.

(2 points)

(d) Since $\left|\vec{F}_B\right| = I\vec{L}\vec{B}$, keeping the current constant in the experiment and measuring different lengths of the wire in the same magnetic field will give the data needed to plot a graph of force versus the length of the wire. The slope of this line will be $\left|\dfrac{\vec{F}_B}{\vec{L}}\right| \propto \vec{B}$. Dividing the slope by the current I will give the strength of the field. $\left|\dfrac{\vec{F}_B}{I\vec{L}}\right| = \vec{B}$. Comparison of the two should give values for the magnetic field that are consistent.

(3 points)

(e) i.

```
        •   •   •   •
    ──┤                ├──────▶ I
       └──────────────○
        ×   ×   ×   ×
```

(1 point)

ii.

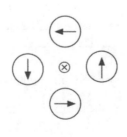

(1 point)

iii. The correct line checked is $\vec{E} = 0$ ___√___. The wire contains an equal number of positive and negative charges. Since there is no net charge, there is no electric field outside the wire. The charges are moving in the wire producing a current. It is the motion of the charges that produces the magnetic field surrounding the wire.

(2 points)

(*College Physics* 9th ed. pages 655–657, 664–666/10th ed. pages 663–667, 676–678)

(L.O. 2.B.1.1, 2.D.2.1, 2.D.3.1, 3.C.3.1)

QUESTION 3

(a) When both switches are closed, the parallel section contains two branches. The top branch consists of two resistors $4.0\,\Omega$ and $2.0\,\Omega$ in series. This resistance is larger than the $3.0\,\Omega$ resistance in the lower branch. The net resistance for the parallel arrangement is less than the smallest resistance in the lower branch. The total resistance for the circuit is the sum of the two external resistors $5.0\,\Omega$ and $1.0\,\Omega$ and the equivalent resistance of the parallel arrangement.

The total current will pass the two resistors $5.0\,\Omega$ and $1.0\,\Omega$ that are in series with the parallel arrangement giving them larger power dissipations than the resistances in the parallel part of the circuit. Kirchhoff's junction rule will apply to the current entering and dividing in the parallel section. The upper branch will get the smaller current. The two resistors in the upper branch $4.0\,\Omega$ and $2.0\,\Omega$ will receive the same current and the smaller resistor, $2.0\,\Omega$, will dissipate the least power. (Power is the product of the current squared times the resistance.) Not needed for the problem but the ranking of the power dissipated is $P_{5\Omega} > P_{3\Omega} > P_{1\Omega} > P_{4\Omega} > P_{2\Omega}$. **(3 points)**

(b) When S_1 is open, the circuit consists of three resistors in a series. The total current will pass through each resistor (Kirchhoff's junction rule applies). Since the $5.0\,\Omega$ resistance is the largest resistor, it will dissipate the most power. **(1 point)**

(c) When the system has reached steady state the capacitor is fully charged and current will no longer flow in the two resistors in the upper branch. The resistance in the circuit is now $1.0\,\Omega + 3.0\,\Omega + 5.0\,\Omega$ in series. They will have the same current. Since power is the product of current squared times resistance, then $P_{5\Omega} > P_{3\Omega} > P_{1\Omega} > (P_{4\Omega} = P_{2\Omega} = 0)$. **(2 points)**

(d) i. When the capacitor in the upper branch has reached steady state, the potential difference across its plates will equal the electrical potential difference across the $3.0\,\Omega$ resistor in the lower branch since they are in parallel. The charge on the plates of the capacitor is equal to the product of the capacitance times the electrical potential difference. **(2 points)**

ii. At steady state the current in the circuit is $I = \dfrac{V}{R} = \dfrac{24.0 \text{ V}}{9.0 \text{ }\Omega} = 2.67 \text{ A}$. The electrical potential difference across the $3.0 \text{ }\Omega$ in the lower branch will equal the electrical potential difference across the plates of the capacitor since they are in parallel.

$V_{3\text{ }\Omega} = (2.67 \text{ A})(3.0 \text{ }\Omega) = 8.0 \text{ V}$. The charge on the capacitor is given by $Q = CV$ and substitution into this equation will give the charge on the plates. $Q = (5.0 \text{ }\mu\text{F})(8.0 \text{ V}) = 40 \text{ }\mu\text{C}$ **(2 points)**

iii. Since the resistance of a resistor depends on four factors, length, cross sectional area, material and temperature, temperature is the factor that will affect the resistance the most.

Use each resistance by itself to see if it obeys Ohm's law by varying the potential difference across the resistor to determine the current through the resistor. A voltage-current graph will be linear if the resistance is ohmic.

If a switch connecting the resistive element is closed for some time, thermal energy dissipated in the resistor will cause the molecules that make up the resistor to gain a larger kinetic energy resulting in dimensional changes as the molecules moving with higher kinetic energy move through a greater range.

The resistivity of a resistor generally is considered as a constant over a wide temperature range, but this is not always true. **(3 points)**

(*College Physics* 9th ed. pages 562–563, 597–598, 617–628/10th ed. pages 573, 607–608, 627–639)
(L.O. 4.E.4.1, 4.E.5.1, 4.E.5.2, 5.C.3.4)

QUESTION 4

(a) The electron beam must be directed into a uniform magnetic field that will direct the electrons to the right. Since the electrons are negative, the magnetic field must be directed into and perpendicular to the page. The magnetic force will bend the electron beam to the right without changing its speed.

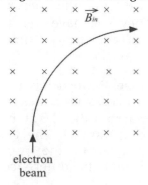

(3 points)

(b) i. To determine the de Broglie wavelength of one of the electrons, its speed must be found. The kinetic energy is 100.0 eV. Kinetic energy is defined as $K = eV = \frac{1}{2}mv^2$. Speed then is $v = \sqrt{\frac{2Ve}{m_e}} = \sqrt{\frac{2(100.0\ eV)(1.60 \times 10^{-19}\ \text{J}/eV)}{9.11 \times 10^{-31}\ \text{kg}}} = 5.93 \times 10^6\ \text{m}/\text{s}$.

The de Broglie wavelength is

$$\lambda = \frac{h}{mv} = \frac{6.63 \times 10^{-34}\ \text{J} \cdot \text{s}}{(9.11 \times 10^{-31}\ \text{kg})(4.19 \times 10^6\ \text{m}/\text{s})} = \mathbf{1.23 \times 10^{-10}\ m}\ .$$

(3 points)

ii. The electron beam will undergo diffraction when it interacts with the crystal, since the de Broglie wavelength is approximately the size of the spacing between the planes of the crystal. **(1 point)**

(c) i. The electrons with a higher energy will crash into the metal and will, after a short distance, come to rest in the metal. **(1 point)**

ii. The electrons, in coming to rest, undergo a negative acceleration. Accelerating charged particles such as electrons radiate electromagnetic energy. Some of the radiated energy becomes thermal energy, giving an increase in temperature of the tungsten. The remaining radiated energy is X-Ray radiation. **(2 points)**

(*College Physics* 9th ed. pages 652–655, 916–920, 922–924/10th ed. 663–667, 929–932, 935–938)

(L.O. 3.A.2.1, 3.C.3.1, 5.D.1.6, 6.F.4.1, 6.G.1.1, 6.G.2.1, 6.G.2.2)